PRINCIPLES

OF

PHYSICAL SCIENCE

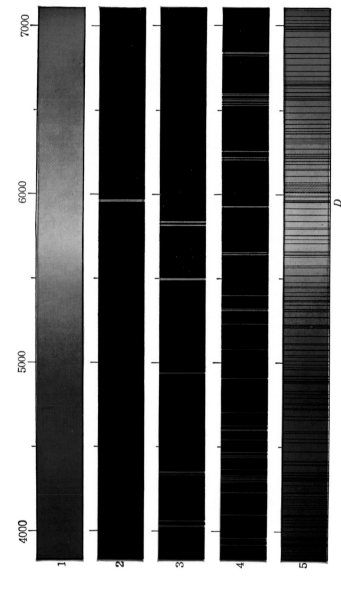

D

Different Types of Spectra* • 1, continuous spectrum from an incandescent solid; 2, bright-line spectrum of sodium; 3, bright-line spectrum of mercury; 4, bright-line spectrum of calcium; 5, absorption spectrum of the sun, showing some of the strongest Fraunhofer lines. Note the coincidence of the bright lines for sodium in 2 and the dark lines D in 5

*Reprinted by permission from *Foundations of College Physics* (Ginn and Company, 1937), by Samuel Robinson Williams.

PRINCIPLES

OF

PHYSICAL SCIENCE

by

FRANCIS T. BONNER

Arthur D. Little, Inc.

and

MELBA PHILLIPS

Washington University

12073

ADDISON-WESLEY PUBLISHING COMPANY, INC.

READING, MASSACHUSETTS, U.S.A.

CONTENTS

v

PREFACE

The science education of the liberal arts student who does not intend to pursue a career in science has been the subject of much interest and debate in recent years. It now seems quite generally agreed that the specialized introductory course offered in conventional curricula falls far short of fulfilling the needs of this student, but there is wide divergence of opinion as to how these needs can best be met. One solution to the problem that has achieved a certain vogue is the presentation of a panoramic "survey" of the whole of natural science, which by its very nature must sacrifice greatly in depth for what is attempted in breadth. Another solution, and one which has had great impact upon the American educational scene, is the method of the scientific "case history," introduced by President J. B. Conant of Harvard University. Born of the deep conviction that understanding of science must be an integral part of the equipment of educated modern man, the method attempts to foster such understanding by detailed examination of a number of important developments in science, all sufficiently remote in the past that full historical perspective is possible, and that their impact on subsequent decades may be appreciated. By its nature, this method sacrifices breadth of coverage and continuity in favor of thorough historical treatment of the rather small number of "cases" that can be studied in a single college course. It is scarcely unique to this plan that achievement of its ultimate objective depends upon the degree to which it is successful in awakening the student's interest in science, hence his willingness and desire to pursue the subject in his leisure reading.

The present text is an outgrowth of several years of experience in the teaching of nonscience liberal arts students at Brooklyn College, during a period in which the authors and many of their colleagues were engaged in a common effort to meet the special requirements of this kind of student. The earliest version of the course was developed by a planning committee under the chairmanship of one of us (MP), and both of us served as lecturers, recitation and laboratory instructors, revisers, advocates, and dissenters during a number of its most formative years. The basic plan of the text corresponds rather closely to that of the course which evolved from this process at Brooklyn College, although its execution is entirely our own. Our approach may perhaps be described as a hybrid between the two extremes of survey and case history, except that we have attempted to show the internal coherence of scientific development on a broad scale.

xiii

We believe it a matter of the utmost consequence that the general student gain appreciation, understanding, and interest in science. We see no reason why less effort and seriousness of purpose should be expected of a student who does not intend to major in a science than of one who does so intend, in an introductory course. The special requirement of the nonscience student, then, resides simply in the fact that his formal education in science will be sharply limited; his college experience of science, therefore, should be made as meaningful as possible in ways that the traditional specialized course can hardly attempt. We are convinced that a broad, connected view of science, if it can be developed without superficiality, should be part of that experience. We have here attempted to develop such a view, with as much depth as is consonant with the limitations of available teaching time and the necessity for nonmathematical treatment.

The central theme of this book is the growth of man's ideas concerning the physical world, from the abstract geometrical astronomy of Greece to modern chemistry, nuclear physics, geophysics, and stellar astronomy. We have attempted to evolve a continuous story, focusing on the fundamental concepts of matter and energy. Our purpose has been to illustrate as clearly as possible what science is, how scientific knowledge is acquired, and how present-day science is related to its historical roots. It is in the sense that we subscribe to the validity of this objective, and at the same time wish to present as broad a view of physical science as is consistent with it, that our treatment may be considered a hybrid. The history of ideas and ideas themselves are not fully separable. Our subject matter is science itself, not its history or philosophy, but we believe that science, especially in its very important dynamic aspects, cannot be properly comprehended or appreciated in ignorance of the growth of its concepts and theories. In the attempt to accomplish our objectives, inclusions and omissions have been chosen with considerable care. We have stressed the emergence of the more fundamental physical laws, and factual material has for the most part been limited to that necessary for the recognition of general principles in historical context, and for the elucidation of their chief consequences.

The subject matter is presented as a unified sequence, without formal recognition of the conventional boundaries of the various fields. We have sought to trace the growth of man's ideas concerning matter and energy so as to indicate both the compellingly logical and the intuitively creative aspects of scientific theory-building, as well as the basic dependence of theory on observation and experiment. Throughout the main body of the book each chapter contributes in an important way to those that follow, in a manner reminiscent of that in which physical theory has actually evolved. This plan has been designed to set the stage for various aspects of modern science, and choice and rearrangement of sequence among several of the later chapters is entirely feasible. While our own experience has been that students enjoy learning something of organic chemistry, for example, much of Chapter 23 and all of Chapter 24 could be omitted without disturbing the continuity. Similarly, the sequence of Chapters 25 through 28 could be left out in a course devoted wholly to physics and chemistry. Chapter 29, which deals with nuclear physics, could be taken up at almost any point after Chapter 19; as it stands, the order is such that nuclear science leads naturally into the fascinating subject of stellar astronomy, with which we conclude this study of physical science. A variety of exercises on several levels of difficulty has been provided, so as to offer some choice. We are convinced that thought-provoking exercises are extremely useful, and have even taken the liberty of occasionally introducing therein physical principles not treated elsewhere in the text. In a brief summary at the end of each chapter attention is called to the most important ideas treated in the chapter, as related to each other and to other aspects of science. Each summary is intended to provide further emphasis, not to constitute a complete résumé of these ideas.

The level of presentation we have tried to achieve is that appropriate to college freshmen; we have presupposed no particular high-school preparation in science, and no mathematical preparation beyond elementary algebra. A review of the mathematical procedures employed is provided in an appendix, and the student would do well to familiarize himself with its contents at the very outset of his study of the text. Although a student laboratory is often not easy to arrange for a liberal arts science course, we are strongly of. the opinion that concurrent use of laboratory exercises designed for the simplest possible illustration of physical principles, as they are taken up in the course, is a most valuable adjunct. For this purpose the laboratory methods should be clear and direct, rather than those aimed at greatest possible accuracy. A few "discovery" experiments (e.g., on factors influencing the period of a simple pendulum) are useful, but most of the laboratory exercises may be modifications (by simplification) of those described in modern laboratory manuals for physics, chemistry, and geology. A planetarium visit, where it can be arranged, is a most helpful aid if the apparent motions of the members of the solar system are shown in relation to the fixed stars. In connection with geological subject matter there is no fully satisfactory substitute for a well-organized field trip, carefully prepared for by a selection of questions appropriate to those geological features available for observation. Whether a student laboratory is available or not, the choice of simple and effective demonstrations throughout the course is of great importance.

No book of this sort can be written without a great deal of help from many sources, although the authors accept full responsibility for the final product. The people who have contributed to our ideas and to the preparation of the manuscript are too numerous to mention individually, but the authors are most gratefully appreciative of their help. We are indebted to our many former colleagues at Brooklyn College, in concert with whom the general contours and much of the detail represented here were originally developed, and to the students who served as sounding boards for our ideas during the book's formative years. We owe especial thanks to Professor Bart J. Bok, who gave very generous advice and encouragement in the preparation of our chapter on stellar astronomy, and to Professor Kirtley F. Mather, whose detailed and constructive suggestions on the geological material were invaluable to us. We are very grateful to Professors Haym Kruglak and R. J. Stephenson, who read the entire manuscript critically and offered numerous helpful suggestions, and to Professor Leonard K. Nash, who criticized portions of the manuscript most helpfully. One of us (FTB) is indebted to the Carnegie Corporation and to Harvard University for making it possible for him to observe and participate in the Harvard program of science in general education during 1954–55. It was during that very stimulating and instructive year that much of his writing on the present work was done.

Our debt to published material is at least partially indicated in the bibliography. We should like to express our gratitude to the many publishing companies and other sources of illustrative material which we have acknowledged throughout the text. Particularly, we wish to thank Mr. Norman Kellogg of Ginn and Co. for making available to us the color plates used as a frontispiece, and Mr. D. E. Jensen of Ward's Natural Science Establishment for his help with the problem of mineralogical illustration. We are indebted to many individuals for their help with the manuscript during its various stages of preparation, particularly to Mrs. Evelyn Bonner. Finally, we should like to acknowledge the cooperation and assistance of the staff of Addison-Wesley Publishing Company, especially the incisive editorial help of Mrs. Olga A. Crawford and the imaginative illustrative work of Mr. Joseph S. Banks.

F. T. B.

January, 1957   M. P.

INTRODUCTION

The word *science,* derived from the Latin *scire,* "to know," is a venerable member of the English language with many different levels of meaning. The particular meaning now most commonly ascribed to the word, the sense in which it is used here, did not enjoy widespread usage before the 19th century. It is not possible to set down a concise definition of science in even this restricted meaning, for a sentence, or a paragraph, can do no more than mention one or a few of its many varied aspects. This entire book represents an attempt to sketch in the broad outlines of just one part of science—that part, defined negatively, which does not deal directly with the phenomenon of life. We shall find it difficult, even on such general terms, to make a sharp separation of the physical from the biological sciences. Geology, for example, cannot properly be placed in either category, and in modern times the sciences of physics and chemistry have become interwoven with biology. At no time in scientific history, in fact, has the division of science into its various branches held more than artificial significance. For example, it was the observation of a nineteenth century ship's doctor that human blood has a more brilliant red color when shed in the tropics than in Europe that led to one of the first formulations of the important physical principle called the Conservation of Energy. Although the branches of science do not fundamentally differ from one another, science as a whole is readily distinguishable from other related fields of human endeavor both in subject matter and in methods. Let us examine, briefly, some of its characteristic aspects.

Physical science is based on man's observation of his inanimate environment, but observation alone is not science. Experiment, or planned observation, plays an indispensable part, for, as Francis Bacon remarked, "the secrets of nature betray themselves more readily when tormented by art than when left to their own course." Science is impersonal: ideally, at least, the scientist attempts to see things as they are, quite apart from his own role of observer, his own wishes or desires. Einstein has said that physics, his own science, is an attempt to grasp physical reality conceptually, as it is thought to exist whether being observed or not. This implies another important ingredient of science: a set of valid concepts, in terms of which we may ask and, hopefully, answer meaningful questions. These concepts, created in the minds of scientists, have distilled, so to speak, from man's long observation of nature. They are not static, but change and develop as knowledge and understanding accumulate. The concept of *motion,* for example, which will concern us throughout this book, is as old as science

1

itself. What is motion? What constitutes change of motion? What influences produce motion, or change of motion? These questions, also as old as science itself, have not declined either in interest or intellectual challenge with the passage of time; during our own century Einstein and many others have been at work improving the answers, bringing them into more complete and consistent accord with the increasingly accurate observations made possible by modern techniques.

Science is at once particular and general. While its ideas are expressed in terms of many abstractions, such as the concept of motion, it is based on the most detailed and accurate possible examination of individual events. Without abstract concepts, which help scientists to generalize and systematize knowledge, and which reflect the relations of different sets of occurrences to one another, science would be little more than a vast catalog of events. As our study of physical science progresses, we shall see that often its most stunning successes have been triumphs of generalization—discoveries of interrelations among phenomena which had previously appeared unrelated. Yet the importance of the phenomena themselves cannot be overlooked. Indeed, the great generalizations have value only so long as they aid exact description and interpretation of *particular* observations, and help scientists to bring new phenomena to light.

One of the most characteristic aspects of science is change: a capacity for continual self-alteration is part of its very nature. The periods of greatest scientific advance have been those in which it has changed itself most rapidly, and from which it has emerged transformed. Since the very methods of science undergo transformation, there can be no recipe for making a great scientific discovery, any more than there can be a prescription for writing a great book or composing a great symphony. The technical skill required of the practitioner of science is at least as great as that required of a writer or composer. Techniques of experimental measurement and mathematical analysis have developed and changed along with the growth of science itself. But just as refined technical skill alone does not suffice to make a great artist, the extraordinary scientist must also possess profound creative ability. Scientific and artistic endeavors, in this sense, are very similar.

More than any other branch of knowledge, science is cumulative, and in a unique way. The scientific knowledge of today comprises all the results of past scientific work that have been proved valid. A "truth," in science, is the result that has survived long, continuous testing by comparison with the behavior of the material world. In the course of such testing, a result may become very different from its original form, however, and the importance of the great innovator in science does not depend upon his success with the details of his innovation. The astronomer Copernicus and the artist Albrecht Dürer were contemporaries, for example. Scientists have not hesitated to change Copernicus' results, and the astronomical framework we continue to call the Copernican system actually represents improvement upon the ideas Copernicus himself entertained. The notion of "improving" Dürer's paintings or etchings by adding brush strokes or changing lines, however, is absurd. Still, the debt of science to Copernicus is probably greater than that of art to Dürer.

For most practical purposes, results are more significant than the methods by which they are achieved. Because change is so integral a part of science, however, no account that omits historical development altogether can pretend adequate representation of science. The progress of science has been remarkably uneven. Great bursts of scientific activity have come at widely separated periods of time—in classical Greece, in 17th century Europe, and again, largely in the western world, in the 19th and 20th centuries. Yet in no other human activity does progress rest so profoundly on what is already known. The very foundations of science are constantly being repaired, while additions to its structure depend in a very fundamental way on what is already there. The scientists of any age, like most other people, see little more than their training has led them to look for. Those whose vision extends notably beyond their predecessors' have their names perpetuated in textbooks like the present one. What they have found contributes to the main stream of science, for all posterity to ponder, to augment and correct, and, if necessary, to discard. It is our present aim to examine some of the most important ideas of physical science, to see how they arose, and how they have had to be corrected and broadened.

Before turning our attention to the subject matter of science itself, we should note that even the function and purpose of the scientific enterprise have changed in the course of its development. Although dependent on both technology and philosophy through much of its history, science came, in time, to affect parts of both earlier traditions profoundly. Until the 19th century most important technological progress occurred independently of formal science. The closeness of relation between present-day science and technology, and the leading role which science now plays in this relation, are often extremely obvious. The importance of interplay between the philosophical and scientific disciplines has been recognized by scientists of virtually all generations. Although our primary concern in this account is science, we should find it impossible, even if desirable, to ignore its many points of contact with technology and philosophy. Just as the branches of science cannot be sharply divided from one another, any attempt to isolate science itself from the fields closely related to it is somewhat artificial, no matter how convenient it may be.

CHAPTER 1

THE SOLAR SYSTEM

1-1 The beginnings of science

The roots of science are to be found in the practical technical achievements of prehistoric society. Benjamin Franklin once defined man as a "tool-making animal"; in a primitive sense, physics began with the invention of the first implement. The taming of fire has been called the beginning of human culture; it might also be said that this event initiated the science of chemistry. The development of early cultures depended on an impressive list of practical arts: those necessary for tilling the soil, for tanning and dyeing, for the making of pottery, for working with metals, and many others. The preservation of these important techniques was usually the responsibility of the priests, who, in time, also served as scribes. The practical and the mythical were not always easily distinguishable in early cultures, for although man gradually gained some control over his environment, his survival remained dependent on events beyond his control, and to these events he tended to ascribe supernatural significance. Man could prepare the soil and plant seeds, for example, but the rest was up to those gods whose task it was to regulate rain and sunshine. Myths of creation form a part of every cultural heritage, and these myths, varying with geographic origin, reflect some aspects of the practical struggles of different peoples to build their own civilizations. The ancient inhabitants of Mesopotamia fought desperately to obtain arable land by swamp drainage, for example, and according to Babylonian mythology the earth was entirely covered with water until the god of creation, Marduk, caused dry land to appear by the exercise of divine powers.

It was the gradual development of the techniques of agriculture, between six and ten thousand years ago, that made urban civilization possible. Once some members of society were able to produce more food than they themselves could eat, others became free to pursue activities not immediately essential to survival. As a result, the techniques of many other practical arts were developed to high states of perfection, in widely separated regions, during centuries that we are still forced to call "prehistoric." More abstract activities also became common in response to the practical demands of rising cities. To help the farmers sustain increasingly heavy burdens of production, astronomical knowledge became necessary for the construction of calendars, geometry for the measurement of fields. Arithmetic developed for the keeping of accounts, and systems of weights and measures for commerce. And, of greatest importance to man's intellectual heritage, art, philosophy and theology—abstract activities whose ends were not immediately practical—began to flourish. Wise men, the priests, began to speculate more rationally than their forebears about their environment, and how it might have come to be as they found it. The beginnings of science, in the modern sense, can be traced to man's earliest attempts to understand the world in an entirely rational way, without direct recourse to supernatural events.

From this viewpoint, science can be said to have first arisen and flourished during the Golden Age of Greece, in approximately the 6th century B.C. Greece inherited most practical aspects of her culture, together with many myths and legends, from the Egyptian, Babylonian, and Sumerian civilizations. The unique contribution of the Greeks was an over-all rational outlook. Thales of Miletus (ca. 625–545 B.C.), the first of the great Greek philosophers, shared the Babylonian view that dry land had separated from an earth once entirely covered with water, but as a result of such observed natural processes as the silting of the River Nile. The significance of Thales' novel approach, in the words of the British classicist Benjamin Farrington, is that "it gathers together into a coherent picture a number of observed facts *without letting Marduk in.*"

Early Greek philosophy, in the sense that it was both rational and realistic, possessed attributes we now consider most characteristic of science. Although the successes of Greek science were most notable in geometry and astronomy, the whole of our own scientific tradition evolved from Greek thought. We shall see that Greek philosophy produced its own limitations and that its ultimate decline was in large part due to overemphasis on an aspect essential to the very existence of either philosophy or science—the tradition of abstract thought. During the period 600–100 B.C., however, science grew at a rate that was not again matched until the 17th century.

1–2 Celestial motion: stars, moon, and sun

The branch of Greek science of most immediate concern to us is astronomy. That the sun, moon, and stars rise in the east and set in the west roughly once a day, and that even the variations in the courses of the sun and moon seem to take place according to some regular scheme, were matters of interest to the most primitive of cultures. Sophisticated urban civilizations maintained detailed, quantitative records of observations of the heavens. The Babylonians constructed particularly elaborate astronomical tables, possibly because of the important role astrology played in their religion. It was the Greeks, however, who first attempted to fit these

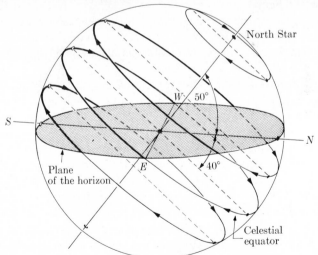

FIG. 1–1. Apparent daily motion of the stars. Directions are marked on the plane of the horizon for a latitude of 50°. Stars below the horizon are invisible. The top picture is an actual time-exposure photograph taken with a fixed camera, and shows that the North Star (very bright trace near the center) is not quite at the pole. (Yerkes Observatory photograph.)

observations into a single rational and comprehensive scheme. The movements of the stars in their fixed constellational patterns are such that they appear to be set inside a giant rotating sphere, and the sun and the moon also seem to describe vast circles. These celestial spheres and circles linked astronomy with geometry, that branch of mathematics which the Greeks developed to a very high level.

Let us examine celestial motions a little more closely. The apparent daily motion of the stars is indicated in Fig. 1–1, and some of the easily recognized constellations are shown on the sky map of Fig. 1–2. Polaris, the North Star, moves so little that it must be very near the axis of rotation of the "sphere of the stars." If we could simultaneously see stars above and below the horizon the sphere would presumably appear complete; the imaginary great circle halfway between its poles is called the *celestial equator*. In northern latitudes, familiar to us and to our cultural forebears, Polaris always remains above the horizon, as do the stars near it, like those of the Great Dipper which circle about the North Star once in twenty-four hours. Other stars appear to describe larger arcs, depending in size on their angular distance* from the celestial pole. Some, like those forming Orion's belt, are about 90° from the pole, on the celestial equator. These stars rise in the east, sweep across the sky somewhat to the south, and set due west, remaining above the horizon twelve hours out of twenty-four. The behavior of typical stars to the north and to the south of the celestial equator is shown on the figure.

The moon also describes a daily circle in the sky, but from evening to evening its position slips eastward with respect to any particular "fixed" star. The time interval between repetitions of any given position of the moon with respect to the stars is called a *sidereal* month. It is as if their relative rates of motion were such that in one month the moon makes one less revolution about the earth than do the stars. The length of an average sidereal month is 27.3 days, but this is not the time between consecutive full, or new, moons. The interval between equivalent *phases* of the moon, 29.5 days, is more than two days longer than the sidereal month, because phases of the moon depend on the sun, not the stars.

Our sun is the celestial object of greatest practical interest to mankind. Its position with respect to the stars is difficult to observe, since it obscures them by its brightness. Observations made just after sunset or just before sunrise show, however, that the sun also slips gradually toward the east with respect to the stars, though more slowly than the moon. Thus, in addition to its daily circle about the earth, the sun describes a second great circle among the stars. One year is the period of time required for the sun

---

*That is, the angle between an observer's line of sight to a given star and his line of sight to Polaris, the pole star.

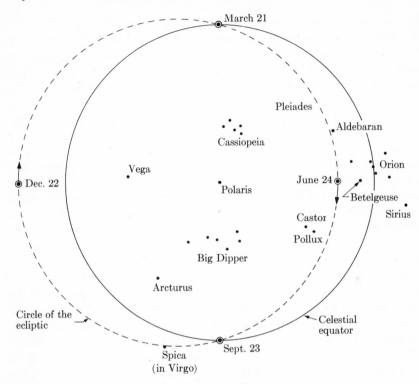

FIG. 1–2. Star map showing the circle traced out by the sun in the course of a year.

to complete a cycle along the path called the *circle of the ecliptic*. The position of this path with respect to the celestial equator marks the annual seasons, as indicated in Fig. 1–2. This sky map, centered at the pole star, shows more of the heavens than could ever be visible at one time. The path of the sun among the stars intersects the celestial equator twice each year, at positions called the *equinoxes*. As spring advances into summer, for example, the sun moves past northerly constellations called the Pleiades and Orion, and approaches the celestial equator at the point of the autumnal equinox. During the winter the sun moves along the circle of the ecliptic to positions south of the equator, i.e., more than 90° from the pole star, as projected on the celestial sphere. Study of Fig. 1–1 will show why daylight extends more than twelve hours in summer and less than twelve hours in winter: in its *daily* motion the sun behaves like any other star in its own part of the sky.

The Greeks were well aware that the sun and moon are much nearer the earth than are the stars and that the moon is the nearest of all celestial objects. Since they had assumed that the stars are fixed to a rotating sphere, the view logically developed that the sun, moon, and even the earth are also spherical. This important step was taken by the Pythagorean school. Pythagoras (ca. 582–500 B.C.), born in Samos, founded a community in southern Italy devoted to the contemplation of mathematics and religion, which were for him very closely related. The Pythagoreans held that the beauties and regularities of the universe must correspond to those of number and geometry, and that the sphere is the geometrically perfect figure. At least two members of the school, Hicetas and Ecphantus, proposed a view that the earth rotates daily on an axis of its own at the center of all things, and that the sphere of stars is fixed and immobile. The moon and sun were required to revolve in circular orbits about the earth, the sun yearly and the moon monthly. According to this scheme, celestial motion becomes slower with increasing distance from the earth. The earth, least perfect of heavenly bodies, has more motion than all others; more remote, hence more "noble," bodies move more slowly; and the stars, truly celestial, do not move at all.

Although some parts of Pythagorean doctrine were considered heretical by the philosophers of Athens, Plato (427–347 B.C.) elaborated and developed the thesis of perfect spheres and circles. According to Plutarch, Plato also absolved astronomy from heresy, "because he made natural laws subordinate to the authority of divine principles." Plato revived the idea of daily motion on the part of the stars, and with it the view that the earth stands still. He also deplored the waste of time involved in actual astronomical observation, as he sought a cosmic view embracing, in the most general possible way, what is seen in the heavens. Unfortunately for the accomplishment of this ideal, the heavens themselves would not conform to any *simple* pattern of regular spheres and circles. The brightest of celestial objects, with the exception of the sun and moon, had long been notable for the irregularity of their paths among the stars. These offenders were the *planets*, whose name derives from the Greek word meaning 'wanderer," or "vagabond." Because of their importance in the development of more satisfactory models of the solar system, we must examine the apparent motions of the planets in some detail.

1–3 The planets and retrograde motion

There are five heavenly bodies visible to the naked eye, like bright stars, whose motions are highly erratic. Although some of them at least were noted for peculiar behavior before historical times, the names that have survived to our own day are those of Roman deities: Mercury, Venus, Mars, Jupiter, and Saturn. The sun, moon, and these planets constituted the seven sacred objects for which the days of the week were named, a practice begun in ancient Babylon. The planets are rather strictly confined to that part of the sky traversed by the sun, i.e., their positions are never far from the circle of the ecliptic shown in Fig. 1–2. Like the sun and moon, they generally lose ground among the stars in their daily (or nightly) processions from east to west, and eventually complete whole cycles. Saturn takes roughly thirty years for its journey, Jupiter nearly twelve, and Mars about two years. The behavior of Venus and Mercury seems different from that of the other planets. Never very far from the sun, they appear, sometimes in the morning and other times in the evening, near the horizon where the sun is about to rise or has recently set. Both planets require less than one year to return to any given position with respect to the sun: about $7\frac{1}{2}$ months for Venus, 3 months for Mercury.

While the general direction of motion of the planets among the stars is eastward, these bodies do not pursue their paths with the regularity observed in the motions of the moon and sun. Indeed, they occasionally seem to be going the wrong way—westward! If the position of a particular planet is recorded at regular intervals, e.g., weekly or monthly, and always at the same time of night, its apparent path among the stars may be plotted and traced out on a star map, as shown in Fig. 1–3. As seen in this diagram, a

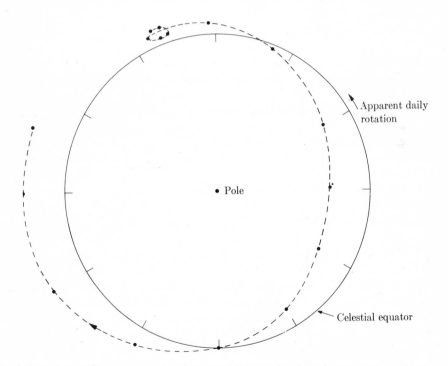

Fig. 1–3. Star map (oriented as in Fig. 1–2) showing the path of Venus during the year 1894.

planet's path seems to describe a loop whenever its eastward motion is interrupted, temporarily reversed, and then resumed. Looped paths, in decided contrast to the regular progression of the sun along the circle of the ecliptic, are described by all the planets. The occasional reversal of planetary motion thus described is called *retrograde motion*. Successive repetitions of the loops in the path of a given planet do not occur in the same part of the sky, and the intervals between them have no easily recognizable connection with such natural terrestrial time intervals as the month or year.

Despite Plato's contempt for "men who paid attention to the heavens but in their simplicity supposed that the surest evidence in these matters is that of the eye," he could hardly fail to appreciate the difficulty involved in including the planets in his philosophy. To his pupils Plato proposed a celebrated problem: "[find] . . . what are the uniform and ordered movements by the assumption of which the apparent movements of the planets can be accounted for." It was Plato's conviction that a complete account of the heavens could be made in terms of the "uniform and ordered" spheres and circles of Greek geometry. He thought that this could be accomplished by speculation and that the importance of observation was secondary.

Yet it was one of Plato's students, Eudoxus (409–356 B.C.), who, in trying to solve his teacher's problem, introduced an element of exactness into theoretical science that we have come to recognize as one of its fundamental characteristics. Eudoxus saw his task as that of making a *geometric model* that would actually represent the observed motions of heavenly bodies, and on which predictions could be based. Predictions of such events as eclipses had been made earlier, but only as a result of noting repetitions of occurrences at regular intervals of time. Eudoxus united quantitative astronomical observation and theoretical speculation in an effort to achieve a physical picture of the actual motions of heavenly bodies. Although Greek astronomy became less realistic and more geometric in the times that followed, i.e., the bodies came to be regarded as geometric points incapable of colliding with each other, it retained Eudoxus' goal of accurate representation.

We need consider only briefly the model ingeniously contrived by Eudoxus. He viewed the motions of the moon, sun, planets, and stars as those of a series of rotating spheres with the earth at the center. Apparent irregularities in the motions of planets were considered *resultants* of the rotations of several spheres. The axis of each sphere was attached to those farther out. A modification of this scheme was accepted by Aristotle (384–322 B.C.), whose views on many other subjects we shall consider further on. It was a later solution of Plato's problem, however, that Greek astronomy bequeathed to the Arabs and to Europe as the "correct" one.

Eudoxus' historical importance results from his contribution to the meaning of science, rather than his actual scientific achievement.

Plato was firm in teaching that the earth stands still, but it was not possible in the intellectual ferment of Greek science that all his contemporaries would agree with him. Heraclides (ca. 373 B.C.) taught that the earth rotates on its axis once in every twenty-four hours, while the remote stars stand still, thus accounting for the apparent diurnal (daily) motions of the stars. He also suggested that Venus and Mercury, never far from the sun, may actually revolve in orbits about the sun while the latter revolves about the earth. Retrograde motion of planets was one of the key problems in astronomy to Heraclides, as it was to Eudoxus. As astronomy progressed, and the making of accurate observations was taken more and more seriously, other problems arose, some of which were handled with great intelligence and ingenuity. Let us examine the most important of these.

1-4 Some achievements of Greek astronomy

Eudoxus' model with its rotating spheres was more or less successful in representing the relative positions of bodies in the skies. But these spheres were centered at the earth and failed to account for the obvious variations in brightness of the planets Mars, Venus, and Mercury, variations which suggest that these planets do not remain at fixed distances from the earth. Eclipses of the sun had been (correctly) attributed, as early as the time of Thales, to the moon's position between the earth and sun. The fact that the sun is totally obscured in some eclipses and an uneclipsed ring of light remains in others seemed to indicate that the earth's distance from the sun is not exactly constant, either. Moreover, the sun does not move quite uniformly with respect to the stellar sphere, so that the four seasons, as measured by the sun's position in relation to the celestial equator, are not quite of the same length.

Among the various Greek scientists who tried to solve one or more of these problems was Aristarchus of Samos (ca. 310–230 B.C.), a man who had very little influence in his own time but whose ideas were destined for revival some eighteen centuries later. His original writings have not survived, but according to his contemporary, Archimedes, he published a number of hypotheses, including the following: "The fixed stars and the sun remain unmoved, but the earth revolves about the sun in the circumference of a circle, the sun lying in the middle of the orbit." We do not know how seriously Aristarchus took this hypothesis, nor do we know whether he also considered the planets to be moving about the sun, an assumption which would have accounted for variations in their brightness. In any case, the hypothesis met with no favor, and gave rise to a charge of impiety against Aristarchus by a contemporary disciple of Plato.

It is hardly surprising that even
the most conventional of Greek
astronomers believed the earth to be
spherical. Some went so far as to
make measurements of the earth's
diameter. The method employed by
Eratosthenes of Alexandria (ca.
284–192 B.C.) to this end is illustrated in Fig. 1–4. He observed that
on midsummer day (when the sun
reaches its position farthest north of
the celestial equator) the sun at
noon, as attested by its illumination
of the bottom of a well, was directly
overhead in Syene, a city in southern
Egypt now called Assuan. On midsummer day in Alexandria light
from the sun at noon made an angle
with the vertical which he measured. Assuming that Alexandria is directly

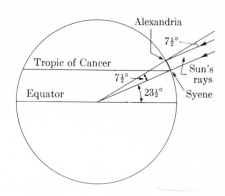

Fig. 1–4. Principle of Eratosthenes'
measurement of the earth's circumference; $360°/7\frac{1}{2}° = 48$, and therefore the
circumference of the earth is 48 times
the distance from Syene to Alexandria.

north of Syene, and knowing the distance between the two cities, he could
compute the circumference (and hence the diameter) as indicated. His
result was in amazingly good agreement with modern measurement, but
unfortunately the value obtained by a later observer, only about one-third
as large as Eratosthenes', was more generally accepted. This mistake was
responsible for the error of Columbus, seventeen centuries later, who
thought he had reached the Orient when he had traveled only one-third or
less of the necessary distance. Modern measurements give the radius of
the earth at the equator as 3963.5 miles or about 6378 kilometers.

Perhaps the greatest astronomer of ancient times, and certainly one of
the greatest astronomical observers of all time, was Hipparchus, who died
about 125 B.C. He was a genius not only in accuracy of observation but in
the discriminating use of earlier observations, and most of his discoveries
continue to hold interest for professional astronomers today. He detected
what is called the *precession of the equinoxes*, i.e., that the times of occurrence of the annual seasons are slowly shifting with respect to the constellations. The circle of the ecliptic (Fig. 1–2) is thus not absolutely fixed;
its points of intersection with the celestial equator rotate, describing a complete cycle once in about 26,000 years. (Hipparchus revised his estimate
several times, but one of his figures is within one percent of the modern accepted value.) This small effect, whose very discovery is a testimony to
Hipparchus' powers of observation, remained inexplicable until the 17th
century. Hipparchus also suggested a solution to Plato's problem which
was acceptable in his own day and survived to the time of Copernicus.

1-5 The Ptolemaic system

The model suggested by Hipparchus became the most successful astronomical system of the ancient world after its details were worked out by Ptolemy (Claudius Ptolemaeus of Alexandria, exact dates uncertain) during the second century A.D. This system depends mainly on two ingenious devices for combining circles, called *epicycles* and *eccentrics*, both simple in principle but very elaborate in application to actual observed motions. We need here be concerned only with the principles. In the system of Hipparchus and Ptolemy, commonly called the *Ptolemaic system*, the earth is stationary. The troublesome retrograde motion of the planets is understood in terms of *epicycles*, the nature of which is made clear in Fig. 1–5. Each planet moves in a small circle whose center moves simultaneously in a larger circle about the earth. This combination of two circular motions gives rise, as shown, to occasional reversals of direction (hence a looped path) in relation to the fixed stars, which were thought, as in the days of earlier astronomers, to be fixed to a rotating crystalline sphere. The *rates* of planetary motion could not be properly represented if these circles were assumed to roll along steadily, and it was necessary to introduce *eccentrics* as well. For example, the slight variation in the sun's speed, already mentioned, could be understood on the assumption that the sun moves uniformly in a perfect circle of which the earth is not quite the center (see Fig.

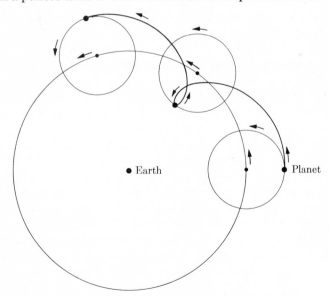

Fig. 1–5. Showing the generation of loops to account for retrograde motion. A planet is assumed to move in a small circle at the same time that the center of the small circle moves in a circular path about the earth.

1-6). In the diagram the distance between the earth and the center of the
sun's orbit has been exaggerated for
clarity.   Epicycles and eccentrics
were combined for representation of
the motions of planets.   A center
other than the one assumed for the
sun's orbit was necessary in some
cases (especially for the planets
Mercury, Venus, and Mars) to account for the observed motions
through the constellations.   Thus
the Ptolemaic system was *not*
strictly geocentric (earth-centered),
but at least the earth was assumed
to stand still.

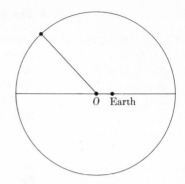

Fig. 1-6.   Eccentric motion.   The
circular orbit is not strictly geocentric,
but both the earth and the center *O* are
stationary.

The model of the solar system which has been sketched so briefly above
was worked out in elaborate detail, and became capable of representing
the careful observations of Hipparchus and others with fair accuracy. The
scheme was an abstract geometrical device, and there is no evidence that
Ptolemy regarded its motions as physically real.   In the introduction to
his *Hypotheses*, for example, he stated: "I do not profess to be able to
account for all the motions at the same time; but I shall show that each
by itself is well explained by its proper hypotheses." However considered,
the Ptolemaic system was a great achievement, the last of the grand
accomplishments, indeed, of ancient astronomy.   The impetus of Greek
science declined as the Hellenistic empire disintegrated and the center of
civilization moved to Rome.   The Romans excelled in engineering but had
little use for science, and it has been said that they took over the content
of Greek science without its method.   Robbed of its capacity for growth,
science could only stagnate.   In seeking the historical roots of ideas we
shall have to return again and again to aspects of ancient Greek thought
but rarely to that of ancient Rome.

A genuine scientific tradition was carried on by the Arabs, who combined
the Greek heritage* with a broader tradition in mathematics inherited from
the Hindu world.   During the Middle Ages, the Ptolemaic system returned
to Europe via translations from the Arabic, together with star catalogs
compiled by Arab astronomers.   In time European interest in astronomy
was rekindled, at least in part because of the practical needs of navigation

---

*The Egyptian city of Alexandria became the principal center of Greek learning
during the third century B.C., and the whole of Egypt was conquered by the
Arabs during the 7th century A.D.

and because the old Julian calendar, in use since the first century B.C., was getting badly out of step with the sun. Theoretical astronomy was taught in the universities that flourished during the Renaissance. Thus the stage was set for the next great step in the theory of astronomy, one which signaled the beginning of a new scientific era.

1–6 The Copernican system

Nikolaus Koppernigk (1473–1543), who used the Latinized form of his name, Copernicus, spent most of his life in his native Poland, but as a young man studied in Italy, where he learned what the universities taught in the way of astronomy. The endless complications of the Ptolemaic system offended and annoyed him and the chief motivation in his work seems to have been an attempt to reinstate the "purity" of the original Pythagorean circles and spheres. He had heard of Aristarchus and the idea that the earth moves in a circle about the sun, and it struck him that by logical elaboration of this idea a vastly simplified picture of celestial motions could be achieved. His model was not really in more complete accord with contemporary observations than Ptolemy's, but it was incontestably simpler (Fig. 1–7). The doubting Père Mersenne (1588–1648), himself a scientist of great repute, said of it: "If I could be convinced that God always did things in the shortest and easiest way, then I should certainly have to

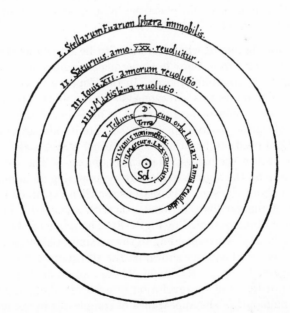

Fig. 1–7. Diagram of the Copernican system, from *The Revolutions* (1543).

recognize the fact that the world does move." The Copernican model, though still based on geometry alone, was capable of physical, as opposed to mere geometrical, representation to a greater extent than the Ptolemaic model.

The Copernican *heliocentric* (sun-centered) view of the solar system, in its essential features, is that taught today. Before seeing how it simplified the difficulties that beset earlier astronomers and mathematicians, let us look at the outline of the system as given by Copernicus himself:

"The first and highest of all the spheres is the sphere of the fixed stars. It encloses all the other spheres and is itself self-contained; it is immobile; it is certainly the portion of the universe with reference to which the movement and positions of all the other heavenly bodies must be considered. If some people are yet of the opinion that this sphere moves, we are of a contrary mind; and after deducing the motion of the earth, we shall show why we so conclude. Saturn, first of the planets, which accomplishes its revolution in thirty years, is nearest the first sphere. Jupiter, making its revolution in twelve years, is next. Then comes Mars, revolving once in two years. The fourth place in the series is occupied by the sphere which contains the earth and the sphere of the moon, and which performs an annual revolution. The fifth place is that of Venus, revolving in nine months. Finally, the sixth place is occupied by Mercury, revolving in eighty days.

"In the midst of all, the sun reposes, unmoving. Who, indeed, in this most beautiful temple would place the light-giver in any other part than whence it can illumine all other parts?"

Some of the details of what has come to be known as the Copernican system are different from those in Copernicus' original formulation, but we may neglect these small differences. In the Copernican view, a daily rotation of the earth on its axis is responsible for the diurnal rising and setting of the sun, moon, planets, and stars. The direction of this axis, to a very good approximation, is fixed in space. It points almost directly toward Polaris, whose position, like those of the other stars, is also fixed. (Temporarily we neglect the precession of the equinoxes.) The apparent motion of the sun among the stars is explained by assuming an annual revolution of the earth about the sun. The seasons are then explained in terms of an inclination of the earth's rotational axis with respect to the plane of its orbit of revolution, as shown in Fig. 1–8. The angle of this inclination is approximately $23\frac{1}{2}°$, corresponding to the maximum difference between the sun and the celestial equator shown on the star-map of Fig. 1–2. Geocentricity is retained only for the moon, whose motion among the stars is accounted for in terms of its revolution in an orbit about the earth with a period of one month. The appearance of complexity in the motions of the planets, in the Copernican view, is due to the combination of their revolu-

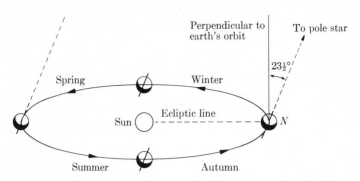

FIG. 1–8. Showing how the seasons depend on the inclination of the earth's axis to the plane of its orbit.

tionary motions about the sun and that of our own planet. The apparent irregularity of Mars, for example, can be accounted for as indicated in Fig. 1–9. The primed numbers, 1', 2', 3', etc., represent the *actual* positions of Mars as it is observed from the earth at times when the latter's successive positions are 1'', 2'', 3'', etc. With respect to the more remote fixed stars, these positions appear to an earthbound observer as 1, 2, 3, etc., and thus include an apparent temporary reversal of the usual eastward trend. Thus the ancient problem of retrograde planetary motion can be understood in a very simple way.

It was evident from the start that the observations did not quite fit into this simple picture, and Copernicus had to introduce a number of eccentrics. For example, the center of the earth's orbit had to be placed slightly to one side of the sun to account for the inequality in length of different quarters of the year. The precession of the equinoxes is more easily interpreted on this model, however, than Copernicus realized. (His own complicated explanation, which we need not consider, resulted from the confusion of data accepted as valid in the 16th century.) It can be described very simply with reference to Fig. 1–10. The direction of the earth's rotation is only approximately fixed in space. The axis itself actually revolves (precesses) slowly about a line perpendicular to the plane of earth's orbit of revolution, always making an angle of $23\frac{1}{2}°$ to this perpendicular. This motion is analogous to that of a spinning top, in which the axis of rotation swings slowly about a vertical line. For the earth this motion is so slow, as we have said, that 26,000 years is required for it to complete a whole cycle. Roughly 13,000 years hence the axis will not point to Polaris, but to a point in the sky some 47° away from that star. The circle of the ecliptic remains unchanged, but the celestial equator (Fig. 1–2), which reflects the earth's orientation, shifts slowly in time so that it crosses this circle at points opposite different constellations in the star background.

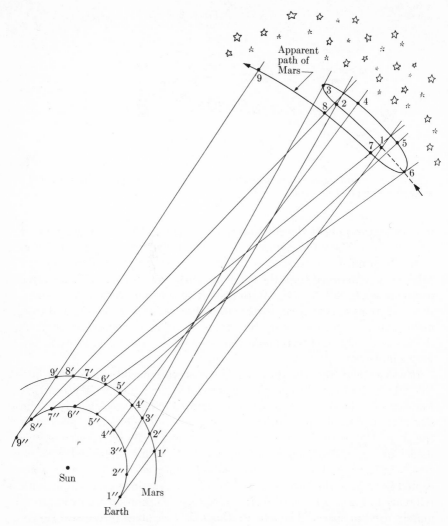

FIG. 1-9.   Interpretation of retrograde motion of Mars on the Copernican theory.

Despite the minor complications that had to be introduced into his system (e.g., eccentrics), Copernicus had restored the "perfect" spheres and circles in such a way that they could be recognized as such, rather than as mere geometric components of more complex motions, as in the Ptolemaic model. This accomplishment pleased him tremendously. He knew that learned men would be prejudiced against his scheme, because reverence for Greek learning was one of the most prominent features of the intellectual

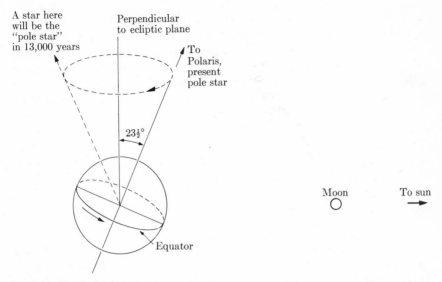

A star here will be the "pole star" in 13,000 years

Perpendicular to ecliptic plane

To Polaris, present pole star

$23\frac{1}{2}°$

Moon

To sun

Equator

FIG. 1–10. The precession of equinoxes is understood as a slow rotation of the axis of the earth about a line perpendicular to the plane of its orbit.

climate of medieval Europe. Copernicus' principal motivation was one of conservatism, however, and there is no evidence that he dreamed of offending religion. He was himself a canon of the Roman Catholic Church, and dedicated his book, *De Revolutionibus Orbium Celestium*, to the Pope. Nevertheless, his work was immediately attacked by Martin Luther, soon proscribed by Hebrew seminaries, and finally placed on the papal index. The conclusion of Catholic officialdom that Copernicus' ideas were heretical did not result from the initial publication of the ideas themselves as much as from later evidence of their physical correctness adduced by a greater scientist, Galileo.

1–7 Confirmation of the heliocentric system

We have said that the system of Copernicus, although simpler than that of Ptolemy, did not give a more accurate representation of those observations of celestial motions that were held acceptable in the 16th century. There was therefore no compelling practical reason for its acceptance, while at the same time there were many reasons of sheer conservatism and prejudice for its rejection. In addition, there was an objection that appeared scientifically valid. As an observer shifts his position on the earth's surface, the relative positions of fixed objects at different distances from the observer give the *appearance* of shifting, a phenomenon known as *parallax*. If the earth moves about the sun in a vast circular orbit, it was argued, and if the stars are fixed to an immobile sphere, their relative positions should exhibit parallactic displacements, i.e., should appear in different relative positions at different seasons of the year. Yet no one had been able to detect parallax of the stars. Copernicus himself worried about this point, since in his own diagram the fixed sphere of stars was placed so near the earth that it would most certainly look different from different parts of the earth's orbit. The correct answer to the dilemma, that the distances of the stars from the earth are so vast in comparison with the dimensions of the solar system that stellar parallax is entirely unobservable to the naked eye, was by no means obvious. The stars are actually "fixed" by distance, some farther from the earth than others, but all so far away that motions within the scope of the earth's orbit bring no changes perceptible to the unaided eye.

Stellar parallax remained undetected until the year 1838, when the German astronomer F. W. Bessel, by telescopic observation, found slight apparent shifts in the position of a star known as 61 Cygni. The nature of these observations is made clear in Fig. 1–11: a relatively near star, observed against the background of more remote stars, appears to describe a circular path (actually elliptical—see Section 1–9) with a period of one year. The maximum parallactic displacement occurs in observations made six months apart, and defines an angle as shown. The largest parallactic angle ever observed is 0.756 *seconds* of arc, for the star alpha-Centauri, which is therefore nearer the earth than all other stars. (The figure has been exaggerated for clarity.) Knowing the length of the base line of observation (the diameter of earth's orbit, 186 million miles) it has been calculated that alpha-Centauri is 4.3 light-years away, i. e., light, traveling at 186,000 miles per second, requires 4.3 years to reach us from the nearest star. This distance corresponds to 25 thousand billion miles. The great majority of stars are so remote that their parallactic displacements cannot be detected with the best available telescopes.

The new and not readily acceptable idea that the stars are almost infinitely remote was vigorously espoused by Giordano Bruno (1548–1600). Although Bruno was neither an astronomer nor a mathematician, and although many of his ideas were not entirely original, he was the first to see some of the logical consequences of deposing the earth from the center of the universe. With considerable contemporary effect, he rejected the idea of a hard crystal sphere containing the stars, an idea that had hardly been doubted since antiquity. Bruno held that the universe is infinite in extent, and that "there are endless particular worlds similar to this of the earth." His shattering of the crystalline, star-laden sphere came to influence not only astronomy but every department of scientific thought. It was his supposition of a "plurality of worlds," which he offered simply as evidence of the power of the Divinity, that brought Bruno his greatest trouble; after

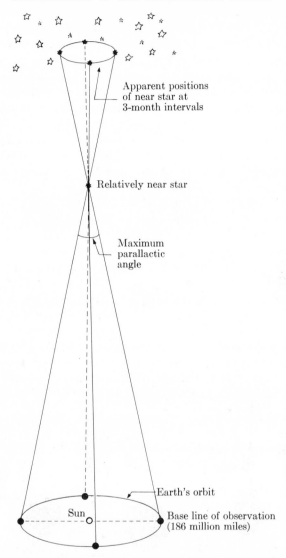

Apparent positions
of near star at
3-month intervals

Relatively near star

Maximum
parallactic
angle

Earth's orbit

Sun

Base line of observation
(186 million miles)

Fig. 1-11. Stellar parallax: apparent shifts in the position of a star due to earth's orbital motion (greatly exaggerated).

eight years of martyrdom at the hands of the Inquisition he was burned at the stake in 1600. Whether or not there are planets of other suns on which life is supported is still a matter for conjecture—something that as yet can be neither proved nor disproved.

Another popular objection to the Copernican system related to the earth's assumed rotation: if the earth is turning so fast, objects on its surface should fly off at a tangent, like drops of water from a spinning wheel. At least, it was argued, an object dropped from a height should fall somewhat to the west if the earth is turning eastward. At last astronomy was related to everyday motions on the earth! The great Italian scientist Galileo Galilei (1564–1642), whose penetrating analyses of terrestrial motions will concern us in the next chapter, was disturbed by the doubt that these considerations cast on the Copernican system. His vindication of that system, however, was not accomplished in terms of direct answers to such objections, but by the use of a newly discovered instrument which enabled him literally to see what had never been seen before, and by inspired recognition of the significance of what he saw.

The telescope was invented in Holland, and after travelers had brought word of it to Italy in 1609 Galileo constructed one for himself and turned it on the skies. Within the short space of one year he made many discoveries, three of which bore particularly significant relations to Copernicus' heliocentric theory. One was the discovery of four of Jupiter's satellites, members of a sort of miniature solar system which can be seen from outside and serve as a model, in a sense, of the larger one. Here at last was proof that there *are* objects in the universe which do not revolve about the earth! More direct confirmation of the heliocentric hypothesis came from Galileo's observations of the *phases* of the planet Venus. We are able to see Venus only by virtue of the sunlight it reflects, and the fraction of its surface which is visible to us at any given time depends on the earth's position relative to both the sun and Venus, as shown in Fig. 1–12. With the unaided eye we

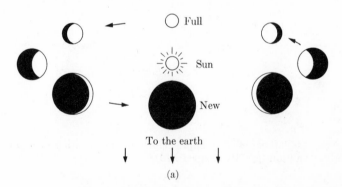

Fig. 1–12. Phases of Venus (a and b) and the moon (c). The photographs in (b) were all taken at the same magnification, and size differences reflect variations in distance from the earth. The photograph at lower left was taken when Venus was almost exactly between the earth and the sun, that at upper left with Venus directly opposite the sun. Unshaded areas in (c) represent those portions of the illuminated moon's surface which we can see from the earth. (Photographs courtesy of Lowell Observatory.)

(b)

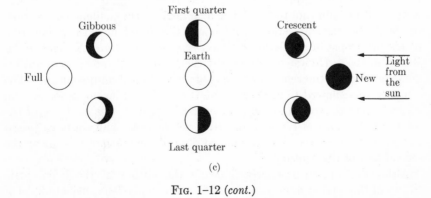

(c)

Fig. 1–12 *(cont.)*

may detect only variations in the brightness of the planet, but through the telescope it is readily seen to pass through a regular cycle of phases—full, crescent, and new—analogous to those of our own moon (Fig. 1–12a,c). That there is considerable variation in the distance from the earth to Venus is shown clearly in the photographs of Fig. 1–12 (b). Such phases of Venus are to be expected on the heliocentric model but not on the geocentric model (Fig. 1–13), and in discovering them Galileo confirmed what Copernicus could have predicted. Finally, Galileo was able to demonstrate that the spherical perfection of heavenly bodies was a complete myth: the sun, observed telescopically, has spots; Saturn has what looked like a bulge around its middle; the moon has mountains. These observations were much more startling in the early 17th century than we can readily believe today. It is said that some of Galileo's fellow professors refused to look through his telescope, but he himself saw enough to confirm his Copernican convictions.

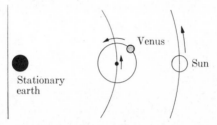

FIG. 1–13. On the Ptolemaic model we should never be able to see the full disk of Venus. Its path, on this model, is inside that of the sun, and since its position is never observed to be far from the sun, the two objects are viewed from the earth in the same general direction.

In 1616 the Pope's consulting theologians held the two propositions that the sun is immovable at the center of the world, and that the earth has a diurnal motion of rotation to be "absurd in philosophy, and formally heretical, because expressly contrary to Holy Scripture." Galileo was warned at that time not to "hold, teach, or defend" the condemned doctrine, but he did not get into serious trouble with the church until the publication of his pro-Copernican *Dialogue Concerning the Two Chief Systems of the World*, in 1632. He was questioned by the Inquisition, forced to recant his views, and spent the remainder of his life in technical imprisonment. The sentence was allowed to mean no more than strict seclusion, however, and he continued to work and write. Nevertheless, with this evidence of the intellectual climate of 17th-century Italy before us we shall not be surprised to find that the center of science had shifted to the north of Europe by the second half of the century.

Although Copernicus was technically the author of the heliocentric theory of the solar system (an acknowledged revival of the ancient model of

Aristarchus) there was good reason to regard Galileo as a greater threat to established ideas. Before him, the Copernican system could be regarded as mere hypothesis, as an alternative mode of thought yielding greater geometric simplicity than the Ptolemaic model. With his telescope, Galileo destroyed the cherished myth of "perfection" in the heavens, and his observations of Venus were hard facts which were in accord with one hypothesis but not the other. Once physical facts of observation had made so decisive an entrance, the Copernican system could no longer be dismissed as a mere mathematical device, or as an interesting mental exercise. Still, we would hardly be justified in saying that Galileo *proved* that the earth moves. It has been the test of time—long-continuing agreement between the model and legions of new and accurate observations—that has led to our present firm conviction of the correctness of Copernicus' essential ideas. The word *essential* must be emphasized, for these very legions of observations have brought alteration to many of the details of the Copernican model, as we shall shortly see.

Bessel's observation of stellar parallax provided striking evidence for the earth's orbital motion, almost tantamount to direct "proof." In Chapter 3 we shall discuss observed effects of the earth's rotation about its own axis, but we may note here that the first popular demonstration of terrestrial rotation was given by the French physicist J. B. L. Foucault at the Paris Exhibition of 1851. The principle of his simple device, the Foucault pendulum, is readily understood by considering what would happen to a pendulum with a heavy bob set swinging at the north pole. The bob itself is nowhere rigidly attached to the earth, and as time goes on the plane in which the pendulum swings appears to rotate slowly with respect to the original line of the swing. What happens is that the plane of swing is maintained while the earth turns under it, rotating through a complete cycle of 360° once in 24 hours. At the equator a Foucault pendulum would show no rotation; if it were set swinging along a north-south line (a meridian), for example, this direction is maintained in space throughout the rotation of the earth. In Foucault's experiment, at the latitude of Paris, the plane of his pendulum rotated through 360° once every 32 hours, in accordance with the detailed theory he had worked out. Apparent rotation of a Foucault pendulum is directly due to the earth's rotational motion.

1–8 Tycho Brahe and accurate astronomical observation

The Copernican system, we have stressed, was no better as a representation of the observed motions of celestial objects than was Ptolemy's, in the sixteenth century. At the time of Copernicus, however, no consistent standards of accuracy for astronomical observations existed. The data Copernicus attempted to fit into his system included those from original Babylonian records, and some of them were very seriously inaccurate. "Good" and "bad" data were not distinguishable, and some observational "facts" actually contradicted others. Where precision of observation was required, personal judgments had to be relied upon.

Difficulties posed by variations in the quality of astronomical observations had to be overcome before real progress could be made in testing the heliocentric and geocentric theories by comparison with facts. The Danish astronomer Tycho Brahe (1546–1601), in recognition of this deficiency of astronomical science, brought naked-eye astronomy to its highest attainable degree of accuracy. Using improved instruments for angular measurement and new ones of his own design, he devoted most of his lifetime to the accumulation of accurate records of the positions of celestial objects. His eyesight must have been superb, and the sum of his patience, consistency, and integrity certainly bordered on genius.

One object of Tycho's search was stellar parallax, since he felt that it was the one phenomenon which, if detected, would support the Copernican model. He failed to observe parallax of the stars, and knowing that his measurements were performed with the greatest accuracy then attainable, he rejected the heliocentric system. Unwilling, at the same time, to return to the endless complexities of the Ptolemaic model, Tycho developed a geocentric system of his own. In this system Mercury and Venus were assumed to revolve around the sun, while the sun and all the outer planets revolve around the earth. This was at least consistent with his failure to detect stellar parallax, and somewhat simpler than the Ptolemaic model. Tycho was not mathematically talented, and the details of his system were never fully worked out. His lasting importance to astronomy does not depend on his hypotheses, but on the vast and unique collection of accurate data which he bequeathed to an Austrian who had been his assistant, Johannes Kepler (1571–1630).

1–9 Kepler's laws of planetary motion

Kepler, an excellent mathematician, was principally motivated by aesthetics and religion, which to him were almost indistinguishable. Of the Copernican system he said: "I have attested it as true in my deepest soul, and I contemplate its beauty with incredible and ravishing delight." In the words of the historian Sir William Dampier: "Kepler was convinced that God created the world in accordance with the principle of perfect numbers, so that the underlying mathematical harmony, the music of the spheres, is the real and discoverable cause of planetary motions." Although Kepler thus had undertaken the solution of Plato's problem as his life's work, his great innovation became possible with his willingness to give up circles and spheres in the face of the "stubborn" facts accumulated by Tycho. He worked long and patiently to systematize Tycho's data, and discovered many regularities in the motions of the planets. While in his own time there was no way of determining which of these relations were of greatest theoretical importance, history has selected three of Kepler's "laws" for permanent commemoration of his name.

The relation known today as Kepler's first law was achieved after more than four years of analysis of Tycho's records of the orbit of Mars. To see how this was done, let us consider the orbit of the planet Mercury, more readily shown on a diagram (Fig. 1–14). At successive times the position of Mercury can be noted against the fixed-star background (not shown). Let us assume, to begin with, that the earth moves in a circle, and indicate the

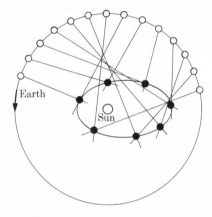

FIG. 1–14. Observations necessary for tracing the orbit of Mercury.

position of the earth in its orbit for each observation. In the diagram, points are shown corresponding to the observation of Mercury through only two complete cycles of its orbit, i.e., about six months. (Actually, we have "cheated" a little in Fig. 1–14, for each of the second set of earth positions was chosen just one of Mercury's years later than a point in the first set. Kepler had to work much harder than this diagram indicates.) The intersection of two lines one cycle apart provides a point on Mercury's orbit, and with many reliable observations that orbit may thus be traced out. It is found, furthermore, that these points cannot be fitted into a circle, no matter where the center is placed. But they *do* fit on a smooth curve, one whose geometric properties had been known to the Greeks, an *ellipse*. This curve has a property which makes it very easy to draw: from every point on an ellipse the sum of the distances to two fixed points is constant (see Fig. 1–15). These two fixed points are called the *foci* of the ellipse. When they are far apart the curve is very long and thin, and ellipses whose foci are close together are very nearly circular.

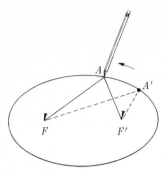

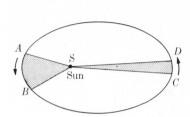

Fig. 1–15. Tracing an ellipse. The sum of FA and $F'A$ is the same for all points A on the curve.

FIG. 1–16. The law of equal areas in equal times (Kepler's second law). Areas ABS and SCD are equal, and a planet traverses arcs CD and AB in equal times.

The discovery Kepler made first about the orbit of Mars was later verified by him for the orbits of the other planets. *Every planet moves in an elliptical path, with the sun at one focus;* this is a statement of Kepler's first law of planetary motion. Ellipses whose foci nearly coincide are difficult to distinguish from the circular orbits of Copernicus, and most planetary orbits are not far from circular. Just these small differences, however, prevented Kepler from fitting the data into circular paths. Because the discrepancies are small, he could not have made his discovery without Tycho's accurate records, even though Copernicus' need for eccentrics stemmed at least in part from the ellipticity of orbits which he did not suspect. The earth's orbit is slightly elliptical, too, but much less so than that of Mars, so that Kepler was able to arrive at the main idea without taking this added complication into account.

Kepler's first law provides a geometrical trace of planetary motion, as though the planet were a pencil tracing out a mark on paper and the mark were more important than the pencil. It does not describe how a planet's changes of position take place in time. Although the orbit itself is important, another law is needed to describe variations in a planet's speed. Kepler's analyses of Tycho's observations convinced him that planets do not move about their elliptical orbits at constant speed, and in time he was able to fit the data to a simple relation between a planet's speed and its position in its path. This relation is called Kepler's second law: *an imaginary line drawn from a planet to the sun sweeps over equal areas in equal times.* The implications of this law are brought out in Fig. 1–16. If a line from a planet to the sun sweeps out the same area in a given time when the planet is near the sun as it does when farther away, then the planet must traverse a greater portion of its orbit in that time, i.e., travel at greater speed, when in the nearer position. The speed of a planet constantly changes, in fact, increasing as it approaches the point in its orbit nearest the sun, decreasing as it recedes from that point. Only in a perfectly circular orbit would a planet travel at constant speed.

Kepler was greatly pleased by the relation now called his second law. He had succeeded in his search for regularity—if not in speed, at least in area. Later, in connection with the work of Newton, we too shall find additional reason to delight in it, although for reasons quite different from Plato's demand for preconceived "sameness." Still Kepler was not satisfied, however. Since the days of early Greek philosophy men had attempted to find relations among the motions of the various planets, without success. The first two laws of Kepler describe the regularities of motion of individual planets, but they do not relate the motions of the various planets to one another. When Kepler finally did succeed in the discovery of such a relation he was overcome with joy: " . . . at last, at last, the true relation . . . overcame by storm the shadows of my mind, with such fulness of agreement between my seventeen years' labor on the observations of Brahe and this present study of mine that I at first believed that I was dreaming . . ." He had long since known that the time required for planets to complete their cycles increased with their distance from the sun. The relation which brought him such ecstasy, now called Kepler's third law, is a *quantitative* statement of the manner of this dependence: *the squares of the times required by the planets for a complete orbital revolution about the sun are proportional to the cubes of their average distances from the sun.* Algebraically, this law may be expressed as

$$T^2 = kR^3, \qquad (1\text{–}1)$$

where T represents the *period* of a planet, or time required for one revolution, R the average distance of the planet from the sun, and k, a constant of proportionality, is the same for all planets. The average radius R is half of that diameter of the ellipse that passes through both its foci, or simply the radius of a very nearly circular orbit. A test of this law is shown in Table 1–1. Measured values of the planetary periods, T, are here shown in earth years, and the unit of distance, R, is the average distance of the earth from the sun. With these units the constant k has the value of unity; therefore, the fact that the values of T^2 and R^3 are nearly identical for each planet (identical, we must assume, within the accuracy of the data), shows the validity of Kepler's third law.*

---

*The Appendix contains a review of mathematical procedures to be employed in this book. The reader for whom the above discussion has raised questions about the meaning of proportionality, or the use of mathematical language in general, is referred to that appendix. The mathematics we shall use is extremely

(*cont.*)

TABLE 1-1

KEPLER'S THIRD LAW OF PLANETARY MOTION

Name of planet	T (period, in years)	R (distance from sun, in units of earth-sun distance)	T^2	R^3
Mercury	0.24	0.39	0.058	0.059
Venus	0.61	0.72	0.37	0.37
Earth	1	1	1	1
Mars	1.88	1.52	3.54	3.50
Jupiter	11.86	5.20	140.7	140.6
Saturn	29.46	9.54	867.6	868

Each of Kepler's laws is *more* than a concise summary of a vast number of meticulous astronomical observations. The laws are extremely useful for prediction, since the pattern of behavior they describe is as valid for the future as for the past. Kepler's mathematical description, based on Tycho's observations, is both accurate and general, and has received confirmation from the wealth of data on the solar system that has been collected since his time. For example, the planets Uranus (discovered 1781) and Neptune (1846) have been found to conform as well to these laws as the more familiar planets. Although the planet Pluto has traversed only about one-tenth of its orbit since it was first seen in 1930, the main features of its path have been computed with confidence on the basis of Kepler's laws. Other objects have come to be recognized as members of the solar system, notably the many small planetoids, or *asteroids*, whose orbits lie between those of Mars and Jupiter. Comets are also members of the solar system, but they suffer such relatively rapid and large changes in their tenuous material that few of them are very regular or permanent. For all planets and planetoids, observations are in accord with Kepler's laws except for deviations, usually small and generally well understood, such as the "perturbation" of one orbit due to the effect of a neighboring planet (see Chapter 4).

---

simple, but its importance cannot be overemphasized: historically, mathematics played a crucial role in the rise of science. To Galileo, for example, the universe could be adequately described only in mathematical language and, as we have seen, Tycho Brahe's accurate observations acquired their greatest importance in the hands of the mathematically talented Kepler.

This last phrase, involving "effect," would not have had much meaning for Kepler. Although he was diligent in seeking a "motive power" for the motions he described, his achievement lay in establishing the existence of regularities, not in explaining them. As concise summaries, or epitomizations, of an array of observational data, Kepler's laws may be called *empirical* laws. It may be argued that they are somewhat more, for Kepler fitted the observations into a hypothetical geometric *model*, one which could be regarded as a representation of actual physical motions. But the laws go no further than precise description, and do not approach causal questions in the modern scientific sense. What regulates the motions in the solar system? What relations do these motions bear to those of bodies here on the earth's surface, or to motion generally? A deeper insight into the meaning of the laws of Kepler became possible only after motion had been more generally studied by his Italian contemporary Galileo, who, ironically, ignored the details of Kepler's work entirely. Before we can achieve a more fundamental grasp of the nature of the solar system we must acquaint ourselves with some of the apparently nonastronomical work of Galileo, the man generally recognized, with good reason, as the "father of modern science."

1-10 Summary

Systematic astronomical observations by early civilizations were used, in about the 6th century B.C., in attempts by the Greeks to formulate a rational cosmology based on geometrical spheres and circles. The outstanding problems encountered in describing the motions of celestial bodies were due to retrograde motions of the planets and to the slight inequality of the four terrestrial seasons. Hellenistic astronomers came to understand solar and lunar eclipses, measured the diameter of the earth, and the greatest of them, Hipparchus, discovered the precession of the equinoxes. The geometrical account of the solar system bequeathed to later civilizations was the geocentric system of epicycles and eccentrics devised by Hipparchus and elaborated by Ptolemy of Alexandria—the Ptolemaic system. In the first half of the 16th century Copernicus, following a suggestion made nineteen centuries earlier by Aristarchus, formulated a heliocentric system according to which the planets (including Earth) revolve in circular orbits about the sun. This idea received confirmation through Galileo's observations with a new instrument, the telescope; Galileo observed the phases of Venus, discovered Jupiter's moons, and spots on the sun. Greater observational accuracy, introduced by Tycho Brahe, made possible Kepler's discovery of several laws of planetary motion. These laws mark the climax of purely descriptive astronomy of the solar system; further progress was impossible without a deeper understanding of motion itself.

REFERENCES*

ARMITAGE, A., *The World of Copernicus*, published earlier as *Sun, Stand Thou Still*.

BAKER, R. H., *Astronomy*. Excellent introduction to astronomical facts.

BERNHARD, H. J., D. A. BENNETT, and H. S. RICE, *New Handbook of the Heavens*. An inexpensive popular introduction to astronomy.

BUTTERFIELD, H., *The Origins of Modern Science*, especially Chapters II and IV.

DREYER, J. L. E., *A History of Astronomy (from Thales to Kepler)*. A detailed account, but one that repays reading even if the technical material is omitted.

FARRINGTON, B., *Greek Science*. An excellent popular survey.

HARGREAVES, F. J., *The Size of the Universe*, Chapters I and II.

HOLTON, G., *Introduction to Concepts and Theories in Physical Science*, Chapters 6 and 7.

PAYNE-GAPOSCHKIN, C., *Introduction to Astronomy*, Chapters I, VII, and VIII.

RUSSELL, H. N., *The Solar System and its Origin*. Popular Lectures.

SARTON, G., *A History of Science: Ancient Science Through the Golden Age of Greece*. The most thorough nontechnical account available, actually a history of culture from the scientific viewpoint.

SHAPLEY, H., and H. E. HOWARTH, *A Source Book in Astronomy*. Excerpts from the original writings of Copernicus (pp. 1–12), Tycho Brahe (pp. 13–19), Kepler (pp. 29–40), and Galileo (pp. 41–57).

WHIPPLE, F., *Sun, Moon and Planets*.

Of the general histories of science, those especially recommended are:

DAMPIER, W. C., *A History of Science*.

MASON, S. F., *Main Currents of Scientific Thought*.

---

*See General Bibliography for publishers and dates.

1. When the sun is on the horizon and the moon is at 90°, as shown in Fig. 1–12(c), we see just half the moon, not more. (a) What does this indicate about the relative distances of the sun and moon from the earth? (b) Draw a diagram with the sun only twice as far from the earth as the moon, and estimate qualitatively how much of the moon's face would then be visible.

2. Careful observation has shown that the moon, throughout its orbit, presents only one face to the earth; an earth-bound observer may never see the back of the moon. Does this indicate that the moon does or does not rotate? If it does rotate, what is its rotational period? Explain.

3. (a) Why are the positions of Mercury and Venus, as observed from the earth, never far from the sun? (b) Draw diagrams indicating the relative positions of the earth, the sun, and Mars when the latter is just on the horizon at sunset, and when it is exactly overhead at midnight.

4. Show that the lunar month (with respect to the sun) should be somewhat over two days longer than the sidereal month (with respect to the stars). This is most easily done by assuming a geocentric model and neglecting the earth's daily rotation. Why is the geocentric explanation valid?

5. If the shadow of a vertical shaft vanishes at noon on one day of the year and points south on all other days, how far is the shaft from the North Pole? Study Fig. 1–4, take the earth's radius to be 4000 miles, and remember that the circumference of a circle is given by the quantity $2\pi r$. [*Ans.*: about 7900 mi]

6. Show that the sun's apparent motion on Fig. 1–1, with successive rotations of the earth, would be a continuous spiral. (a) What part of the celestial sphere would be traced out by this spiral from midwinter to the vernal equinox? (b) How many turns would the spiral contain in this interval?

7. Is Venus the only planet that exhibits regular phase variations? Draw diagrams of the relative positions of the earth, sun, and Mercury, and of the earth, sun, and Mars at different orbital positions, and decide whether either Mercury or Mars could be expected to show phase variations.

8. On Tycho Brahe's model of the solar system Mercury and Venus were

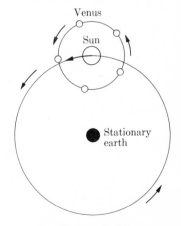

FIGURE 1–17.

thought to revolve around the sun, while the resulting system of three bodies revolves around the earth. Study the diagram of earth, sun, and Venus (Fig. 1–17) and decide whether it would be possible to distinguish Tycho's scheme from that of Copernicus on the basis of the phases of Venus.

9. The orbits of the moon and planets are near but not quite coincident with the plane of the earth's orbit, called the *plane of the ecliptic.* (a) If they lay precisely in the plane of the ecliptic, how often would solar eclipses occur? (b) About how often would Venus appear to cross the disk of the sun? (c) Do these considerations suggest a reason for use of the word ecliptic? If so, state it.

10. Can you explain why Mercury and Venus are sometimes seen on the horizon in the morning ("morning stars") and at other times in the evening ("evening stars")?

11. What combination of circumstances brings about (a) an eclipse of the sun, (b) an eclipse of the moon? (c) While in some solar eclipses the sun's disk is totally obscured, in others (annular eclipses) a thin, complete ring of light remains visible. Can you suggest a reason for this?

12. A distant planet like Saturn shows retrograde motion at intervals of a little more than one earth year, and always when the earth is on the same side of the sun as the planet. Construct a diagram similar to Fig. 1–9, and explain.

13. Uranus is 19.2 times farther from the sun than is the earth, and its period of revolution is 84 years. Neptune is 30.1 times farther from the sun than the earth and has a period of 165 years. Do these planets conform to Kepler's third law?

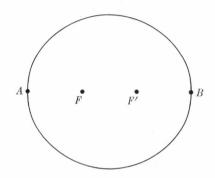

FIGURE 1–18.

14. The ellipse shown in Fig. 1–18 is constructed so that the distances AF, FF', and $F'B$ are equal. If this were the path of a planet, with the sun located at focus F, what would be the ratio of the planet's speed in the vicinity of A to that in the vicinity of B? Use Kepler's second law.

CHAPTER 2

TERRESTRIAL MOTION
FALLING BODIES AND NEWTON'S LAWS

The concept of natural law matured first in astronomy, because of the many regularities observed in the motions of celestial objects   Some regularities were also noted in the motions of terrestrial bodies, although the greater variation in these motions made generalization more difficult. No evidence of the "perfect" circular paths apparently traced out by stars was exhibited by bodies here on the earth. Instead, the most obvious generalization about terrestrial motion is that objects will fall *down*, i.e., vertically, if not supported. Aristotle (384–322 B.C.) contrived a rational view of the whole universe by making a sharp division between the realm of the earth and that of the skies. There could be no conflict between the "perfection" of the heavens and the obviously irregular earth if the two simply had nothing to do with each other. We must admit that Aristotle's view, which later turned out to be quite wrong, was entirely justifiable in terms of the state of knowledge of his time. His generalizations concerning terrestrial motion were accepted as "true" for nearly two millenia. In this chapter we shall see how they were ultimately superseded by generalizations more truly representing the behavior of moving bodies.

2-1 Aristotelian physics

Aristotle was perhaps the greatest of all Greek philosopher-scientists. No other individual of the ancient world collected the knowledge of his time so comprehensively or recorded it so systematically as did Aristotle. His encyclopedic lecture notes were destined to serve as the accepted basis of all science until the time of Galileo, and his importance to the history of science is therefore supreme. Although Aristotle was without doubt a great innovator, the influences of earlier Greek schools were clearly discernible in his work. For nearly twenty years he was a member of Plato's Academy in Athens, and the philosophy of Plato, himself a student of Socrates, encompassed much of the learning of earlier schools, particularly the Pythagorean. It was during a period of twelve years as head of his own school, the Lyceum in Athens, that Aristotle's most original works were produced. Aristotelian philosophers came to be known as the *Peripatetics*, because, when engrossed in thought, the great man and his colleagues habitually strolled about the Lyceum grounds.

Much of the weakness in Athenian science was inherent in the assumption that manual techniques are vulgar and despicable, and that the philosopher should be content to observe and reason. Aristotle acquired this attitude, undoubtedly an outcome of the Athenian institution of slavery, during his long years of study at the Academy. Although Plato had relegated even observation to a position of secondary importance, and held that "correct" answers could be obtained by exercise of the mind alone, Aristotle was more truly a scientist in his belief that generalization should proceed from experience. In one connection, for example, he wrote that ". . . we must partly investigate for ourselves, partly learn from other investigators, and if those who study this subject form an opinion contrary to what we have now stated, we must esteem both parties, indeed, but follow the more accurate." Because of his contempt for manual techniques, however, Aristotle had no concept of the method of experiment and no use for precise measurement. His method was fruitful in biology, to which science his contributions went unmatched for many centuries, buↄ it led to few advances in physical science. Although the method of experimentation *was* practiced by later Greek scientists, notably the great practical inventor, engineer, geometer, and physicist Archimedes (287–212 B.C.), the difficult physical problem of *motion* was not tackled by any of them, and Aristotle's views on this subject remained unchallenged.

According to Aristotle, man's environment, "below the sphere of the moon," was composed of the four elements Earth, Water, Fire, and Air, while the "quintessence," or ether, filled the skies. We shall consider the nature of these elements in Chapter 5, but are here concerned only with their motions. Each terrestrial element had a "natural" place which it tended to seek: Water and Earthy bodies fall, Air and Fire rise. If Fire is added to Water it comes to resemble Air, and ascends. Thus it was believed that the motion of a body was produced by tendencies, or "desires," intrinsic to itself. *"Natural"* terrestrial motion was vertical, that of a predominantly Earthy body being downward toward the center of the earth, which was thought to be the center of the universe. Any motion other than "natural," Aristotle believed, required the application of continued effort, or force. The *speed* of "natural motion" was thought to depend on the amount of Earth in a falling body, i.e., heavy bodies fall faster than lighter ones. These generalizations, the gist of Aristotle's teachings on motion, were based on a great deal of qualitative observation and did not rely on precise measurement.

Although classical learning suffered almost total eclipse in Europe for many centuries following the fall of Rome, the details of Greek achievement were known during the same period throughout the world of Islam.

Despite the many Arabic contributions to mathematics and science, very little progress was made in the understanding of motion. When translations of Greek treatises from the Arabic were introduced into Western Europe between the 11th and 13th centuries Aristotle's works were foremost among them. Aristotle gained more disciples at this time than he could ever have had in his own era. It is not altogether strange that his words, viewed by European scholars against the background of the Dark Ages, were accepted without question. To the new Aristotelians, emerging from a thousand years of relative ignorance, they seemed to contain the whole of all possible knowledge. In the words of Herbert Butterfield: "So in the middle ages men found themselves endowed with an explanation of the physical universe and the workings of nature which had fallen out of the blue, and which they had taken over full-grown and ready made. And they were infinitely more the slaves of that intellectual system than if they had actually invented it for themselves, developing it out of their own original researches and their own wrestlings with truth."

Although only geocentric astronomy would fit into Aristotle's general picture of the universe, Copernicus had not been aware that in making the earth move he was upsetting the entire foundation of established physical science. Galileo, on the other hand, attacked the Aristotelian structure on many fronts. Though by no means the first European scholar to oppose Aristotle's doctrines, he can truly be said to have laid the foundation for the new intellectual system which replaced them. From the perspective of the present it is difficult to visualize the magnitude of this task. The founders of modern science had to "destroy one world and replace it by another. They had to reshape the framework of our intellect itself." Yet they did possess the advantage of new tools. Europe had produced a number of great technical inventions by Galileo's time (for example, the telescope) and a number of powerful new mathematical techniques. Let us see how Galileo made use of these advantages and his own genius to achieve deeper understanding of the phenomenon of motion.

2–2 Galileo's view of falling bodies

The Aristotelian teaching that bodies fall at rates in proportion to the amount of "Earth" they contain is equivalent to saying that the speed of a falling body is proportional to its weight. This view may be attacked on purely logical grounds. Consider, said Galileo, two identical tiles, each of which would fall in the same way, whether side by side or one after the other. Will they fall twice as fast if glued together at the start so that they constitute a single tile twice as heavy? Quite to the contrary, they would fall at the same rate side by side or one on top of the other, as before. The argument was not original with Galileo, but he found it a powerful one, and such arguments were more useful than experiments in refuting contemporary misconceptions. In part, this was because the nature of experiment was not yet generally understood, but also because those experiments that were performed on falling bodies did not entirely support Galileo's contention, as we shall see.

The writings of Galileo do not indicate that he ever performed the experiment of dropping light and heavy bodies from the tower of Pisa, a popular story which originated long after the supposed fact. Actually Galileo does say, in one of his youthful writings, that he had tried dropping a lump of lead and a block of wood from a height, and that the lead reached the ground first. His later analysis of this experiment was itself used to attack the Aristotelian position. Galileo's own account is better than any paraphrase. He presented his scientific work in dialogue form, and in the following excerpt Salviati, representing Galileo, is addressing Simplicio, who represents the Aristotelians:

"But, Simplicio, I trust you will not follow the example of others who divert the discussion from its main intent and fasten upon some statement of mine that lacks a hairbreadth of the truth, and under this hair, hide the fault of another which is as big as a ship's cable. Aristotle says that an iron ball of one hundred pounds falling from a height of one hundred cubits reaches the ground before a one-pound ball has fallen a single cubit. I say that they arrive at the same time. You find, on making the experiment, that the larger outstrips the small by two fingers breadth . . . Now you would not hide behind these two fingers the ninety-nine cubits of Aristotle, nor would you mention my small error and at the same time pass over in silence his very large one."

Galileo held that all bodies would fall at the same rate, regardless of weight, in the absence of resistance of the air. The observed differences between the rates of fall of light and heavy bodies were real, though generally small. It is easy for us to believe that they are completely attributable to air resistance: in an evacuated cylinder, a feather and a coin do indeed fall side by side. However, vacuum pumps had not yet been invented and very little was known about air resistance in Galileo's day. It is unlikely that any number of experiments on free fall could alone have convinced a confirmed Aristotelian of Galileo's view.

Galileo's conviction, despite his lack of direct experimental evidence on the relation between weight and rate of free fall, serves to underscore our previous statement that science is not based on observation *alone*. Clearly defined concepts are necessary, together with logic and a considerable amount of imagination. The kind of imagination required in science must not be confused with fantasy. Like that needed for the development of a fugue or a sonata, it must be at once free and well disciplined. In the example of the two tiles Galileo conducted what we might call a "thought experiment," asking himself "what would happen if . . . ?," and arriving at an answer by following a path of principled reasoning. The final test of any such conclusion is experiment, however, even though the scientist may purposely have focused his attention only on essentials and omitted small factors which will affect actual observations. If experimental results undeniably contrary to his conclusions are obtained one of several things may be wrong. He may not have grasped the essentials correctly, he may have made tacit assumptions which are unjustified, or his reasoning may have been faulty. In any case, he, or someone else, must begin all over again. Discoveries are sometimes made almost by mere chance, but more often they are sought, even though they can never be fully anticipated.

Galileo's conclusions about motion required the crucial test of experiment, and the experiments he devised to test them led to further discovery. Before we can follow the progress of his discoveries on the nature of motion, we must make sure that the concepts we shall use to describe motion are sharp, both mathematically and measurably.

2–3 Linear motion

Let us at first confine our attention to motion in a straight line. The *position* of a body, whether it be a car on a highway, a rolling billiard ball, or a falling stone, can be described by giving the distance of the body from some particular point on its line of motion (Fig. 2–1), and may be measured in miles, feet, meters, or any other proper unit of length. (See the Appendix, section on units of measurement.) We shall represent this distance by the symbol d. If a body is in motion, d changes as time goes by; in mathematical language we say that d is a "function" of time. The simplest kind of motion is that in which the body traverses equal distances in equal times—a car traveling at constant speed on a straight road, for example. If a stopwatch were used to measure the time intervals required for such a car to traverse the distances between the equally spaced mileposts of Fig. 2–1, these intervals would be found equal. A graph showing distance plotted against time would be a straight line, as shown in Fig. 2–2. In these circumstances we may say that *distance is directly proportional to time* or, algebraically,

FIG. 2–1. The position of the car may be described by citing its distance from the milepost at the left.

$$d = (\text{constant}) \times t, \qquad (2\text{-}1)$$

where t stands for the time interval required to traverse any distance d. But from this relation we see that the distance traveled per unit time, d/t, which is defined as the *speed* of a moving body, is constant. Linear (straight-line) motion at constant speed, or velocity, is called *uniform*, i.e., unchanging, motion. (The words *speed* and *velocity* are synonymous for linear motion in a single direction, although we shall later draw an important distinction between them for motion of other kinds.)

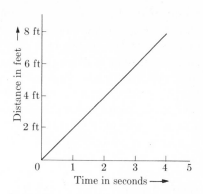

Fig. 2–2. Distance plotted against time for a body moving with the uniform speed of 2 ft/sec.

The *average* speed of a moving body during an interval of time is defined as the total distance traveled divided by the total time. We shall represent speed by the symbol v and average speed by $\bar{v}$. Our definition becomes

$$\text{average speed} = \bar{v} = \frac{\text{total distance}}{\text{total time}} = \frac{d}{t}. \qquad (2\text{-}2)$$

If the motion of a body is uniform, its speed during one time interval is the same as that during any other equal interval, and there is no distinction between speed and average speed. For nonuniform motion, however, the difference is very distinct, and the definition given above must be used in computing $\bar{v}$. If a car is driven 30 mi at 30 mi/hr then 30 mi at 60 mi/hr, its *average speed* over the entire time interval involved ($1\frac{1}{2}$ hours) is only 40 mi/hr computed according to the definition (2–2).

Speed is a *derived* quantitative concept: it is obtained by dividing one measured quantity (distance) by another (time). When Aristotle spoke of the speed of a body there is no evidence that he had anything quantitatively measurable in mind: he may have watched falling bodies, but he did not "torment" them with yardsticks and clocks. Although Aristotle was not inclined to make the attempt at all, measurements on the speeds of falling bodies are in fact difficult to make. Distances are not hard to determine, but before the invention of accurate timing devices the time required for a body to fall was not easily measured. We shall see how Galileo, by a combination of ideas and instruments, overcame this difficulty.

2–4 Quantitative description of free fall

Aristotle had held that the speed of a falling body is determined entirely by its content of Earth, i.e., how heavy it is. Taken quantitatively, this means that the speed of a particular body is constant, and is independent of the time or distance of fall. Galileo and some of his precursors were sure that bodies *gain* speed as they fall. Let us assume, with Galileo, that "these increases take place in a manner which is exceedingly simple and fairly easily apprehended by everybody," and see where we are led. We might guess that a body gains speed as it falls so that its average speed, over any interval of time, is proportional to the distance it has fallen. Or, again, its average speed over any time interval t may be proportional to the time itself. These *hypotheses* are shown in mathematical form, along with Aristotle's belief that bodies fall at constant speed, in Table 2–1. For each, the defined quantity d/t is substituted for average speed $\bar{v}$, with the logical consequence shown. Wherever it appears, the letter K simply represents a constant, the same for all times and distances.

TABLE 2–1

1. Aristotle	2. Galileo (a)	3. Galileo (b)
$\bar{v} = K$	$\bar{v} = Kd$	$\bar{v} = Kt$
$d/t = K$	$d/t = Kd$	$d/t = Kt$
$\therefore d = Kt$	$\therefore 1/t = K$	$\therefore d = Kt^2$

Galileo first considered the possibility reflected in column 2, Table 2–1, that average speed is proportional to distance traversed, but we can see that it results in a logical absurdity. The time interval t is a variable, increasing during the motion, so that $(1/t)$ cannot be constant, as the hypothesis predicts. If speed of fall is constant (Aristotle, column 1) then the prediction that distance of fall is proportional to time of fall ($d = Kt$) should be experimentally verifiable. If average speed of fall is proportional to time of fall (Galileo, column 3), on the other hand, then a direct proportionality between distance and the *square* of time ($d = Kt^2$) must be observable. The simplest possible hypotheses have here been set forth, but with no guarantee that either will be in accord with observable fact, and more complicated possibilities are not automatically excluded.

Since bodies fall freely at high speeds and short times are difficult to measure, Galileo utilized the assumption that bodies roll down hill for the same reason that they fall, whatever that reason might be. The experiments he describes in his writings were measurements on bodies moving

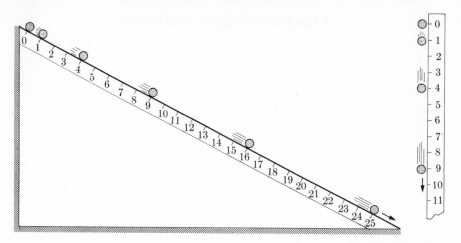

FIG. 2–3. A body rolls down a smooth inclined plane; its positions, observed at equal time intervals, are as shown. Distances from the starting position are related to one another as 1 : 4 : 9 : 16 : 25, i.e., the *square* of the total elapsed times 1, 2, 3, 4, and 5. Galileo concluded that a body falling freely would exhibit the same relation between distance and time, as shown on the right.

down a very smooth inclined plane along which he could measure distances accurately. These distances were traversed in time intervals sufficiently long so that he could use his own pulse rate for accurate time measurements.* He found that the hypothesis reflected in column 3, Table 2–1, was correct: for any given inclination of his plane the distance traversed by a body was proportional to the square of time, as indicated in Fig. 2–3. Different inclinations of the plane gave different constants of proportionality, K in $d = Kt^2$ being greater the more nearly vertical the plane. Galileo concluded that for free fall (corresponding to a perfectly upright plane) the same relation would be observed.

In Galileo's own words: "The spaces described by a body falling from rest with uniformly accelerated motion are to each other as the squares of the time-intervals employed in traversing these distances." But what is "uniformly accelerated" motion? Galileo defined it as motion in which equal amounts of velocity are added in equal times. If we confine our attention to

---

*Galileo also used a water clock: "As for measuring the time, we kept a large pail full of water tied up above, from which, through a very small funnel soldered at the bottom, poured a fine thread of water which was collected in a small glass all the time the ball rolled down the groove and its parts; then the particles of water so collected were weighed each time with a very exact scale, their weight differences and proportions giving us the differences and proportions of the lengths of time; and this with such accuracy, as I have said, that such operations, repeated many many times, never differed a perceptible amount."

linear motion, *acceleration* may be defined as the *time rate of change of speed:*

$$\text{acceleration} = a = \frac{v_2 - v_1}{t}, \qquad (2\text{--}3)$$

where v_1 and v_2 represent the speed of a body at the beginning and end of time interval t. For motion that is *uniformly* accelerated the quantity a is the same for all time intervals, i.e., a constant for the motion. If a body begins its motion from rest, $v_1 = 0$; we can replace v_2 in Eq. (2–3) by v, the speed at the end of any time interval t, and write

$$a = v/t, \qquad (2\text{--}4)$$

or

$$v = at. \qquad (2\text{--}5)$$

For motion with constant acceleration, according to Eq. (2–5), speed is proportional to time. A plot of v against t should therefore be a straight line, as shown in Fig. 2–4(c), even though distance varies nonuniformly with time (Fig. 2–4b). In *uniform* motion (i.e., at constant speed) there is no acceleration at all (Fig. 2–4a).

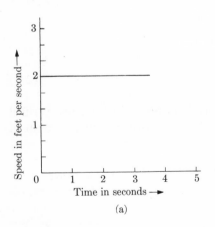

(a)

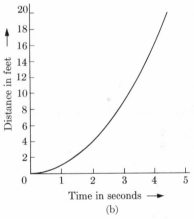

(b)

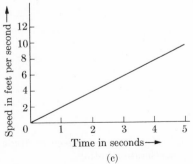

(c)

Fig. 2–4. (a) Speed plotted against time for uniform motion at 2 ft/sec. (b) Distance plotted against time for uniformly accelerated motion ($a = 2$ ft/sec²). (c) Speed plotted against time for uniformly accelerated motion as in (b).

As we have seen, it was Galileo's contention that falling bodies are accelerated, and that their acceleration is uniform, i.e., constant. Let us see whether we can *derive* the relation Galileo verified by experiment, that distance is proportional to the square of time, from his assumption of uniform acceleration. Let a body start from rest at the instant we begin to measure time, so that its acceleration a, as in Eq. (2–4), is

$$a = v/t.$$

From the definition of average speed,

$$d = \bar{v}t. \tag{2–6}$$

What is the relation between v, the speed of the body after time t has elapsed, and $\bar{v}$, its average speed over the entire interval t? The average of any quantity which increases at a regular rate is simply the *arithmetic* average, i.e., one-half the sum of its initial and final values. The initial speed of the body is zero, and if its final speed at the time t is v, its average speed $\bar{v}$ over the time interval t is therefore simply $v/2$ (see Fig. 2–5). Substituting this result in Eq. (2–6),

$$d = \bar{v}t = vt/2;$$

and since by (2–5), $v = at$,

$$d = \tfrac{1}{2}at^2. \tag{2–7}$$

The result $d = Kt^2$, for a body starting from rest, which Galileo verified with his inclined plane experiments, is identical with the derived result of

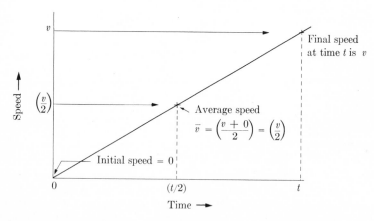

Fig. 2–5. Relation between final speed attained and average speed during a given time interval for a body with uniformly accelerated motion.

t (seconds)	$d \; (= \frac{1}{2}gt^2)$	$v \; (= gt)$
0	0	0
1	16 ft	32 ft /sec
2	64 ft	64 ft /sec
3	144 ft	96 ft /sec
4	256 ft	128 ft /sec
5	400 ft	160 ft /sec

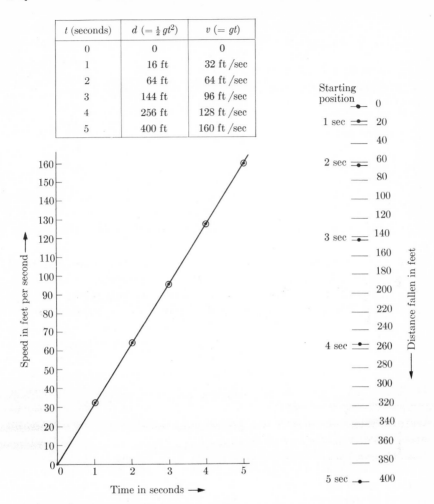

FIG. 2–6. Distance and speed of free fall during first 5 sec, starting from rest.

Eq. (2–7) if the quantity $a/2$ is the same as the previous constant K. Since a is constant, there is no trouble on this score. We have thus arrived at the same relation between time and distance of fall as before, but with the advantage that the constant K has been identified in terms of a concept useful to the description of motion, i.e., acceleration. Equation (2–7) is known as Galileo's *Law of Free Fall*.

A word must be added about the units in which acceleration may be expressed. From the definition of this concept we can see that acceleration is *change in velocity per unit time,* which is equivalent to distance per unit time per unit time, or *distance/time²*. Appropriate units are then *feet per second per second*, abbreviated *ft/sec²*, or *miles/hour/sec*, or, in the metric system, *centimeters per second per second* (*cm/sec²*). The measured acceleration of free fall on the earth's surface (the acceleration due to gravity) is very nearly 32 ft/sec² at sea level, or 980 cm/sec². (See the Appendix for the relation between metric and English units.) Free fall is such an important kind of uniformly accelerated motion that its acceleration is designated by a special letter, g, so that the relation between distance and time of free fall for an object starting from rest becomes

$$d = \tfrac{1}{2}gt^2.$$

This relation, using the numerical value of g given above, is illustrated in Fig. 2–6.

2–5 Significance of Galileo's study of motion

Galileo's conclusions concerning falling bodies have been amply confirmed since his time. Except for air resistance, which is minimal for dense compact bodies, all bodies do fall with the same acceleration at any one place near the earth's surface. The acceleration due to gravity, g, is not an absolute constant, but a local one. Later we shall be in a position to understand the small observed variations of g with locale—why it is somewhat smaller on the equator than at the poles, and smaller on a high mountain than at sea level. Much later we shall also see how the careful measurement of g has become a useful tool in geology, since it can yield information about the inaccessible interior of the earth. For the continuation of our present story, however, our immediate concern is that Galileo, in discovering the laws of motion of falling bodies, succeeded in clarifying ideas of motion in general. We have defined uniform motion as motion at constant speed in a straight line. The motion of falling bodies, we now know, is not uniform but is *uniformly accelerated*, with an acceleration which is the same for all bodies, whatever their weight. These results, important in themselves, symbolized the overthrow of Aristotelian physics, and seemed to clear the way for a rational study of terrestrial motion and, eventually, of all motion. Galileo had shown conclusively that Aristotle was fallible.

It has not yet been made clear that there is any connection between Galileo's study of falling bodies on the earth and our problem of understanding "celestial" motions, in particular those of the solar system. The two are intimately related, however, in a way that was shown with transcendent clarity by Sir Isaac Newton (1642–1727). Both problems involve *gravity*, as that influence that causes bodies to fall toward the earth, whatever it might be, was called. Before the effects of gravity could be understood it was necessary to imagine what would happen if it did not exist. What sort of motion would then take place? The answer to this question, implicit in Newton's first law of motion (Sec. 2–7), was stated directly by the great Dutch scientist, Christian Huygens (1629–1695): "If gravity did not exist, nor the atmosphere obstruct the motion of bodies, a body would maintain forever a motion once impressed upon it, with uniform velocity in a straight line." This remarkable conclusion was published in 1673, fourteen years before the appearance in print of Newton's laws of motion. It had been implicit in Galileo's concentration on *changes* in motion, rather than on uniform motion, in bodies initially at rest. We shall have more than one occasion to remark that great discoveries are rarely made singly. In this instance the work of Galileo and others had prepared the way, and the time was ripe by the second half of the 17th century for a deeper understanding of motion and gravitation.

2–6 Science in the 17th century

The 17th century has been called "The Century of Genius," a characterization that seems amply justified in the realm of science. The significant work of Galileo and Kepler was accomplished early in this century, and before its close an apparently perfect system of celestial and terrestrial *mechanics* encompassed these great achievements and many more. In following the main outlines of this vast accomplishment we may note two general tendencies: a growing awareness of the nature and importance of science, and a geographical trend in scientific achievement from the south of Europe toward the commercial north. The Englishman Sir Francis Bacon (1561–1626) and the Frenchman René Descartes (1596–1650) were chief among those of the early 17th century who thought deeply about the purpose, nature, and methods of science and whose influence, widely felt, contributed substantially to the increasing awareness of science.

Bacon, who held that the goal of science was to give man control over nature, worked out an inspired but somewhat narrow and rigid set of rules for gaining this control. Impressed by the inadequacy of knowledge inherited from the past, Bacon urged that science be organized for the efficient and systematic discovery of new knowledge. A champion of what might be called "enlightened" (i.e., organized) empiricism in science, he glorified what is known as the *inductive* method, by which laws of nature would emerge, he thought, as obvious generalizations from the results of well-organized series of experiments and observations. In the attack on a problem, all available facts were first to be collected and checked with meticulous care. Then specific experiments were to be designed and performed to add new facts to the collection. After all possible information related to the problem was collected, it was to be brought together and examined. Features common to all facts, presumably, would be readily discernible, and these were to form the basis for grand generalizations.

Generalizations obtained in this manner, in turn, might suggest new avenues of observation and experiment, ultimately leading to new generalizations of even greater scope. Bacon's influence on the methodology of science was justifiably great, although he made no notable advances in scientific discovery itself. That his view of the ideal method of science was tied too closely to empiricism and gave too little scope to the role of imagination is exemplified by the fact that he heartily disapproved of Galileo and his "thought experiments."

Descartes, on the whole a much greater scientist and philosopher than Bacon, believed profoundly in the *deductive* system of reasoning. He was a mathematician and logician of immense accomplishment, and attempted to establish natural laws by the exercise of these talents. He believed it possible, beginning with a very limited number of affirmed premises or "primary truths," to deduce the grand generalizations of nature correctly, and hence to explain individual facts. He paid much less attention to establishing the validity of a fact than to explaining it by his deductive system, and hence underestimated the role of experiment in science as much as Bacon had overestimated it. The kind of excess to which this attitude may lead is exemplified by his attempt to explain how lightning may be turned into a stone. Still, Descartes may fairly be said to have anticipated the mathematical scientific theory of today, and certainly his influence loomed large on the 17th-century horizon of science. We owe much to him, including the geometric interpretation of algebraic relationships by which we make graphical representations—a debt commemorated in the term *cartesian coordinates.*

The attempts of Bacon and Descartes to reduce science to sets of rules were fruitful, even though doomed to failure in any absolute sense. Inductive and deductive thought are *both* valuable tools of science, but the great discoveries of science have never resulted from the following of any rigid system. Those who have made such discoveries, in fact, have not only contributed to the factual and theoretical content of science, but have also contributed greatly to scientific methodology, by their example.

Huygens in Holland criticized both Bacon and Descartes, the former for lack of emphasis on mathematical theory, the latter for lack of devotion to experiment. The culmination of the century's genius, and with it the achievement of an inspired and powerful balance between the roles of theory and experiment, came in England, particularly in the person of Sir Isaac Newton. Newton's contributions to mathematics alone, or to optics, would suffice to establish him as one of the greatest thinkers of all time. We shall here be concerned, however, with his work in the sciences of mechanics (motion) and astronomy, to which he made contributions which have never been equaled. Yet he wrote extensively on theology, spent his later years as a man of affairs in charge of the Mint, and it has been estimated that he devoted more time and effort to fruitless alchemical experiments than to the mathematical and physical researches that made him famous. He was indeed a giant, though not an isolated one. Many of his discoveries were anticipated, and some of his greatest ideas were also "in the air" among his contemporaries. Still, his combination of mathematical genius and physical intuition made him unique, even in the "Century of Genius."

2-7 The first law of motion

Thus far we have *described* simple types of linear motion in terms of length (distance) and time. Newton codified the laws of general motion and set the stage for a mechanical era in science by introducing two additional precise concepts, *mass* and *force*. Using these terms, he was able to write three rules which furnished a basis for the whole science of mechanics. To this day these laws constitute the foundation of the science of motion: every possible result in mechanics can apparently be derived from them. Even the modifications of Newton's laws that have come with Einstein's theory of relativity involve essentially their *re*interpretation, not their renunciation.

The first law states: *every object persists in its state of rest or uniform motion unless acted on by some external unbalanced force.* This is often called the *law of inertia,* inertia being defined as that property by virtue of which a body resists changes in its motion. Huygens' statement, quoted in Section 2-5, contains the same information for the special cases of two forces, gravity and the "obstruction" of the atmosphere, but like much of Galileo's work it implies awareness of the general law. What the law means is that a push or pull (force) of some kind is necessary to put an object into motion, and equally necessary to stop it, but that in the *absence* of any external influence (force), *uniform straight-line motion persists indefinitely.* Aristotle had held that a force is necessary to *keep* a body in motion, as, for example, in the case of a heavy object pushed along a rough floor. A person pushing an object at constant speed actually does exert a force on it, but so does the floor. The *frictional* force exerted by the floor is equal, and opposite in di-

(a)	(b)

Fig. 2-7. Moving an object along a rough floor by exertion of a steady push. (a) While object is in motion at constant speed, frictional force of floor exactly opposes push, hence no *net* force acts. (b) When push is interrupted, unopposed frictional force quickly brings object to rest. The frictional force indicated exists only so long as motion persists.

rection, to the push, so that the *net* force on the object is zero (Fig. 2–7). At the beginning and end of the motion, however, there must be some net force exerted to *change* the object's state of motion. On a very highly polished floor the body continues to slide, once it is put into motion. A body on which there is *no* net force, whether at rest or in uniform motion, is said to be *in equilibrium.*

In terms of Newton's first law and the new concept of force, then, gravity must be a force. For whatever it may be, it is certain that gravity changes the states of motion of bodies—bodies at rest in precarious positions tend to start moving downward and bodies which are falling freely are undergoing constant change of motion, since their speeds are not constant. Looking ahead a little, we may also conclude that if Newton's first law is valid some force or forces must constantly act on the earth and all other planets, since in the absence of unbalanced forces their paths would be straight lines. The first law, however, gives us no idea as to *how much* force would be required in given circumstances to produce a particular change in the motion of a body. Indeed, it contains very little hint of how we might measure force and the other quantities involved. Let us proceed to the investigation of changes of motion in quantitative fashion.

2–8 The second law of motion

In his second law Newton answered the question of *how* force is related to change of motion. Change in motion involves *acceleration*, which may or may not be constant, and acceleration is rate of change of velocity, as defined by Eq. (2–3). According to the first law, the velocity of a body will not change in the absence of forces, so we may conclude that acceleration can be produced only by a net force. The second law, which relates force to acceleration, may be stated: *the acceleration imparted to any body by a net force is directly proportional to the force applied, and in the same direction.* Qualitatively, this is certainly reasonable: if we want to change the motion of a body very rapidly, we must push it harder than if only a slow change is required, and the change produced is undoubtedly in the same direction as the push. For linear motion a push must be directed *against* the motion to slow the body, *with* the motion to speed it up.

We shall return to the problem of measuring forces quantitatively a little later. Let us first note that the same push will not ordinarily produce the same acceleration in *different* bodies. A greater force is required to produce a given acceleration in a body we would call heavy than to produce the same acceleration in a light body. In other words, some objects offer more resistance to changes in their motion than others and thus possess more of the property of *inertia* postulated in the first law. The measure of the quantity of inertia of a body is called its *inertial mass*, or simply its *mass*. The more mass a body has, the greater the force which must be applied to impart a given acceleration to it. The force needed to produce an acceleration a in a body of mass m is then proportional to both a and m, a conclusion that may be stated mathematically in the relation

$$F = K\,ma,$$

where F is the net force acting on the body and K is a constant of proportionality. Before making numerical applications of this law we shall be able to adjust the units of F, m, and a so that the constant K is unity, and the relation is usually stated in the form:

$$F = ma. \tag{2–8}$$

This last equation, one of the most important in the whole of science, merits considerable thought. Formally it gives a simple algebraic relation between three physical quantities: force, mass, and acceleration. We were able to define velocity, and hence acceleration, in terms of distance and time, which can be measured by means of yardsticks and clocks. Force we know intuitively as pushing and pulling, and we have said that mass is a quantity of inertia, the property by which bodies resist changes in motion. Do we have *independent* methods for measuring force and mass, so that we can verify this famous equation? There has been much discussion of this question, and the answer is not altogether simple.

There *is* a method of comparing forces that does not depend on motion. Robert Hooke (1635–1703) announced in 1678 the principle of the spring balance: the stretch experienced by a good spring is proportional to the force applied to it, i.e., doubles when the force is doubled, etc. In principle, we could then perform the experiment illustrated in Fig. 2–8, in which the magnitude of a force is determined by reading the scale on a spring balance, and the acceleration imparted by this force to a body is measured by determining distances and times. Mass may then be regarded simply as the constant for the proportionality between force and acceleration for a given body. This is certainly a perfectly *logical* and self-consistent scheme for determining force, mass, and acceleration, although undeniably a "thought experiment," difficult to carry out in practice.

Fig. 2–8. In principle, force necessary to produce unit acceleration in mass m may be measured with a spring balance.

2–9 Units for mass and force

In practice, mass is not determined by peforming measurements of forces and accelerations. Instead, some particular body is arbitrarily called a standard, and copies of it are made for comparison with unknown masses. The standard mass generally accepted for scientific work is a piece of platinum alloy kept in Paris, called one *kilogram* (kgm) of mass. One one-thousandth of this mass is called the *gram* (gm). The unit of mass in the English system of units is the pound, which is now defined in terms of the standard kilogram. There are about 2.2 pounds in one kilogram. (See the Appendix for a summary of useful relations among units.)

Comparisons of mass are usually made indirectly, by comparing *weights*. The weight of a body is the force exerted on it by gravity, i.e., the force that will cause it to fall toward the earth unless it is supported. If Galileo was right in stating that all bodies fall to earth with the same constant accelera-tion, and if the force that makes a given body fall (i.e., its weight) is propor-tional to mass times this constant acceleration, then *weight must be propor-tional to mass* in any given locality. If a body is hung on a spring balance, its weight (a downward force) is balanced by an equal upward pull of the spring, as shown in Fig. 2–9. Two masses are equal if their weights are equal, in which case they will stretch the spring by equal amounts. Note that this method depends on the observed constancy of g, the acceleration of gravity, in a given locality. If an object is moved to a place where g is different, its weight changes but not its mass. The standard kilogram could be moved to the top of Mt. Blanc and remain the standard kilogram of mass, but its weight would be somewhat diminished and it would not stretch a spring quite so much as in Paris. *Comparisons* of mass would be equally valid in the new circum-stances, however, since at any one place g is the same for all masses.

The standards of length and time are as arbitrary as that of mass: a *meter*, equal to 39.37 inches, is de-fined as the distance between two fine scratches in a certain platinum bar, and forms the international standard of length. One hundredth of a meter, called a *centimeter* (cm), is a unit smaller than the inch: 2.54 cm equal one inch. The meter and kilogram, and their decimal frac-tions and multiples, make up the

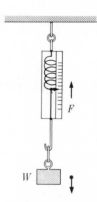

FIG. 2–9.   Body hung on spring balance.   Downward weight W is balanced by upward force F of stretched spring.

metric system of units, used almost universally in scientific work and adopted for commercial use in all major countries except Britain and the United States. Even in these countries the metric system forms the basis for certain practical units of electricity and of heat. Metric units were devised in France and the system was adopted there in 1793. A more ancient unit, used for measuring time, is common to the metric and English systems. The *second* is based on the average rotational period of the earth, i.e., the day. The *mean solar day* is the average interval between successive passages of the sun across the meridian. The *mean solar second* is simply 1/86,400 of the mean solar day.

The practice of defining units of mass, length, and time in terms of arbitrary standards leaves us with the problem of defining a unit of force. As we have remarked, this may be done in such a way that a constant of proportionality becomes unnecessary in Newton's second law: if we consider a mass of one gram, and take as a unit of acceleration one centimeter per $\sec^2$, our unit of force will be defined for us if $F = ma$, since F must then also equal one unit. A satisfactory unit of force is thus *one gram centimeter per second per second* (abbreviated, 1 gm · cm/sec^2), and is called one *dyne*. In words, we may say that one dyne is that force which, when acting on a body whose mass is one gram, will produce an acceleration of one cm/sec^2 in that body. The dyne is a *derived* unit, as are the units of velocity and acceleration. These and all other mechanical units can be expressed in terms of units of length, mass, and time. When no numerical factors are introduced, derived units are sometimes not of very convenient size for ordinary purposes. A dyne, for example, is something like the weight of a mosquito, and would be highly inconvenient for expressing our own weights. In practice, we avoid reference to Newton's second law altogether, since in expressing weights we are not primarily concerned with falling bodies, and instead say that we weigh some number of pounds, or some number of kilos (kilograms). A pound or a kilogram, in this usage, is the force exerted by gravity on one pound or one kilogram of mass.

The weight of a 1–gm mass may be easily expressed in dynes by applying the relation $F = ma$, substituting g for a. Where the value of g is 980 cm/sec^2, the weight of a 1-gm mass is 980 dynes. The weight of a 1-kgm mass is 9.8×10^5 dynes, a number whose size reflects the smallness of the dyne as a unit of force. (See the Appendix for a review of the manipulations involved in using exponential notation.) The dyne is a dynamical unit of force; that is to say, it is a proper unit for quantitative treatment of *changes* of motion, appropriate for use in the relation $F = ma$. Only when the forces of interest are balanced, so that no changes of motion can occur, is it permissible to use the same units for force and mass. In the "thought experiment" illustrated in Fig. 2–8, the spring balance would have to be adjusted to give readings in dynes, if mass is measured in grams.

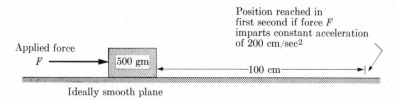

Fig. 2–10. Mass accelerated on a smooth table.

A numerical example will serve to illustrate the magnitude of the force involved in producing a given acceleration. Suppose that a 500-gm mass rests on a perfectly smooth (ideally frictionless) horizontal table (Fig. 2–10), and that you wish to impart to it a constant horizontal acceleration of 200 cm/sec^2:

$$F = ma = 500 \text{ gm} \times 200 \text{ cm/sec}^2 = 10^5 \text{ dynes.}$$

If the table is not perfectly smooth a *net* force of 10^5 dynes will still produce the required acceleration, although the applied force in that case must be enough larger to balance frictional resistance to its motion.

2–10 The third law of motion

Until now we have spoken of *single* bodies and their behavior when forces act on them. Newton's third law takes into consideration whatever influence produces a given force, as well as the body to which the force is applied, and says that the relation between these is *reciprocal* or, to use another word, *symmetrical*. A common statement of the law is that *for every action there is an equal and opposite reaction*, but this sentence can mean very little until we have analyzed it carefully. Newton explained: "If you press a stone with your finger, the finger is also pressed by the stone." If a person pushes against a door, the door pushes equally against him, and this is true whether he is accelerating the door or not. The *equal* and *opposite* forces described by Newton's third law can never balance each other, *because they do not act on the same body.* Examples will help to clarify this rather surprising law.

Take the case of a small stone, for instance. We shall soon see, and the reader certainly already knows, that the earth exerts a force on the stone. The third law tells us that the stone exerts an equal and opposite force on the earth. This is true whether the stone is falling from a height, or lying at rest on the table (Fig. 2–11). If the stone is falling, it is accelerated by the force exerted by the earth, in accord with the second law of motion. Is the earth also being accelerated by a force due to the stone? The answer is yes,

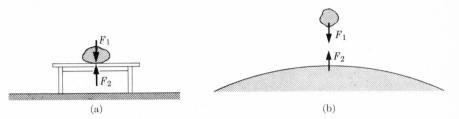

Fig. 2–11. Newton's Third Law: (a) A stone lying on a table exerts a force F_1 equal and opposite to that of the table on the stone, F_2. (b) A stone falling freely toward the earth experiences a force F_1 exerted *by* the earth, and exerts an equal and opposite force F_2 *on* the earth.

but the mass of the earth is so very great that the acceleration produced in it by a small force is immeasurably small. If, on the other hand, the stone lies on a table, another pair of forces is involved: an upward force exerted by the table on the stone is equal and opposite to that of the earth on the stone, so that the net force on the stone is zero and no acceleration takes place. These two balancing forces are *not* those described in the third law, however: the "reaction," equal and opposite to the "action" of the table on the stone, is a force exerted *by* the stone on the table. The stone pushes downward on the table as hard as the table pushes upward on the stone.

There are no exceptions to the third law, although some of its applications are much more complicated than the case of the stone and table. During the firing of a gun a force is exerted on the bullet which accelerates it to a high velocity. There is a force of reaction on the gun itself equal to the action on the bullet. These two forces are equal and opposite, but the body of a gun is so much more massive than that of a bullet that it is accelerated to a relatively small extent. The shooting of a projectile comparable in mass to that of the gun would lead to serious trouble if no arrangement were made to allow for the recoil.

In his three laws of motion, Newton established the framework for general study of motion in terms of mass and force. Our own considerations have thus far been confined to motions in a single straight line. Before we can venture back to the skies, however, we must take account of the fact that even on the earth bodies are not constrained to move in straight lines, vertically, horizontally, or otherwise. Again we shall start with ideas that originated in the thought of Galileo, who effectively broke the spell that the inherited system of Aristotle had held over men of learning. The great achievements of Newton and his contemporaries were fruits of the freedom to seek new knowledge of the world as they found it, made possible by Galileo.

2-11 Summary

Aristotle was able to achieve a rational over-all view of the world by assuming that motion observed in terrestrial objects is in no way related to the presumably "perfect" spheres and circles traced out by celestial bodies. The center of the earth was taken as the center of the universe, and terrestrial bodies were thought to fall toward this center at a rate depending on their content of the "element" Earth. Motions other than this "natural" motion were held to require the continued exertion of effort. Aristotle's whole scheme was attacked and essentially overthrown by Galileo, who established that all bodies are equally *accelerated* toward the earth in falling. It became apparent that uniform (unaccelerated) motion is maintained unaltered in the absence of external influences, and that force is involved only in *changes* of motion. The concept of mass as a measure of inertia and the quantitative relation of force to acceleration were defined by Newton, whose laws of motion form the basis of mechanics and have played a fundamental role in all science since his time.

REFERENCES

BROWN, G. B., *Science, Its Method and Philosophy*. Chapters III, IV, and V contain lively accounts of the lives and scientific contributions of Aristotle, Francis Bacon, and Isaac Newton.

BUTTERFIELD, H., *The Origins of Modern Science*, especially Chapters V and VI.

GALILEO GALILEI, *Dialogues Concerning Two New Sciences*, or excerpts found in pp. 1–17 of:

MAGIE, W. F., *A Source Book in Physics*. In this translation the word momentum is used—momentum is the velocity multiplied by the mass of a moving body.

NEWTON, I., excerpt from the *Principia*, found in *A Source Book of Physics*, pp. 31–39. There are some matters here which we shall study in Chapter 3.

HOLTON, G., *Introduction to Concepts and Theories in Physical Science*. Chapters 1, 2, and 3 furnish a more complete account of linear motion than we have given here.

1. On the basis of Aristotelian physics, how would you explain the behavior of (a) an ascending balloon, (b) a descending balloon?

2. (a) Show that the average speed of the journey described in the text, in which the first 30 mi are traversed at 30 mi/hr and the second 30 mi at 60 mi/hr, is 40 mi/hr. (b) Suppose that after driving half the journey at 30 mi/hr the driver thinks he would like to average 45 mi/hr for the entire trip, how fast would he have to drive to achieve this? [Hint: First find the *time* in which he must travel the second 30 mi.] [*Ans.*: 90 mi/hr]

3. Galileo pointed out in his *Dialogues Concerning Two New Sciences* that if the speed of a falling body were proportional to its distance of fall, all distances would be traversed in equal lengths of time. Show that this is a logical conclusion to be drawn from hypothesis (2) of Table 2–1, and develop a "thought experiment" to demonstrate that the hypothesis is absurd.

4. A small, compact object is allowed to fall freely from the top of a tower 576 ft in height. Knowing that the acceleration of a freely falling body is 32 ft/sec², determine how much time is required for the object to reach the ground. [*Ans.*: 6 sec]

5. Two heavy balls are dropped simultaneously from two high windows, one of which is 10 m above the other. Do the balls remain 10 m apart as they fall to the ground? Justify your answer.

6. An automobile, initially at rest, is constantly accelerated for 2 sec to a speed of 30 mi/hr (44 ft/sec). Determine (a) the average speed during the 2 sec, (b) the acceleration, (c) the total distance traversed during this time, (d) the instantaneous speed (speedometer reading) at the end of the first second.

7. Density is defined as mass per unit volume. Newton gave as a definition of mass: "the quantity of matter is the measure of the same, arising from its density and bulk conjointly," i.e., mass equals volume multiplied by density. Later scientists have said that he was guilty of "circular reasoning" in this definition. What do they mean?

8. A man in a parachute does not fall freely, but descends at constant speed, for example, 5 m/sec. (a) What is his acceleration in these circumstances? (b) If the man and his parachute weigh 70 kgm, what is the force of air resistance?

9. How much acceleration will be produced in a 20-gm mass by (a) a net force of 10 dynes, (b) a net force of 100 dynes?

10. A 100-gm weight is allowed to slide down a smooth incline, as shown in Fig. 2–12. Careful measurement shows that it slides 980 cm in 2 sec after starting from rest. (a) What is its

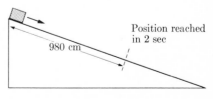

Position reached in 2 sec

980 cm

FIGURE 2–12.

acceleration? (b) What force acts in the direction of the motion? [*Ans.*: 490 cm/sec^2; 49 × 10^3 dynes]

11. Construct a graph showing how the acceleration of a 100-gm mass varies with the force applied to it.

12. Construct graphs of distance against time, speed against time, and acceleration against time, typical for (a) uniform motion, (b) uniformly accelerated motion, (c) nonuniformly accelerated motion.

13. What is the *average* speed of a freely falling body, in cm/sec, during its first second of fall? During its second, third, fourth, and fifth seconds?

14. A man standing on shore gives a push to a boat in the water. Imagining the *complete absence of frictional forces*, describe what would happen and explain the motions of the boat and the man.

15. A stone dropped from the top of a building requires exactly 8 sec to reach the ground. How high is the building? [*Ans.*: 313.6 m or about 1024 ft]

16. A 100-lb boy and a 200-lb man are standing on separate carts with a rope stretched between them, as shown in Fig. 2–13. The boy pulls on the rope while the man simply holds it, yet the boy moves toward the man much more rapidly than the man moves toward the boy. Explain.

200 lb   100 lb

FIGURE 2–13.

CHAPTER 3

MOTION AND FORCES IN MORE THAN ONE DIMENSION

There are reasons other than the challenge of the solar system, stars, and planets for us to consider motion in more than one direction. Even without benefit of aircraft we move in a three-dimensional world, going upstairs or down, to the right or left, forward or back. Our own motions are too complicated for mathematical analysis or simple description, but one of the earliest practical problems involving motion was that of projectiles, objects whose motions are simple enough to be controlled in some degree by the way they are started. Apart from its beginning and end points the path of a projectile was difficult for the ancients to trace, but one thing was clear: only when it is shot vertically (up or down) is the motion of a projectile in a single straight line. In order to send a projectile from one point to another point on the same horizontal level it must be directed somewhat upward at the beginning, as shown in Fig. 3–1. To the ancients the intermediate part of its path was a mystery, and the problem was first solved by Galileo, on

Fig. 3–1. A cannon or a catapult must direct a projectile at an angle above the horizontal line to hit a distant object on the same level.

the assumption that a projectile *falls* vertically as it moves horizontally. We know now that changes from linear motion must be attributed to the action of forces. We shall see how Galileo's analysis, in terms of the forces which produce curvature, aided the description of curved motions in general, so necessary for the study of the recurring motions of celestial bodies.

3–1 Directed quantities: vectors

There is an infinite number of directions in which a body may move, each slightly different from all others. Any one of these directions can be fully described, however, in terms of three *independent* ones, which is what we mean by saying the world is three-dimensional. The three chosen independent directions must not lie in the same plane, and it is most convenient to take them at right angles to one another. Although the selection is arbitrary, the customary set of directions for a fairly small region of the earth's surface is (1) the east-west line, (2) the north-south line, and (3) the vertical, or altitude line.

A *directed quantity*, such as the *displacement* of the point of a pencil from one place on a notebook page to another, or of a person from his house to the top of the nearest hill, is called a *vector*. Displacement is "as the crow flies"; that is, *relative* position depends only on initial and final positions and is independent of the path between. It can be represented by a straight line, an arrow beginning at the starting point and ending at the destination. The displacement shown in Fig. 3–2 is one inch to the right and one inch above the starting point O, but can be represented by a single straight line. On the two-dimensional plane of the paper it may be specified by giving *two* numbers, the distance to the right and the distance toward the top of the page. If Fig. 3–2 is considered as a map the displacement could be called one inch *east* and one inch *north* of O. Equivalent information is given by saying that the displacement is 1.4 inches *north-east*. In addition to the *length* of displacement, this specifies by the term "north-east" that the displacement makes an angle of 45° with the east-west line. If a given displacement should be such that its endpoint were out of the plane of the paper, a third number (corresponding to the third dimension of space) would have to be given, specifying altitude.

The displacement in Fig. 3–2 is the same whether a pencil point is moved directly along the diagonal line or in two stages, one inch east from O, then one inch north. In the latter alternative two actual displacements are made, but they result in the single vector OP. In this sense, vector OP is the *sum* of vectors OA and AP, even though the total distance $OA + AP$ is greater than the length of OP. These intermediate displacements need not occur along directions chosen as coordinates. In Fig. 3–3, for example, the vector **C** is the sum of the individual vectors **A** and **B**. The displacement **C** is the

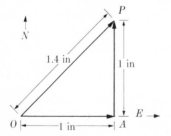

FIG. 3–2. Displacement from O to P.

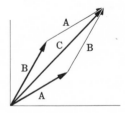

FIG. 3–3. Displacement **C** is the sum of displacements **A** and **B**.

final effect, or *resultant*, of displacements **A** and **B**. A convenient way of finding the sum of two vectors is also indicated in Fig. 3–3: when the parallelogram of which **A** and **B** are sides is constructed, its diagonal (**C**) is the desired vector sum. Care must be taken that the original direction of every vector is maintained in finding a sum: note that the actual path of a displacement proceeds from the tail to the head of the arrow which represents it.

Directed quantities other than displacements can be represented by arrows on a diagram, even though they may refer to single points and have no actual extension in space. The force on a body, for example, can be

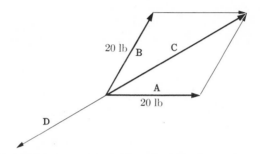

FIG. 3–4. The vector sum of forces **A** and **B** is **C**. **D**, equal and opposite to **C**, cancels the effect of **C** alone, or of **A** and **B** combined.

shown by a line segment whose length represents its *magnitude* in accord with some predetermined scale, and whose *direction* is that of the force. Two forces acting at the same point, but in different directions, are so represented in Fig. 3–4. The two may be added as though they were displacements, and the magnitude of their vector sum, or *resultant*, can be measured on the diagram. In Fig. 3–4, $\frac{1}{2}$ in. represents 10 lb, and it can be determined that the two 20–lb forces are equivalent to a single force of about 36 lb, directed as shown. Let us note emphatically that this is not a space diagram; the lengths represent pounds (or other units of force), and use of the diagram is possible only because forces, like displacements, are directed, or vector, quantities.

Force diagrams are often used to find what force must be applied to a body in order to cancel the effects of other forces acting upon it. A body on which there is no net force, and which therefore experiences no acceleration, is said to be in equilibrium. Force equilibrium considerations are particularly important in structural design: bridges, buildings, even such simple devices as chairs, tables, and curtain rods, must be constructed to withstand stresses, and it is necessary to know how these stresses are distributed. Although very large forces may be involved in an equilibrium,

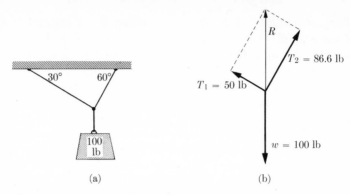

(a)   (b)

FIG. 3–5. The physical problem of supporting a 100-lb object by two strings in the manner shown in (a) may be analyzed by a force diagram (b). The resultant sum R of the forces T_1 and T_2 exerted by the strings must be equal and opposite to weight w. This requirement is met if $T_1 = 50$ lb and $T_2 = 86.6$ lb.

their *vector sum* is zero. Two equal and opposite forces acting on the same body add to zero and thus cancel each other. This observation, together with the method for adding vectors, enables us to find the force necessary to produce equilibrium in the general case. In Fig. 3–4, for example, **C** is equivalent to forces **A** and **B** together. If a force **D**, equal and opposite to **C**, is applied to the body on which **A** and **B** act, the net force on the body is zero, and there will be no acceleration. It can be stated as a condition for equilibrium that the vector sum of all acting forces (in this case **A**, **B**, and **D**) must vanish. This is, in a sense, only a restatement of the first law of motion, since equilibrium is *defined* as an absence of acceleration. A detailed diagram showing just how forces are distributed in a given equilibrium is nonetheless extremely useful in practice (see Fig. 3–5).

We must now draw a distinction between the concepts of *speed* and *velocity*. The former is a nondirected quantity, and can be specified by an expression of magnitude alone; complete specification of velocity must include a statement of direction, as well as of magnitude. For example, we say that the speed of a car is 60 mi/hr, but that its velocity is 60 mi/hr southwest. Velocities, which are directed quantities of the same general kind as displacement and force, may also be represented by vector diagrams, and their vector sums determined. For example, if a flier set his course by the compass and headed due north at 100 mi/hr his velocity would be 100 mi/hr north. If a 75 mi/hr gale came up out of the west, however, and he did not correct his course, his ground velocity would be 125 mi/hr in the direction indicated in Fig. 3–6. (Check this result, remembering the right triangle theorem of Pythagoras.) Note that Fig. 3–6, which is a velocity diagram, is applicable only to individual instants of time; it gives no indication of the distance traveled under the conditions described, or how long those conditions prevail. In practice, a single velocity can be specified by giving its magnitude (*speed*) and appropriate angles for describing its direction, but a diagram is invaluable for determining the net result of two simultaneous velocities. The same is true of other vector quantities, which include *acceleration* as well as those we have discussed. Although we shall be concerned most frequently with ordinary space diagrams indicating the paths of moving bodies, we must always remember to specify the directions as well as the magnitudes of all vector quantities we do consider.

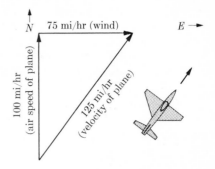

Fig. 3-6. Addition of velocities.

3-2 Motion of projectiles

We have mentioned the behavior of projectiles as an example of motion in two dimensions. Fundamental understanding of this behavior came much later than the craft of technical use. Early explanations of the behavior of rocks shot from catapults and of cannon balls may now seem amusing: a force from the sending mechanism was supposed to persist until it was "worn out," whereupon the "natural" motion of free fall suddenly took over and the body fell straight down. Galileo disregarded such fallacious views. Indeed, we can achieve correct answers at once in terms of Galileo's discoveries about falling bodies and the most elementary ideas contained in Newton's laws.

Let us consider the simple case of a projectile fired horizontally from a height. It can readily be demonstrated that if one ball is simply dropped while another at the same level is simultaneously fired horizontally, the two reach the ground at the same instant (Fig. 3-7). This observation can be made understandable by simple analysis. One ball has only the vertical motion of free fall. The other ball falls, too, but at the same time is traveling horizontally. The vertical force of gravity acts on both, and produces the same downward acceleration in both, so that it is no wonder they reach the ground at the same time. Meanwhile, no horizontal forces act on either ball, once motion in the air has begun. According to the law of inertia a state either of rest or of uniform motion in the *horizontal* direction is then maintained unaltered. The resulting motion of the ball which is fired is one in which equal horizontal distances are traversed in equal times, while the vertical distance traveled is proportional to the square of the time of fall. The path traced out by this ball is of the kind called a *parabola*. Galileo worked out the parabolic path for a projectile without explicitly invoking forces; he simply assumed that the horizontal motion was uniform, while the simultaneous downward motion was uniformly accelerated.

We have neglected the effect of air resistance in this example, which is justified if the objects observed are steel balls, but not if they are feathers or balls made of pith or paper. The important point is that the motion of the horizontally fired ball, neglecting air resistance, is made up of two independent but simultaneous parts, manifested in two perpendicular directions.

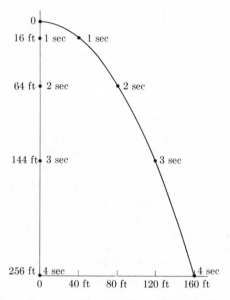

FIG. 3–7. Positions shown are those at the end of the 1st, 2nd, 3rd, and 4th seconds of fall from a tower 256 ft high. The path on the left is that of a body which is dropped, and the curved (parabolic) path that of a body fired horizontally at a speed of 40 ft/sec.

By superposing these parts we get the actual path, actual velocities at different instants, and other features of the motion. The same consideration holds for the projectile of Fig. 3–1. A ball fired horizontally begins to fall at once, and would simply plow into the earth if fired at ground level. On the other hand, a ball thrown vertically upward is slowed by the downward acceleration g, comes to a halt at a height dependent on its initial speed, reverses its path, and falls downward. If it is shot at an angle, part of its velocity is horizontal, and this part remains unchanged. This can be demonstrated rather spectacularly by means of a cart that fires a ball

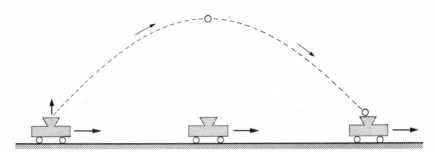

Fig. 3–8. Ball projected upward from a cart in uniform motion keeps abreast of the cart as it rises and falls.

vertically in the air while moving uniformly in a horizontal direction (Fig. 3–8). Uniform horizontal velocity is maintained by the ball in its flight, and if the cart also moves at steady speed it will catch the ball when the latter returns to the horizontal level from which it was fired. If a gun is shot straight up in the air from a plane the pilot must swerve or change speed afterward if he wishes to avoid being hit by the returning shell!

3–3 Uniform circular motion

On a flat earth a shot fired horizontally from the top of a tower or high mountain would always strike the ground somewhere, subject as it is to the acceleration of gravity, and the curvature of our earth is so small that no appreciable error is made in assuming it flat for all ordinary projectile speeds. As an object is fired with increased velocity it strikes the earth farther from its source, at a time determined by its distance of fall, i.e., the height of the tower. Only if there were no force of gravity (and no air resistance) would the object, in Huygens' words, "maintain forever a motion once impressed upon it." In the absence of forces, however, since the earth *is* curved, the object would progressively recede from the earth's surface, as shown in Fig. 3–9.

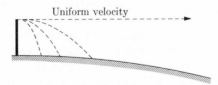

Uniform velocity

Fig. 3–9. Object fired horizontally from top of tower at various speeds strikes earth at various distances. With uniform velocity it would recede from the earth's surface.

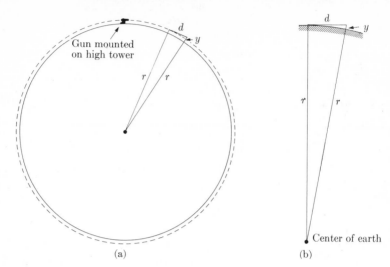

Fig. 3–10. Imaginary projectile fired around the earth in a circular orbit. Details for derivation of required acceleration are shown in (b).

For projectiles subject to the inescapable influence of gravity, fired at great horizontal speeds, the effect of the earth's curvature would be to make the time of fall a little greater than that expected from Galileo's law of free fall. In principle, it should be possible to fire a bullet with a speed so great that it falls toward the earth at the same rate that the earth's surface recedes from it because of the earth's curvature. In that case, *if there were no air friction and no obstacles*, it could continue to go around the earth at a constant distance from its center. Let us imagine this to be possible, and see whether we can find what relations would pertain among the various quantities describing the motion. Again, we are performing a "thought experiment" of the kind we have attributed to Galileo, although this particular example is due to Newton.

Let us shoot a projectile horizontally, then, at exactly the speed that will permit its rate of fall to equal its tendency to escape due to the curvature of the earth. In Fig. 3–10 d represents the distance such a projectile *would* travel in a time t if there were no gravity. Let y represent the distance fallen in this same time, such that the projectile maintains its original distance from the center of the earth. (The fall, directed centrally, is continuously changing in direction, but if d is sufficiently small compared with the radius r of the earth this change is *very* small and may be neglected.) Since d is perpendicular to the radius of the earth at the starting point we may use the theorem of Pythagoras:

$$r^2 + d^2 = (r + y)^2 = r^2 + 2ry + y^2. \tag{3–1}$$

Subtracting r^2 from both sides, we obtain

$$d^2 = y^2 + 2ry. \qquad (3\text{–}2)$$

Since y is very small in comparison with both d and r, y^2 is very small compared with $2ry$. Therefore a close approximation is obtained by neglecting y^2, with the result that

$$d^2 = 2ry, \qquad (3\text{–}3)$$

and hence

$$y = \frac{d^2}{2r}. \qquad (3\text{–}4)$$

Now y represents the distance fallen freely in the time interval t and, according to Galileo's law of free fall,

$$y = \tfrac{1}{2}at^2, \qquad (3\text{–}5)$$

where a is the acceleration the projectile experiences. Equating the two expressions for y (Eqs. 3–4 and 3–5), we see that

$$\frac{1}{2}\frac{d^2}{r} = \frac{1}{2}\,at^2, \qquad (3\text{–}6)$$

which may be rearranged in the form

$$\frac{d^2}{t^2} = ar. \qquad (3\text{–}7)$$

The quantity d/t is simply the initial horizontal speed of the projectile, which is maintained without change, and if we represent this speed by v it is clear that

$$v^2 = ar. \qquad (3\text{–}8)$$

Dividing both sides of this equation by r, we obtain

$$a = \frac{v^2}{r}, \qquad (3\text{–}9)$$

which is an expression for the acceleration in terms of speed and radius. The acceleration required to make an object moving with speed v travel in an arc of a circle whose radius is r, is thus v^2/r.

It may be argued, and soundly, that Eq. (3–9) lacks more than approximate validity because in its derivation we have neglected the term y^2 in Eq. (3–2). As the time interval t is made successively smaller, however, both d and y diminish in size while radius r remains unchanged. The statement that y is negligible with respect to r, hence also y^2 with respect to $2ry$, then increases in validity, i.e., the approximation becomes more and more exact. It is possible to imagine time intervals so small that our approximation would introduce essentially no error at all. By use of the branch of mathematics called the *calculus*, Eq. (3–9) can be rigorously derived.

In the example of our imaginary projectile $a = g$, the acceleration of free fall, which is known. In Eq. (3–8), $v^2 = ar = gr$, we could use the radius of the earth and solve for v, the speed the projectile must have to continue moving round and round the earth if there were no atmosphere or other obstruction. It may be amusing to attempt to guess how great this speed would have to be; calculation of its actual value is left to a problem.

Our "thought experiment" has given us much more than the necessary speed for making a projectile into a satellite on a hypothetically smooth and airless earth. *The formula $a = v^2/r$ represents the acceleration that any body must have if it is to travel in a circular path with speed v at radius r.* This acceleration is always directed toward the center of the circle, and while it continuously changes the *direction* of the object's velocity it has no effect on the *magnitude* of v; that is, the *speed* is constant. Such motion, called *uniform circular motion*, is not uniform motion, since an acceleration is involved.

To keep a body moving in a circular path, i.e., to produce the acceleration $a = v^2/r$, a force is needed. Like the acceleration, this force is directed toward the center of the circle. In the case of the projectile considered above the force is that of gravity, directed toward the center of the earth. If a weight is whirled on a string, the string exerts a force toward the center of the weight's circular path. Such a central force, necessary for all revolving bodies, is called a *centripetal force*. This force is exerted *on* the revolving body, and produces an acceleration in the body in accord with Newton's second law:

$$F = ma.$$

Substituting the expression for a given by Eq. (3–9), we obtain the equation

$$F = \frac{mv^2}{r} \tag{3-10}$$

for centripetal force in uniform circular motion.

This important equation gives the relation between the force necessary for circular motion of radius r, and the mass and speed of the body.

There is often some confusion between the *centripetal* force *on* a rotating body, and the *centrifugal* force exerted *by* the body. The two are simply the forces of action and reaction described by Newton's third law. The projectile of our "thought experiment" exerts as great a force on the earth as the earth exerts on it; the mass of the earth is so much greater, however, that no perceptible acceleration of the earth would result. A stone whirled on the end of a string exerts a force on the string, thence on the hand that holds the string (Fig. 3–11). It is the force exerted by the string on the stone, the centripetal force, which makes it move in a circle. Although

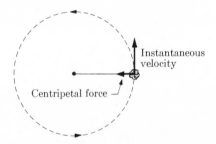

FIG. 3–11. The string exerts a force on the stone equal to the mass of the stone times its centripetal acceleration. The direction of this force is toward the center of rotation.

centrifugal force may cause the string to break, it is a mistake to say that after the string breaks the stone flies off at a tangent *because* of centrifugal force. The centripetal and centrifugal forces are both radial, equal, and oppositely directed along the string. The velocity of the stone at every instant of its path is directed along a tangent to the circular orbit. Tension in the string may cause it to break, but once it has broken there is no longer *either* centripetal or centrifugal force. The stone continues in a straight line, in a direction identical with that of its instant of release, and with the same speed, since *no* force now acts on it. Newton's first law again! We could rephrase this by saying that the body was not in equilibrium before the string broke; there was a net force acting on it, so that it was accelerated. Upon the breaking of the string it attained equilibrium, hence its motion became uniform. In actual practice, of course, the force of gravity here on the earth would add the motion of free fall to the stone's uniform motion, as in the case of a projectile fired at relatively low speed.

3–4 Effects of the earth's rotation

One reason that Copernicus' contemporaries largely rejected the idea of the earth's daily rotation was based on the observation that a force is required to hold a body in rotation. The string is essential to keep the stone pictured in Fig. 3–11 moving in its circular path, but objects remain on the surface of the earth without being tied down. To understand how this can be so, despite the earth's rapid rotation, we must make a quantitative estimate of the centripetal acceleration a body experiences at the earth's surface.

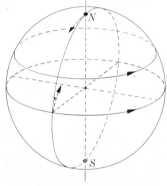

Fig. 3–12. The broken arrows indicate the paths of rockets fired along a meridian at the north pole and northward from the equator. The deviation at the pole is due to turning of the meridian during the motion. That at the equator is not quite as great as shown; the meridian north of the equator turns, but not fast enough to keep up with the rocket.

By examining Fig. 3–12 we may see that the rotational speed of an object on the earth's surface will be greatest at the equator. There a distance equal to the entire circumference of the earth, 25,000 miles, is traversed daily, hence at a speed in excess of 1000 mi/hr. But on computing v^2/r, the acceleration required to hold a body in place on the equator, we find that it amounts to only about $3\frac{1}{2}$ cm/sec^2, or about $\frac{1}{3}$ of one percent of 980 cm/sec^2, the acceleration of gravity. Thus the force of gravity is much more than sufficient to hold terrestrial objects down at the equator; at all other latitudes, where rotational speed is smaller, the required centripetal acceleration is even less. If we assume that g would be the same at all points on the surface of a *stationary* earth, it follows that the observed acceleration of gravity should be somewhat smaller at the equator than at the poles of a *rotating* earth. That is, gravitational force must provide *two* separate accelerations, centripetal and vertical, at the equator, but only the latter at a pole. To quote some actual measurements: on Karajak Glacier, Greenland, latitude 70°27′ North, the observed value of g is 982.5 cm/sec^2;

at Batavia, Indonesia, latitude 6°11′ South, $g = 978.2$ cm/sec^2. It has been inferred from an abundance of measurements in the relatively accessible portions of the earth that g should have the value 978.039 cm/sec^2 at the equator and 983.217 at either pole, if measured at sea level. The difference between these values is small, although greater than the $3\frac{1}{2}$ cm/sec^2 we have calculated for centripetal acceleration at the equator. This discrepancy largely results from the fact that the earth is not a true sphere, but is slightly flattened at its poles and possessed of an equatorial bulge. Objects at the poles are thus very slightly nearer the earth's center than are those at the equator, hence experience greater gravitational force, for reasons that will be made clear in the next chapter. (It must be remembered that purely *local* variations in g remain to be accounted for.)

The development of modern projectiles has brought the possibility of direct observation of the earth's rotation. To a stationary observer watching above the north pole the earth rotates in a counterclockwise direction. A rocket fired in any direction from the north pole would continue in that direction, while the object at which it is fired rotates to the left. To an observer on the earth near the pole the rocket would appear to deviate to the right (Fig. 3–12). Now let us consider what would happen to a projectile fired northward from the equator. The launching mechanism itself is traveling eastward at more than a thousand miles per hour, and the projectile is automatically endowed with this same horizontal velocity. As it flies northward it passes over parts of the earth that are moving at progressively smaller linear speeds, while it maintains its own original eastward component of motion. Thus it "gets ahead" of the meridian along which it was fired, and is also apparently deviated to the right. Effects of this sort have been observed. In practice, error is avoided by making an appropriate correction in the firing of a long-range projectile. In the northern hemisphere the aim must be slightly to the left of the direct line to the target. In the southern hemisphere the rotation of the earth produces a deviation in the opposite direction; a long range missile appears to deviate to the left if fired along a north-south line, and must be aimed slightly to the right of its target.

The motions of winds and ocean currents are also affected by the rotation of the earth, but in such a complicated and almost undecipherable way that the observed effects can hardly be cited as "proof" of the earth's rotation. Meteorologists simply *assume* the rotation of the earth on the basis of other evidence, then find the assumption very helpful in explaining some features of the complex motions of air masses.

Since our first introduction of the concept *force* we have referred constantly to the force of *gravity*. The term has done no more for us, however, than to permit convenient reference to the familiar tendency of objects to fall toward the earth's surface. Is gravity a mysterious power of attraction exercised, uniquely, by the earth on all terrestrial objects? In Aristotle's view, as we know, the phenomenon of free fall *was* peculiar to the "mundane sphere," although he ascribed it more to bodies themselves than to the earth. We are now in a position to understand how Newton, building on the results of his anti-Aristotelian predecessors, was able to bridge the centuries-old gap (in the thoughts of man) between events in the heavens and those on earth. And we shall find that the same kind of force that causes terrestrial objects to fall, gravity, holds the solar system together.

3–5 Summary

The world is three-dimensional, and changes in motion may include changes in *direction* as well as in speed. Galileo was able to achieve the first satisfactory account of projectile motion by analyzing it into two simultaneous motions, one uniform in the horizontal direction, and the other uniformly accelerated in the vertical direction. Directed quantities called vectors, necessary for the simple description of motion and forces, may be represented by directed line segments, and combined graphically. A body in uniform circular motion is accelerated toward the center of the circle although its speed remains constant, and a force (called centripetal) is required to produce this acceleration. The rotation of the earth about its axis involves such forces, although the effects are so small as to escape detection unless they are explicitly sought.

REFERENCES

EINSTEIN, A., and L. INFELD, *The Evolution of Physics*. The problem of motion, including vectors, is treated in the first thirty pages of this nontechnical book.

GALILEO GALILEI, *Dialogues Concering Two New Sciences*, Fourth Day.

HOLTON, G., *Introduction to Concepts and Theories in Physical Science*, especially Chapter 3.

LUHR, O., *Physics Tells Why*. A very engaging account of vectors and motion generally is to be found in Chapter 2.

MAGIE, W. F., *A Source Book in Physics*, pp. 19–22 (Galileo on projectiles), 28 (Huygens).

SEMAT, H., *Physics in the Modern World*, especially Chapter 2

TAYLOR, L. W., *Physics, the Pioneer Science*, Chapters 2 and 3. This text is a valuable reference for much of the subject matter of the present book, since Taylor has traced the development of physics historically.

1. A boat is steered due south at a speed of 12 mi/hr but is meanwhile carried east by the tide at 5 mi/hr. Draw a careful diagram showing the boat's velocity.

2. How could you find the sum of *three* vectors? Find the sum of the three forces acting on the cart shown in Fig. 3–13.

3. A raindrop falling vertically at a constant speed of 5 m/sec enters the top of a long tube. The tube is moving horizontally with a speed of 5 m/sec, and if it is held vertically the raindrop will hit its side. At what angle will the tube have to be held so that the drop will fall along its axis? Construct a carefully labeled diagram, and indicate its scale. [*Ans.*: 45°]

4. A ball is thrown from a mountain top at a horizontal speed of 10 m/sec. (a) How far does it fall below the horizontal line of throw in the first second? (b) How far does it travel horizontally in the first second? (c) Show on a diagram the *displacement* of the ball during the first second. (d) Make another diagram showing the *velocity* of the ball at the end of the first

second. (e) Make similar calculations and diagrams for the second, third, and fourth seconds.

5. Suppose you allow an object to fall from the ceiling of a train which is moving with uniform velocity. (a) Will it hit the floor of the car at the same spot it would strike if the car were standing still? (b) Would the answer be the same if the object fell while the train was slowing down?

6. Approximately how fast would an object have to be shot horizontally to describe the circular path shown in Fig. 3–10, assuming no air resistance and no obstacles? Take the earth's radius as 6.4×10^6 meters and g as 10 m/sec². [*Ans.*: 8000 m/sec, or 8 km/sec. This is about 5 mi/sec.]

7. For artificial satellites to complete many revolutions about the earth they must be carried well over one hundred miles above the earth's surface before being "put into orbit" at a speed of approximately 5 mi/sec. Why? Why should the lifetime of such a satellite be relatively short even at a height of two hundred miles above the surface of the earth?

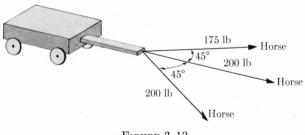

FIGURE 3–13.

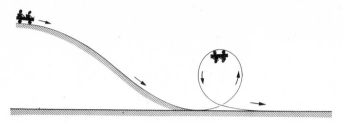

FIGURE 3–14.

8. In 1803 an experiment was performed in Germany to determine whether free fall from a high tower is truly vertical. It was found that objects fall slightly to the *east* of the vertical. Why?

9. Imagine yourself at the south pole, and show by a diagram that a rocket fired in any direction would be apparently deviated to the left of the meridian line along which it was fired. If you fired a rocket southward from the equator, which way would it appear to be deviated?

10. In rounding a curve, it is progressively more difficult to control an automobile as its speed is increased. Why?

11. A roller coaster car traveling at sufficient speed can execute a "loop-the-loop" (Fig. 3–14) without losing its passengers. Why?

12. If a stone weighing 200 gm is whirled once each second in a circle of radius 100 cm, what acceleration does it experience? What is the magnitude of the centripetal force involved? of the centrifugal force? On what bodies do these forces act, respectively? [*Ans.*: $a = 400\pi^2 \simeq 4000$ cm/sec^2; F is about 8×10^5 dynes.]

13. The driver of an automobile pushes down harder on the accelerator pedal in order to climb a straight, steep hill at constant speed. (a) Is the automobile accelerated as it climbs? Will it be accelerated (b) if he removes his foot from the accelerator pedal, (c) if he negotiates a slight curve in the road at constant speed?

CHAPTER 4

THE LAW OF UNIVERSAL GRAVITATION

We are now in possession of all the significant pieces of information that led Newton to his famous law of gravitation. Newton's chain of reasoning resulted in deeper understanding not only of the solar system but of the behavior of matter everywhere. The essential ingredient of the process—indeed the most revolutionary idea involved—was his conviction that the *laws of motion are the same everywhere,* in the heavens and on the earth. This is an assumption: it is not possible for us to travel over the universe to verify the statement directly. Its validity is tested at second hand, by the logical consequences to which it leads. It was an assumption implicit in much of the work of Galileo, although his attack on Aristotelian physics did not explicitly include this point. By the latter part of the 17th century the idea had gained in acceptability, but was still so novel that it was difficult for most people to comprehend. Even so great a scientist as Huygens, who published the formulas for uniform circular motion well before Newton, seems never to have thought of applying these results to planetary motions.

4-1 Component parts of Newton's synthesis

It was, according to Newton's own account, during "the two plague years of 1665 and 1666, for in those days I was in the prime of my age for invention, and minded Mathematicks and Philosophy more than at any time since," that he first conceived the law of gravitation. In 1666 he was 24 years old. There is no extant documentation of his work during these years, and his results on gravitation were not published until 1687. Nevertheless we can trace a possible line of proof. Let us recapitulate the information that was available.

First, there were Kepler's laws of planetary motion:

1. Planets move in elliptical paths, with the sun at one focus of the ellipse.

2. The line from a planet to the sun sweeps over equal areas in equal times, during all parts of its path.

3. For all the planets, $T^2 = KR^3$, where T, called the *period* of the orbit, is the time for one complete revolution about the sun, R is the average distance of the planet from the sun, and K is a constant.

Next, there was the law of free fall, stating that all bodies falling from rest are accelerated at the same rate at any given place, and the distance traversed from the starting point is given by $d = \frac{1}{2}gt^2$, where t is the time of fall and g is the acceleration of gravity. Newton himself had clarified what we know as his three laws of motion: the law of inertia; the law giving the relation between force, mass, and acceleration, $F = ma$; and the law of action and reaction. In addition, he had worked out for himself the law of force required to keep a body moving uniformly in a circle, $F = mv^2/r$.

To test his results quantitatively Newton needed certain astronomical measurements as well as values for such physical constants as the acceleration of gravity. We shall see just what information of this sort was required as we proceed to develop Newton's ideas.

Newton assumed, as we have said, that the laws of motion hold everywhere. Reasoning from his own laws of motion, it was clear to him that force is required to keep planets moving around the sun and the moon moving around the earth in circular paths. He assumed that these forces are of exactly the same kind as that acting on objects at the earth's surface, i.e., that the force is a gravitational one in every case. Even without this assumption he was able to show that Kepler's second law (the law of equal areas) should be expected to hold if the forces on planets always act toward a *center*. To see this, let us examine the relation between the areas swept by a line from a moving body to a center and the direction of the forces acting on that body.

4–2 Law of equal areas for central forces

In the absence of forces, a body moves along a straight line with uniform speed and it will travel equal distances, AB, BC, etc., as in Fig. 4–1, in equal intervals of time which we may designate Δt. (The symbol Δ is used to indicate a small change in the quantity following: thus Δt is a small change of time.) If we establish a point outside the line of motion as a "center" (O in Fig. 4–1) *a line from this center to the moving body sweeps over equal areas in equal times*. The proof of this statement follows at once from the rule that the area of a triangle is $\frac{1}{2}$ its base times its altitude: triangles ABO, BCO, etc., have equal bases and the same altitude, and hence have the same area.

Now suppose that when the body is at B it is given a sharp instantaneous blow *toward the center*, point O. As a result of this impact it will gain a velocity toward O. Imagine the velocity to be such that if the body had been standing still at point B in Fig. 4–2, it would have traveled to B' in the succeeding time interval Δt. Without the blow its initial uniform motion would have carried it to C in this same interval, however, and the combination of its two motions will bring the body to point C'. In other words, its actual displacement BC' is equal to the vector sum of the two component

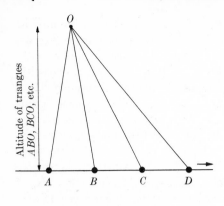

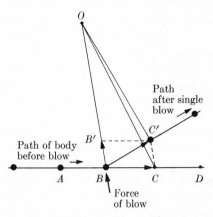

FIG. 4-1. Law of equal areas for a body in uniform motion.

FIG. 4-2. Law of equal areas in the case of an impact directed toward the center O.

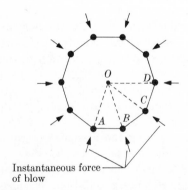

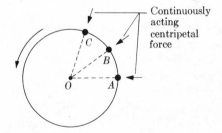

FIG. 4-3. A body moving with uniform speed is subjected to successive sharp blows at regular intervals. If the blows are always of the same size and always directed toward center O the path of the body will be as shown. Areas OAB, OBC, OCD, etc., are equal.

FIG. 4-4. A body moving at constant speed but subjected to a continuous force, constant in magnitude and directed at all times toward center O, travels in a circular path. Areas OAB, ODC, etc., are equal, where arcs AB, BC, etc. are distances traversed by the body in equal times. Figure 4-3 reduces to Fig. 4-4 if the time interval between blows is made vanishingly small.

displacements BB' and BC. Now the areas of the triangles OBC' and OBC are equal. They share one side, the base OB, and since CC' is parallel to BB' their altitudes are equal.* Therefore our conclusion for uniform motion,

---

*To appreciate that BB' and CC' must be parallel, remember the parallelogram method for combining vectors. *Since* they are parallel, the two lines joining OB to C' and C, both perpendicular to OB (that is, the altitudes of OBC' and OBC), must be of equal length.

that equal areas are swept out by a line from the center O to the moving body in equal times, is unchanged by the intervention of a force directed toward that center. The process could be repeated as often as we like without altering this result, so long as the force, and thus the change in velocity, is toward the center (Fig. 4–3). A completely general theorem follows: *If there are no forces acting on a body except those toward a fixed center, the line from that center to the moving body sweeps over equal areas in equal times.*

If a central force acts *continuously* the velocity of the body changes continuously and its path is a curve. If this curve is to be a circle the force must act constantly toward its center (Fig. 4–4). Newton was able to show, probably in 1682, that if the path is an *ellipse* the center of action of force must be one of its foci. Thus an assumption that the forces acting on planets are at all times directed toward the sun, and are perhaps exerted *by* that body, was shown to be in complete accord with Kepler's second law.

4–3 The law of gravitation for circular orbits

Let us assume that the motions of the planets and moon are circular, forgetting for the moment those discrepancies which led Kepler to his first law. Newton himself first approached the problem of gravitation in this way, although later he had to make sure that elliptical paths could be quantitatively accounted for. Deliberate simplification of a problem to achieve a provisional solution is a very useful device often employed in science. It must be kept in mind that this is done only for initial convenience, however, and that we are not denying the existence of those features we temporarily neglect. This is quite different from the demand made by Plato for circles and nothing but circles. Our concern at first will be the main features, not the details, of the effect of gravitation. Even so, we shall not be led far astray, for the orbits of most planets are, in fact, *nearly* circular.

It was Newton's belief that the central force constantly acting on planets to maintain their orbital motions was one of gravitation exerted by the sun. He demonstrated, by combining Kepler's third law of planetary motion with the law of centripetal force, that this force must be inversely proportional to the square of the distance between the sun and any planet. If a planet traverses a circle of radius R in time T, its *speed* v is the circumference ($2\pi R$) divided by the time period T, hence

$$v = \frac{2\pi R}{T}. \tag{4–1}$$

Let us substitute this expression for v in the formula for centripetal force:

$$F = \frac{mv^2}{R}, \tag{3–10}$$

therefore

$$F = \frac{4\pi^2 m R}{T^2}. \tag{4–2}$$

Equation (4–2) would be true for any circular motion, even though m, R, and T may here refer to a particular planet. But Kepler had found that for the planets

$$T^2 = KR^3, \tag{1–1}$$

where the value of the constant K is the same for all. If we substitute KR^3 for T^2 in the denominator on the right side of Eq. (4–2), we obtain

$$F = \frac{4\pi^2}{K} \frac{m}{R^2} = K' \frac{m}{R^2}, \tag{4–3}$$

where m is the mass of the planet and K' simply represents the new constant factor $(4\pi^2/K)$.

According to Eq. (4–3), the force exerted by the sun on a planet is inversely proportional to the square of the planet's *distance from the sun*, if its orbit is circular. Imagine a planet first traveling in a circle of radius R, then somehow transported to a new circular orbit whose radius is twice as large, i.e., $2R$. If the force exerted on the planet in the first orbit is $F = K'm/R^2$, and that in its new orbit is $F' = K'm/(2R)^2$, the *ratio* of these forces will be

$$\frac{F'}{F} = \frac{K'm/4R^2}{K'm/R^2} = \frac{1}{4},$$

that is, $F' = \frac{1}{4}F$. When the planet's distance from the sun is doubled, the force it experiences is quartered. If the radius were trebled, the force would become only $\frac{1}{9}$ as great; if quadrupled, only $\frac{1}{16}$ as great, and so on. These imaginary operations simply serve to illustrate the meaning of the inverse-square relation between F and R shown in Eq. (4–3); actual members of the solar system are not spaced so conveniently. If Kepler's third law and the equation for centripetal force are correct, there can be no doubt of the validity of this relation for circular orbits, for it has been derived from them by purely deductive means.

There is another important relation brought out in Eq. (4–3) which we have not as yet considered: the force F is proportional to the mass m of the planet. Thus the sun pulls on a given planet with a force proportional to the planet's mass, and by Newton's third law of motion the planet must pull on the sun with equal force in an opposite direction. Thus the *two* bodies act on each other mutually, even though greatly separated by distance. If their *mutual* force of attraction depends upon the mass of one of the bodies (the planet), as indicated by Eq. (4–3), why should it not equally depend on the mass of the other (the sun)? Perhaps it is proportional to the *product* of the masses of planet and sun, in which case the quantity K', Eq. (4–3), would contain within it the constant mass of the latter. If so, a new equation may be written:

$$F = G \frac{mM}{R^2},\qquad (4\text{--}4)$$

in which M represents the mass of the sun, and G a new constant of proportionality (K' with M factored out). The assumption that the force acting between a planet and the sun is proportional to *both* their masses, based upon what might be called an *argument of symmetry*, is representative of Newton's great intuition. Thus far in our development, however, we may regard it as little more than an inspired guess that will have to be checked carefully against the available evidence.

Equation (4–4) has been developed specifically in terms of forces between the sun and planets, and for the ideal case of circular orbits at that. Its more general applicability will be illustrated in succeeding pages, but we may glimpse ahead at the almost breathtaking extension Newton was bold enough to envisage. As we have said, he assumed nearly from the start that the force causing terrestrial free fall and those causing curvature in the paths of planets and satellites were similar. Extending this argument, he dared to imagine that such forces of attraction are *universal*, manifested between all material objects, everywhere. In this greatly widened sense, F in Eq. (4–4) would represent the mutual force with which *any* two objects of masses m and M attract each other when separated by a distance R. The quantity G, a *universal constant of gravitation*, would be independent of any mass or distance, the same for all pairs of bodies wherever they may be. In words, Newton's *law of universal gravitation* may be stated:

Every body in the universe attracts every other with a force which is directly proportional to the product of their masses and inversely proportional to the square of the distance between them.

4–4 A test of the law of gravitation

The consistency of the law of gravitation with the law of equal areas and, for circular orbits, with Kepler's third law is promising but not enough to warrant acceptance. The results of such reasoning in science must always be weighed in the impartial balance of further factual observation. One of Newton's first tests involved observation of the moon. It was a partial test, not of the universality of Eq. (4–4), but of the validity of the inverse-square relation when applied to pairs of bodies *other* than the sun and planets. This test was certainly necessary for the validation of Eq. (4–4), although it could not, of itself, guarantee that the law is unexceptionally correct.

In Newton's view it is gravitational attraction of the earth for the moon that accelerates the latter, hence keeps it in its orbit. Also, the earth's attraction for an object at its surface is responsible for the acceleration of free fall. If this view is correct, the moon's constant "fall" toward the earth and the downward motion of a stone released from a cliff may be ascribed to the same cause (see Fig. 4–5). The acceleration of the moon, at its greater distance, must be considerably smaller than that of the stone if the inverse-square relation between force and distance holds. How much smaller? Before we can make a quantitative estimate, we must choose some single point of reference from which to reckon the two distances. If the center of the earth is selected for this purpose, it is implied that that point is the center of action of the earth's gravitational force, even though the earth's mass is distributed through a large volume. We shall return to this question; for the moment let us assume that this is true.

Gravitational force, like any other, must satisfy Newton's second law of motion. Therefore we may write

$$F = \frac{GmM}{R^2} = ma, \qquad (4\text{–}5)$$

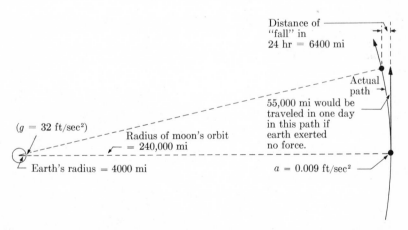

FIG. 4–5. Earth's gravitational force causes the moon to "fall." The moon's speed in its orbit ($v = 2\pi r/T$) is such that in one day it would move 55,000 mi in a straight path if no forces acted on it. At the same time it "falls" a distance ($d = \frac{1}{2}at^2$) of 6400 mi toward the earth, since the latter's gravitational force, at a distance of 240,000 mi, imparts an acceleration of about 0.009 ft/sec².

in which a is the gravitational acceleration of a body of mass m (here either the moon or stone) at a distance R from another body of mass M (here the earth). Solving for a, we note that m cancels, and that

$$a = G\,\frac{M}{R^2}. \tag{4-6}$$

The distance from the earth's center to that of the moon is known to be roughly 240,000 mi, and the radius of the earth about 4000 mi. The acceleration a of the moon should then be

$$a = \frac{GM}{(240,000)^2}, \tag{4-7}$$

and the acceleration g of a stone at the earth's surface should be

$$g = \frac{GM}{(4000)^2}. \tag{4-8}$$

At this stage we know neither G, the gravitational constant, nor M, the mass of the earth. However, if we divide Eq. (4-7) by Eq. (4-8) both of these quantities will cancel, and we will obtain an expression for the *ratio* of a to g:

$$\frac{a}{g} = \left(\frac{4000}{240,000}\right)^2 = \frac{1}{3600},$$

hence

$$a = \frac{1}{3600}\,g.$$

Equation (4-4) has thus been used to make a prediction: if the equation is correct, our assumption in taking distances from the earth's center is valid, and the actual measurements employed are not seriously in error, then the moon's *observed* acceleration should be only about 1/3600 as large as g. Since the measured value of g is 32 ft/sec², the moon should be accelerated toward the earth at the rate of about 32/3600 ft/sec².

To obtain a value for the moon's acceleration by observation of its orbit, we may simply combine Eq. (4-2) with Newton's second law of motion:

$$F = ma = \frac{4\pi^2 m R}{T^2},$$

hence

$$a = 4\pi^2\,\frac{R}{T^2}. \tag{4-9}$$

[Equation (4–2) is an expression for centripetal acceleration in uniform *circular* motion, hence the value for *a* computed from Eq. (4–9) will not be quite right because of the slight actual ellipticity of the moon's orbit.] The period T of the moon (the time it requires for one complete revolution in its orbit) is one sidereal month, 27.3 days; R has the same value employed above, 240,000 mi. Therefore the acceleration of the moon, in ft/sec^2, is

$$a = \frac{4\pi^2 R}{T^2} = \frac{4 \times (3.14)^2 \times 240,000 \text{ mi} \times 5280 \text{ ft/mi}}{(27.3 \text{ days} \times 24 \text{ hr/day} \times 3600 \text{ sec/hr})^2}. \quad (4\text{–}10)$$

When the arithmetic of Eq. (4–10) is performed, the result checks very well with the predicted value of 32/3600 ft/sec^2 [32/3600 = 0.00889 ft/sec^2; calculated result, Eq. (4–10), = 0.00896 ft/sec^2]. It was in this way that the first independent test of the inverse-square gravitation law was successfully met. As Newton put it, he had "compared the force requisite to keep the Moon in her orb with the force of gravity at the surface of the earth, and found them to answer pretty nearly."

4–5 Elliptical orbits and extended masses

Planetary orbits are not perfect circles, as assumed in the derivation of Eq. (4–4), and the mass of the earth is not actually concentrated at its center, as assumed in the "falling moon" test. By 1684 the inverse-square law for circular orbits had been derived from Kepler's third law by at least three scientists other than Newton: Robert Hooke (who had discovered the law of the spring balance), Edmund Halley (of Halley's comet fame), and Christopher Wren (best remembered as a great architect). Whether the inverse-square law would account for *elliptical* orbits remained an unanswered question.

During a visit Halley made to Newton in Cambridge, in 1683, he mentioned his concern over the problem of elliptical orbits, which seemed to defy solution. Much to his surprise, the great man told him that he had succeeded in demonstrating, two years earlier, that a body traveling in a closed path other than a circle, and continuously pulled by a central force which varies inversely with the square of distance, *must* travel in an ellipse. And, furthermore, that the center of action of the force must be one focus of the ellipse. The problem had been solved! When Newton looked for the notes containing his proof he found that he had mislaid them, so that he was forced to perform the detailed mathematics all over again. The problem had appeared insoluble to Halley and others because of limitations in the available mathematical techniques. Newton's success was facilitated by his invention of an entirely new kind of mathematics called the *calculus**, which made the calculation of elliptical motions and many other difficult computations relatively simple. With calculus it is readily shown that for a body moving in an elliptical path, the acceleration toward one focus is just that described by the inverse-square law (see Fig. 4–6). Since the sun is at one focus of all the planetary ellipses, planetary motions can be fully attributed to forces of the kind given by Newton's gravitation formula, Eq. (4–4).

It can also be shown by the methods of the calculus that if a quantity of matter is distributed with *spherical symmetry* about a point (i.e., uniformly

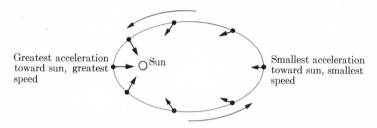

Greatest acceleration toward sun, greatest speed   Sun   Smallest acceleration toward sun, smallest speed

FIG. 4–6. Planetary orbit of greatly exaggerated ellipticity. Vectors represent forces on the planet, or its accelerations at different points on its orbit. Force varies with distance from the sun in accord with Eq. (4–4).

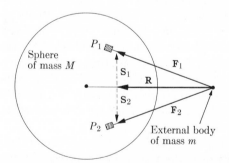

FIG. 4–7. Particles P_1 and P_2 inside a symmetrical sphere exert forces $\mathbf{F}_1$ and $\mathbf{F}_2$ on a mass m outside the sphere. These forces have equal and opposite sidewise components $\mathbf{S}_1$ and $\mathbf{S}_2$, which cancel. Each also has a component $\mathbf{R}$ toward the center; the net force exerted by particles P_1 and P_2 on m is thus force $2\mathbf{R}$. When forces due to all particles composing the mass are added, the symmetry of opposing sideward forces results in a single force directed toward the center.

---

*The calculus was developed independently by Leibnitz on the continent of Europe, and there was considerable controversy over priority. The developments were truly independent, however, and we may stress again that great discoveries are rarely made singly.

along all radial directions from the
point) then, for all points outside the
sphere, it acts as though it were concentrated at that central point.
Proof of this assertion also depends
on the inverse-square law of gravitational attraction, and is thus consistent with the *universality* Newton
assumed for his law. As shown in
Fig. 4–7, there are *sideward* components of attraction exerted by the
parts of a spherical body on a small
mass m above its surface which cancel one another. The sum of all the
components that do not cancel but
add to one another is a net attraction directed toward the center. To

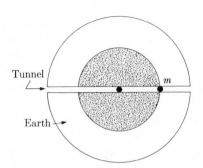

Fig. 4–8. Only the shaded portion of
the sphere is effective in attracting m
toward the center. The net attractive
effect of the outer shell on m vanishes.

whatever extent the earth *is* symmetrical about its central point we are
justified in assuming that its entire mass is concentrated at that point, as
we did in the test of the "falling moon." This implies that the earth is perfectly rigid and perfectly regular; despite the fact that it is neither, as we
shall see, the assumption leads to remarkably little error in calculation.

The inverse-square law yields a curious result for the gravitational attraction on an object *within* a massive sphere. Suppose that it were possible to
make a narrow tunnel through the earth, and for a man to "weigh" himself
at various points, as shown in Fig. 4–8. The net attraction exerted on him
by the earth would become *smaller* as he descends from the surface. That
part of the sphere below him at any point can be considered as though it
were concentrated at the center, but the shell of matter *above* his level pulls
in all directions, upward as well as down, so that its net effect is zero. (What
would he weigh at the exact center of the earth?) The problems of elliptical
orbits and extended masses are not difficult to solve by the methods of
calculus, but the learning of new mathematical techniques takes so much
time and practice that we must here be content with the statements of results given above.

With the encouragement of Halley, Newton prepared his work for publication, and the result was the appearance in 1687 of his *Principia Mathe-
matica Philosophiae Naturalis,* or *Mathematical Principles of Natural
Philosophy.* This is probably the greatest scientific book ever to have been
published. It contains the laws of motion, the law of gravitation and many
of its consequences, and much of Newton's great mathematical achievement.

4-6 Further consequences of the law of gravitation

Once the law of gravitation was finally established, it was found to possess powerful explanatory and predictive value. Newton was able to employ it, for example, in offering the first rational explanation of the phenomenon of tides. Although the details are complicated by shore and ocean floor variations and by rotation, the main features of tides are caused by gravitational attraction of the moon for the earth. Water on the side of the earth toward the moon is pulled out a little, since it is closer to the moon than the rest of the earth and thus experiences greater force per unit mass than the earth as a whole. For the same reason the *earth* is pulled a little away from the ocean on the side *opposite* the moon. Since the earth rotates there are thus *two* tides per day at any ocean location, although it is clear from an examination of Fig. 4–9 that they are not likely to be of equal height. This is because the orbit of the moon lies close to the plane of the ecliptic, with respect to which the earth's axis is tilted. On Fig. 4–9, point A travels in 12 hours to A', where the tidal effect on the side opposite the moon is much smaller than that near the moon. Point B, on the other hand, travels from a region of small tidal bulge facing the moon to one of large bulge opposite the moon. Figure 4–9 represents an idealized earth, uniformly covered with water; tides are complicated on a real earth by land masses, which are much more rigid than the oceans. The sun also contributes to the occurrence of tides, and must be taken into account. The highest tides occur about twice a month, when the sun, earth, and moon are all in positions along the same line. The sun is less than half as effective as the moon in causing tidal bulges, however.

It was first deduced from the law of gravitation that recurring comets are part of the solar system, moving in highly elliptical orbits and visible only when near the sun. Comets have very little mass, however large they

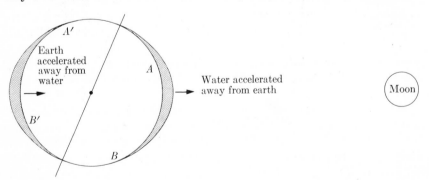

Fig. 4–9. Earth and moon, showing tidal bulges (exaggerated) on an ideal earth. A and A' change places in half a day, and it is clear that the two tides will be of unequal height.

may be in volume, and are relatively unstable members of the solar family. Their paths show that their travel is subject to the gravitational force of the sun, however. Halley's Comet is perhaps the most famous of the comets that appear regularly, and there is evidence that it has done so for at least two thousand years, at intervals of about 75 years. Some comets are seen only once, others several times at most.

More "new" permanent members of the solar system were also found by application of the law of gravitation. We remember that the law presumes to apply to *every* pair of bodies, although the sun is so very massive that its gravitational effect almost entirely governs the motion of the planets. One of the most remarkable achievements of Newton's theory, however, came from studying *perturbations* of orbits, small deviations from perfect ellipticity due to gravitational effects of the planets on *each other*. The paths of some of the more remote planets exhibited perturbations which could not be attributed to planets already known. The existence of the planets Neptune and Pluto was predicted from such discrepancies before they were actually seen.in the telescope. In the case of Neptune, an astronomer in Berlin found the planet with his telescope on the very evening he received a letter from the Paris mathematician Leverrier telling him where to look! The latter had made extensive calculations, based on Eq. (4–4), of the probable path of a planet near Uranus, capable of causing the perturbations that had been observed in that planet's orbit. (These calculations were made independently by the English mathematician Adams.)

With the law of gravitation it is easy to see why there should be variations in g, the acceleration of gravity, as we go from place to place on the earth. Changes in altitude alone would produce an effect: g is smaller at the top of Pike's Peak than at its base, smaller on the 100th floor of the Empire State Building than at street level, for the same reason that the acceleration of the moon is less than that of free fall on the earth. From Eq. (4–6), $g = GM/R^2$, and R, the distance to the center of the earth, varies with altitude. There are more interesting causes of variation, as well. As we know, the earth is not a perfect sphere but more nearly a spheroid, flattened at the poles and bulging somewhat around the middle. Its equatorial radius is about 13 miles greater than its polar radius, and this is one of the reasons why g is found to be larger near the poles than at the equator. In Chapter 3 we spoke of another reason, the rotation of the earth.

Further, more localized variations in the acceleration of gravity have found their most significant interpretations in the field of geology. Masses of rock in high mountains affect the value of g in their vicinity and also the very *direction* of free fall. The attraction of a mountainous mass for a body falling near it pulls the body sidewise; a plumb line near mountains does not point exactly to the center of the earth. Hidden features of the

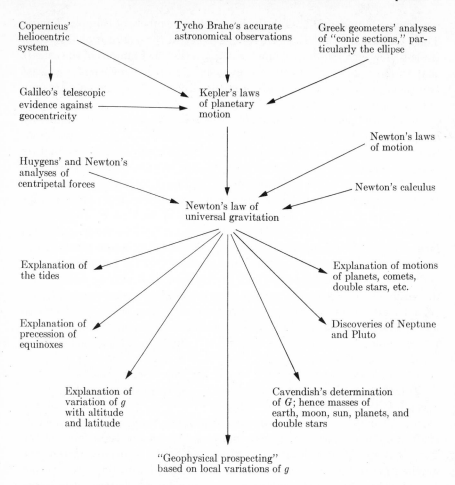

FIG. 4–10. Outline of the Sources and Consequences of Newton's Law of Gravitation. (After E. H. Green.)

earth may be detected by measurement of local variations in g. For example, at the same latitude and elevation g would differ if in one case it were measured over a vast cave and in another it were measured over a deposit of lead or gold. We shall return to this subject when we consider the interior structure of the earth.

The effect of the earth's equatorial bulge on the gravitational attraction of the moon and, to a lesser extent, of the sun was shown by Newton to account for an ancient astronomical mystery. We have mentioned the "precession of the equinoxes," known to Hipparchus, as a slow shift of the seasons with respect to the constellations. This can be interpreted as a slow rotation of the earth's rotational axis, rather like the rotation of the axis of a spinning top about a vertical line, as shown in Fig. 1–10. Since the moon's orbit lies very nearly in the plane of the ecliptic it constantly exerts an oblique force on the earth's equatorial bulge which steadily changes the direction of the earth's axis, but not its angle of inclination. While the details of the theory are too complex to consider here, Newton was able to account quite quantitatively for the secondary, or *precessional*, rotation of the earth in these terms.

The principal sources and some of the more important consequences of the law of gravitation are summarized in Fig. 4–10. Newton's great generalization produced a decided change in the character of astronomy. From the time of Hipparchus through that of Kepler astronomers had striven for empirical geometrical descriptions of the apparent motions of celestial bodies. Plato conceived his problem simply as an exercise in geometry, and Kepler's laws are essentially geometric relations. With Newton, astronomy and dynamics (the science of motion in terms of forces) became inseparable. By this marriage astronomy was both deepened and widened, and simultaneously the study of the earth was enriched as well. Still, many of the most impressive quantitative applications of the law of gravitation were not possible until more than a hundred years after publication of the *Principia*, when an experiment to which we now turn our attention was first performed.

4–7 The determination of G: "weighing the earth"

In any fixed system of units of mass, distance, and force, the physical content of the law of gravitation can be expressed mathematically only by including the factor of proportionality, which, in accord with custom, we have designated G in Eq. (4–4). This factor must be the same for all masses and all distances if Newton's law is universal, but a test such as that of the "falling moon" provides no clue to its numerical value. Both G and M, the (unknown) mass of the earth, canceled out of the equations leading to our comparison of g with the moon's acceleration. The first successful precision determination of G was made by the Englishman Henry Cavendish (1731–1810), who published his result in 1798. Cavendish attributes the idea for this particular experiment, together with the rough preliminary apparatus, to one "late Rev. John Michell . . . who did not live to make any experiments with it."

The Cavendish apparatus consists of a *torsion* balance, operating on a principle similar to that of the spring balance: here a wire is twisted, rather than stretched. If two equal masses m are suspended from a wire in the manner shown in Fig. 4–11 they will assume a definite position of equilibrium. Any sideward force on either or both of the masses will cause the wire

FIG. 4–11. A torsion balance, show-   FIG. 4–12. The attraction between
ing the initial position of masses m. m and M will produce a small angular
                                                 displacement of the balance in the di-
                                                 rection indicated.

to twist. The amount of twist produced, as determined from the new positions of the masses, can be related to the amount of force applied, and
hence serves as a direct measure of that force. If two large spheres of equal
known mass M are placed near the small masses m, as shown in Fig. 4–12,
the law of gravitation predicts that there will be a force of attraction which
should cause the wire to twist. If the magnitude of this force is determined
from the amount of twist, and if the distances between masses M and m are
measured, the only remaining unknown quantity in Eq. (4–4), $F = GMm/R^2$, is G, which may then be found. The actual forces observed in the
Cavendish experiment amounted to only about one five-millionth of the
weight of the small masses m, and extreme care had to be taken to shield the
apparatus from such outside disturbances as air currents resulting from
temperature variations. The most careful of modern measurements, using
improved versions of essentially the same apparatus, yield the value

$$G = 6.67 \times 10^{-8},$$

if the masses are expressed in grams, distance in centimeters, and force in
dynes. In other words, two one-gram masses one centimeter apart attract
each other with a force of less than one ten-millionth of a dyne! It is almost
miraculous that gravitational forces between masses small enough to be
handled in the laboratory can be measured at all.

Cavendish, in observing the small gravitational attraction between ordinary terrestrial masses, strengthened immeasurably the assumption that
gravitational force is *universal*. Also, his achievement of a numerical value
for G, the universal gravitational constant, greatly heightened the quantitative utility of Newton's law. A consequence of immediate interest that he
was able to deduce, for example, was the mass of the earth. It is sometimes

said that Cavendish succeeded in "weighing the earth," although the proper meaning of the term *weight* is the gravitational force exerted on a body *by the earth*. According to Eq. (4–6), the acceleration *a* imparted to a body by the gravitational attraction of mass M is given by

$$a = GM/R^2.$$

Solving this for M, we obtain

$$M = R^2 a/G. \tag{4-11}$$

To find the mass of the earth, we need merely substitute values for the radius of the earth R, the acceleration of gravity g, and the gravitational constant G:

$$M = \frac{(4000 \text{ mi} \times 5280 \text{ ft/mi} \times 12 \text{ in/ft} \times 2.54 \text{ cm/in})^2 \times 980 \text{ cm/sec}^2}{6.67 \times 10^{-8}}.$$

$$\tag{4-12}$$

(Distance must be expressed in cm and acceleration in cm/sec^2 because the given value of G is based on cgs units of measurement.) When the arithmetic of Eq. (4–12) has been done, the result is very nearly 6×10^{27} gm, which is equivalent to 6×10^{24} kgm, or 6.6×10^{21} tons. This number is so large that it hardly carries meaning in terms of our everyday experience. A more significant quantity is the mass of the earth divided by its total volume, i.e., the *average density* of the earth, which turns out to be 5.52 times greater than the density of water. The value originally obtained by Cavendish was 5.48; the slight discrepancy between his value and the modern one gives some indication of the exquisite care and precision with which he carried out his measurement of G with the techniques available to him.

Once the mass of the earth is known, the masses of the sun, moon, and planets can be found by further application of the law of gravitation. Most of the mass of the solar system is concentrated in the sun, as we should expect from the fact that it appears to stand still at the center of the system. It is more than 333,000 times as massive as the earth. The sun's volume is so very great, however, that its mass per unit volume, or density, is only 1.4 times that of water. Of all the members of the solar system our own planet is densest. Saturn, for example, contains less mass than it would if it were composed of water, yet has so large a volume that its mass is almost as great as that of the earth.

With modern telescopes it has been found that many stars are actually double, consisting of two stars which revolve about each other. The relative motions of these stars can be observed and traced out in time, and in some cases distances between the two members can be ascertained. Application of the law of gravitation, using the numerical value of the gravitational constant G, then enables astronomers to determine their masses. Thus Cavendish's experiment has contributed to our knowledge of parts of the universe remote from the solar system.

4-8 Are mechanics and gravitation universal?

The most spectacular successes of the law of gravitation have resulted from its application to motions within the solar system. This region, vast as it is, makes up only an infinitesimal part of the universe, and it may well be asked whether the same law of gravitation applies everywhere, as Newton believed. Analysis of the motions of double stars, mentioned above, indicates that Newton's laws of motion and law of gravitation are certainly valid for such pairs. But if the law applies universally, why doesn't gravity cause all the matter in the universe to coalesce? As for our own galaxy, that community of stars of which our sun is an inconspicuous member, the reason seems to be similar to that which explains the stability of the solar system. The galaxy as a whole is rotating, and gravitational forces are just sufficient to hold its members together. But the relations, if any, among the countless different galaxies in the universe are not understood. There is considerable evidence that they are actually receding from each other. Astronomers and mathematicians have long been at work on the problem, but their results are still highly speculative. It is certain that more than Newton's law is involved in the mystery. Modern refinements are based on a theory of gravitation originated by Einstein, in which Newton's law of gravitation is taken to be a first approximation, with limited, although wide, applicability.

There is no doubt that the great work of Newton marked a culmination of the study of motion. Building on the work of Galileo, Kepler, and others, Newton was able to give what appeared to be a complete solution to the problem of heavenly bodies and at the same time explain the behavior of all parts or particles of matter here on the earth. To many people, and in particular to the French mathematician and astronomer Pierre Laplace (1749-1827), it seemed that all the *essential* answers to all possible problems of the physical world had been given, and that what remained to be done was only to work out the details. Laplace thought that by the laws of mechanics (motion) all future behavior of the universe could be predicted, in principle, if the present is known. It is certainly true that such phenomena as eclipses, comets, and tides are rather accurately predictable, but the Newton-Laplacian conception of the universe turned out to be vastly oversimplified. Historically, Newton's laws of motion have stood up very well indeed, even though they have required slight modification in our own century by Einstein's theories of relativity. The more serious defect of the Laplace view is that it has not proved possible to solve *all* problems merely by application of the laws of motion.

Newton and his contemporaries left entirely out of account many fundamental aspects of the physical world. Gravitation is only one kind of force, universal in that it does exist wherever there is mass, but sometimes so small in comparison with other forces that it may be neglected with much more justification than our neglect of air resistance in considering projectiles. Gravitation has very little to do with the inherent cohesiveness of most kinds of matter, for example. It could never explain why one can lift an object by taking hold of it at the top. Why do gases expand, upward as readily as downward? How does one substance become transformed into another? What causes lightning, and what is heat? How profound an understanding can we attain of matter itself? Newton's mechanical laws are very useful in *helping* to provide answers to some of these questions, yet do not entirely suffice.

More than once it has appeared that the long-sought answer to a given problem has solved all possible problems, as Laplace thought Newtonian mechanics had done. And indeed, an inspired answer often serves far beyond the confines of the problem for which it was designed. In perspective, however, every advance in science appears to have raised *more* questions than it answered, and to have opened fields for investigation that were hitherto unknown or neglected. The history of science seems to indicate that man's constant increase in knowledge is steadily expanding the horizons of his ignorance!

4–9 Summary

On the assumption that the laws of motion apply everywhere, Newton showed that Kepler's laws are consistent with a universal law of gravitation: all bodies attract each other with a force that varies directly with the product of their masses and inversely with the square of their mutual distance. The free fall of terrestrial bodies toward the earth is due to gravitational attraction between them and the earth. To test his theory, Newton showed that gravitational force between the moon and the earth can account for the motion of the moon. He was able to account at least qualitatively for tides in gravitational terms, and for the precession of the equinoxes. He extended his calculations to the elliptical planetary orbits and to extended masses by means of a new mathematical tool, the calculus. By determining experimentally the constant of proportionality in the law of gravitation, Cavendish found the average density of the earth, and made it possible to determine the masses of members of the solar system and of double stars. Application of the laws of motion to celestial mechanics was so successful that some scientists tended to overestimate the completeness of mechanical description, and to conclude that only details remained to be discovered.

REFERENCES

BUTTERFIELD, H., *Origins of Modern Science*, Chapters VII and (especially) VIII.

BROWN, G. B., *Science, Its Method and Philosophy*, Chapter V.

DAMPIER, W., *A History of Science*, Chapter IV.

HOLTON, G., *Introduction to Concepts and Theories in Physical Science*, Chapter 11.

MAGIE, W. F., *A Source Book in Physics*. An excerpt from Newton's *Principia*, pp. 92–93, and Cavendish's description of his celebrated experiment, pp. 105–111.

MASON, S. F., *Main Currents of Scientific Thought*, Chapter 17.

Sir Isaac Newton, 1727–1927. A publication of the History of Science Society, containing essays on various aspects of Newton's life and work.

RANDALL, J. H., *The Making of the Modern Mind*. Chapters 11 and 12 contain a fascinating account of the impact of Newton's mechanical views on the thought of his own and succeeding generations.

SHAPLEY, H., and H. E. HOWARTH, *A Source Book in Astronomy*. Excerpts from Newton's *Principia*, pp. 74–93.

TAYLOR, L. W., *Physics, the Pioneer Science*, Chapter 13.

1. The motion of a body on which only central forces act, i.e., forces directed toward the same point in space, is confined to a single plane. Can you demonstrate that this must be so?

2. Check the arithmetic of Eqs. (4–10) and (4–12).

3. How large is g, the acceleration of gravity toward the center of the earth, for a meteorite (a) 4000 mi above the earth's surface? (b) 8000 mi? (c) 12,000 mi? [*Ans.*: 8 ft/sec^2; 3.6 ft/sec^2; 2 ft/sec^2]

4. The moon's radius is about 0.27 times that of the earth, and its mass is about 1/81 that of the earth. Prove from the law of gravitation that a body at the surface of the moon should experience an acceleration of free fall about 1/6 that on the earth.

5. Tides are produced as a result of the *difference* between a gravitational pull on the water of the oceans and a pull on the earth as a whole. The gravitational force exerted by the sun on the earth is much greater than that exerted by the moon, yet the moon is more effective in producing tides. Why?

6. A 1-kgm mass and a 2-kgm mass, in a given location at the earth's surface, experience the same acceleration of free fall, g. Does this mean that they are subject to identical gravitational forces? How is it that they experience the same acceleration?

7. (a) What would happen to the *weight* of a body at the equator if the speed of the earth's rotation were somehow increased? (b) What would happen to the weight of a body at either pole?

8. From Eq. (4–4) it can be calculated that two bodies of mass 120 million kilograms (1.2 $\times$ 10^8 kgm or 1.2 $\times$ 10^{11} gm), when 1 km apart (10^5 cm), exert a mutual force of 10^5 dynes. What would this force be if the bodies were placed, respectively, $\frac{1}{2}$, $\frac{1}{4}$, 2, 3, 4, 5, 10, and 100 km apart? Use your results to construct a graph of gravitational force against distance.

9. Suppose that the two bodies of Exercise 8 are now held at a constant separation of 1 km, but that the masses of either or both may be augmented or diminished at will. (a) What would the force be if one mass were reduced by half? (b) If both were reduced by half? (c) If one were doubled, then trebled, then quadrupled? (d) If both were doubled, then trebled, then quadrupled? Construct a graph showing how gravitational force varies with mass.

10. Prepare an outline of the content of Newton's law of gravitation along the following lines: On what basic hypotheses does it rest? Of these, which are directly verifiable, which not? For those that you have listed as "verifiable," what tests have been applied? How can one be led to accept those that you have listed as "not directly verifiable"? What assumptions, hypotheses, laws, or measurements, which were initially independent of the law of gravitation, were essential to the latter's formulation, and of these, which had been directly verified? In what ways can you say that the law of gravitation is "true" in any absolute sense? Discuss.

11. (a) The mass of a certain laboratory table is 20 kgm; what is its weight? (b) The mass of the moon is about 7.4 $\times$ 10^{22} kgm; what would you say its weight is?

CHAPTER 5

MATTER AND ITS CLASSIFICATION

In the preceding chapters we have learned to describe the motions of bodies, the relation between force and motion, and the universal force of gravitation. We began by examining and describing the motions of very large and remote bodies and found, contrary to Aristotle's philosophy, that understanding them required quantitative description of the more commonplace motions we continually see around us on the earth's surface. In all our considerations of the behavior of material objects, however, no distinctions have been drawn between different *kinds* of matter. A cannon ball and a snowball fall to earth with the same acceleration, and each will describe a parabolic path if thrown from a cliff. The gravitational force between the earth and a gram of hydrogen gas is the same as that acting between the earth and a gram of gold metal. The properties of matter which have been examined so far are thus common to all of its forms. In this chapter we shall turn our attention to some of those properties of matter which distinguish one form from another.

The primary object of science is the interpretation of natural phenomena, and we have already seen that exact description can be an essential prelude to fruitful interpretation. In the case of free fall starting from rest, description may take the form of the single equation $d = \frac{1}{2}at^2$, which is a highly condensed statement, in mathematical language, that is valid for all objects in uniformly accelerated motion. This statement, abstracted from systematic experience, serves the purpose of economy in thought. In the case of the forms of matter, which are variegated to an almost bewildering extent, description is accomplished in terms of convenient distinguishing *properties*, greatly aided by the process of *classification*. Abstraction from experience again is involved: sets of properties common to different kinds of matter are used to establish conceptual classes, or categories. And again the device may be regarded as one of economy: thinking about matter is greatly facilitated by the establishment of a successful, broad classification system.

Obviously, there are many possible points of view which may serve as starting points for the classification of matter. One might choose simply to divide the kinds of matter into the categories gas, liquid, and solid, for example, or to classify on the basis of color. The key concept in the classification system which has proved most useful to science is that of *element*, whose origins we shall attempt to trace in succeeding sections. Our discussion cannot be restricted to questions of classification alone, but will require some consideration, as well, of those activities of man to which classification of matter has borne important relation.

5-1 The Four Elements

Important discoveries in the skills of metallurgy, ceramics, textiles, dyeing, and brewing were achieved independently by such widely separated early civilizations as those of China, India, Mesopotamia, and Egypt. The essential process involved in extraction of copper from its ore, for example, appears to have been known to the Egyptians at least 5000 years ago. Techniques for the preparation and casting of bronze (early bronzes were mixtures of copper and tin) were early discoveries of Egyptian and Mesopotamian civilizations. The relatively difficult extraction of iron from its ore was practiced by the Hittites 4000 years ago. The glazing of pottery has been placed at least as far back as 3400 B.C., and the production of glass at about 2000 B.C., in Egypt. Egyptian fabrics dyed with indigo at least 4000 years ago are still in existence. These processes, developed empirically, required the discovery of useful transformations, as well as useful properties, of matter. However, there is no evidence in the records of early civilizations that attempts were made to understand the qualities of matter that made such remarkable procedures possible.

Advanced techniques in the practical arts, the heritage of earlier civilizations, were an integral feature of classical Greek culture. We have noted that the Greeks were the first peoples to inject an over-all rational outlook into speculation about natural phenomena; it is also in the writings of Greek philosophers that we find the first systematic attempts to interpret material phenomena in terms of broad principles. In particular, the idea that all matter consists of irreducible *elements* appeared, and Empedokles (490–430 B.C.) made the speculative selection of Earth, Air, Fire, and Water as the sum total of those elements. We do not imply that the philosophic concept of element arose *directly* out of the practical arts; indeed, many of the Greek philosophers were, in effect, barred from manual activity by the institution of slavery. It is true, however, that various of the transformations involved in practical processes could be, and were, interpreted in terms of this concept; the consequences of these interpretations will be examined in the next section.

The well-known hypothesis of Four Elements, although not originated by Aristotle, was formalized in his writings; hence Earth, Air, Fire, and Water are often called the Aristotelian elements. Aristotle emphasized the qualities of wetness, dryness, hotness, and coldness, which he associated with the elements (Fig. 5–1), and it was his belief that variations in the *proportions* of elements accounted for the characteristic differences between kinds of matter. Each of the elements, to Aristotle, was an idealized conception: for example, the "perfect" cold dry Earth was believed to be unavailable for inspection, since all common matter consisted of "imperfect" mixtures of the elements.

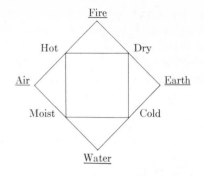

FIG. 5–1. The Four Aristotelian Elements and their associated qualities.

From our present perspective it is easy to lose sight of the truly rational character of the Aristotelian scheme. We must remember that the Greeks made no *systematic* observation of matter and its properties. We should also be aware that many commonplace qualitative observations—the solution of salt by water, the deposition of silt by rivers, the "consumption" of wood by flame—can readily be interpreted as transformations involving the alteration of proportions of the supposed Four Elements. As a speculative hypothesis the Aristotelian conception of matter had considerable beauty and even utility. The idea of irreducible elements, contributed by Greek philosophy, has remained fruitful in human thought to the present day; it has been only the definition of the "true" elements that has required revision in succeeding ages.

5–2 Alchemy

The idea of *transmutation* of matter, i.e., transformation of one kind into another, is implicit in Aristotelian philosophy. If different kinds of matter differ only in their relative proportions of the Four Elements it is logical to suppose that alteration of these proportions will bring about transmutation. It was with this orientation of thought that the art of *alchemy* had its origin, in the city of Alexandria during the early centuries of the Christian era. It was reasonable that Alexandria should be the seat of this development: the city had been founded by the Greeks, and its scholars, trained in the philosophical tradition of Greece, were at the same time close to the long practical traditions of Egypt..

The problem which the Alexandrian alchemists sought to solve was the production of the "perfect" metal, gold, from less valuable ("base") metals—certainly a rational goal within the framework of Aristotle's

philosophy. Although they made no
notable progress toward this goal,
their efforts resulted in the development of techniques of basic importance to the present-day science we
call chemistry (Fig. 5–2). Alexandrian manuscripts contain full descriptions of the techniques of distillation, filtration, crystallization,
and sublimation, as well as char-
acterizations of many new materials
discovered in the course of alchemical investigation.   Unfortunately,
the goal of Alexandrian alchemy was
not one which could sustain disin-

FIG. 5–2. Distilling apparatus, after
an Alexandrian manuscript illustration.
(From *The Alchemists*, by F. Sherwood
Taylor, Abelard-Schuman, Inc.)

terested inquiry, and some manuscripts describe procedures for coloring
lead and other metals to make them *look* like gold. Both fraudulence and
mysticism gradually gained footholds in the new field of investigation.

The Alexandrian alchemical treatises were translated into Arabic, and
great interest in the art developed among the Arab peoples following their
conquest of Egypt in 640 A.D. Although alchemy was primarily confined
to Arabian men of learning from approximately 700 to 1200, it should be
noted that it was also practiced in China (from as early as 100 A.D.) and
in India (from about 700 A.D.), probably as a result of communication between these countries and Alexandria. The introduction of alchemical
knowledge and techniques into western Europe occurred in the 12th and
13th centuries *via* Spain, where Latin translations of Arabic manuscripts
were prepared. Europe became the main locus of alchemical activity, and
remained so until the final demise of the art in the late 18th century.

The fraudulent and mystic components of the long alchemical enterprise
could easily tempt one to overlook its real contributions to knowledge.
These contributions were many and important: many experimental techniques were developed and refined; new substances were discovered, among
them phosphorus, antimony, bismuth, zinc, alcohol, several of the mineral
acids, and large numbers of salts; and several worthwhile attempts were
made to extend the classification of matter. Despite these constructive
aspects, it is fair to say that the over-all gain from alchemical endeavor was
hardly worth the length and intensity of the enterprise. It is ironic that
"transmutation" has finally been accomplished in our own time, although
by methods which could not have been anticipated by the alchemists.
(Means for the production of radioactive gold from mercury, for example,
are described in Chapter 29.)

5-3   Medical chemistry

Transmutation of "base" metals to gold was not the sole objective of alchemy. A parallel (and equally deceptive) goal which arose early in its history was the preparation of an "elixir" of eternal life. More important, however, is the fact that a tradition of rational devotion to knowledge was somehow kept alive throughout the long history of alchemy, and that philosophic consideration of matter never really stopped. For example, Arabian alchemists formulated the hypothesis that metals are composed of two *principles*, mercury and sulfur, in addition to the Four Elements. The Arabian scholar ibn-Sina (980–1036), later known in Europe as Avicenna, was the first of the alchemists to state the belief that transmutation of metals is impossible. Avicenna's treatises strongly influenced the earliest European alchemical scholars, including the Dominican priest Albertus Magnus (1193–1280) and the Franciscan Roger Bacon (1214–1292). While the latter remained a firm believer in transmutation, he felt that "improvement" upon Nature by alchemical techniques should be applied to such things as medicinals, and only incidentally to gold. Bacon's emphasis upon medicine was an anticipation of the later rise of a tradition of Medical Chemistry which gradually absorbed most of the genuinely scholarly element of alchemy.

Theophrastus Bombastus von Hohenheim (1493–1541), more commonly known as Paracelsus, is generally considered the founder of Medical Chemistry, or, as it was contemporarily called, Iatrochemistry. Paracelsus' training was primarily medical, and he devoted his life to an attempted reform of the medical profession. He also pleaded a case for alchemical reform, urging that the techniques of alchemy and the attention of alchemists should be turned to the discovery of medically effective substances. In addition to his medical treatises, Paracelsus wrote speculative tracts concerning the nature of matter. He believed in transmutation and in the Four Elements; to the two Arabic principles, sulfur and mercury, he added a third, *salt*. In Paracelsus' scheme the Four Elements manifest themselves in the form of these three principles, sulfur associated with the property of combustibility, mercury with liquidity, and salt with solidity.

Perhaps the greatest of the medical chemists was the physician Johann Baptista van Helmont (1577-1644) of Brussels, who was one of the first western scholars to reject the Aristotelian Four Elements. He rejected Paracelsus' three principles as well, holding that there are only two *primary* elements, air and water. Solids could be derived from water, according to this view, and van Helmont "proved" in a celebrated experiment that the solid substance of a willow tree forms from water alone (see below). Each kind of solid was thought to have an alchemical "spirit" in addition to its primary matter, and van Helmont succeeded in isolating and characterizing

some "spirits" (vapors), for which he coined our word *gas*. He could find
no relation between air and water, however, hence regarded air as a second
element. Van Helmont emphasized genuine experimentation in all his
work, and although his ideas of elements were wrong, we have already
noted the importance to European science of those who first undertook to
question the authority of Aristotle.

Van Helmont's account of his famous willow-tree experiment runs as follows:
"For I took an Earthen Vessel, in which I put 200 pounds of Earth that had been
dried in a Furnace, which I moystened with Rain-water, then I implanted therein
the Trunk or Stem of a Willow Tree, weighing five pounds; and at length, five
years being finished, the Tree sprung from thence, did weigh 169 pounds, and
about three ounces; But I moystened the Earthern Vessel with Rain-water or
distilled water (alwayes when there was need) and it was large, and implanted into
the Earth, and lest the dust that flew about should be co-mingled with the Earth,
I covered the lip or mouth of the Vessel, with an Iron-plate covered with Tin,
and easily passable with many holes. I computed not the weight of the leaves that
fell off in the four Autumnes. At length, I again dried the Earth of the Vessel, and
there were found the same 200 pounds, wanting about two ounces. Therefore
164 pounds of Wood, Barks, and Roots, arose out of water onely." A large fraction of a willow tree *is* water, but another large fraction consists of compounds of
carbon, formed from carbon dioxide gas in the atmosphere. The thought that a
component of the atmosphere plays a role in plant nutrition could not have
occurred to van Helmont, and was not, in fact, established until more than a
century after his death.

5–4 Robert Boyle on elements

The school of Medical Chemistry was a direct antecedent of the modern
science of chemistry, as may be partially inferred from the fact that Robert
Boyle (1627–1691), often referred to as the "father" of modern chemistry,
was strongly influenced by the writings of van Helmont. Boyle, a son of the
Earl of Cork, was a tireless experimenter and writer whose interests ranged
across the whole of natural philosophy and even beyond. A true follower
of Francis Bacon's philosophy of empiricism in science, he strongly under-
scored the importance of experimentation, as opposed to speculation, in the
study of matter. He was one of the first to emphasize a distinction between
pure substances and mixtures, pointing out the necessity for experimentation with pure materials when possible. Perhaps the principal reason Boyle
is said to have "fathered" modern chemistry is that he went beyond the
traditions of both alchemy and medicine, and proposed that chemistry be
considered a subject worthy of investigation in its own right.

Boyle's discoveries and his influence were far-reaching, and we shall meet
him in connection with quite different aspects of science in later chapters.

For the moment, however, our interest centers upon his ideas of elements. The vigor of his attack on the Aristotelian position is evident in this quotation from Boyle's *The Sceptical Chymist*:

"Nothwithstanding the subtile reasonings I have met with in the books of the Peripateticks, and the pretty experiments that have been shew'd me in the Laboratories of Chemists, I am of so diffident, or dull a Nature, as to think that if neither of them can bring more cogent arguments to evince the truth of their assertion than are wont to be brought, a Man may rationally enough retain some doubts concerning the very number of those materiall Ingredients of mixt bodies, which some would have us call Elements, and others Principles . . . When I took the pains impartially to examine the bodies themselves that are said to result from the blended Elements, and to torture them into a confession of their constituent Principles, I was quickly induc'd to think that the number of Elements has been contended about by Philosophers with more earnestness, than success."

Among the experiments referred to here was the prolonged exposure of metallic gold to fire, a procedure which was popularly supposed to "torture (bodies) into a confession of their constituent principles," but which Boyle found without effect on gold. Thus Boyle rejected the Greek Four Elements, Paracelsus' three principles, and van Helmont's two elements as hypotheses insufficiently grounded in observation. A later passage in *The Sceptical Chymist* contains his own definition of an element:

"I mean by Elements . . . certain Primitive and Simple, or perfectly unmingled bodies; which not being made of any other bodies, or of one another, are the Ingredients of which all those call'd perfectly mixt Bodies are immediately compounded, and into which they are ultimately resolved."

In speaking of "perfectly mixt Bodies" Boyle refers to specimens of matter which are neither elements nor mere physical mixtures—kinds of matter which today we call *compounds*.

Boyle's distinction between element and compound is nearly identical with that in more modern chemical usage. It is controversial, however, whether his actual mental conception of elements was at all like that which developed later. He was notably noncommittal, for example, as to the *specific* substances he considered to be elements. In some of his writings he speaks of the elements as composed of a *single* kind of primordial matter, an attractive hypothesis which can be traced back to Greek philosophy. Moreover, Boyle was greatly impressed by van Helmont's willow-tree experiment, and felt moderately certain of the possibility of transmutation. Thus despite the apparent clarity of his distinction between element and compound, one can say only that Boyle produced a turning point in the gradual evolution of these concepts, and not a dramatic break with past tradition. His great contribution was insistence that elements be sought on an observational rather than a speculative basis. He had no way of knowing how many elements there are, and would undoubtedly have been surprised by later developments which showed that the number is large (101, as of 1956); his caution about labeling specific kinds of matter as elements can only be admired. It was nearly a century after Boyle's death that more positive identification of the elements became possible, and during most of the intervening years the Aristotelian elements, particularly Fire, continued to hold the center of the chemical stage.

5–5　The hierarchy of matter

Boyle's admirable definition of an element could not come into its own until many careful observations of chemical transformations had made it possible to pinpoint the fundamental ingredients of matter. We shall trace the significant aspects of this development in the next chapter. Meanwhile, Boyle's definition has sufficient validity so that we may proceed to use it in considering the broad classification of matter in modern terms.

We may regard the categories used in classifying matter as forming a "hierarchy" of abstractions, those of higher order embracing others of lower order, and all essential to the scheme as a whole. The highest concept, then, is that of matter itself—a concept which hardly requires elaboration but which, for the sake of elegance, we may define as *all that which possesses inertia*. Most samples of matter available for our immediate everyday inspection, such as rocks, dirt, air, and seawater, are *mixtures*. In many of these the presence of different kinds of matter is apparent to the unaided eye. Inspection of a piece of granite, for example, will readily reveal its *heterogeneous* makeup; it contains crystal grains of different colors, some shiny, some dull. Other mixtures, of which air and seawater are examples, are uniform in their properties and composition, i.e., they are *homogeneous*. Homogeneous mixtures are usually called *solutions*; we can be certain that they are mixtures only upon separation of their components. If seawater is subjected to distillation, for example, a residue of salt remains in the distilling vessel, and water, recovered by condensation, appears in the receiving vessel (Fig. 5–3). Thus we can be sure that seawater is a mixture of at least two components. The separation of air into its constituent gases is not so simple, and it is not surprising that it was long held to be an elemental substance.

Several techniques commonly used to separate the components of mixtures are illustrated in Figs. 5–3 through 5–6. The pure, separated kinds of matter obtained by application of these techniques and others are said to be *substances*. Clearly, substances must be homogeneous, but how shall we

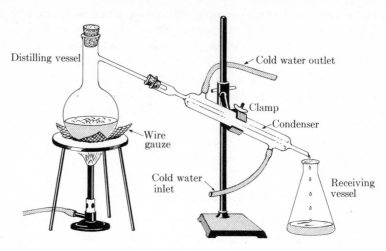

Distilling vessel

Cold water outlet

Clamp

Condenser

Wire gauze

Cold water inlet

Receiving vessel

FIG. 5–3. Distillation: dissolved solids remain in distilling vessel as liquid boils off.

FIG. 5–4. Filtration: suspended solid is retained by filter paper as liquid passes through.

FIG. 5–5. Flotation: particles of dense solid remain at bottom of vessel, while less dense particles are carried off in overflowing water. (Example: "panning" for gold.)

FIG. 5–6. Crystallization: less soluble solids separate from solution first, leaving those of higher solubility in the dissolved state.

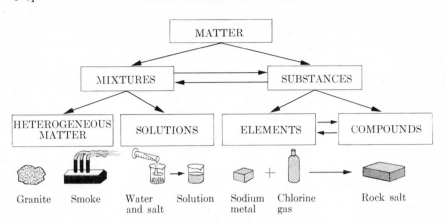

FIG. 5-7. The Hierarchy of Matter.

distinguish them from solutions? We may base our criterion upon constancy of composition: *substances exhibit constant composition; mixtures exhibit arbitrarily variable composition.* While a deeper understanding of this statement will be made possible in Chapter 7, we may illustrate it for present purposes by reference to the substances salt and water. Suppose that to any given quantity of water we were to add a very small pinch of salt, forming a solution of one concentration. The addition of a second small pinch would result in a mixture of a second concentration, and so on; we would find that, between limits, it is possible to vary the proportions of salt and water at will. It is not possible to alter either salt or water individually, however, by any of the processes commonly used for the separation of mixtures. Constancy of composition and *purity* are identical, although we should bear in mind that satisfactory criteria of purity had to evolve from long experience with mixtures and their component substances.

The category *substance* embraces two other categories, those of *element* and *compound*. Rephrasing and slightly extending the point of view of Boyle, we may say that *the chemical elements are substances that cannot be decomposed to form simpler substances by any chemical means.* Compounds, then, are simply all substances which are *not* elements. Iron, sulfur, hydrogen, and oxygen are examples of elements; iron oxide, or rust, is a compound of the elements iron and oxygen, hydrogen sulfide ("rotten-egg gas") is a compound of sulfur and hydrogen, and water is a compound of hydrogen and oxygen. Each of these compounds may be decomposed to its elements, but none of the elements can be further decomposed chemically. Here the criteria are most difficult to establish: how can we be *sure* that a given substance cannot be broken down to simpler components by methods presently unavailable to us, and what is meant by "simplicity" in this connection?

These questions are, of course, central to the science of chemistry, and satisfactory answers required a long time to evolve, as will be detailed in succeeding chapters. Once evolved, the answers were not final, for in our own century means *have* been found for subdivision of the chemical elements; it is this fact which is anticipated by appending the phrase "by any chemical means" to the definition of element.

5–6 Properties and transformations of matter

The categories described above are the broadest in our classification system for matter. There are many narrower categories; the elements, for example, may be divided into the classes metal and nonmetal, the metals into the classes active and inert, etc. The entire scheme has value, however, only insofar as it permits generalization about the multitudinous forms of matter, and thus depends upon our ability to recognize these on the basis of their individual characteristic *properties*.

The properties of matter are usually divided into the two classes *physical* and *chemical*, although the distinction is not always entirely sharp. Physical properties, of which melting point and mechanical strength are examples, are *intrinsic* properties of pure substances under specified conditions. For instance, under ordinary conditions of temperature the metallic element zinc is a moderately lustrous bluish-white solid. It conducts heat and electricity well, and is unaffected by the presence of a magnet. Its density (mass per unit volume)* is 7.14 gm/cm^3 at 20° Centigrade (C). When heated to a temperature of 419°C zinc melts to a liquid, and at the much higher temperature of 907°C the liquid boils and zinc vapor appears. Some properties, notably density, of the liquid and vapor differ markedly from each other and from those of the original solid. There is no alteration, however, that would lead us to believe that the liquid and vapor are any substance other than zinc; on cooling zinc vapor we observe condensation at 907°C, crystallization (freezing) at 419°C, and at ordinary temperatures the properties of the solid are found to be the same as before heating. Melting and boiling points are related to transformations among the *states* of matter: gas, liquid, and solid. Transformations which do not lead to the appearance of new substances are called *physical changes*; the properties of zinc mentioned in this paragraph are called *physical* properties. Some

---

*Neither the mass of an object nor its extension in space (volume) can be used to identify it, since each depends upon the particular sample at hand. The *ratio* of mass to volume for a given substance, however, is the same for every sample of that substance, provided all measurements are made under identical environmental conditions. A ratio of 7.14 gm/cm^3 is observed whether the sample of zinc examined weighs one-tenth gram or one thousand grams. Density is thus an important *defined* numerical property.

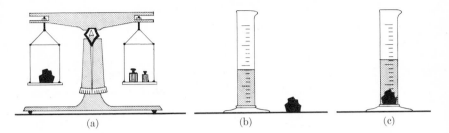

FIG. 5–8. One way to determine the density of a solid body: (a) weigh it, (b) measure the volume of an arbitrary quantity of water, (c) remeasure the volume of water after immersion of the solid body. The body displaces a volume of fluid equal to its own, hence its density may be calculated by dividing result (a), mass of body, by result (c) minus result (b), volume of body.

e.g., color) may be noted by simple visual observation, others (e.g., density) are determined by the performance of simple quantitative measurements (Fig. 5–8), but all are intrinsic to the single substance zinc, being observable by examination of that substance alone.

Chemical properties, on the other hand, may be observed only in the course of *chemical change,* in which new substances *are* formed. To illustrate, let us consider the consequences of placing some zinc in a solution of another substance, hydrochloric acid. When this is done a vigorous bubbling occurs, the temperature of the solution arises, and the zinc gradually disappears. At first-sight one might believe that the zinc is undergoing the physical process of dissolving, but if the solution is afterward evaporated to dryness a white solid quite unlike zinc is found in the vessel. Furthermore, if the bubbling of the solution is watched closely it will be seen to accompany the evolution of a gas; this gas, if tested appropriately (Fig. 5–9), is found to be inflammable. The over-all change actually leads to the disappearance of zinc and the appearance of two new substances, the white solid (zinc chloride) and the gas (hydrogen), and is a chemical change. The statement that hydrogen is given off whenever zinc is added to hydrochloric acid solution specifies a *chemical property* of each of the substances, zinc and hydrochloric acid. Other examples of chemical properties are the combustibility of hydrogen and the tendency of iron to rust.

We shall not atempt to make an exhaustive listing of useful chemical and physical properties at this stage; these will be introduced as we have need for them. We should note, however, that identification of a substance cannot be based upon a single property; rather, the concordance of a set of characteristics must be relied upon. The worthless mineral pyrite, for example, has a lustrous yellow appearance similar to that of gold, and is commonly called "fool's gold" in commemoration of the many unfortu-

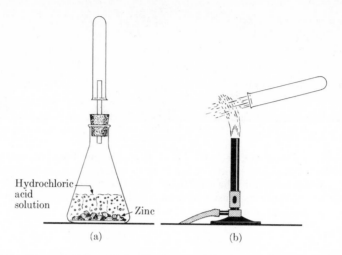

Hydrochloric
acid
solution
Zinc

(a)   (b)

FIG. 5–9. Zinc reacting with hydrochloric acid; (a) collection of evolved hydrogen gas, (b) hydrogen-air mixture explodes with a sharp pop when mouth of test tube is placed near an open flame.

nate prospectors who have thus misidentified it. The density of gold, however, is 19.3 gm/cm³, whereas that of pyrite is only about one-fourth as great, and this property provides a ready basis for distinction. Mere distinction between gold and pyrite does not mean positive identification of either, of course; for such identification, properties other than color and density would have to be examined.

The development of the concepts we have used here to discuss the properties and the classification of matter was a long and even a painful process. We have taken advantage of Boyle's precocious definition of element to introduce modern terminology, but this terminology will become more meaningful as we trace some of the difficulties of its growth. There are so many kinds of matter that it was historically impossible to anticipate which, if studied, might lead to observations of interpretive significance. Moreover, of the many properties of matter, how could one make the best selection for comparison of different substances? We have seen that Aristotle's particular selections, hotness, wetness, coldness, and dryness, led to a great deal of trouble; we shall see other instances in which emphasis was placed on misleading properties, particularly in connection with the subject of our next chapter.

5–7 Summary

Chemistry, the study of matter and its transformations, originated in the earliest of the practical arts. Aristotle formalized the description of matter in terms of four qualitative "elements," Earth, Air, Fire, and Water. The alchemists, seeking to transmute abundant matter into more valuable forms, discovered many new substances, but added relatively little to organized knowledge. In the 17th century Boyle defined chemical *element* in very nearly the modern sense, but the idea was not further exploited for well over a century. In modern usage the term *substance* is confined to homogeneous matter of constant composition, which may be either an element or a *compound* of elements. *Mixtures* of substances may be homogeneous (solutions) or inhomogeneous. Substances may be identified in terms of such *physical properties* as color, density, and boiling point, and also by the changes in which they may participate that result in the formation of new substances, i.e., their *chemical properties*.

REFERENCES

FARRINGTON, B., *Greek Science*, especially Chapter 8, on Aristotle.

HOPKINS, A. J., *Alchemy, Child of Greek Philosophy*. Concerns primarily the sources of alchemy.

LEICESTER, H. M., and H. S. KLICKSTEIN, *A Source Book in Chemistry*, pp. 16–20 (Paracelsus), 23–27 (van Helmont), 33–47 (Boyle).

MORE, L. T., *The Life and Works of the Honorable Robert Boyle*.

PARTINGTON, J. R., *A Short History of Chemistry*, Chapters I through IV.

PAULING, L., *General Chemistry*, Chapter 2.

READ, J., *Prelude to Chemistry*. Contains much interesting material relating alchemical endeavor to its contemporary literature, art, and music.

TAYLOR, F. S., *The Alchemists*. An excellent brief account of the entire history of alchemy.

1. Suppose that a king's crown, made entirely of metal, weighs 2 kgm, and that a carefully graduated cylinder like that of Fig. 5–8 is available for immersing it. (a) If the crown is of pure gold (density 19.3 gm/cm^3), what displacement volume would be observed? (b) If the crown is 25% gold by volume and 75% silver (density 10.5 gm/cm^3), what would be the displacement volume? [*Ans.*: (a) 104 cm^3; (b) average density is 12.7 gm/cm^3, so that volume is 158 cm^3]

2. A problem similar to that above arose in ancient Syracuse: after King Hiero received a new crown for which he had allotted gold from his treasury, he was struck by the terrible thought that the artisans might have realized an illicit profit by alloying the gold with silver. The great Archimedes (287–212 B.C.) was consulted but, in those days, no graduated cylinders were available for volume measurements. His attack on the problem culminated in his recognition (while taking a bath) of the principle of buoyancy, according to which the buoyant force on a body in a fluid is equal to the weight of the fluid displaced by the body. He determined the volume by weighing the crown in air and then in water, subtracting one from the other, and dividing the difference by the density of water. Given that the density of water is 1 gm/cm^3, find the buoyant force (loss of weight in water) on each of the crowns of Exercise 1.

3. Wood burns with a bright flame and copious production of smoke, condensed moisture can be detected on a cold surface placed nearby, and a small amount of white residue (ash) remains after the burning. When magnesium metal is ignited an even brighter "flame" is observed, no moisture can be detected, and the amount of white residue left is considerably greater in proportion to the initial quantity of sample than in the case of wood. Can you give an interpretation of these changes in terms of the Four Elements?

4. The element iron has metallic luster, a density of 7.86 gm/cm^3, good conductivity of electric current and heat, malleability and ductility; it is attracted by a magnet; it is virtually insoluble in all solvents; when added to hydrochloric acid solution it appears to dissolve while hydrogen gas evolves; when heated in air it gives rise to red rust. The element sulfur is yellow, lusterless, nonmagnetic, very soluble in the solvent carbon disulfide but unaffected by hydrochloric acid solution; its density is 2.1 gm/cm^3; when heated carefully it melts at 113°C; when ignited it burns with a quiet blue flame and a colorless, pungent gas (sulfur dioxide) forms. An intimate mixture of 7 parts iron to 4 parts sulfur by weight, when heated with an open flame, glows to red heat. After the glowing ceases and the product material is cooled, a tough, solid, black-brown mass is found. This product has a density of

4.8 gm/cm^3; it is unaffected by a magnet and insoluble in carbon disulfide; when added to hydrochloric acid solution it appears to dissolve as a colorless, vile-smelling gas (hydrogen sulfide) is given off.

(a) List separately the physical and chemical properties of the substances described in the paragraph above.

(b) Describe as many ways as you can think of for separating powdered iron and sulfur from a mixture of the two.

(c) Of the changes alluded to above, which are chemical? which physical? Be specific about the criteria employed in each case.

CHAPTER 6

COMBUSTION AND THE INTERPRETATION OF CHEMICAL CHANGE

Man has always attached great importance to the phenomenon of burning, and it is not surprising that the first broad theory of chemical change was centered on the process of combustion. The *phlogiston theory* of the 18th century derived essentially from the Greek concept of the element Fire. Thus the authority of Aristotle, although it had waned in other sciences with rejection of the idea of "natural motion," lasted in chemistry nearly to the beginning of the 19th century. Rational advance in chemistry along the lines of Boyle's work was retarded for more than a century. Still, there was an advance inherent in the phlogiston theory. The problem of chemical change, whose outlines had hitherto been but vaguely defined, became centered upon the changes related to combustion. It was this line of study that led eventually to more rational interpretation of chemical processes in general. Modern chemistry cannot be said to have begun until the phlogiston theory was overthrown, yet it was just in the process of overthrowing this theory that it got its start.

6-1 Combustion and calcination

Let us review some of the facts about combustive processes that were known at the beginning of the 18th century. The word *combustion* was applied to flame-producing processes in general. These, as everyday experience teaches, are accompanied by radical transformations of matter. When wood burns, for example, all that is left behind is an ashy residue, small in quantity if compared with the original wood; when charcoal is burned virtually no solid residue remains. The fact that air is essential to combustion has been known since antiquity, and the fact that enclosed air contracts in volume while supporting combustion (e.g., Fig. 6-1) was certainly known in the 17th century.

Metals are not combustible in the usual sense, but most of them undergo radical transformation when exposed to intense heat while in contact with air. The alchemists were well acquainted with the *calcination* of metals, i.e., their alteration upon heating in air. The product of calcination of a metal, called a "calx" by the alchemists, is a substance completely unmetallic in properties. Red rust, the calx of iron, for example, is nonlustrous, a poor

114

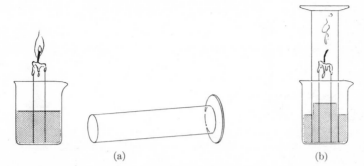

FIG. 6–1. (a) Burning candle mounted in beaker of water and empty cylinder about to be inverted over it. (b) Candle flame quickly goes out, and water level rises in cylinder.

conductor, nonmagnetic, and has little mechanical strength; the powdery product of calcination of magnesium is similarly unlike magnesium in properties. The production of metals from their calxes, i.e., the reverse of calcination, was in several instances part of the ancient lore of the practical arts. When a mixture of a calx and charcoal is heated, the metal corresponding to the calx is produced (Fig. 6–2); the ancient processes for extraction of several of the metals from their ores, e.g., copper and iron, depended upon knowledge of this fact.

The processes of combustion and calcination resemble each other in many ways (both generally occur at high temperatures, and both depend on air) and for that reason they have long been interpreted together. The phlogiston theory was devised to encompass both sets of phenomena and also the reverse of calcination, known as *reduction*. The theory was even extended to embrace animal respiration, a process which also depends on air. While most early investigations of matter, in the Aristotelian tradition, focused primarily on the *qualities* of substances, an important *quantitative* difference between combustion and calcination was known during the 16th century, and was certainly common knowledge in the scientific community during the entire period of the phlogiston theory. This difference is the following: after *combustion*, the weight of residue is always strikingly less than that of the sample burned, while upon *calcination*, metals invariably undergo a small *increase* in weight.

Air, so necessary to both combustion and calcination, was traditionally regarded as an irreducible element. Gases distinct from air were not recognized by the majority of early 18th century chemists despite the work of van Helmont, who had identified a number of gases as the products of combustion and other chemical changes. The gas that van Helmont called *gas*

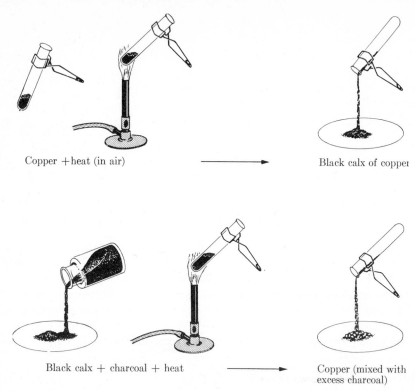

Copper +heat (in air)   ⟶   Black calx of copper

Black calx + charcoal + heat   ⟶   Copper (mixed with excess charcoal)

FIG. 6–2. Recovery of copper metal from its calx.

sylvestre is the substance we call carbon dioxide today, but its importance to the interpretation of combustion did not become clear until near the end of the 18th century.

6–2 The phlogiston theory

Significant experiments on combustion and calcination were carried out by Boyle and several of his contemporaries. If investigation had continued uninterruptedly along similar lines, it is conceivable that the modern theory of combustion might have arisen many decades earlier than it did. However, modifications of traditional ideas proved to have wider appeal than the more revolutionary ideas of Boyle. The German chemist Johann Joachim Becher (1635–1682), in speculating about matter, extended Paracelsus' idea of *three earths*. It was his belief that matter consists of the *elements* air and water, plus *principles* of inflammability, fusibility, and "mercurial nature." Paracelsus' earthy "principles," it will be recalled, were sulfur, salt, and mercury; Becher placed emphasis upon certain properties, or *essences*, of these materials. Another German, Georg Ernst Stahl (1660–

1734), popularized and extended Becher's philosophy in his own writings. His *Fundamenta Chymiae*, published in 1723, was the most influential chemistry text of the early 18th century. It was Stahl who introduced the name *phlogiston* (Greek, *phlox* = "flame") for Becher's *essence of inflammability*; the word thus represents nothing more than the ancient Aristotelian element Fire in sophisticated form.

The Becher-Stahl phlogiston theory, as originally presented, can be reduced to two underlying hypotheses. First, it assumes that all combustion and calcination processes are accompanied by the liberation of phlogiston from the material involved. Second, it assumes that air must be present to absorb phlogiston, and that the capacity of a given volume of air for phlogiston is limited. From these postulates Stahl developed a broad framework of explanation which satisfactorily encompassed most of the knowledge of his time concerning combustion and calcination. The fact that this theory gained almost immediate acceptance and became *the* chemical theory of the 18th century was largely because it was the first major conceptualization of its kind in chemistry. It was impressive that so large a number of factual observations, previously more or less isolated from one another, could be related by a single theory. Let us examine some of the relations between observation and theory.

When wood burns, phlogiston is given up and ash remains; is not wood, then, a "compound" of ash and phlogiston? The flames of a wood fire can be made to rise higher, and the burning to proceed faster, if air is blown over it. Isn't pure (elemental) air therefore required to carry the phlogiston away from the wood? Obviously, air near the surface of burning wood must be heavily laden with phlogiston, and a supply of unphlogisticated air should increase the rate at which burning can continue. And what could be more consistent with this interpretation than the fact that the flame of a candle survives but a brief moment in a small enclosure? Clearly, the candle flame quickly imparts as much phlogiston to the air as it can absorb, and air saturated with phlogiston cannot support further combustion.

Again, when metals liberate the "fiery principle" during calcination their calxes appear; isn't metal therefore a "compound" of its calx and phlogiston? It is true that no way was ever found to put ashes and phlogiston back together to recover wood, but there is a very simple way to recover a metal from its calx: mix calx and charcoal together, heat, and metal reappears. And if we stop to consider the properties of charcoal we find that they are beautifully consistent with the phlogiston scheme. Charcoal is almost completely consumed by flame, and thus apparently consists of nearly pure phlogiston. Wouldn't it seem that it is the presence of so rich a source of phlogiston that makes possible the reformation of the "compound" (i.e., metal) from its calx? For the case of lead, for example, calcination and its reverse might be represented schematically as follows:

lead (calx + phlogiston) = lead calx + phlogiston;
lead calx + charcoal (phlogiston) = lead.

The major interpretative achievements of the phlogiston theory were those implied in the last two paragraphs. There was good reason for including animal respiration within this same framework. Since animals require a continuous supply of fresh air, and long-respired air becomes incapable of sustaining life *or* combustion, it was natural to assume that animal metabolism is itself essentially a combustion process, in which phlogiston is given up. Thus the area of successful interpretation within a single theoretical context was materially broadened.

The observation that air contracts in volume as it supports combustion and calcination could not be explained directly by the phlogiston hypotheses, nor was it considered significant by most early 18th century chemists. (It could be accounted for, however, by assuming that phlogistication *causes* air to shrink in volume.) Similarly, the gain in weight that accompanies calcination was not predicted by the theory, and was generally regarded as unimportant. Stahl disposed of it with the added assumption that phlogiston given off in combustion has *positive* weight, while that given off by metals has *negative* weight, a remarkable proposition in view of the inertia concept, which was firmly established in physics at the time. There is no evidence that this hypothesis was widely held, however; to most chemists of the phlogiston period changes in the weights of substances during chemical transformations bore no direct relation to the transformations themselves.

The phlogiston theory was abundantly successful in its time. Its basis, two underlying postulates, was simple, yet the range of factual knowledge it embraced was impressively broad, especially in a science which had previously known no such unifying theory. Yet there were some undeniable aspects of combustion and calcination that could be reconciled with the phlogiston postulates only with great difficulty. The usefulness of any theory depends on continuing agreement with factual knowledge as the latter increases. If the original hypotheses upon which a theory rests are sufficiently valid, new observations will be interpretable in terms of them without fundamental alteration, i.e., the *simplicity* of the postulates will be maintained. If the underlying hypotheses lack general validity, on the other hand, explanation of newly discovered regularities requires the introduction of *new* hypotheses. The theory will then become less and less simple, and when it becomes so complex that it can no longer perform its functions of correlating large numbers of facts and successfully predicting new ones, it must be abandoned. In a general sense this is what happened to the phlogiston theory. Vast improvements in the techniques of chemical experimentation accompanied the quest for knowledge in the 18th century.

Their use led to the discovery of new properties and new regularities in the behavior of matter which the phlogiston theory could accommodate only by the addition of new assumptions quite distinct from the two original postulates. The theoretical superstructure became top-heavy and threatened to collapse of its own weight, although it was in fact not abandoned until, late in the century, a new and more promising theory was proposed by Lavoisier.

The complete history of phlogiston is complicated. The theory changed as the 18th century progressed, and different versions were often simultaneously in use by different investigators, versions which sometimes had little in common except the two basic postulates. The intermediate stages of phlogiston theory are of considerable interest to the historian of science, but their exploration is not greatly instructive in following the growth of fundamental scientific concepts. More important for our present purpose are some of the mid-18th century discoveries which preceded establishment of Lavoisier's oxygen theory.

6–3 Pneumatic chemistry

Although van Helmont initiated the study of gases, no *systematic* investigation of such substances was carried out before the 18th century because techniques for collecting and storing them had not yet been developed. The introduction of *pneumatic* techniques for the manipulation of gases was largely the work of the rural English vicar Stephen Hales (1677–1761). Hales' principal interest lay in biological systems, which he found to contain considerable quantities of "air" (to him an element). Hales collected the gas by displacing water in an apparatus like that shown in Fig. 6–3, and made many measurements of the volume of "air" expelled when specimens of various plants were heated over a hot fire. He also collected gases given off on heating coal, saltpeter, and several other substances, but failed to recognize these as substances distinct from air.

Joseph Black (1728–1799), a Scottish physician and chemist whose important investigations of heat will concern us in a later chapter, was responsible for the first of many important chemical discoveries to result from the use of pneumatic techniques. He collected and studied with meticulous care the gas which is evolved when basic magnesium carbonate is heated. (Magnesium carbonate is modern terminology; the name employed by Black was *magnesia alba*.) Later he found that the same gas forms when limestone is heated to yield quicklime. This gas is incapable of supporting combustion, is moderately soluble in water, and is completely absorbed by solutions of *alkali* (e.g., sodium hydroxide). Black called it "fixed air," since it is retained in the solid state by limestone. This gas, identical to the *gas sylvestre* described by van Helmont, is now called *carbon dioxide*. Although

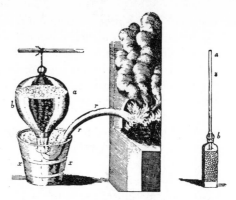

FIG. 6–3. Hales' gas collection apparatus. Metal tube (r) was sealed at heated end. Gas evolved at that end was conducted to the water-filled globe (ab); water was displaced downward to the tub (xx) and gas thus collected in globe.

he used the word *air* to describe it, Black recognized the essential difference between carbon dioxide and ordinary atmospheric air (gases were generally called "airs" during the 18th century, despite van Helmont's coined word).

Black found that quicklime, the product of heating limestone, is capable of recapturing "fixed air," with consequent restoration of limestone. Thus he had discovered a *reversible* chemical system:

limestone = quicklime + "fixed air";
quicklime + "fixed air" = limestone.

Using this system, Black performed one of the first significant *quantitative* chemical experiments, in which he demonstrated that a given quantity of limestone loses weight as its "fixed air" is driven off, but that its original weight is restored upon recombination with "fixed air." (We shall see that this kind of approach to chemical experimentation was crucial in the later advances made by Lavoisier.) Moreover, Black's discovery of reversibility in the limestone system gave him a simple test for the presence of his "fixed air": if this gas is passed into limewater (quicklime in water), the latter turns cloudy as the result of precipitation of limestone (Fig. 6–4). With this chemical property as an index, Black made the important discoveries that "fixed air" is present in respired air and in air which has been blown over glowing charcoal.

Henry Cavendish also made important contributions to the chemistry of gases and to the techniques for their manipulation. He was the first to recognize the extensive water-solubility of Black's "fixed air," which he prepared by adding acids to marble; to avoid loss of the gas through dissolu-

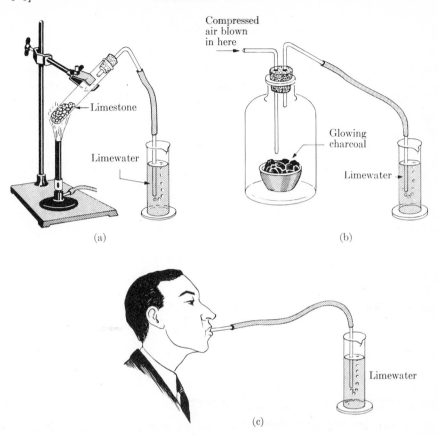

(a)   (b)

(c)

FIG. 6–4. Limewater test for "Fixed Air." In each case a positive test is observed, i.e., the limewater becomes cloudy as limestone precipitates.

tion, he collected it by displacement of mercury. The inflammable gas that we call *hydrogen* today was first intensively investigated by Cavendish, although it had been known to van Helmont and Boyle. Cavendish prepared this gas, which he called "inflammable air," by the action of acids on several metals, and concluded from his observations that the gas arose from the metal rather than from the acid. One of the later forms of the phlogiston theory, incorporating the assumption that "inflammable air" is itself phlogiston, was the product of this (erroneous) conclusion. Cavendish, a glimpse of whose great experimental prowess we have already seen in the measurement of the gravitational constant, was a firm believer in the kind of quantitative chemical experimentation which Boyle and Black had practiced before him and which was later to play so important a role in the work of Lavoisier.

6-4 The emergence of the oxygen theory

The all-important discovery of 18th century chemistry, that of the gaseous substance oxygen, was made independently by Carl Wilhelm Scheele (1742–1786) in Sweden and Joseph Priestley (1733–1804) in England. Although Scheele's work predated that of Priestley there was a delay of several years in publication of his findings; during that interval the work of Priestley came to the attention of the French chemist Antoine Laurent Lavoisier (1743–1794). Since the new *oxygen theory* was the creation of Lavoisier, Priestley's work holds greater interest for our purpose than Scheele's.

Priestley's work in pneumatic chemistry was carried out over a long period of time and involved a great variety of substances. Among the gases (or "factitious airs," as he called them) that Priestley was the first to collect and examine were ammonia, hydrogen chloride, carbon monoxide, sulfur dioxide, and nitrous and nitric oxides. His work with oxygen began with the observation in 1774 that the red calx of mercury, unlike all other calxes then known, could be decomposed by heating in the *absence* of charcoal. The reaction upon which his attention was focused was thus reversible in a simple way; the red calx forms when mercury is heated in air, yet decomposes by itself when more vigorously heated:

mercury metal + heat yields red calx;
red calx + heat (at higher temperature) yields mercury metal.

Priestley, in whose work pneumatic techniques had reached a high state of refinement, collected the gas evolved by mercury calx upon heating (Figs. 6–5 and 6–6), and soon noted that it supported the combustion of a candle flame much more brilliantly than ordinary atmospheric air. At first he identified the product with a gas he had previously discovered and called "dephlogisticated nitrous air" (today it is known as nitrous oxide, or "laughing gas"), but in the course of new experiments conducted in March 1775 he found his new gas to have very striking and unique properties. Not only did it support combustion exceedingly well, it also seemed to stimulate life processes when breathed. Priestley found that mice placed in an enclosed space filled with this gas survived much longer than in an equal volume of common air.

The fact that the properties of his newly discovered gas were related to those of air, yet were more intense, led Priestley to call it "dephlogisticated air." To him it was air completely devoid of phlogiston, hence capable of absorbing great quantities of the substance supposedly given off in combustion. Priestley saw no conflict between his new discovery and the phlogiston theory, and defended the latter vigorously to the end of his life. His experiments on "dephlogisticated air," however, brought to light just that information needed for the elaboration of a new theory.

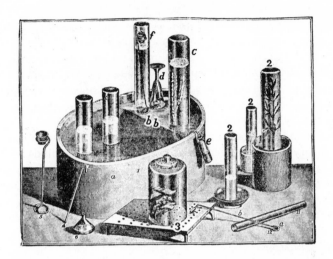

FIG. 6-5. Priestley's pneumatic trough (from his book *Experiments and Observations on Different Kinds of Air*, 1774). Inverted, water-filled bottles are placed on shelf (*bb*), ready to receive gas from gas-evolving vessel (*e*). Gas samples are stored in main part of trough, and may here be added to one another by underwater manipulation. Other gas-handling equipment is shown outside the trough, as well as arrangements for work with plants (2) and small animals (3).

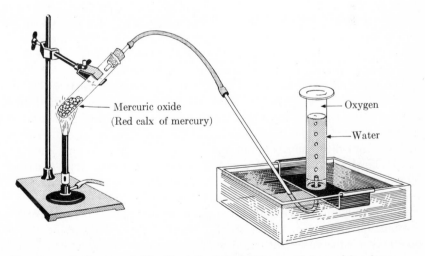

Mercuric oxide
(Red calx of mercury)

Oxygen

Water

FIG. 6-6. Collection of "dephlogisticated air" (oxygen) formed by decomposition of the red calx of mercury (mercuric oxide).

Lavoisier, in France, had formulated the hypothesis (at least as early as 1772) that an "atmospheric principle" is *taken up* from the atmosphere during combustion and calcination. He had been led to this view by observations of very large contractions in volume and increases in weight accompanying the calcination of phosphorus. Changes of this magnitude could not be ignored, nor could they be readily explained by the phlogiston theory. Lavoisier was therefore prepared to abandon the phlogiston theory. Although it may now seem clear that factual knowledge by 1775 had become more than the phlogiston theory could handle, it must be remembered that the theory was deeply ingrained upon the scientific minds of the time. Scientists as great as Priestley and Cavendish were basically unaware of the chaos contemporary discovery (much of it their own) had brought to chemical science and its old interpretations. In the circumstances, it needed genius to stand above the chaos and to reinterpret all the varied facts in an entirely new context; certainly genius is the only word appropriate to the abilities of Lavoisier.

Lavoisier repeated Priestley's experiments on "dephlogisticated air" soon after he learned of them, and was rapidly convinced that this "eminently respirable and combustible air" was the *atmospheric principle* whose existence he had postulated in 1772. The grand synthesis of explanation in terms of his single hypothesis took shape over the ensuing years. In September 1775 he published a moderate attack on the phlogiston theory, as he put it, ". . . not to substitute a rigorously demonstrated theory but solely a hypothesis which appears to me more probable, more conformable to the laws of nature, and which appears to me to contain fewer forced explanations and fewer contradictions." In a flood of publications during succeeding years he gradually increased the force of his attack, until by 1781 he was ready to present a fully formulated theory and to assert that the phlogiston hypothesis was unnecessary. He gave the name *oxygen* (Greek "acid-former") to Priestley's "dephlogisticated air" because of his belief (later found to be erroneous) that all acids contain this substance.

The principal explanations of combustion phenomena in terms of the oxygen theory are summarized in Table 6–1. First, air is not an irreducible element but a *mixture*: approximately one-fifth of air is capable of supporting combustion, calcination, and respiration, and is called *oxygen*. The remaining four-fifths, incapable of supporting combustion, is now known to consist largely of the gas *nitrogen*, with several other gases (argon, carbon dioxide, water vapor, neon, helium, krypton, and xenon) present in small proportion. Thus when a candle burns in an enclosed space combustion continues only until the available oxygen is consumed (Fig. 6–1). Secondly, combustion and calcination are both chemical changes involving a *combination* of substances with atmospheric oxygen. Many of those substances commonly called combustible contain the element *carbon*, which

TABLE 6-1

	Observation	Phlogistic explanation	Oxygen theory explanation
1	Candle burns	Candle gives off phlogiston	Material of candle reacts chemically with oxygen
2	Flame goes out in enclosed space	Air becomes saturated with phlogiston	Oxygen, required for combustion, is used up
3	Air after (2) is less than its original volume	No single explanation agreed upon	Air is a mixture, containing only $\frac{1}{5}$ oxygen by volume
4	Metals form calxes when heated in air	Metals are compounds of calx and phlogiston	A calx is a compound of metal and oxygen
5	Charcoal leaves little residue when burned	Charcoal is nearly pure phlogiston	Charcoal is largely carbon, which combines with oxygen to form carbon dioxide gas
6	Some calxes turn to metal when heated with charcoal	Phlogiston from charcoal is restored to calx	Oxygen in calx combines with carbon in charcoal to form carbon dioxide gas
7	Combustible materials lose weight on burning	Weight loss corresponds to weight of phlogiston given off	Oxygen combines with carbon in material (e.g., wood) to form carbon dioxide, which escapes
8	Metals gain weight on calcination	None (although phlogiston of negative weight was suggested)	Weight gain corresponds to weight of oxygen taken up by metal to form calx, or oxide
9	Mouse dies in enclosed space	Mouse saturates the air with phlogiston from lungs	Mouse exhausts oxygen supply in limited volume of air

combines with oxygen to form the compound *carbon dioxide* (Black's "fixed air"); this substance escapes as a gas, thus giving the impression that the burning material loses weight. Charcoal consists almost exclusively of carbon, hence its combustion to carbon dioxide leaves negligible residue:

$$\text{charcoal (carbon)} + \text{oxygen} = \text{carbon dioxide.}$$

Calcination differs from combustion only in that no gas is given up during the combination of a metal with oxygen; the increase in weight during calcination, therefore, simply reflects the added weight of oxygen taken from the atmosphere. The calcination of iron to form *iron oxide* ("calx of iron" to the alchemists and phlogistonists; "rust" in common parlance) may be represented as follows:

$$\text{iron} + \text{oxygen} = \text{iron oxide.}$$

Combustion is also accompanied by an increase in weight of the material burned, a fact that can be demonstrated only by collecting and weighing all gaseous products of the process. Finally, animal respiration involves absorption of oxygen and evolution of carbon dioxide, and is thus correctly viewed as a process closely related to combustion.

Lavoisier performed many experiments in the attempt to overthrow the phlogiston theory, although his greatest contribution to science was in the field of theory. One of the most impressive experiments he designed to establish the identity of his "atmospheric principle" was that of heating mercury in an enclosed volume of air (Fig. 6–7). A quantity of mercury was heated for twelve days in contact with 50 in.³ of air. The red calx of mercury (mercuric oxide) was observed to form slowly during that time on the surface of the mercury, and the volume of air in contact with it slowly contracted to 42 in³. When the contraction appeared to have ceased the red mercury compound was carefully collected and portions of the remaining air were tested. It was found that animals placed in this air died at once,

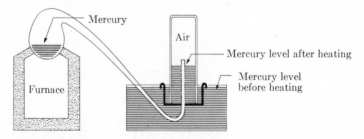

FIG. 6–7. Lavoisier's experiment on heating of mercury in an enclosed volume of air.

and the air could not support combustion. The red oxide was then placed in another container and heated to a high temperature, all the gas evolved was collected, and after gas evolution had ceased it was found that a total of 8 in.[3] (just the quantity by which the volume had contracted in the first part of the experiment) had been given off. Part of this gas was tested and found to have all the properties of Priestley's "dephlogisticated air." When this second gas and that remaining from the first part of the experiment were mixed in their original proportions, no manifestation of chemical change was observed, yet the product was indistinguishable, by all standard tests of the time, from common atmospheric air. That air is a mixture, and that mercury calx is a compound of mercury and one component of that mixture, could hardly be more convincingly demonstrated. The experiment was made possible by the comparatively ready reversibility of the mercury-oxygen reaction, which may be represented as follows:

$$\text{mercury} + \text{oxygen} \xrightarrow{\text{(heat)}} \text{mercuric oxide ("red calx");}$$

$$\text{mercuric oxide} \xrightarrow{\text{(at higher temperature)}} \text{mercury} + \text{oxygen.}$$

In 1783 Lavoisier wrote:

"I do not expect that my ideas will be adopted all at once; human nature bends toward one viewpoint, and those who have invisaged nature from a certain point of view during a part of their career change only with difficulty to new ideas; it is for time, then, to confirm or destroy the opinions which I have presented. In the meanwhile I see . . . that the young people who are commencing to study the science without prejudice . . . believe no longer in a phlogiston in the sense that Stahl presented it and regard all the doctrine as a scaffolding more encumbering than useful for continuing the edifice of chemical science."

These words effectively summarize the manner in which the new oxygen theory gained acceptance in chemistry. The number of established scientists who accepted it at the time of its enunciation was small, although this minority did include such celebrated chemists as Joseph Black and Claude Louis Berthollet. The oxygen theory was almost universally accepted among the rising generation of younger chemists, however, so that by the end of the 18th century the phlogiston theory was essentially dead. New chemical discoveries, readily interpretable in terms of the new theory, also played an important role in the rapid establishment of the oxygen theory. Of these, one which must be mentioned was the discovery that water is *not* an irreducible element, but a compound of oxygen and hydrogen ("inflammable air"). It was Cavendish (in 1782) who first made a careful study of the formation of water droplets when mixtures of hydrogen and either air or oxygen are exploded. While Cavendish was able to "torture" the phlogiston theory into an explanation of his observations, to the partisans of Lavoisier they constituted a striking example of the superior simplicity of the new theory.

In combating the phlogiston theory, Lavoisier succeeded in bringing about the complete abandonment of the Aristotelian hypothesis of elements as vague *qualities*, and in setting chemistry on its present foundations. We must note, however, that phlogiston was not the last of the "subtle" invisible fluids. It is tempting (and sometimes helpful) to invent a "subtle fluid" to explain any process not understood in terms of observable components. The appearance of heat during chemical change found no ready explanation on the oxygen theory, and yet it was a phenomenon to be reckoned with; Lavoisier accepted the idea of a weightless invisible kind of matter, *caloric*, to account for it. In a later chapter we shall see what became of this theory of heat. Another subtle substance, the "quintessence" or *aether* of the Greeks, has been mentioned in an earlier connection and will play an important role in later chapters.

6–5 Chemical change and the quantitative method

Lavoisier's contributions to chemistry went far beyond the interpretation of combustion and related processes: following the same lines of reasoning that led to the oxygen theory he completely altered the chemist's conception of *all* kinds of chemical change. Just as Stahl's *Fundamenta Chymiae* was the most influential chemistry treatise of its time, Lavoisier's *Traité Élémentaire de Chimie*, published in 1789, became a model for the chemistry texts of several generations. Boyle's definition of element could, at last, become a working base for chemical science: Lavoisier's quantitative methods, and his convincing assertion of the ponderability of chemical elements, provided a means for effective distinction between element and compound.

Quantitative chemical experimentation, as we have seen, was not original with Lavoisier; shifting emphasis from qualities to quantities of substances was a continuing feature of 18th century chemistry, and reached its culmination with Lavoisier. The use of the balance, and of reasoning based on quantities of materials, is inevitably predicated upon belief in the *indestructibility* of matter. This belief was stated very explicitly by Lavoisier in his *Traité Élémentaire de Chimie*:

". . . nothing is created in the operations either of art or of nature, and it can be taken as an axiom that in every operation an equal quantity of matter exists both before and after the operation, that the quality and quantity of the principles remain the same and that only changes and modifications occur. The whole art of making experiments in chemistry is founded on this principle: we must always suppose an exact equality or equation between the principles of the body examined and those of the products of its analysis."

The *Law of Conservation of Matter*, frequently cited as a fundamental law of chemical change, is identical with the conviction here expressed by Lavoisier: matter can be neither created nor destroyed. (We shall find in a later chapter that this statement requires modification to take account of the relation between mass and energy. This modification does not alter the interpretation of chemical change here presented, however.)

We have already noted Black's experiment with limestone, which actually constitutes an illustration of the law of conservation of matter. Lavoisier tested his "axiom" as rigorously as possible in another of his own celebrated experiments, that of carrying out the calcination of tin in a sealed vessel (Fig. 6–8). First a weighed quantity of tin was introduced into a weighed retort. Next the neck of the retort was drawn out to a capillary, without removing any of the glass; the vessel was then heated to expel part of the air inside, and while hot, the capillary neck was sealed. (If the vessel had been sealed while cold, expansion of air on subsequent heating would have caused it to burst.) The retort was then reweighed and heated to high temperature for an extended period of time, during which the formation of the black oxide of tin was observed. Only a fraction of the tin was thus transformed, since there was not sufficient oxygen present to transform all of it. Upon cooling and reweighing the sealed retort, Lavoisier found that its weight was the same (within reasonable experimental error) as it was after expulsion of air but before calcination. He then opened the retort, allowing atmospheric air to enter, and on weighing again found that it weighed *more* than the tin and unsealed retort had originally weighed. Next he removed the tin and tin oxide, and found that together they showed a weight increase which agreed almost exactly with the increase observed upon entrance of air. This correspondence seemed to him convincing evidence that the black oxide is a compound of tin and a component (oxygen) of the air which was enclosed with it. Lavoisier's actual quantitative results in this experiment are summarized in Table 6–2.

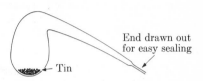

FIG. 6–8. Retort for Lavoisier's experiment with tin.

End drawn out for easy sealing

Tin

We shall witness the fruits of the quantitative method in chemistry in many of the succeeding chapters. Here we must touch briefly upon the manner in which it makes possible the identification of elements, which Lavoisier (following Boyle) defined as "the last point which analysis is

TABLE 6–2

LAVOISIER'S EXPERIMENT ON THE CALCINATION OF TIN

Object weighed	Weight in grams*
1. Tin sample	244.72
2. Unsealed retort	160.73
3. Tin + retort (Wt. 1 + Wt. 2)	405.45
4. Tin + retort, heated and sealed	405.15
5. Air expelled (Wt. 3 − Wt. 4)	0.30

- -

6. Sealed retort, tin, and black oxide after calcination	405.14
7. Wt. 4 − Wt. 6	0.01
	(Wts. 6 and 4 are identical within experimental error)

- -

8. Retort, tin, and oxide after entrance of air	405.62
9. Weight increase during calcination (Wt. 8 − Wt. 3)	0.17

- -

10. Retort fragments after removal of tin and oxide	160.73
	(identical with Wt. 2)
11. Uncalcined tin	239.06
12. Black oxide	5.83
13. Tin + oxide (Wt. 11 + Wt. 12)	244.89
14. Weight increase in tin due to combination with oxygen (Wt. 13 − Wt. 1)	0.17
	(Wts. 14 and 9 identical)

---

*Lavoisier's results were expressed in the units (*onces, gros,* and *grains*) in use in France during his lifetime, and have been converted to grams for this table. Although Lavoisier was a member of the French commission which developed the metric system of measurement, that system was not adopted in France until 25 years after the date of this experiment.

capable of reaching." For example, when a weighed sample of mercuric oxide is decomposed by heating, and the quantities of mercury and oxygen produced are weighed, an *analysis* of the substance has been performed. The fact that each product (oxygen, mercury) is *less* in weight than the original (mercuric oxide), and that the sum of the product weights is *equal* to that of the original, constitutes the evidential criterion that oxygen and mercury are simpler substances of which mercuric oxide is composed. Now if each of these simpler substances is subjected to all known means of chemical decomposition (i.e., further analysis), and neither of them can be made to give rise to other substances which are simpler than themselves by the same criterion, they may be classified as elements. This criterion is a pragmatic operational one, and it is for this very reason that it succeeded in chemistry where earlier speculative criteria had failed. There is nothing in this view of the chemical elements which either assumes or precludes the possibility of further simplicity underlying their purely chemical behavior. It is a view which requires the investigator to be alert to the possible existence of substances which, as Lavoisier put it, ". . . since we have not hitherto discovered the means of separating them, . . . act with regard to us as simple substances." Of Lavoisier's list of 33 elements in his *Traité Élémentaire*, 26 appear in our modern table of elements; of the remaining seven, two were the "imponderables," light and heat, not actually considered proper *chemical* elements by Lavoisier, and five were metallic oxides which no one succeeded in decomposing until the 19th century.

Three entries in the list of 26 elements, Lavoisier's "radical muriatique, radical fluorique, and radical boracique," correspond to the elements chlorine, fluorine, and boron; while chlorine was known as such in Lavoisier's time, the latter two elements had not yet been prepared from their compounds and their existence was assumed by Lavoisier by arguments of analogy. It is interesting that while Lavoisier listed the oxides of calcium, magnesium, barium, aluminum, and silicon as elements, he did not similarly list those of sodium and potassium, which he was convinced could one day be broken down to simpler constituents.

In considering the beginnings of modern chemistry, let us note that neither of the two principals in the development was a professional scientist in the modern sense; the rise of scientific professionalism was a 19th century phenomenon. Priestley, the conservative phlogistonist, was a radical theologian. He wrote prodigiously on matters of religion; as a minister of dissident congregations he was poor throughout most of his lifetime, and indulgence in his beloved hobby, science, required an abundance of ingenuity despite the generosity of certain friendly manufacturers and noblemen. Lavoisier, born to wealth, never lacked the best available apparatus and assistants for the performance of scientific experiments. Although he was able to devote a much larger fraction of his energies to science than was Priestley, the externals of Lavoisier's career were those of successful financier, tax collector, and public servant. The lives of both men were profoundly affected by the French Revolution. Priestley's religious radicalism and political liberalism caused him to be suspected of seditious tendencies in an England made jittery by the fall of the Bastille. In 1791 his house in Birmingham was ransacked by a mob shouting loyalty to "Church and King"; he fled to London and finally emigrated to America (1794), where he spent the last decade of his life in Pennsylvania. Lavoisier, identified with the hated tax-collection agency (Ferme Général) of monarchist France, was guillotined in 1794, during the brief terrorist regime of Robespierre. The great French mathematician Lagrange, when informed of Lavoisier's fate, said: "It took only a moment to sever that head but France will not produce another like it in a century."

6–6 Summary

The Greek element Fire was adapted in the guise of phlogiston, early in the 18th century, to furnish a theoretical account of the phenomena of combustion and calcination. The existence of the subtle substance phlogiston could not be confirmed, but the phlogiston theory served to focus attention on a set of problems that led to fundamental discoveries. The importance of gases in combustion and calcination was recognized, and techniques were developed for characterizing them. After the discovery of oxygen by Priestley and Scheele the crucial role of oxygen in both combustion and calcination was established by Lavoisier, whose new theory quickly displaced the phlogiston concept and led directly to the establishment of modern chemical science. Lavoisier stressed quantitative measurement, and intuitive recognition of the law of conservation of matter was implicit in much of his work. He utilized the modern definitions of element and compound, and made the first extended list of elemental substances.

REFERENCES

CONANT, J. B., The Overthrow of the Phlogiston Theory (Number 2 of the Harvard Case Histories in Experimental Science). An excellent detailed treatment of the work of Priestley and Lavoisier between 1775 and 1789 and the resultant revolution in chemical thought.

FRENCH, S. J., Torch and Crucible, the Life and Death of Antoine Lavoisier.

LEICESTER, H. M., and H. S. KLICKSTEIN, A Source Book in Chemistry: pp. 55–63 (Becher and Stahl), 80–91 (Black), 112–125 (Priestley), 134–153 (Cavendish), and 154–180 (Lavoisier).

MASON, S. F., Main Currents of Scientific Thought, Chapter 26.

McKIE, D., Antoine Lavoisier.

PARTINGTON, J. R., A Short History of Chemistry, Chapters V, VI, and VII.

1. When wood burns, both carbon dioxide and water can be detected as products; when charcoal burns, only carbon dioxide is evolved. Interpret in terms of the oxygen theory.

2. When sulfur burns in air no residue remains; a pungent colorless gas (called sulfur dioxide) is given off, but neither carbon dioxide nor water can be detected. When phosphorus burns no gases are evolved, but a white solid, weighing considerably more than the original sample of phosphorus (and called phosphorus pentoxide) is formed. Interpret these facts in terms of both the phlogiston and oxygen theories.

3. Does the increase in weight when phosphorus is burned indicate that this substance is a metal? The answer, of course, is *no*; point out the fallacies underlying a *yes* answer.

4. Does the evidence in Exercise 2 indicate that sulfur and phosphorus are compounds or elements? What procedures should be followed to settle this question?

5. Refer back to Exercise 5–2; interpret the changes described there in terms of (a) the phlogiston theory and (b) the oxygen theory.

6. Analysis shows that mercuric oxide contains 92.6% mercury by weight; the rest is oxygen. If the density of oxygen gas had been 2.0 gm/in.^{3} under the conditons of Lavoisier's experiment (Fig. 6–7), find what weight of mercuric oxide gave rise to his 8 in.^{3} of oxygen. [*Ans.*: 216 gm]

7. Accurate measurement has shown that atmospheric air contains 21% of oxygen by volume. How close did Lavoisier come to this value in his experiment (Fig. 6–7) with mercuric oxide?

8. Using Lavoisier's data (Table 6–2), calculate the percentage of oxygen by weight in the black oxide of tin. [*Ans.*: 2.9 percent. The black oxide of tin actually contains about 12% oxygen, and Lavoisier's separation of tin from the oxide was probably incomplete.]

9. We have said that Cavendish "tortured" the phlogiston theory into an explanation of the appearance of water when hydrogen is exploded with oxygen. He assumed that hydrogen ("inflammable air") consists of water plus phlogiston, and oxygen ("dephlogisticated air") of water with phlogiston removed. Using these assumptions, could you explain the fact that copper oxide, when heated in the presence of hydrogen, gives rise to copper and water? (Remember that copper oxide is a calx, which in phlogiston theory is metal that has lost its phlogiston.) What is the oxygen-theory explanation?

10. At the end of Chapter 5 it was promised that we should in the present chapter see instances of misplaced emphasis on certain properties of matter. Could you now state some of these misleading properties, and say in what manner they turned out to be misleading?

CHAPTER 7

THE ATOMICITY OF MATTER

In his famous work *De Rerum Natura* ("On the Nature of Things") the Roman poet Lucretius (98–55 B.C.) wrote:

"All nature then, as it exists by itself, is founded on two things: there are bodies and there is void in which these bodies are placed and through which they move about . . ."

The hypothesis stated in this passage was not original with Lucretius. The "bodies" he mentions are identical with the *atoms* (Greek, *atomos* = "indivisible"), ultimate particles of matter, proposed by certain early Greek philosophers. Lucretius' poem is devoted to exposition of the philosophy of Epicurus (342–270 B.C.), and is the most complete record of Greek atomism available today. Epicurus' philosophy derived, in turn, from that of Democritus of Abdera (468–370 B.C.), whose original writings are unfortunately lost. The idea that matter consists of minute indivisible particles was rejected by later schools of Greek learning, however, and in particular by those of Plato and Aristotle. Atomistic thought suffered eclipse through the long Dark Ages of intellectual history, but was revived during the Renaissance and gradually gained wide acceptance in Western philosophy. Belief in the atomic constitution of matter was an essential ingredient of natural philosophies as important as those of Isaac Newton and Robert Boyle.

The atomism of the Greeks and of 17th and 18th century Western scholars was largely speculative. This does not mean that it was a viewpoint entirely unrelated to observation of nature, since there are many familiar natural phenomena which lend themselves to interpretation more readily when atoms are assumed to exist than when they are not. For example, a given quantity of water, when vaporized, gives rise to many times its own volume of steam, a fact readily interpreted in terms of "atoms" of water which are greatly separated from one another by vaporization, so that the "void" space between them is increased. This interpretation, though perhaps more satisfying than any possible alternative, must be called speculative in the context of pre-19th century science because it was not susceptible to experimental test in any way. There were no known phenomena through which the atomic hypothesis could be subjected to the scrutiny of experiment until early in the 19th century, when the English chemist John Dalton (1766–1844) devised a detailed theory based upon quantitative chemistry. By that time the stage had been set for such a theory by the labors of Lavoisier.

Today atomism is a commonplace. No one has ever actually seen an individual atom, and the notion that void spaces pervade all the seemingly solid materials of everyday existence might appear to run counter to our sensory perceptions. Yet 20th century man's belief in the real existence of atoms is profound. The overwhelming agreement of atomic theory with observation, and its great fruitfulness in predicting hitherto unknown phenomena, have been so impressive that existence of atoms is often (perhaps incautiously) referred to as a "fact" of nature. Let us see how this modern atomic theory arose.

7-1 The Law of Definite Proportions

Stimulated by the example of Lavoisier, the chemists who followed him came to regard quantitative experimentation as one of the cornerstones of their science. Out of the widespread quantitative investigation carried on during the closing years of the 18th century there developed a famous controversy, in which the protagonists were the French chemists Joseph Louis Proust (1754-1826) and Claude Louis Berthollet (1748–1822). Proust, then a professor in Madrid, first stated his conviction in 1799 that the weight ratios of the elements present in a compound are *fixed*, and do not depend on the origin of the particular sample examined:

"A compound . . . is a privileged product to which Nature assigns fixed ratios; it is, in short, a being which Nature never creates even when through the agency of man, otherwise than with her balance in hand . . . No differences have yet been observed between the oxides of iron from the South and those from the North. The cinnabar of Japan is constituted according to the same ratio as that of Spain. Silver is not differently oxidized or muriated in the muriate of Peru than in that of Siberia . . ."

Proust's conclusions, here expressed, culminated a long period of careful experimentation. Yet Berthollet in Paris, at about the same time, had reached the opposite conclusion, namely, that elements combine in weight ratios which are variable, within limits. In support of Berthollet's position was his observation that the metals copper and tin, when heated in air, give the appearance of forming a continuous series of "compounds" of varying colors and compositions. He also cited the existence of solutions, alloys, and glasses as evidence of "compounds" of variable composition.

On turning his attention to the question of copper and tin Proust made the important discovery that each of these elements forms *two* compounds with oxygen. In the case of copper, one of these oxides is red and, Proust found, exhibits a *fixed* copper-to-oxygen weight ratio; the other is black, and exhibits a copper-to-oxygen weight ratio *different* from that of the red compound. Proust's reply to Berthollet, then, was that the latter's apparent continuous series of copper oxides consisted of a series of *mixtures* of the two compounds, possibly containing unreacted copper as well, which should indeed show wide variation in color and composition. Solutions, alloys, and glasses, on the other hand, posed a different sort of problem, since their compositions are not definite. These, Proust could only maintain, are not "true" compounds.

The Proust-Berthollet controversy continued for several years, accompanied by intensive experimental effort, and it gradually became clear that Proust was right—at least about the oxides. Berthollet was famous and Proust little known at the outset of their controversy; in consequence the latter had to labor with impressive diligence to establish his position. His investigations of the compositions of numerous compounds, and his discovery that several pairs of elements (such as copper and oxygen) form more than one compound, proved of great value. Perhaps his most important contribution to chemistry, however, was his suggestion of constancy of composition as the *criterion* for existence of a compound. In maintaining that all compounds exhibit definite composition by weight, and then excluding solutions, alloys, and glasses from the category of compound because they *do not* exhibit definite composition, Proust may be accused of circularity. But the distinction he made was significant, and the effect of his position was to *define* the term compound in terms of the new criterion, constant composition.

Proust's conclusion, that *compounds are substances containing two or more elements combined in definite proportions by weight*, serves as our definition of compound today. Frequently this definition is cited as one of the empirical *laws* of chemical change, called the *Law of Definite Proportions* (Fig. 7–1). Armed with this law, and with the empirical data related to it, we are in a position to solve many practical problems. Water, for example, is now known to be a compound of hydrogen and oxygen in the fixed weight ratio $1 : 8$. Nine pounds of water, on decomposition, will thus give rise to 1 lb of hydrogen and 8 lb of oxygen. But how much hydrogen and oxygen could be expected upon decomposition of a sample of water weighing 19.8 gm? Bearing in mind the $1 : 8$ ratio, it is a simple matter to find the answer: 2.2 gm of hydrogen, 17.6 gm of oxygen. Or, again, what quantity of water may be expected to result from explosion of 24 gm of oxygen in the presence of 4 gm of hydrogen? Here we can see that the quantity 24 gm (oxygen) stands in 8:1 ratio with just 3 gm (hydrogen); the answer, then, is that 27 gm of water will form, while 1 gm of hydrogen remains uncombined. Finally, we may feel confident that *any* sample of pure water, whether

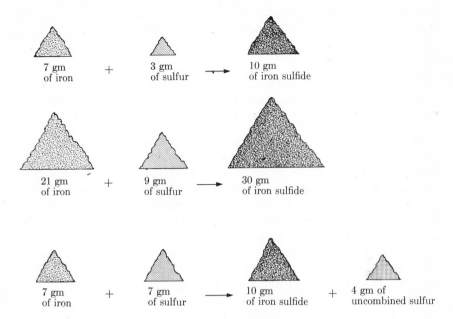

FIG. 7–1. The Law of Definite Proportions.

synthesized in the laboratory, or collected from the North Pole or the South Seas, will exhibit the 1:8 weight ratio characteristic of that compound. (This statement, though entirely valid for our present purposes, will require modification when we learn of the existence of different kinds (*isotopes*) of hydrogen and oxygen.)

7–2 Dalton and the chemical atomic theory

During the period of the Proust-Berthollet controversy John Dalton was independently taking the first steps toward establishment of his atomic theory. Almost entirely self-taught, Dalton spent most of his life as a teacher in Manchester, where his most important scientific work was done. He possessed little skill as an experimental scientist; it was remarkable perseverance, combined with a penetrating mind, that enabled him to fit masses of existing data into the single coherent scheme of his theory. Dalton's concern with atoms appears to have originated with his intense interest in meteorology, which led him to attempt an explanation of the fact that the atmosphere is a homogeneous mixture of gases. The actual route traveled by him from this concern to the postulates of the atomic theory is a marvel of obscurity which we shall not attempt to unravel. For our purpose, it suffices to note that Dalton eventually arrived at the assumption that different elements possess unlike atoms, and began to inquire into their *relative weights*. His first announcement of this investigation was made in 1803:

"An enquiry into the relative weights of the ultimate particles of bodies is a subject, as far as I know, entirely new: I have lately been prosecuting this enquiry with remarkable success."

Emphasis on the weights of atoms was, indeed, Dalton's great contribution, since there was nothing new in the atomic hypothesis itself. Proust's *definite proportions*, in turn, made possible the exploitation of Dalton's idea. On this level only two views of the ultimate nature of matter are possible: either it is *continuous* or it is *discrete*. If continuous, matter must be infinitely subdivisible; for example, if one were to break a piece of chalk in half, each half in half, etc., it should be possible in principle to continue the process indefinitely. If matter is discrete, i.e., atomic, the subdivision may be continued in principle only to the limit of some ultimate indivisible particle. If two elemental substances consist of continuous matter, there would be no particular reason to suppose that they would combine in fixed ratios by weight; rather, the indefinite proportions of Berthollet would seem reasonable. If they contain atoms, on the other hand, combinations of elements should consist of combinations of atoms. If all the atoms of one element are alike in weight, all the atoms of the second like one another yet unlike those of the first, and if the atoms of the two elements combine in fixed ratio (one atom of the first element combining with only one of the second, for instance), then a fixed *weight* ratio for the combination must be expected. Furthermore, the fixed weight ratio itself will depend on the relative weights of *individual* atoms of the two elements (Fig. 7–2). This argument embodies the basic assumption of Dalton's atomic theory. Although its conception was actually independent of Proust's struggle over definite proportions, the mutual dependence of the two developments was quickly recognized. Final resolution of the Proust-Berthollet controversy, in fact, coincided with the favorable reception of Dalton's theory.

Perhaps the most persuasive feature of this theory, when first proposed, was the success with which it *predicted* the existence of a new kind of quantitative chemical relation. This prediction concerned those pairs of elements which form two or more compounds, several of which Proust had discovered. In distinct compounds of the same elements, Dalton reasoned, the atoms must combine in different numerical ratios. Let us represent two elements by the symbols A and B; then one compound might contain one B atom per A atom, the other two B atoms per A atom. If so, and if all B atoms are alike in weight, the weight of B combined with a given weight of A in the second compound should be exactly *twice* the weight of B combined

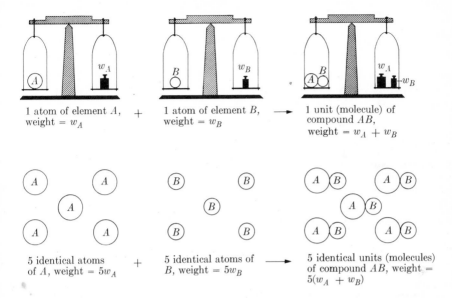

1 atom of element A, + 1 atom of element B, ⟶ 1 unit (molecule) of
weight = w_A weight = w_B compound AB,
     weight = $w_A + w_B$

5 identical atoms + 5 identical atoms of ⟶ 5 identical units (molecules)
of A, weight = $5w_A$ B, weight = $5w_B$ of compound AB, weight =
     $5(w_A + w_B)$

FIG. 7–2. Atomistic representation of chemical combination between atoms of elements to give a compound of fixed composition. (The operation of weighing individual atoms on a balance is an imaginary one.)

with the *same* weight of A in the first compound (Fig. 7–3). If the atom ratios in the compounds were not 1:1 and 1:2, Dalton argued, they should at least be simple; comparison of the weights of B combined with a fixed weight of A in the compounds should therefore disclose a small whole number ratio.

Considerable evidence confirming Dalton's prediction was available in the chemical literature of his time. The existence of such small whole number ratios had not been previously noted, however, because they had not been sought. They were not readily noticeable, since quantitative analytical results were often presented in the form of *percentage compositions*. The two oxides of tin, for example, contain 88.2% and 78.8% of tin, respectively; neither these numbers nor the corresponding percentages of oxygen, 11.8 and 21.2, exhibit integral relations. But the ratio $11.8/88.2 = 0.134$ gives the weight of oxygen combined with one gram of tin in the first compound, and $21.2/78.8 = 0.268$ gm of oxygen per gram of tin in the second; thus the amount of oxygen per unit weight of tin is twice as much in the second oxide as in the first. In selecting the arbitrary weight of one gram of tin, according to Dalton, we have chosen a fixed *number* of identical tin atoms; there are thus twice as many atoms of oxygen *per atom of tin* in the second compound as in the first.

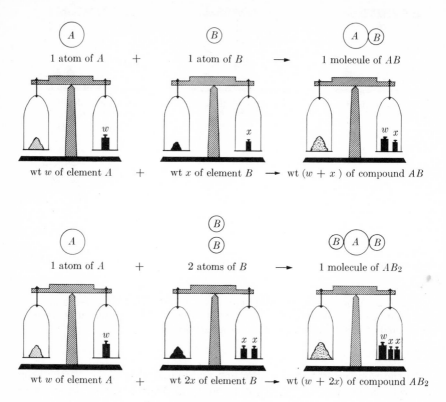

Fig. 7–3. Multiple proportions.

The empirical observations stemming from Dalton's prediction are traditionally summarized in the *Law of Multiple Proportions*: *when more than one compound is formed from the same pair of elements, the weights of one element which combine with a fixed weight of the other are related to one another by small whole number ratios.* Further illustration of the Law of Multiple Proportions is afforded by Table 7–1, in which it is applied to the several oxides of nitrogen.

Dalton did not publish a complete exposition of his atomic theory until 1808, when his book *A New System of Chemical Philosophy* appeared, although many of the essentials of the theory had been published previously (with Dalton's permission) by his admirer Thomas Thomson. The main features are those described above, but it is instructive to summarize them more formally as four *assumptions*:

1. Elements consist of minute, discrete, indivisible particles called atoms; atoms are unchanged by all physical and chemical processes.

TABLE 7–1

THE LAW OF MULTIPLE PROPORTIONS,
AS IT APPLIES TO THE OXIDES OF NITROGEN

Compound	Weight (in grams) of oxygen combined with 1.00 gm of nitrogen in compound	Numerical ratios of oxygen weights to one another: Column 2 divided by 0.571 gm, least weight of oxygen
Nitrous oxide	0.571	1
Nitric oxide	1.14	2
Nitrogen dioxide	2.28	4
Nitrogen tetroxide	1.14	2
Nitrogen pentoxide	2.86	5

2. All atoms of a given element are identical in mass and in all other physical and chemical properties; the atoms of different elements are unlike in mass and other properties.

3. Chemical combination between two (or more) elements consists in the union of the atoms of these elements in fixed ratios to form the simplest units, called *molecules,** of a compound.

4. Atoms of the same elements can sometimes unite in more than one ratio to form more than one compound.

These assumptions contain the essence of Dalton's atomic theory, although not in his words. The fourth statement will be recognized as the result of his search for confirmation of the theory; it leads back to, hence explains, his observations of multiple proportions. Modern *physical* knowledge has required some modification† of statements 1 and 2, but these four assumptions continue today to underlie all our interpretations of *chemical* events.

---

*The unit particles of compounds were called "compound atoms" by Dalton; to avoid confusion we shall confine ourselves to the use of the modern term *molecule*.

†These modifications will be treated in detail later, but may be briefly mentioned here. First, it has turned out that atoms are *not* indivisible: they possess substructure, and can be "split" in certain circumstances. Second, atoms of the same element of unlike mass (isotopes) are known; many of the elements consist of mixtures of atoms of slightly different mass, but with relative percentages so fixed that the fact cannot ordinarily be discerned by chemical means.

7-3 The problem of atomic weights

Dalton's concern with the *relative weights* of atoms can perhaps best be expressed in these words, taken from his *A New System of Chemical Philosophy:*

"Now it is one great object of this work, to shew the importance and advantage of ascertaining the relative weights of the ultimate particles, both of simple [elemental] and compound bodies, the number of elementary particles which constitute one compound particle, and the number of less compound particles which enter into the formation of one more compound particle."

To illustrate the utility of Dalton's "great object," let us suppose we know that element *A* will combine with element *B*, and wish to know what weight of *B* is necessary for complete combination with one pound of *A*. The answer could be found experimentally by carrying out the combination with an excess of *B*, then weighing the quantity of compound formed, and similar empirical answers can be found for all other possible pairs of reacting elements. However, atomic theory provides a basis for systematizing all such empirical information. For example, if we should somehow know that the atoms of *A* are 10 times heavier than those of *B*, and that the compound formed between them contains 2 atoms of *A* per atom of *B*, we could state immediately that the weight ratio of *A* to *B* in the compound is 20 : 1. The answer to our practical question would then be that 1/20 pound of *B* will combine completely with one pound of *A*.

Dalton's "great object" thus poses two questions: what are the relative *weights* of the atoms, and what are their relative *numbers* in compounds? The two questions are actually inseparable. Consider the two oxides of tin, whose compositions have been cited above:

tin oxide 1: 1.00 gm of tin + 0.134 gm of oxygen;
tin oxide 2: 1.00 gm of tin + 0.268 gm of oxygen.

If we *assume* that the molecules of oxide 1 contain one oxygen atom per tin atom, it follows (by the arguments of multiple proportions) that those of oxide 2 must contain two oxygen atoms per tin atom. Furthermore, the relative weights of tin and oxygen atoms must then be $(1.00/0.134) = 7.4$, that is, tin atoms are 7.4 times heavier than oxygen atoms. But it is equally consistent with the evidence to assume that oxide 1 contains 2 oxygen atoms per tin atom; oxide 2 would then contain 4 oxygen atoms per tin atom, and it would follow that tin atoms are $(2 \times 1.00/0.134) = 14.8$ times heavier than oxygen atoms. Clearly, any number of possible atomic ratios could be chosen on the basis of the two tin oxide weights alone.

The element carbon also forms two oxides, with the following compositions:

Carbon oxide 1: 1.00 gm carbon + 1.33 gm oxygen;
Carbon oxide 2: 1.00 gm carbon + 2.67 gm oxygen.

Again, if we assume an atomic ratio (carbon to oxygen) of 1:1 for oxide 1, the ratio must be 1:2 for oxide 2. Moreover, comparison of tin oxide 1 with carbon oxide 1 reveals that nearly 10 times as great a weight of oxygen combines with one gram of carbon as with one gram of tin. If the molecules of carbon oxide 1 and tin oxide 1 are *both* assumed to possess 1:1 atomic ratios, this observation leads to the conclusion that tin atoms are nearly 10 times heavier than carbon atoms. (1.33 grams of oxygen must contain nearly 10 times as many oxygen atoms as 0.134 gram; therefore there must be nearly 10 times as many carbon atoms in one gram of that element as there are tin atoms in one gram of tin.) Such information would have great utility, but is here based upon addition of one arbitrary assumption to another. It is clear that reliable *atomic weight ratios* (relative weights of atoms) can be computed only when *atomic ratios* (relative numbers of atoms in the molecules of compounds) are known with certainty.

The arguments of the foregoing paragraphs may be rephrased in a more formal and general manner. Consider a compound of the elements A and B, containing x atoms of A and y atoms of B per molecule. (A molecule of the compound might then be symbolized by the formula $A_x B_y$.) Let us designate the weights of *individual* A and B atoms as w_A and w_B, and suppose that we wish to determine the atomic weight ratio w_A/w_B. In the laboratory a sample of the compound of arbitrary size, containing an unknown large number of molecules, say N, is subjected to analysis. We now know, empirically, the relative weights of elements A and B present in the compound. The weight of A per molecule, however, must be w_A multiplied by x; the weight of A in N molecules is therefore $N x w_A$. Similarly, the weight of B in N molecules may be represented by $N y w_B$. The empirical weight ratio may then be written as:

$$\frac{\text{Weight of } A \text{ in sample}}{\text{Weight of } B \text{ in sample}} = \frac{N x w_A}{N y w_B}.$$

The quantity N cancels out of this expression, indicating that the arbitrary size of the sample selected for analysis is of no consequence to the ultimate *relative* result. The equation may be rearranged to give the ratio of the atomic weights explicitly:

$$\frac{w_A}{w_B} = \frac{\text{Weight of } A \text{ in sample}}{\text{Weight of } B \text{ in sample}} \times \frac{y}{x},$$

from which it is quite clear that we must know the value of the atomic ratio, y/x, in order to determine the relative atomic weights. To generalize: there are three ratios in the equation, namely, relative weights of elements present, relative weights of atoms, and relative numbers of atoms per molecule. When values for *any two* of these are known, the third may be found, but when a value is known for only one the other two remain uncertain.

The problem Dalton set himself, then, was a difficult one; it could not be solved uniquely in his own day. Elemental weight ratios (i.e., Proust's definite proportions) for many compounds were available, but no method was known for determining relative numbers of atoms per molecule. Dalton took the only avenue open to him: he guessed. In the conviction that Nature behaves simply, he proposed an arbitrary set of rules for atomic ratios. When only one compound of two elements was known, he assumed its molecules to consist of one atom of each; when two were known, he assumed one to have atomic ratio 1:1, the other 1:2; more complicated cases were covered by similar rules. For example, water was the only compound of the elements hydrogen and oxygen known to Dalton; he therefore assumed that water molecules consist of one atom of hydrogen combined with one atom of oxygen. According to his (inaccurate) analysis, water contained 7 parts of oxygen to 1 of hydrogen by weight, and therefore oxygen atoms must be 7 times heavier than hydrogen atoms. Similarly, analysis of ammonia, the only nitrogen-hydrogen compound Dalton knew, led him to a weight ratio of 5:1 for the atoms of nitrogen and hydrogen. The method could be extended to give atomic weights relative to hydrogen of elements not known in combination with hydrogen itself: for the compound now called sulfur dioxide, to which he assigned 1:1 atomic ratio, Dalton found 1.9 parts sulfur per part oxygen by weight; since sulfur atoms thus appeared to be 1.9 times heavier than oxygen atoms, he computed that they are $(7 \times 1.9) = 13$ times heavier than hydrogen atoms. To the two oxides of carbon he assigned carbon-oxygen atomic ratios 1:1 (carbon monoxide) and 1:2 (carbon dioxide), and from analytical data he deduced an atomic weight of 5 for carbon relative to hydrogen.

By combining analytical measurement with his arbitrary number rules in this way, Dalton was able to compile a list of the atomic weights relative to hydrogen of twenty elements. An integral part of this effort was assignment of *molecular formulas* to many compounds, and for this purpose he introduced symbols to represent atoms, for example, $\odot$ for hydrogen and $\bigcirc$ for oxygen. His molecular formula for water, with assumed 1:1 atomic ratio, was thus $\odot\bigcirc$. The Swedish chemist Berzelius, in 1813, proposed the use of a less cumbersome *letter* symbolism which continues in use today. In this system Dalton's formula for water would be HO, for ammonia NH, for carbon monoxide CO, and for carbon dioxide CO_2.

TABLE 7-2

DALTON'S RELATIVE ATOMIC WEIGHTS

Element	Dalton's symbol	Modern symbol	Dalton's atomic weight (H = 1.00)	Modern atomic weight (O = 16.0000)
Hydrogen	⊙	H	1	1.008
Carbon	●	C	5	12.010
Nitrogen	⊖	N	5	14.008
Oxygen	◯	O	7	16.00
Phosphorus	⊗	P	9	30.98
Sulfur	⊕	S	13	32.066
Iron	Ⓘ	Fe	38	55.85
Zinc	Ⓩ	Zn	56	65.38
Copper	Ⓒ	Cu	56	63.54
Lead	Ⓛ	Pb	95	207.21
Silver	Ⓢ	Ag	100	107.88
Platinum	Ⓟ	Pt	100	195.23
Gold	Ⓖ	Au	140	197.2
Mercury	✸	Hg	167	200.61

A portion of Dalton's original atomic weight table, as published in *A New System of Chemical Philosophy*, is reproduced in Table 7–2. Modern atomic weights, shown for comparison, are all relative to the weight of the oxygen atom, which is arbitrarily assigned the value of 16.0000. The modern *unit* of atomic weight is thus 1/16 the weight of the oxygen atom, rather than the weight of one hydrogen atom, as in Dalton's scale. The selection of a basis for atomic weights is an arbitrary matter, since these quantities are *relative*, not absolute. When oxygen is selected as 16 a high percentage of individual atomic weights are nearly integers (though none except oxygen is exactly so); the choice is thus one of convenience.

Dalton's atomic weight values were in error for two reasons. First, the analytical data upon which they were based were generally inaccurate; the art of quantitative chemical analysis was then in its infancy, and Dalton himself was not an accomplished experimentalist. Second, the atomic ratios that derived from Dalton's guesswork were frequently wrong. We know now, for example, that water contains hydrogen and oxygen atoms in the ratio 2:1 (formula, H_2O), and that nitrogen and hydrogen atoms are present in the ammonia molecule in the ratio 1:3 (formula, NH_3). In fact, Dalton's mistakes were such that his relative weights were often wrong by a factor of two or more, as shown in Table 7–2. But these errors do not detract from the value of Dalton's contribution to science. His theory constituted a crucial advance in the understanding of chemistry, and remains valid in principle even though the details have had to be corrected. His assumptions of simple atomic number ratios have not proved tenable, but they were the most reasonable ones possible in his time. Indeed, chemical science did not achieve reliable means for atomic ratio determination until Dalton's proposals were more than fifty years old. Meanwhile, other valuable evidence contributing to the theory was being accumulated.

7–4 The Law of Combining Volumes

In 1808 the French chemist Joseph Louis Gay-Lussac (1778–1850), a superb experimentalist, discovered an arresting regularity in the combination of gases. On combining hydrogen and oxygen and measuring carefully the *volumes* of gases involved, he found that very nearly *twice* as much hydrogen entered into the combination, by volume, as oxygen. In his most precise experiment he found the volume ratio (hydrogen to oxygen) to be 1.9989:1.0000, and thought that the difference between this result and an exact 2:1 ratio might be ascribed to experimental error. Turning to observation of other gaseous combinations, Gay-Lussac found very nearly integral volume ratios in every case. Not only did he find simple numerical relations between volumes of *reactant* gases, but between those of reactants and *products* as well, for cases in which the products were also gaseous. To illustrate Gay-Lussac's discovery:

2 vol hydrogen + 1 vol oxygen = 2 vol steam;
2 vol nitrogen + 1 vol oxygen = 2 vol nitrous oxide;
1 vol nitrogen + 1 vol oxygen = 2 vol nitric oxide;
1 vol nitrogen + 2 vol oxygen = 2 vol nitrogen dioxide;
1 vol carbon dioxide + charcoal (solid) = 2 vol carbon monoxide;
1 vol nitrogen + 3 vol hydrogen = 2 vol ammonia.

The word *volume* (vol) is used in the above equations as an abbreviation for the phrase "parts by volume," and represents *any* arbitrarily selected volume. Thus 5 liters of hydrogen will combine with 2.5 liters of oxygen, giving rise to 5 liters of water vapor (steam). The integral ratios shown are observed only when the volumes involved are measured under similar conditions of temperature and pressure.

Gay-Lussac's observations are commonly summarized in the formal *Law of Combining Volumes: the volumes of gases participating in chemical reactions are related by simple numerical ratios.* Gay-Lussac recognized that such volume regularities are confined to the gaseous state of matter, and are quite unrelated to the *weights* of combining substances. In these circumstances he thought he had discerned "... a new proof that it is only in the gaseous state that substances are in the same circumstances and obey regular laws."

If we have accepted the idea that atoms of elements combine to form molecules of compounds, how are we now to interpret the appearance of new integral ratios between *volumes* of combining gaseous elements? Surely there must be a relation between the two sets of integers, and the mind fairly leaps to the inference that *equal volumes of gases contain equal numbers of particles.* Equal volumes of nitrogen and oxygen combine to form nitric oxide, for example; if these contain equal numbers of atoms of each element, the integral volume relation would simply indicate combination in 1:1 atomic ratio. But how can equal volumes of nitrogen and oxygen give rise to *two* volumes of nitric oxide? Dalton felt certain that the particles present in gaseous elements must be *atoms;* one atom of nitrogen, on combining with one atom of oxygen, could yield only one molecule of nitric oxide. The volume of nitric oxide formed, then, if equal volumes of gases contain equal numbers of particles, should be *equal* to the initial volume of each element, not twice that volume.

Moreover, the combining volumes for hydrogen and oxygen suggest that *two* hydrogen atoms combine with one oxygen atom to form water, in disagreement with Dalton's assumption. Dalton was strengthened in his resistance to the idea of equal numbers of particles in equal volumes by the knowledge that the *density* of water vapor is less than that of oxygen gas. If hydrogen atoms are added to oxygen atoms, forming a product that contains *less* mass per unit volume than does oxygen itself, how could these volumes contain equal numbers of particles? Finally, Dalton's mental picture of a gas was one in which individual particles, at rest, are in physical contact through interacting "spheres of caloric." He therefore believed that differences in gas volumes could be related only to differences in *sizes* of individual atoms and molecules.

7-5 Avogadro's Hypothesis

A solution to the apparent conflict between Gay-Lussac's law of combining volumes and Dalton's atomic theory was proposed by the Italian physicist Amadeo Avogadro (1776–1856) in 1811. This proposal took the form of a two-part hypothesis:

1. Equal volumes of gases under the same conditions of temperature and pressure contain the same number of particles.

2. The ultimate *physical* units of elemental substances may be different from their ultimate *chemical* units.

The first of these assumptions had occurred to others, although it is now identified with the name of Avogadro. The second was a novel idea, and constituted the most promising basis for reconciliation of the law of combining volumes with the atomic theory.

Two volumes of hydrogen combine with one of oxygen; according to the first part of Avogadro's hypothesis, two of the particles present in hydrogen gas must therefore combine with one of those present in oxygen gas. If these particles are single atoms, then the number of water molecules formed (each containing two hydrogen atoms and one oxygen atom) should be equal to the initial number of oxygen atoms. The resulting volume of water vapor should then be equal to the volume of oxygen used up; actually it is twice that volume. Suppose, said Avogadro, that the ultimate physical units of hydrogen and oxygen are *not* atoms, but molecules, each of which contains two like atoms. Two such *diatomic* hydrogen molecules plus one diatomic oxygen molecule would contain a total of four hydrogen atoms and two oxygen atoms, from which two water molecules could be formed. The volume of water vapor would then be twice that of reactant oxygen and equal to that of reactant hydrogen, as observed (Fig. 7–4). Avogadro's interpretation may be written in the form of an equation, in which the subscript 2 indicates the assumed presence of two like atoms in a single molecule:

$$2 \ H_2 \text{ molecules} + 1 \ O_2 \text{ molecule} = 2 \ H_2O \text{ molecules}.$$

Avogadro's original explanation assumed formation of a double water molecule, H_4O_2, followed by its splitting to form two single molecules. The assumption of a transient intermediate molecule is not essential to the argument, nor does it represent the actual path of reaction in this case. It should also be mentioned that Avogadro was aware that he had no way of knowing that there are only two atoms per hydrogen and oxygen molecule. It would have been just as consistent with the evidence to assume 4 atoms in each and a formula H_4O_2 for the single water molecule.

For another illustration of Avogadro's thesis, let us consider the formation of ammonia. Here the volume ratios are 3 (hydrogen) to 1 (nitrogen), yielding 2 (ammonia). The 3:1 ratio of hydrogen to nitrogen volumes indicates, according to Avogadro, that these elements are present in the ammonia molecule in 3:1 atomic ratio, rather than 1:1 as assumed by Dalton. The 2:1 volume ratio of ammonia to nitrogen again implies twice as many ammonia molecules formed as nitrogen particles combined. The whole process may be described by

$$1 \ N_2 \text{ molecule} + 3 \ H_2 \text{ molecules} = 2 \ NH_3 \text{ molecules}.$$
$$\text{(1 volume)} \qquad \text{(3 volumes)} \qquad \text{(2 volumes)}$$

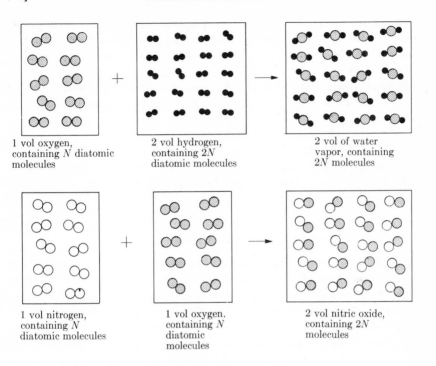

1 vol oxygen, containing N diatomic molecules

2 vol hydrogen, containing $2N$ diatomic molecules

2 vol of water vapor, containing $2N$ molecules

1 vol nitrogen, containing N diatomic molecules

1 vol oxygen, containing N diatomic molecules

2 vol nitric oxide, containing $2N$ molecules

Fig. 7–4. Avogadro's proposal.

As a final illustration, the formation of nitric oxide (Fig. 7–4), in which the volume ratios are 1 (nitrogen) to 1 (oxygen) to 2 (nitric oxide), may be formulated as

$$1 \ N_2 \text{ molecule} + 1 \ O_2 \text{ molecule} = 2 \ NO \text{ molecules.}$$
$$\text{(1 volume)} \qquad \text{(1 volume)} \qquad \text{(2 volumes)}$$

Dalton's objection that the density of oxygen is greater than that of water vapor could also be met by Avogadro's proposal. If an oxygen molecule contains two atoms it *must* be heavier than a water molecule, which contains only one oxygen atom plus two very light hydrogen atoms. Therefore, if equal volumes contain equal numbers of particles, the density of oxygen would be greater than that of water vapor.

Avogadro's twofold hypothesis was *capable* of contributing great clarity to chemistry at the time it was put forward. Rationally deduced atomic ratios, for compounds of gaseous elements at least, would have aided substantially in solving the difficult problem of atomic weights. But the proposal was not given serious consideration by Avogadro's contemporaries. One reason was that most chemists of the time, like Dalton, preferred to think of gases as containing particles in mutual contact. As Avogadro correctly pointed out, the hypothesis that two unlike gases contain equal numbers of molecules in equal volumes virtually demands belief that gas molecules are widely separated from one another. A second reason was the widespread reluctance to believe that two like atoms could form a stable union with each other. This reluctance stemmed from a popular theory of chemical combination, due to Jons Jacob Berzelius (1779–1848), that assumed electric charges on individual atoms; according to this theory like atoms possess like charge, and should therefore repel each other. For these and other reasons Avogadro's hypothesis was virtually unutilized until 1858, when it was revived and put to significant use by his countryman Stanislao Cannizzaro (1826–1910).

7–6 Cannizzaro's method for atomic weight determination

The atomic theory did not stand still between the time of Avogadro and that of Cannizzaro. One development of great significance to the atomic weight problem was a nearly Herculean accomplishment of the great Swedish chemist Berzelius. A scarcity of reliable combining weight data was inhibiting chemical progress; Berzelius devoted ten years to the acquisition of such data. With the greatest accuracy then possible he determined the elemental weight proportions of some 2000 compounds. These results, in turn, became the basis for an improved atomic weight table. But for selection of atomic ratios Berzelius made his own set of rules which, though superior to those of Dalton, led to frequent error.

Two other developments in the period 1811–1858 proved significant to the atomic weight question. First was the discovery of an interesting empirical relation between the specific heats (see Chapter 11) and atomic weights of *solid* elements.* This relation led to the selection of correct atomic ratios in a large number of cases. Second was the perfection by

---

*The Law of Pierre Dulong (1785–1838) and Alexis Petit (1791–1820), who observed that the *product* of specific heat (in calories per gram) and atomic weight is approximately 6 for nearly all known solid elements. While postponing our inquiry into the nature of specific heat, we may nevertheless illustrate formally the utility of this law. Consider the case of silver. Berzelius' analysis of silver oxide showed 13.5 parts silver per part oxygen by weight. If the atomic ratio (silver to oxygen) in this compound were 1:1 (AgO) the atomic weight of silver, relative to oxygen 16, would be $13.5 \times 16 = 216$; if 2:1, the atomic weight of silver should be 108; and if 1:2, the answer is 54. The specific heat of silver is measured as 0.056 calorie per gram, so that by the Law of Dulong and Petit its atomic weight should be $6/0.056 = 107$. In view of the approximate nature of the law, this result indicates that the second computation above is correct: 108 may be assigned as the correct atomic weight of silver, and 2:1 the correct ratio of silver to oxygen atoms in the compound silver oxide (Ag_2O).

Jean Dumas (1800–1884) of an ingenious method for precise determination of the densities of vapors. This method made possible, for the first time, the measurement of *gas* densities for many substances normally liquid or solid at ordinary temperatures.

Cannizzaro's contribution, dependent in theory on Avogadro's twofold hypothesis, and equally dependent in application on Berzelius' analytical data and Dumas' vapor density method, proved decisive in the final systematization of chemistry. Cannizzaro's method, in outline, is presented in the columns of numbers shown in Table 7–3. Let us consider first just those numbers pertaining to gaseous compounds of hydrogen, Part A. In the first column are listed values of the densities (grams per liter) of elemental hydrogen and several of its compounds, all measured under like conditions of temperature and pressure. In the second column are *percentages of hydrogen by weight* in each of these gases, as determined by analysis. The third column contains, for each compound, the *product* of gas density and hydrogen percentage, i.e., column 1 multiplied by column 2; in effect, each number in column 3 represents the *weight of hydrogen present in one liter* of the gas considered. Inspection of column 3 reveals the striking fact that its numbers are integrally related; each is a multiple of the smallest value present, that obtained for the compound hydrogen chloride. Values of these multiples are listed in column 4. Parts B and C of Table 7–3 contain similar data for gaseous compounds of oxygen and chlorine, respectively. Again, the products of gas density and percentage composition are integrally related.

How are these striking numerical relations to be explained? First, argued Cannizzaro, we must admit the full validity of Avogadro's hypothesis: equal volumes of gases contain equal numbers of particles, hence in comparing the densities of gases we are comparing the *weights of equal numbers of molecules*. When the density of a gas is multiplied by its weight percentage of hydrogen, the result is weight of *that element* per unit volume. The numbers in column 3 (Part A) thus represent weights of hydrogen present in a fixed number of molecules. In a series of hydrogen compounds the number of hydrogen atoms per molecule would be expected to vary from one compound to the next. A compound containing two hydrogen atoms per molecule must contain twice as much hydrogen by weight, in a fixed number of molecules, as a compound whose molecules contain only one hydrogen atom; a compound containing three hydrogen atoms, three times as much hydrogen by weight, etc. The integers in column 4, then, give the *number of hydrogen atoms present in one molecule of each compound*. Similarly, the integers in Parts B and C indicate numbers of oxygen and chlorine atoms per molecule of their various compounds.

Accepting Cannizzaro's interpretation of these results (and the similar results for other elements), we immediately find verification for the second

TABLE 7-3

CANNIZZARO'S METHOD OF ATOMIC WEIGHT DETERMINATION

Substance	1. Density, grams per liter*	2. Percentage of element of interest, by weight	3. Products of values in 1 and 2	4. Values in 3 divided by least value
A. Hydrogen and Its Gaseous Compounds				
Hydrogen	0.0659	100	0.0659	2
Hydrogen chloride	1.19	2.76	0.0329	1
Water	0.589	11.2	0.0659	2
Ammonia	0.557	17.7	0.0986	3
Methane	0.524	25.1	0.132	4
B. Oxygen and Its Gaseous Compounds				
Oxygen	1.05	100	1.05	2
Water	0.589	88.8	0.523	1
Sulfur dioxide	2.09	50.0	1.05	2
Carbon monoxide	0.916	57.1	0.523	1
Carbon dioxide	1.44	72.7	1.05	2
C. Chlorine and Its Gaseous Compounds				
Cholorine	2.32	100	2.32	2
Hydrogen chloride	1.19	97.2	1.16	1
Chloroform	3.90	89.1	3.48	3
Methylene chloride	2.78	83.5	2.32	2
Carbon tetrachloride	5.03	92.2	4.64	4

*All gas densities in this table are reported for the conditions 100°C and one atmosphere pressure.

part of Avogadro's hypothesis. The weight of hydrogen present in one liter of elemental gas is exactly twice the *least* weight, i.e., that observed for hydrogen chloride. Elemental hydrogen does *not* consist of individual atoms, then, but of molecules, each containing two atoms. From the results for oxygen and chlorine we may similarly deduce that each of these elemental gases consists of diatomic molecules. Cannizzaro's method had at long last provided means for establishing the *number* of atoms in the molecule of any gaseous element. The smallest physical particle and the smallest chemical unit of an element are *not* necessarily identical, and indeed we now know that those elements whose atoms travel singly in the gaseous state constitute a minority.*

We have called Cannizzaro's contribution a method for the determination of *atomic weights*, yet our concern so far has been entirely with numbers of atoms of a given kind per molecule. But we have seen again and again that no certainty in atomic weights was possible without certainty in atomic ratios; the triumph of Cannizzaro's scheme was the clarity it brought to the latter question. The compound water, for example, appears in both A and B of Table 7–3; its weight of hydrogen (Part A) is twice the least weight of that element, while its weight of oxygen (Part B) is equal to that element's least weight. According to Cannizzaro's interpretation, hydrogen and oxygen atoms must then be present in 2:1 ratio in water molecules. Use of the known analytical result that the *weight* ratio of hydrogen to water is very nearly 1:8 leads to the conclusion that oxygen atoms must therefore be $2 \times 8 = 16$ times heavier than hydrogen atoms. Basic to such determinations, and in fact to successful operation of Cannizzaro's entire scheme, was his *assumption* that each of his list of compounds of a given element included at least one compound whose molecules contain only one atom of that element. This assumption, risky though it may seem, has worked out well in long-range practice.

Cannizzaro's proposals and their acceptance brought order to the previously confused assignment of atomic ratios and atomic weights. The principal chemists of Europe had assembled at an international congress in Karlsruhe, Germany, in 1860, in an attempt to resolve the chaos that prevailed in the use of atomic weights and the writing of molecular formulas. The conference was disappointingly inconclusive, but at its close copies of Cannizzaro's pamphlet, *Sketch of a Course in Chemical Philosophy*, pub-

---

*This minority includes all the so-called inert gas elements: helium, neon, argon, krypton, xenon, and radon. It also includes mercury. Our statement applies, in practice, only to those elements whose vapors form under moderate conditions, since at extremely high temperatures molecules in general are not stable but dissociate readily into single atoms. Molecules of some gaseous elements contain more than two atoms: those of phosphorus contain four atoms (P_4), and sulfur vapor molecules occur in two forms, S_2 and S_8.

lished two years earlier, were distributed to the participants. Its impact can be illustrated by the words of the German chemist Lothar Meyer, who wrote that after reading it "the scales fell from my eyes, doubts vanished, and a feeling of calm certainty came in their place."

7-7 The utility of atomic and molecular weights

Since Cannizzaro's time great effort has been applied to the determination of chemical atomic weights, and modern values are reliable in some cases to as many as six significant figures. A complete listing of modern atomic weights is shown in Table 7-4. These values are based on the arbitrary assignment of 16.0000 as the atomic weight of oxygen; the atomic weight of any element on this scale thus represents the weight of an atom of that element in units 1/16 the weight of an oxygen atom. For example, 107.880 as the atomic weight of silver means that silver atoms are 107.880/16.0000 times heavier than oxygen atoms. Beryllium atoms, on the other hand, are lighter than oxygen atoms, by the fraction 9.013/16.0000.

In dealing with molecules it is convenient to compute quantities called *molecular weights*. Given the numbers and kinds of atoms present in a molecule, we may find the molecular weight by simply adding the atomic weights of those atoms. The molecular weight of oxygen gas (O_2), for example, is $2 \times 16.0000 = 32.0000$; that of sulfur dioxide (SO_2) is $32.066 + (2 \times 16.0000) = 64.066$. Molecular weights are proportional to the densities of the corresponding gases, under similar conditions of pressure and temperature.

The list of numbers shown in Table 7-4 may seem an unromantic end product of so much effort, but it is of untold value in performing useful quantitative chemical computations. Suppose we know, for example, that a certain compound contains 21.9% sulfur (by weight), the rest fluorine; we can immediately calculate the relative numbers of sulfur and fluorine atoms in a single molecule of the compound. Or suppose we know the atoms of iron and oxygen to be present in a certain compound (ferric oxide) in 2:3 ratio; the table would then enable us to compute the quantity of iron that should be weighed out to obtain 5 gm of the compound. These examples represent only two variations on a theme whose practical importance cannot be overestimated.

The practical validity of the atomic theory has never been questioned, but the question may be raised whether this proves that atoms actually exist. The answer can only be "no." The mere *workability* of any theoretical framework, such as the atomic theory, does not constitute "proof" of its underlying assumptions. There were several 19th century scientists, some of them eminent, who maintained that atoms are merely a "con-

TABLE 7–4

ATOMIC WEIGHTS OF THE ELEMENTS

Name	Symbol	Atomic weight	Atomic number**
Actinium	Ac	227	89
Aluminum	Al	26.98	13
Americium	Am	(243)*	95
Antimony	Sb	121.76	51
Argon	A	39.944	18
Arsenic	As	74.91	33
Astatine	At	(210)*	85
Barium	Ba	137.36	56
Berkelium	Bk	(245)*	97
Beryllium	Be	9.013	4
Bismuth	Bi	209.00	83
Boron	B	10.82	5
Bromine	Br	79.916	35
Cadmium	Cd	112.41	48
Calcium	Ca	40.08	20
Californium	Cf	(246)*	98
Carbon	C	12.010	6
Cerium	Ce	140.13	58
Cesium	Cs.	132.91	55
Chlorine	Cl	35.457	17
Chromium	Cr	52.01	24
Cobalt	Co	58.94	27
Copper	Cu	63.54	29
Curium	Cm	(243)*	96
Dysprosium	Dy	162.46	66
Einsteinium	E	(253)*	99
Erbium	Er	167.2	68
Europium	Eu	152.0	63
Fermium	Fm	(255)*	100
Fluorine	F	19.00	9
Francium	Fr	(223)*	87
Gadolinium	Gd	156.9	64
Gallium	Ga	69.72	31
Germanium	Ge	72.60	32
Gold	Au	197.2	79
Hafnium	Hf	178.6	72

(cont.)

*The elements whose atomic weights are given in parentheses do not occur in nature, but have been produced "artificially" by nuclear reactions. The number given, in each case, is the mass number of the longest-lived known radioactive isotope; see Chapter 29.

**See Chapter 9 for the meaning of atomic number.

ATOMIC WEIGHTS OF THE ELEMENTS (*cont.*)

Name	*Symbol*	*Atomic weight*	*Atomic number*
Helium	He	4.003	2
Holmium	Ho	164.94	67
Hydrogen	H	1.0080	1
Indium	In	114.76	49
Iodine	I	126.91	53
Iridium	Ir	193.1	77
Iron	Fe	55.85	26
Krypton	Kr	83.80	36
Lanthanum	La	138.92	57
Lead	Pb	207.21	82
Lithium	Li	6.940	3
Lutecium	Lu	174.99	71
Magnesium	Mg	24.32	12
Manganese	Mn	54.93	25
Mendelevium	Mv	(256)*	101
Mercury	Hg	200.61	80
Molybdenum	Mo	95.95	42
Neodymium	Nd	144.27	60
Neon	Ne	20.183	10
Neptunium	Np	(237)*	93
Nickel	Ni	58.69	28
Niobium	Nb	92.91	41
Nitrogen	N	14.008	7
Osmium	Os	190.2	76
Oxygen	O	16.0000	8
Palladium	Pd	106.7	46
Phosphorus	P	30.975	15
Platinum	Pt	195.23	78
Plutonium	Pu	(239)*	94
Polonium	Po	210	84
Potassium	K	39.100	19
Praesodymium	Pr	140.92	59
Prometheum	Pm	(145)*	61
Protactinium	Pa	231	91
Radium	Ra	226.05	88
Radon	Rn	222	86
Rhenium	Re	186.31	75
Rhodium	Rh	102.91	45
Rubidium	Rb	85.48	37
Ruthenium	Ru	101.7	44
Samarium	Sm	150.43	62
Scandium	Sc	44.96	21
Selenium	Se	78.96	34

ATOMIC WEIGHTS OF THE ELEMENTS (*cont.*)

Name	Symbol	Atomic weight	Atomic number
Silicon	Si	28.09	14
Silver	Ag	107.880	47
Sodium	Na	22.991	11
Strontium	Sr	87.63	38
Sulfur	S	32.066	16
Tantalum	Ta	180.95	73
Technetium	Tc	(99)*	43
Tellurium	Te	127.61	52
Terbium	Tb	158.9	65
Thallium	Tl	204.39	81
Thorium	Th	232.12	90
Thulium	Tm	168.9	69
Tin	Sn	118.70	50
Titanium	Ti	47.90	22
Uranium	U	238.07	92
Vanadium	V	50.95	23
Wolfram (Tungsten)	W	183.92	74
Xenon	Xe	131.3	54
Ytterbium	Yb	173.04	70
Yttrium	Y	88.92	39
Zinc	Zn	65.38	30
Zirconium	Zr	91.22	40

venient fiction," having no necessary relation to reality in the structure of matter. This position has become insupportable only during our own century, in which physical science has, as we shall see later, found convincingly direct demonstrations of the behavior of *individual* atoms and molecules.

7–8 Summary

The ancient philosophical view that matter is composed of indivisible *atoms* became a useful chemical theory only after the discovery (by Proust) that elements combine in definite proportions by weight. Dalton, in 1803, was first to realize that weight relations in chemical change may be used to draw inferences about the combinations of atoms. He concluded that small whole numbers of atoms combine to form the units (molecules) of compounds. He predicted and demonstrated the relation known as the law of multiple proportions. Relative atomic weights could not at first be established with certainty. Gay-Lussac discovered that the volumes of gases participating in chemical reactions are related by simple numerical ratios, and the relation between this law of combining volumes and Dalton's atomic theory was made understandable by Avogadro's hypothesis that equal volumes of gases under the same conditions contain the same number of particles. A wealth of experimental data helped to confirm the atomic theory, and Cannizzaro's method for unambiguous determination of atomic weights made it possible to systematize chemistry in a consistent fashion.

REFERENCES

GREGORY, J. C., *A Short History of Atomism.*

LEICESTER, H. M., and H. S. KLICKSTEIN, *Source Book in Chemistry*, pp. 202–205 (Proust), 208–220 (Dalton), 293–299 (Gay-Lussac), 231–238 (Avogadro), 406–417 (Cannizzaro).

LUCRETIUS, *De Rerum Natura.* Several good translations are available, for example that by Ronald Latham (*On the Nature of the Universe*) in the Penguin series.

NASH, L. K., *The Atomic-Molecular Theory* (Number 4 of the Harvard Case Histories in Experimental Science). An excellent account of the development of atomic theory from Dalton to Cannizzaro, set in its historical context.

PARTINGTON, J. R., *A Short History of Chemistry*, Chapter VIII.

SISLER, H. H., and others, *General Chemistry, a Systematic Approach.* The atomic theory is treated in many elementary textbooks on chemistry, of which this is a good example.

VAN MELSEN, A. G., *From Atomos to Atom, the History of the Concept Atom.*

1. Cinnabar, a mineral investigated by Proust (see Section 7–1), is known to contain the elements mercury and sulfur in the weight ratio 6.25 to 1. (a) What quantity of mercury could be obtained from 250 kgm of cinnabar? (b) What quantity of sulfur will combine with 100 gm of mercury to form cinnabar? [*Ans.*: (a) 216 kgm; (b) 16 gm]

2. The compound mercuric oxide, which played so prominent a role in the work of Priestley and Lavoisier, can be formed by heating mercury in air. If a 100-gm quantity of mercury is completely converted to mercuric oxide, the latter is found to weigh 108 gm. (a) What weight of oxygen may be obtained by decomposition of 500 gm of mercuric oxide? (b) What is the percentage by weight of mercury in this compound? (c) What is the weight ratio of mercury to oxygen (grams of mercury per gram of oxygen) in mercuric oxide? [*Ans.*: (a) 37 gm; (b) 92.6 percent; (c) 12.5:1]

3. Use the mercury-sulfur weight ratio given for cinnabar in Exercise 1 and the mercury-oxygen ratio calculated for mercuric oxide in Exercise 2(c) to compute the weights of mercury and sulfur atoms relative to the weight of the oxygen atom defined as 16, assuming that mercury and oxygen atoms combine in 1:1 ratio, and that mercury and sulfur atoms combine in:
(a) 1:1 ratio; (b) 2:1 ratio; (c) 1:2 ratio; (d) 3:2 ratio. The 1:1 ratio assumed for mercuric oxide is correct; check your results against those in Table 7–4 to see which of the assump-

tions (a)–(d) is correct. [*Ans.*: (a) 32, (b) 64, (c) 16, (d) 48, for the atomic weight of sulfur]

4. The element copper forms two compounds with the element chlorine; the copper-chlorine weight ratio in one of these is 1.79:1, in the other 0.895:1. (a) Do these compounds conform to the law of multiple proportions? (b) If one of these compounds contains copper and chlorine atoms in 1:1 ratio, what must be the ratio in the other compound? Which compound is which?

5. Iron and oxygen form two compounds, one containing 77.8% of iron by weight, the other 69.9%. (a) Demonstrate that these compounds conform to the law of multiple proportions. (b) Indicate two possible sets of atomic ratios consistent with your results in (a).

6. According to Dalton's arbitrary atomic ratio rules, when three compounds of the elements A and B are known, one of these must contain A and B atoms in 1:1 ratio (AB), one in 2:1 ratio (A_2B), and the third in 1:2 ratio (AB_2). A case of this sort which attracted Dalton's attention was that of the three compounds of nitrogen and oxygen which were then known. These contain 63.6%, 46.6%, and 30.4% of nitrogen, respectively. By inspecting these numbers, can you tell what atomic ratios Dalton would have assigned to each? It is of interest to note that in this instance Dalton's rules led to the correct result.

7. Carbon monoxide contains carbon and oxygen in weight ratio 3:4; water contains hydrogen and oxygen in weight

159

ratio 1:8. For the carbon-hydrogen compound methane the weight ratio of carbon to hydrogen is 3:1. Having arbitrarily assigned atomic ratios of 1:1 for the first two compounds, Dalton was able to *deduce* an atomic ratio for methane. What was his answer? [*Ans.*: ratio of carbon to hydrogen atoms = 1:2]

8. Dalton's assignment of 1:1 atomic ratio for carbon monoxide was correct, but the hydrogen-oxygen ratio in water, of course, is 2:1. How does this alteration affect the atomic ratio deduced for methane in Exercise 7?

9. What volume of nitrogen, at 25°C and 1 atm pressure, would be required to react completely with 2.50 liters of hydrogen as measured under the same conditions? What volume of ammonia would be produced? (See Section 7–4 for volume relations in this reaction.) [*Ans.*: 0.833 liter, 1.67 liters]

10. Explain the volume relations shown in Section 7–4 for the formation of nitrous oxide and nitrogen dioxide in terms of Avogadro's hypothesis. Can you write chemical equations for these reactions similar to those shown in Section 7–5?

11. In certain circumstances elemental chlorine and fluorine combine to form a compound. Three volumes of fluorine combine with one of chlorine to form two volumes of the compound. In the light of Avogadro's hypothesis: (a) What is the atomic ratio of the two elements in the compound? (b) Do elemental fluorine and chlorine consist of single atoms or of molecules? If molecules, how many atoms in each?

12. Gas densities and weight percentages of fluorine are shown below for fluorine and four of its compounds. Following the method of Cannizzaro: (a) Determine the probable number of fluorine atoms per molecule of each of these five substances. (b) Determine the probable atomic weight of fluorine, relative to O = 16. The density of elemental oxygen gas, under the same conditions as the densities above, is 1.31 gm/liter.

13. Use the information of Exercise 12 and the known atomic weights of hydrogen, carbon, and sulfur (Table 7–4) to deduce atomic ratios for compounds 2, 3, and 4 of Exercise 12.

	Density	% Fluorine (by weight)
1. Pure fluorine	1.56	100
2. Fluorine-hydrogen compound	0.820	95.0
3. Fluorine-carbon compound	3.61	86.5
4. Fluorine-sulfur compound	5.99	78.0
5. Fluorine-hydrogen-carbon compound	2.13	73.1

CHAPTER 8

THE LANGUAGE AND ARITHMETIC OF CHEMISTRY

Chemistry deals with a vast number of phenomena, since it is the science of matter, and matter is virtually unending in its variation. It is the task of science to unify factual knowledge by the discovery of features common to broad sets of observables, and hence to formulate statements which can be applied to many facts. Perhaps the most important generalization in chemistry is the one we have examined in the last chapter: elements consist of unit particles called atoms, which unite to form molecules, the unit particles of compounds. Yet this statement is useful only to the extent that it can be focused upon *individual* observations and experiments, and invoked in their explanation. The value and the validity of abstract and general laws and theories in science rest upon interpretation and prediction of single observable events.

Since chemical phenomena are both abundant and complex it is highly inconvenient to deal with them in words alone. (Think how difficult ordinary arithmetic would be if all the numbers had to be written out in words!) For this reason the science of chemistry, over its long history, has evolved a shorthand nomenclature, or language, of its own. Some of this language has entered into common parlance—to say H_2O instead of water is almost to use a kind of slang. We have anticipated the writing of formulas in the previous chapter, but we should investigate the language of chemistry more systematically before attempting to trace further development of the science. The rudiments of chemical notation are an almost indispensable aid in tracing the history of chemical thought and in understanding the lofty generalizations chemical science has achieved.

The language of chemistry contains *symbols* for the representation of atoms, *formulas* for the representation of molecules, and *equations* for the description of chemical events at the atomic and molecular level. It is a system predicated on the basic concepts of the atomic theory, and we may be stretching a point to call it a system for the description of macroscopic (large-scale) *facts*. But the *concepts* of atom and molecule are so closely related to the laboratory *operations* that gave rise to them that a chemical equation can be regarded as a factual statement.

161

8-1 Symbols

The chemical symbolism in use today follows the system devised by Berzelius in the 19th century: characteristic letters, or pairs of letters, are used to represent atoms of the elements. The letter H, for example, represents *one atom* of the element hydrogen, C an atom of carbon, and N an atom of nitrogen. Since there are 101 elements and only 26 letters, pairs of letters must be frequently used. The element boron is symbolized by B, bromine by the combination Br. Sulfur atoms are represented by the symbol S, selenium by Se, silicon by Si, scandium by Sc, strontium by Sr, and samarium by Sm. In the cases of several of the metallic elements, symbols are based on Latin (rather than English) names. These are sodium: symbol Na for Latin *natrium*; antimony: Sb (*stibium*); copper: Cu (*cuprum*); gold: Au (*aurum*); iron: Fe (*ferrum*); lead: Pb (*plumbum*); mercury: Hg (*hydrargium*); potassium: K (*kallium*); silver: Ag (*argentum*); and tin: Sn (*stannum*). A complete listing of the elemental letter symbols is found in Table 7–4.

8-2 Formulas

Molecules of the compound carbon monoxide contain one atom of carbon and one atom of oxygen. The *formula* for carbon monoxide, representing a *single molecule* of that compound, simply consists of the two atomic symbols placed side by side: CO. Carbon dioxide, whose molecules contain two oxygen atoms and one carbon atom, is represented by the formula CO_2. Similarly, the formula for water, H_2O, contains a subscript 2 on the symbol H to indicate the presence of two hydrogen atoms per molecule. Phosphorus pentoxide molecules contain 2 phosphorus atoms and 5 oxygen atoms, and are represented by the formula P_2O_5. The formula for chloroform is $CHCl_3$, for sodium dichromate $Na_2Cr_2O_7$, for sugar $C_{12}H_{22}O_{11}$. (These formulas are given as examples, not to be memorized!) It is important to remember that each formula represents a single molecular unit, and that the atomic symbols and subscripts convey complete information as to the kinds and numbers of atoms present in each such unit.

8-3 Names of compounds

Formulas, as described above, provide the symbolic representation of compounds essential to chemical shorthand. Each known compound also requires verbal representation, corresponding to the formula as *twelve* does to the symbol 12. We are already familiar with several compounds, such as water (H_2O) and ammonia (NH_3), whose commonly used names reveal nothing about chemical composition. But most compounds are given systematic names which do carry chemical information. It would not be useful or desirable to give a complete account of this system here, but a brief introduction is necessary to facilitate our further discussion.

(a) When two elements form but a single compound, the name of that compound usually consists of the name of one element followed by a modification of the name of the second carrying the suffix *-ide*. If one of the two elements is metallic, its name forms the first part of the name of the compound. Thus $NaCl$ is called *sodium chloride*, CaO *calcium oxide*, PbI_2 *lead iodide*, Mg_3N_2 *magnesium nitride*, and Al_4C_3 *aluminum carbide*. If neither element is metallic, their order of appearance in the name is immaterial, although usually fixed by convention. In translating a formula to a name it is customary to list first the name of the element whose symbol appears first in the formula.

(b) When two elements form more than one compound, names are assigned according to alternative conventions. The first of these is to add a prefix (*mono-, di-, tri-, tetra-, penta-, hexa-*, etc.) to the name of the second element to indicate the number of atoms of that kind present per molecule of the compound. For example, CO and CO_2 are called carbon *mon*oxide and carbon *di*oxide, respectively; SO_2 and SO_3 are called sulfur *di*oxide and sulfur *tri*oxide, PCl_3 and PCl_5 are called phosphorus *tri*chloride and phosphorus *penta*chloride. The second convention, usually applied to the compounds of metals, consists of adding a suffix, either *-ous* or *-ic*, to the name of the element appearing first in the name of the compound. For two compounds of the same elements, *-ous* designates the smaller number of atoms of the second element per atom of the first, *-ic* the greater number. $CoCl_2$ and $CoCl_3$, for example, are called cobalt*ous* chloride and cobalt*ic* chloride, respectively; CrO is called chrom*ous* oxide, and Cr_2O_3 chrom*ic* oxide. For those elements whose symbols are based upon them, Latin names are frequently used in naming compounds. Thus SnO and SnO_2 are known as stannous and stannic oxides, Cu_2S and CuS as cuprous and cupric sulfides, $FeBr_2$ and $FeBr_3$ as ferrous and ferric bromides.

Occasionally both these conventions are invoked in the naming of a series of compounds, as in the oxides of nitrogen (Table 7–1). Here N_2O and NO are called nitrous and nitric oxide, respectively, and prefixes are employed in naming the higher oxides, e.g., nitrogen tetroxide for N_2O_4.

(c) Compounds which contain atoms of more than two elements are simply named, in many cases, because of the presence of groups of atoms known as *radicals*. Chemical experience has shown that many such groups tend to *act as units* in chemical change. For example, the compound known as calcium nitrate has a known composition for which we could write the formula CaN_2O_6. In many of its reactions, however, the group consisting of one nitrogen atom and three oxygen atoms ($-NO_3$), called the *nitrate* radical, acts as a unit. Therefore a formula which comes closer to representation of the nature of calcium nitrate is $Ca(NO_3)_2$, indicating the presence of one calcium atom and two nitrate radicals in each molecular unit* of the compound.

Table 8–1 contains the names and formulas of some of the more common and important radicals. To name compounds which contain them it is simply necessary to recognize these group formulas. The compound whose formula is Ag_2SO_4, for example, is called silver sulfate; Na_2CO_3 is called sodium carbonate, $KClO_3$ potassium chlorate, $Ca(OH)_2$ calcium hydroxide, $FeCrO_4$ and $Fe_2(CrO_4)_3$ ferrous and ferric chromates, $(NH_4)_2SO_4$ ammonium sulfate.

TABLE 8–1

RADICALS

Name	Formula
Hydroxide	$-OH$
Ammonium	NH_4-
Nitrate	$-NO_3$
Nitrite	$-NO_2$
Carbonate	$-CO_3$
Phosphate	$-PO_4$
Sulfate	$-SO_4$
Sulfite	$-SO_3$
Cyanide	$-CN$
Chromate	$-CrO_4$
Dichromate	$-Cr_2O_7$
Chlorate	$-ClO_3$
Perchlorate	$-ClO_4$
Permanganate	$-MnO_4$

The formulas and names of the radicals in Table 8–1, with one exception, are conventionally placed last in the formulas and names of the compounds that contain them. The single exception is the important *ammonium* group,

---

*Later (Chapter 20) we shall find that calcium nitrate and most of the other compounds of radicals discussed in this section (as well as many other compounds) do not actually consist of "molecular units" at all! This surprising result, related to the existence of radicals, cannot be made meaningful at this stage in our story. We shall continue to speak of "molecules" in *all* compounds, but may expect that some readjustment of thought on the subject will be required eventually.

NH_4—, which also has the distinction of being the only radical in the list which forms compounds with the others.

(d) *Acids*, unique and important substances, are given special names. Hydrogen chloride (HCl), for example, dissolves in water to form a solution with characteristic acid properties (iron, zinc, and other metals liberate hydrogen on contact with it; it has a sour taste; it changes the color of the vegetable dye *litmus* from blue to red). The name given the solution is *hydrochloric* acid. The prefix *hydro-* and suffix *-ic*, combined in this manner, indicate an acid whose molecules contain only two elements, one of which is hydrogen; HBr is called hydrobromic acid, for example. The molecules of some other acids consist of one or more hydrogen atoms combined with radicals. Thus HNO_3, *nitric* acid, could be called hydrogen nitrate. Its special name is derived from the nitrate radical alone, by replacing the suffix *-ate* with *-ic*. Similarly, H_2SO_4 is called *sulfuric* acid, H_2CO_3 *carbonic* acid, and $HClO_4$ *perchloric* acid. H_2SO_3, which contains the same elements as sulfuric acid, is distinguished from it by use of the *-ous* suffix, i.e., *sulfurous* acid; HNO_2 is called *nitrous* acid.

8–4 Equations

As symbols and formulas correspond to the letters and words of a language, *equations* may be considered complete chemical sentences. The combustion of charcoal, for example, may be represented by the equation

$$C + O_2 \rightarrow CO_2.$$

In words, this equation says: "One atom of carbon combines with one molecule of oxygen to form one molecule of carbon dioxide." Or, again,

$$2H_2 + O_2 \rightarrow 2H_2O,$$

which says: "Two molecules of hydrogen combine with one molecule of oxygen to form two molecules of water." A formula represents a single molecular unit, it will be recalled, and a number placed in front of a formula applies to the entire unit. $2H_2O$ thus represents two water molecules, containing a total of 4 hydrogen and 2 oxygen atoms.

There is nothing speculative about writing a chemical equation. The starting point is knowledge of those substances which participate and those which are formed in an observed chemical change. Formulas for these substances, as determined by analytical methods, are set down in an appropriate order. Finally, since atoms are neither created nor destroyed in chemical change, the equation must be *balanced* so that the same numbers of atoms of each kind appear on both sides. The equation for combination of hydrogen and oxygen, above, has been balanced by placing the number 2 in front of the formulas for hydrogen and water. With a little practice, many equations can be balanced by inspection. For example, it is known that sulfur dioxide can combine with oxygen to form sulfur trioxide. Setting the three formulas down in appropriate order we obtain the *un*balanced equation

$$SO_2 + O_2 \rightarrow SO_3.$$

While there is one sulfur atom on each side of this equation, there are four oxygen atoms on the left and only three on the right. The smallest factor we could apply to the right-hand side is 2; 2 SO_3 molecules contain 2 sulfur atoms, so that to maintain a balance for that element there must be 2 SO_2 molecules on the left. We then have 6 oxygen atoms on the right and 6 on the left (4 in $2SO_2$ and 2 in O_2), and the whole equation is balanced:

$$2SO_2 + O_2 \rightarrow 2SO_3.$$

As a further example of equation balancing, consider the decomposition of potassium chlorate, which results in formation of potassium chloride and oxygen gas:

$$KClO_3 \rightarrow KCl + O_2.$$

This preliminary equation is unbalanced with respect to oxygen, as there are three atoms of that element on the left and only two on the right. To rectify this imbalance, we may put 3 in front of the formula for oxygen and 2 in front of that for potassium chlorate, giving 6 oxygen atoms on each side of the equation. The 2 in front of $KClO_3$, however, applies to the entire formula unit; balance of the elements potassium and chlorine must be achieved by multiplying KCl by 2. The final balanced equation is thus:

$$2KClO_3 \rightarrow 2KCl + 3O_2.$$

A convention frequently used in equation writing, which we shall use occasionally here, is to indicate the evolution of a gaseous reaction product by an upward arrow beside the gas formula. Examples are afforded by the equations

$$(NH_4)_2Cr_2O_7 \rightarrow N_2 \uparrow + Cr_2O_3 + 4H_2O$$

and

$$2HCl + Na_2CO_3 \rightarrow CO_2 \uparrow + H_2O + 2NaCl.$$

A downward arrow is often used to indicate precipitation of an insoluble reaction product from solution, as illustrated by the equations

$$AgNO_3 + NaCl \rightarrow AgCl \downarrow + NaNO_3$$

and

$$Pb(NO_3)_2 + 2KI \rightarrow PbI_2 \downarrow + 2KNO_3.$$

8-5 Weight relations in chemical change

A chemical equation, according to the discussion of the preceding section, conveys information about processes that we *assume* to take place at the atomic and molecular level. Our assumptions about atoms and molecules, however, are based on the observed behavior of matter in bulk. The equation

$$Fe + S \rightarrow FeS,$$

for example, implants an image in the chemist's mind of tangible quantities of black metallic iron and soft yellow sulfur mixed together, combining to form brown ferrous sulfide. (The equation does not tell him about the colors of reactants or that the iron-sulfur mixture must be heated to high temperature to initiate the reaction; information of this sort must supplement an equation for *full* description of a chemical change.) But, what is more important, the equation and its associated atomic weights, in combination, make possible the precise prediction of practical *weight* relations. Since the atomic weights of iron and sulfur are 55.85 and 32.07, respectively, and since the equation indicates that they combine atom for atom, we know with certainty that 55.85 grams, pounds, or tons of iron will combine with 32.07 grams, pounds, or tons of sulfur to form 87.92 grams, pounds, or tons of ferrous sulfide. Let us consider some illustrative applications of the quantitative information available in atomic weights, formulas, and equations.

For example, we may determine what quantity of iron must be weighed out to make just 3.00 gm of ferrous sulfide. We have seen that 55.95 gm of iron, combined with sulfur, will form 87.92 gm of ferrous sulfide, i.e., that the weight ratio of chemically equivalent quantities of Fe and FeS is 55.85/87.92. We also know that the weight ratio of Fe to FeS will have this value no matter what quantity of iron is involved, i.e.,

$$\frac{\text{Weight of Fe combined}}{\text{Weight of FeS formed}} = \frac{55.85}{87.92}.$$

To solve the problem, let (x) represent the quantity of iron required; then

$$\frac{(x)}{3.00 \text{ gm}} = \frac{55.9}{87.9},$$

whence

$$(x) = \frac{3.00 \times 55.9}{87.9} = 1.91 \text{ gm.}$$

As a second example, let us compute the weight of hydrogen that will combine with one ton of nitrogen to form ammonia, according to the equation

$$N_2 + 3H_2 \rightarrow 2NH_3.$$

Here we must deal with *molecular* weights: $2 \times 14.01 = 28.02$ for nitrogen, $2 \times 1.008 = 2.016$ for hydrogen, and $14.01 + 3 \times (1.008) = 17.03$ for ammonia. Since one molecule of nitrogen combines with three of hydrogen to form two of ammonia, the relative weights of these substances involved are $28.02 : 6.048 : 34.06$. The combining weight ratio of hydrogen to nitrogen in this reaction is then $6.048/28.02$, and the quantity of the former required to combine with 1.00 ton of the latter is

$$(x) = \frac{1.00 \text{ ton} \times 6.05}{28.0} = 0.216 \text{ ton.}$$

The problem above could have been solved without reference to a balanced equation, on the basis of the formula for ammonia alone. Since NH_3 contains hydrogen and nitrogen in weight ratio $3.024/14.01$, multiplication of this ratio by 1.00 ton gives the desired result at once. A more complicated example, which *does* require a balanced equation for its solution, is afforded by the reaction between zinc arsenide and hydrochloric acid to form zinc chloride and arsine (AsH_3):

$$Zn_3As_2 + 6HCl \rightarrow 3ZnCl_2 + 2AsH_3.$$

How much arsine can be obtained from 5.00 gm of zinc arsenide? The molecular weights of interest are $(3 \times 65.4 + 2 \times 74.9) = 346$ for Zn_3As_2, and $(74.9 + 3 \times 1.01) = 77.9$ for AsH_3. The relative weights of AsH_3 and Zn_3As_2 involved in this reaction are then 156 and 346, and the quantity of the former obtainable by reaction of 5.00 gm of the latter is

$$(x) = \frac{5.00 \times 156}{346} = 2.26 \text{ gm.}$$

Finally, let us review the procedure for deducing formulas from empirical data. The metal aluminum is known to combine with oxygen to form aluminum oxide (common name *corundum*), and chemical analysis shows the latter to contain 53.0% of aluminum by weight. Can we write an equation for its formation? So far, all we know is that 100 parts by weight of the compound contains 53 parts of aluminum and 47 parts of oxygen, i.e., that the weight *ratio* of oxygen to aluminum is $47/53 = 0.886$. To find a formula, we may apply an equation developed in Section 7–3:

$$\frac{\text{Wt. of O in cmpd.}}{\text{Wt. of Al in cmpd.}} = \frac{\text{No. of O atoms/molecule} \times \text{Wt. of O atom}}{\text{No. of Al atoms/molecule} \times \text{Wt. of Al atom}}.$$

The ratio on the left we have found to be 0.886. The atomic weight ratio of oxygen and aluminum atoms, from the atomic weight table, is $16.0/27.0$. If we represent the unknown formula by Al_xO_y, the equation becomes

$$0.886 = (y/x) \times (16.0/27.0),$$

and hence $(y/x) = 0.886 \times (27.0/16.0) = 1.50$. Oxygen and aluminum atoms, then, combine in the ratio $1.5:1$, or $3:2$, and as a formula for aluminum oxide, we may write Al_2O_3. This formula, in turn, enables us to write an equation for reaction between aluminum atoms and oxygen molecules:

$$4Al + 3O_2 \rightarrow 2Al_2O_3.$$

8–6 Volumes of gases in chemical change

For chemical changes involving gases, the *volume* relations between gaseous reactants and products can be explored by application of Gay-Lussac's law of combining volumes. In the reaction

$$N_2 + 3H_2 \rightarrow 2NH_3,$$

for example, one volume of nitrogen is known to combine with three of hydrogen, yielding two volumes of ammonia. The numerical coefficients in the balanced equation, it will be observed, correspond exactly to these volume ratios. Since one N_2 molecule reacts with three H_2 molecules, and since we assume, with Avogadro, that equal volumes of gases contain equal numbers of molecules, there is nothing surprising in this observation. For the reaction

$$2CO + O_2 \rightarrow 2CO_2,$$

in which reactants and product are all gases, we could state at once that 2 liters of carbon monoxide will combine with 1 liter of oxygen to form 2 liters of carbon dioxide, and that 0.286 in^3 of carbon dioxide would require 0.143 in^3 of oxygen and 0.286 in^3 of carbon monoxide for its production, if all gas volumes are measured under the same environmental conditions.

Since similar numbers of molecules of different gases occupy equal volumes, we should expect the *weights* of equal volumes to be proportional to the molecular weights of the gases. Careful measurement has shown that a quantity of any gas whose weight is equal to its *molecular weight in grams* (*called gram-molecular weight*), at 0°C and 1 atmosphere pressure, occupies the volume 22.4 liters.* The quantities 32 gm of oxygen, 2 gm of hydrogen, 64 gm of sulfur dioxide, 44 gm of carbon dioxide, and 46 gm of nitrogen dioxide, all occupy 22.4 liters each under the conditions specified. Note that conditions must be specified, for gas volumes change with pressure and temperature. The particular conditions, 0°C and 1 atm, are called *Standard Temperature and Pressure*, usually designated simply STP.

Knowledge of the volume of one gram-molecular weight enables us to determine gaseous volume relations in chemical reactions. If a 2.00-gm sample of carbon monoxide were available, what volume of oxygen would be required to combine with it? Now 28.0 gm of CO occupy 22.4 liters at STP, so that the volume of 2.00 gm is $(2.00/28.0) \times 22.4 = 1.60$ liters. Since carbon monoxide combines with oxygen in the volume ratio 2:1 (see balanced equation above), 0.80 liter of the latter (STP) would be required.

In the decomposition of solid potassium chlorate, oxygen gas is produced:

$$2KClO_3 \rightarrow 2KCl + 3O_2 \uparrow .$$

What volume of oxygen (STP) can be obtained by decomposition of 1.00 gm of $KClO_3$? Use of the atomic weight table and the above equation shows us that $2[39.1 + 35.5 + (3 \times 16.0)] = 245$ gm of $KClO_3$ can give rise to $3 \times 22.4 = 67.2$ liters of O_2 at STP. The volume of O_2 available in 1.00 gm of $KClO_3$ is therefore

$$(x) = 1.00 \times 67.2/245 = 0.274 \text{ liter (or 274 milliliters)}.$$

Examples are numerous, for the method is obviously quite general for gaseous reactants or products.

8–7 Avogadro's number

Avogadro's hypothesis was of great value, as shown in Chapter 7, long before any method was available for determining actual numbers of molecules in given volumes. Only in the 20th century have methods been devised for counting molecules, so to speak. We shall find that some of these methods are conceptually very simple, but they depend on developments we have not as yet considered. Nevertheless it is appropriate here to note

---

*Deviations from this volume *do* occur, as we shall find in Chapter 13. For ordinary purposes the figure 22.4 liters is entirely acceptable, however.

that the number of molecules in any macroscopic quantity of matter is staggeringly large. The number of molecules contained in 22.4 liters of gas at STP, an important constant called *Avogadro's number*, is 6.02×10^{23}. This is the number of hydrogen molecules in 2 gm of hydrogen, of oxygen molecules in 32 gm of oxygen, etc. Although introduced here in terms of the gram-molecular volume of gases, its significance is not restricted to gases; it is the number of molecules present in one gram-molecular weight (or *atoms* in one *gram-atomic* weight) of any substance.

To try to gain an idea of the size of Avogadro's number, we may make a comparison. The distance between the earth and the sun is approximately 93 million miles, or 1.5×10^{14} millimeters. If a chain were constructed having 6×10^{23} links, each a millimeter in length, it could be stretched to the sun and back a total of two billion times! No human lifespan could possibly suffice for counting 6×10^{23} objects of any kind, and a number of such magnitude is beyond our sensory comprehension. Conversely, atoms are incomprehensibly small. With Avogadro's number we can calculate the mass of an individual atom: since 1 gram-atomic weight of hydrogen, 1.01 gm, contains 6.02×10^{23} atoms, each must weigh $1.01/6.02 \times 10^{23}$ gm $= 1.66 \times 10^{-24}$ gm. Again, a mass so small lies entirely outside our range of sensory experience.

8–8 Summary

The great variety and complexity of chemical substances is simplified by a consistent shorthand notation. Atoms of elements are represented by letter symbols corresponding to abbreviations of their names (although not always their English language names). A single molecule of any substance may be represented by a formula showing the kind and number of atoms it comprises, for example, H_2O, CO_2. The names of many compounds also carry chemical information, in accord with a set of systematic conventional terms. Chemical reactions are simply and conveniently represented by equations between the reactant and product substances; in balanced equations the molecular formulas have numerical coefficients so that the total number of atoms of any given kind is the same on the left and on the right, although their molecular distribution is different. With the aid of a table of atomic weights, a chemical equation exhibits the weight relations involved in any chemical reaction, and the law of combining volumes may be applied to obtain information on the volumes of gaseous reactants and products.

REFERENCES

The material of this chapter is covered (in more detail than is given here) in standard introductory chemistry texts. See, for example, H. H. Sisler and others, *General Chemistry, A Systematic Approach*.

1. Assign appropriate chemical names to each of the following compounds:

RbCl $CdSO_3$

HNO_3 HI

CaC_2 $PbCO_3$

BaI_2 MgO

$SrSO_4$ KCN

$Ca_3(PO_4)_2$ $NaClO_4$

NH_4CN Ag_2Se

Al_2S_3 H_2SO_4

SiC $KMnO_4$

2. Assign appropriate chemical names to the following compounds:

ICl and ICl_3,

$Mn_2(SO_4)_3$ and $MnSO_4$,

Hg_2O and HgO,

SnO and SnO_2,

$OsCl_2$, $OsCl_3$, $OsCl_4$, OsF_6 and OsF_8.

3. Translate the following chemical equations into word sentences:

(a) $Cu_2O + H_2 \rightarrow 2Cu + H_2O$,

(b) $NH_4NO_3 \rightarrow N_2O + 2H_2O$

(c) $4FeCrO_4 + 8K_2CO_3 + 7O_2 \rightarrow 2Fe_2O_3 + 8K_2CrO_4 + 8CO_2 \uparrow$,

(d) $4NH_3 + 5O_2 \rightarrow 4NO + 6H_2O$.

4. Write balanced equations for each of the following chemical changes:

(a) The formation of phosphorus pentoxide (P_2O_5) from the elements phosphorus (P_4) and oxygen.

(b) The reaction between nitric oxide and oxygen to form nitrogen dioxide.

(c) The reaction between cupric nitrate and phosphoric acid (H_3PO_4) to form cupric phosphate and nitric acid.

(d) The reaction between silicon dioxide and hydrofluoric acid to form silicon tetrafluoride and water.

(e) The reaction between ferric oxide (Fe_2O_3) and carbon monoxide to form iron metal and carbon dioxide.

5. How much nitric acid can be produced from 1 kgm of nitrogen dioxide in the reaction below? [Ans.: 0.875 kgm]

$$3NO_2 + H_2O \rightarrow 2HNO_3 + NO \uparrow.$$

6. What quantity of uranium metal could be recovered from one ton of the oxide U_3O_8? (U_3O_8 is the chemical form of uranium found in the mineral *pitchblende*.) [Ans.: 1700 lb]

7. Calculate the weight of chromic oxide produced by decomposition of 25.2 gm of ammonium dichromate according to the equation

$$(NH_4)_2Cr_2O_7 \rightarrow N_2 \uparrow + Cr_2O_3 + 4H_2O.$$

What volume of nitrogen gas, measured at STP, is evolved during this decomposition? [Ans.: 15.2 gm of chromic oxide; 2.24 liters of nitrogen]

8. Calcium carbide (CaC_2) is a convenient source of acetylene gas (C_2H_2) by virtue of the reaction

$$CaC_2 + 2H_2O \rightarrow C_2H_2 \uparrow + Ca(OH)_2.$$

If an oxyacetylene torch burns acetylene at the rate of 1 liter (STP) per minute, what weight of CaC_2 would be required to supply it for one hour? [*Ans.*: 172 gm]

9. A compound of fluorine and iodine contains 51.2% of fluorine by weight. Find its formula and write a balanced equation for its formation from the elements.

10. A compound of calcium, carbon, and oxygen contains 48.0% of oxygen and 12.0% of carbon by weight. What is its formula?

11. Calculate the (approximate) number of individual hydrogen and oxygen atoms which combine in the formation of one milligram (0.001 gm) of water.

12. (a) Compute the mass of an individual atom of gold.

(b) The density of gold is 19.3 gm/cm^3. If you make the (dubious) assumption that gold atoms are minute cubes packed tightly together in the solid, can you calculate the volume occupied by each atom?

(c) Does your result in (b) give you any insight into the approximate dimensions of a gold atom? Compute the length of one side of the assumed cube.

CHAPTER 9

PERIODIC CLASSIFICATION OF THE ELEMENTS

Lavoisier's list of the elements, published in 1789, contained only 26 of those that appear in modern tables. Between his time and our own 75 elements have been discovered, bringing the total to 101. This fact provides an index to the rate of growth of chemistry in the past century and a half, though not of chemical science *alone*: the discoveries of many of the elements have resulted from important developments in related fields. Some of these developments will be traced later in our story, but we may note in advance that early in the 19th century, for example, Volta's discovery of the electric battery enabled Sir Humphrey Davy to prepare the elements sodium, potassium, magnesium, calcium, strontium, and barium. In mid-19th century, study of the properties of light with an instrument called the spectroscope led Bunsen and Kirchhoff to discover cesium and rubidium. The late 19th-century researches of Rayleigh and Ramsay, dependent in part upon newly developed gas-liquefaction techniques, led to the discovery that the atmosphere contains traces of several hitherto unsuspected elements, the inert gases helium, neon, argon, krypton, and xenon. In the 20th century, investigation of radioactivity has resulted in many additions to the list of elements, including radium, the most celebrated find of Pierre and Marie Curie. Eleven of the elements discovered since 1940 do not occur naturally in the earth's crust, but are produced by recently developed "artificial" means.

To the chemists of Lavoisier's time the existence of as many as 26 elements was a great surprise. Since antiquity "the elements" had implied a *small number* of kinds of irreducible, primordial matter, e.g., the Four Elements of Aristotle. An attempt to restore simplicity to the growing list of elements was made by the English physician William Prout (1785-1850) in 1815. Observing that most of the atomic weights then determined were approximately integral multiples of the atomic weight of hydrogen, he suggested that all heavier atoms may be composed of hydrogen atoms in varying numbers. On this basis there would be but a *single* primordial matter, hydrogen, of which all other matter is composed. Prout's hypothesis, amply supported by the atomic weight data of 1815, was attractive, and for a time widely held. Later, more accurate weight determinations showed that no elemental atomic weight is an *exact* multiple of that of hydrogen, and that some are very different from multiples (e.g., chlorine, atomic weight 35.46), as we have seen in Chapter 7. That the hypothesis nevertheless contained an important germ of truth, and that the hydrogen atom *has* turned out to be a building block of other atoms, is a 20th-century tale to which we shall return in a later chapter.

Prout's hypothesis was but one manifestation of a widespread 19th-century search for order among the elements. Similarities in the properties of several groups of elements had long been apparent. Just as Kepler, 300 years earlier, had applied himself to a search for the regularities of planetary motion, the minds of many 19th-century chemists were captivated by the possibility of discoverable regularity in the properties of the elements. The search, aided by steady growth in the list of elements and by important new conceptual developments in chemistry, finally rewarded the Russian chemist Dmitri Ivanovich Mendeleyev (1834–1907) with success in 1869. Before considering the nature of the discovery itself, we shall have to examine some of the background essential to it.

9–1 Metals and nonmetals

Perhaps the simplest (and oldest) classification scheme of the elements consists of the two categories *metal* and *nonmetal*. The properties most generally associated with the first category are metallic luster and marked ability to conduct heat and electricity, properties which nonmetals (e.g., sulfur) lack. Metals in general exhibit a strong tendency to combine chemically with nonmetals, but not with one another. While nonmetallic elements frequently do combine with each other (nitrogen forms several compounds with oxygen, for example) their reactions with metals are usually more vigorous than those with fellow nonmetals. Metals outnumber nonmetals, in the list of elements, by a rather large majority.

Both metallic and nonmetallic elements exhibit gradations in the properties typical of their classes. A property typical of some metals is ability to liberate hydrogen from water; the reaction between sodium and water, for example, is summarized by the equation

$$2Na + 2H_2O \rightarrow H_2\uparrow + 2NaOH.$$

Cesium, potassium, and calcium are also capable of liberating hydrogen from water, and qualitative observation readily shows that cesium does so much more vigorously than potassium, potassium more vigorously than sodium, and calcium less vigorously than sodium. Magnesium cannot liberate hydrogen from liquid water at ordinary temperatures, yet does react with steam at high temperature. Zinc, iron, and tin are examples of metals which cannot liberate hydrogen from water, but can liberate it from solutions of acids:

$$Zn + 2HCl \rightarrow H_2\uparrow + ZnCl_2.$$

Copper, gold, and other elements, although typically metallic in most properties, cannot liberate hydrogen from either water or acids. Thus there is continual gradation in this property, from very *active* cesium to *inactive* gold. Similarly, gradation is observed in the vigor of typical nonmetal reactions, such as combination with sodium. Fluorine and oxygen are the most active of the nonmetals, selenium and iodine among the least active.

Because there are gradations in properties, the metal-nonmetal division of elements is not a sharp one. Between the most strongly metallic and nonmetallic elements lie all those of intermediate character, including some that do not belong to either camp. Examples of such "borderline" elements are boron, silicon, germanium, arsenic, and tellurium. The last-named element, for example, has metallic luster and conducts electric current, although very slightly in comparison with iron and copper. Most (but not all) of its *chemical* properties are those of a nonmetal, however. "Borderline" elements thus have some of the properties of both metals and nonmetals. The unique inert gases, with none of the properties of either class, add further to the list of elements that cannot be placed in so simple a classification.

9-2 The concept of valence

The task of seeking relations among properties of elements within the broad classes metal and nonmetal was considerably lightened, in 1852, by the emergence of a useful concept called *valence*. This concept, proposed by the English chemist Edward Frankland (1825-1899), attempts to express the *relative capacities of atoms for combination with one another*. Its application depends upon the successful determination of formulas for great numbers of individual compounds.

Let us examine the formulas for the oxides and chlorides of a number of elements, as shown in Table 9-1. One oxygen atom combines with *two* atoms of lithium, sodium, or potassium, but a single chlorine atom combines with only *one* atom of each of these elements. One oxygen atom combines with a single atom of beryllium, magnesium, or calcium, but two chlorine atoms are required to combine with one atom of each. For each of the first six elements in Table 9-1, we could say that the *combining capacity of oxygen is just twice that of chlorine*. Similarly, 3 oxygen atoms to 2 aluminum atoms indicates twice as much combining capacity as 3 chlorine atoms to 1 aluminum atom. Comparing CO_2 with CCl_4 (ignoring CO, which has no chloride counterpart), FeO with $FeCl_2$, Fe_2O_3 with $FeCl_3$, etc., we

TABLE 9–1

FORMULAS FOR THE OXIDES AND CHLORIDES OF SEVERAL ELEMENTS

Element	Formula for oxide	Formula for chloride
Lithium	Li_2O	$LiCl$
Sodium	Na_2O	$NaCl$
Potassium	K_2O	KCl
Beryllium	BeO	$BeCl_2$
Magnesium	MgO	$MgCl_2$
Calcium	CaO	$CaCl_2$
Aluminum	Al_2O_3	$AlCl_3$
Carbon	CO_2 (and CO)	CCl_4
Iron	FeO and Fe_2O_3	$FeCl_2$ and $FeCl_3$
Copper	Cu_2O and CuO	$CuCl$ and $CuCl_2$
Tin	SnO and SnO_2	$SnCl_2$ and $SnCl_4$

can conclude that in all these pairs of compounds the combining capacity of oxygen, its *valence*, is twice that of chlorine.

Further inspection of Table 9–1 reveals that the elements lithium, sodium, and potassium all have the same valence, equal to that of chlorine and just half that of oxygen. Moreover, the combining power exhibited in common by beryllium, magnesium, and calcium is equal to that of oxygen and twice that of chlorine, lithium, sodium, and potassium. Aluminum and ferric iron have valences three times, carbon (in CO_2 and CCl_4) and stannic tin four times, ferrous iron, cupric copper, and stannous tin twice, the valence of chlorine. The valence of cuprous copper, half that of cupric copper, is equal to that of chlorine.

A numerical scale of valences of the elements has been built up from intercomparisons similar to those of the preceding paragraphs. When all the elements are considered it is found that, except for the inert gases that have no tendency to combine at all, chlorine is among the elements whose atoms have the smallest capacity for combination with others. Assigning the valence number 1 to chlorine and other elements in this category, which includes hydrogen, bromine, iodine, lithium, sodium, and potassium, we may then proceed to assign appropriate numbers to elements with different combining powers. Oxygen, having twice the combining capacity of chlorine, is assigned the valence number 2, as are beryllium, magnesium, and calcium; aluminum and ferric iron have valence 3, carbon (in many of

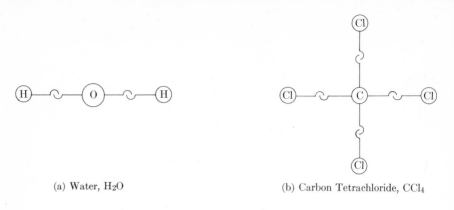

(a) Water, H₂O   (b) Carbon Tetrachloride, CCl₄

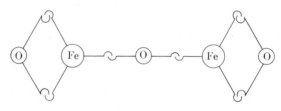

(c) Ferric Oxide, Fe₂O₃

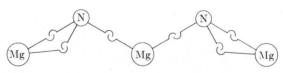

(d) Magnesium Nitride, Mg₃N₂

FIG. 9–1. Imaginary representations of molecules composed of atoms with "valence hooks."

its compounds) and stannic tin have valence 4, ferrous iron and cupric copper have valence 2.

At this stage in our account of scientific development we cannot *explain* the valence concept, but may make use of it, as it was introduced, empirically. It may be helpful to think of the valence of an element as indicating a number of (imaginary) hooks on its individual atoms, each of which must be satisfied during compound formation by engaging a complementary hook from another atom. An oxygen atom, for example, would have two hooks, a hydrogen atom one; formation of a water molecule would then require that two hydrogen atoms hook onto each oxygen atom, as indicated in Fig. 9–1. In ferric oxide each iron atom has three such imaginary hooks, so that binding with oxygen atoms, each having two hooks, would require two iron atoms and three oxygen atoms. Carbon tetrachloride and magnesium nitride are also represented in Fig. 9–1.

Many elements in addition to the last three of Table 9–1 exhibit more than one valence. The valence of 1 which we have assigned to chlorine, for example, is nearly always valid for that element in simple two-element compounds, but in other compounds chlorine may show valences as high as 7. We already know something of the series of nitrogen oxides, in which the valence of nitrogen ranges from 1 in N_2O to 5 in N_2O_5. It is helpful to remember some elements whose valences are invariable. In the compounds of hydrogen, lithium, sodium, and potassium, these elements always exhibit a valence of 1. The valence of combined oxygen is always 2 except in those compounds, which we shall rarely encounter here, called peroxides, e.g., hydrogen peroxide, H_2O_2. The valences of magnesium and calcium in their compounds are always 2, and that of combined aluminum is always 3.*

9–3 Families of elements

Early in the 19th century it became clear that while no two elements are identical, some of them do display similarities so strong that they might be said to belong to the same "family." With steadily increasing chemical discovery, and with the valence concept as a guide, scientists were able to delineate such groups, and to explore the extent of similarity within them. Let us illustrate the meaning of elemental family characteristics by describing the properties of several of these groups.

The elements fluorine, chlorine, bromine, and iodine, here listed in order of increasing atomic weight, constitute the family of elements called *halogens*.† They are all nonmetals, with atomic weights ranging from 19 (F) to 127 (I). Fluorine and chlorine are gases at ordinary temperatures, bromine is a liquid and iodine a solid; there is a regular increase in their boiling points with atomic weight, i.e., fluorine boils at −187°C, chlorine at −35°C, bromine at +59°C, and iodine at +184°C. Fluorine is pale yellow, chlorine greenish yellow, bromine reddish brown, and iodine deep violet. The order of their nonmetallic activities, as reflected by the relative vigor of their reactions with sodium, for example, is that of decreasing atomic weight; fluorine is in fact the most active of all the nonmetals. In simple compounds (*halides*) containing a halogen plus one other element, all of the

---

*The convention of expressing valences as either plus or minus, which we have omitted thus far, contributes greatly to facility in use of the valence concept. We shall delay its introduction until we are in a position to understand its true significance, however.

†A fifth member, *astatine*, is among the elements of recent discovery. Its properties are so little known that we cannot discuss it on a par with the others, however.

halogens exhibit valence 1. Their hydrogen compounds, HF, HCl, HBr, and HI, are all acids. They all combine readily with metals to form compounds of a class called *salts*. (The name halogen, derived from the Greek, means "salt former.") Formulas for some halide salts are: NaF, NaCl, NaBr, NaI, CaF_2, $CaCl_2$, $CaBr_2$, and CaI_2. Finally, the vapors of the elemental halogens all consist of diatomic molecules: F_2, Cl_2, Br_2, and I_2.

It is evident from the above paragraph that family character involves both gradations and absolute similarities. Thus the properties nonmetallic activity and boiling point vary in a regular way through the halogen group, while predominant valence remains fixed. Both kinds of group character are important, and we shall see them recurring in our further examples.

The *alkali metals* consist of the elements lithium, sodium, potassium, rubidium, and cesium.* Their atomic weights range from 6.94 (Li) to 133 (Cs). They exhibit regular gradation in melting point, ranging from 186°C (Li) to 28.5°C (Cs). They are "light" metals, the highest density (1.99 gm/cm^3) being that of cesium and the lowest (0.53 gm/cm^3) that of lithium. They are all very active metals, capable of liberating hydrogen from water. The order of their increasing activity lies with *in*creasing atomic weight, and cesium is the most strongly metallic of all the elements. If exposed to air these metals combine readily with the oxygen of the atmosphere. All of them have the single valence 1, and hence their compounds with other elements all have similar formulas: LiCl, NaCl, KCl, RbCl, CsCl; Li_2O, Na_2O, K_2O, Rb_2O, Cs_2O.

The *alkaline earth metals* are a family consisting of the elements beryllium, magnesium, calcium, strontium, barium, and radium, ranging in atomic weight from 9.2 (Be) to 226 (Ra). They are all active metals, although generally less so than the alkali metals, and like the alkali metals they exhibit increasing activity with increasing atomic weight. In their compounds they show but one valence, 2. All form chlorides that are water-soluble, and carbonates that are insoluble in water.

The elements oxygen, sulfur, selenium, tellurium, and polonium constitute a family known as the *oxygen group*. Here the evidences of group character are not as striking as in the other families we have discussed. Oxygen is strongly nonmetallic, but we have previously noted tellurium as an element on the metal-nonmetal border; although not a "true" metal, polonium is more metallic than tellurium. Yet this apparent lack of group character fits in well with the kind of gradation we have observed in other groups: nonmetallic activity *de*creases with increasing atomic weight or, alternatively phrased, metallic character *in*creases. Oxygen, as we have

---

*Again, recent discovery has turned up a new member of this group, *francium*; its properties, like those of astatine, are too little explored to form a part of this discussion.

seen, has a characteristic valence 2 which is very nearly its only valence. The other elements exhibit different valences as well, but 2 is a characteristic valence of the group. All of the oxygen group elements form compounds with hydrogen, for example, with formulas H_2O, H_2S, H_2Se, H_2Te, and H_2Po.

As a final example we shall mention the inert gas family, consisting of helium, neon, argon, krypton, xenon, and radon. None of these elements, it must be stressed, had been isolated by 1869, the year of Mendeleyev's discovery of the periodic law. Although the presence of helium in the sun had been detected by Norman Lockyer in 1868 (see Chapter 18), the first detection of an inert gas on the earth came in 1894, when argon was discovered in the atmosphere. In 1892 Lord Rayleigh (1842–1919) had observed that the density of nitrogen prepared by removal of oxygen from air is slightly higher than that prepared by decomposition of nitrogen-containing compounds such as ammonia. This observation led him to suppose that air contained a previously unsuspected constituent. In collaboration with Sir William Ramsay (1852–1916) he performed experiments which resulted in separation of nitrogen and the new gas, argon. Ramsay, in succeeding years, discovered the gases neon, krypton, and xenon by distilling *liquefied* argon prepared from the atmosphere. Of the inert gases found in air, argon (constituting 0.93% by volume) is most abundant, and xenon ($8 \times 10^{-6}\%$ by volume) the least abundant. Helium and radon were discovered as constituents of radioactive minerals, and traces of the former were ultimately found in the atmosphere.

The outstanding characteristic of this group of elements is *lack* of chemical properties: its members do not enter into chemical combinations. The valence is thus zero, i.e., inert gas atoms have *no* combining capacity. They do not even combine with each other to form diatomic molecules, as do the atoms of hydrogen, nitrogen, oxygen, and the halogens. In physical properties the inert gases show gradations similar to those observed in other groups. Their boiling points, for example, increase regularly from $-269°C$ for helium (the lowest boiling point for any substance) to $-62°C$ for radon.

9–4 Mendeleyev's periodic law

By the middle of the 19th century at least five distinct groups of elements were known. Recognition of families had been stimulated (in part) by the observation of J. W. Döbereiner (1780–1849) in 1829 that the atomic weight of strontium is very nearly equal to the *average* of the atomic weights of calcium and barium.* Similar "triad" relations were soon observed within

---

*With modern atomic weights, [40.1 (calcium) + 137.4 (barium)]/2 = 88.7, and the observed atomic weight of strontium is 87.6. Döbereiner offered no explanation for his "triads," and no complete one can be given today.

other groups, e.g., chlorine, bromine, iodine. Growth in the list of elemental families, combined with this evidence of atomic weight regularities within them, produced several attempts to correlate, systematically, the atomic weights and properties of *all* the known elements. J. A. R. Newlands (1836–1898), for example, proposed a "law of octaves" in 1863, according to which properties are repeated at equal intervals when the elements are arranged in order of increasing atomic weight. While Newlands' proposal proved incapable of systematizing the properties of more than a few of the elements, it represented a tentative foray in a direction later pursued, with brilliant success, by Mendeleyev.

The first three of Newlands' "octaves" are shown below:

1	2	3	4	5	6	7
H	Li	Be	B	C	N	O
8	9	10	11	12	13	14
F	Na	Mg	Al	Si	P	S
15	16	17	18	19	20	21
Cl	K	Ca	Cr	Ti	Mn	Fe

According to his "law" the elements in vertical columns should resemble one another closely. With the exception of hydrogen and fluorine, pairs of elements in the first two "octaves" *do* show strong mutual resemblances. The scheme breaks down entirely after Newlands' element 17, however; chromium, titanium, manganese, and iron do not resemble the elements listed above them.

Mendeleyev, fourteenth child of a Siberian school teacher, journeyed thousands of miles to St. Petersburg for schooling. He arrived in that city in 1848 at the age of 14, and rose to great prominence as a professor in its university between the years 1867 and 1890. His contributions to chemical science were many and important, but he is best remembered for his Periodic Law and periodic classification of the elements. Actually, the Periodic Law was independently and nearly simultaneously developed by Mendeleyev in Russia and Lothar Meyer (1830–1895) in Germany. Its association with the single name of Mendeleyev is quite justifiable, however, in terms of the greater wealth of application achieved by the Russian chemist.

If the word *periodic* is understood to mean *repeating at intervals*, the best statement of the Periodic Law is that of Mendeleyev himself: *"The properties of the elements are in periodic dependence upon their atomic weights."* In other words, if the elements are arranged in order of increasing atomic weight, their properties will be observed to go through a repeated cycle of

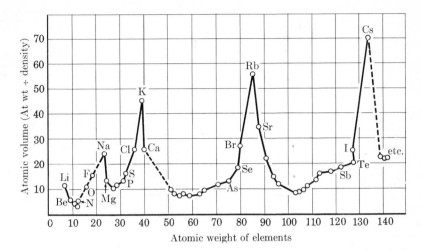

Fig. 9–2. Periodic variation in atomic volumes of the elements. (After Lothar Meyer's original plot, but using modern values; density values employed have been measured at the melting points of the elements.)

changes, similar elements appearing at intervals. An excellent illustration of such periodicity, first employed by Lothar Meyer, is afforded by the physical property of *atomic volume*. The atomic volume of an element, or the volume occupied by one gram-atomic weight, is simply determined by dividing atomic weight by density. Figure 9–2 is a graph of the atomic volumes of the elements plotted against their atomic weights. The curve is cyclic, or *periodic*; it reaches to successively higher maxima, each of which corresponds to one of the elements in the alkali metal family. Points representative of similar elements appear, from cycle to cycle, in fixed positions with respect to the members of neighboring families.

It is true that the Periodic Law was anticipated in the proposal of Newlands. Mendeleyev's brilliance manifested itself in his application of the law to achieve a workable *periodic classification* of the elements. Where Newlands had sought repeating periods of seven members each throughout the list of known elements, Mendeleyev allowed himself to be guided by the properties of the elements themselves, without apparent preconception about the sizes of periodic intervals. One of Mendeleyev's principal guides was valence. Because the element tin, like carbon and silicon, exhibits a valence of 4, for example, he dared to group it with those elements despite the fact that it is a metal, which carbon and silicon are not.

The earliest (1869) version of Mendeleyev's periodic table of the elements is shown in Table 9–2. In this version six *periods* of elements,

TABLE 9–2

MENDELEYEV'S PERIODIC TABLE, 1869

				Ti = 50	Zr = 90	? = 180
				V = 51	Nb = 94	Ta = 182
				Cr = 52	Mo = 96	W = 186
				Mn = 55	Rh = 104.4	Pt = 197.4
				Fe = 56	Ru = 104.4	Ir = 198
				Ni Co = 59	Pd = 106.6	Os = 199
H = 1				Cu = 63.4	Ag = 108	Hg = 200
	Be = 9.4	Mg = 24		Zn = 65.2	Cd = 112	
	B = 11	Al = 27.4		? = 68	U = 116	Au = 197?
	C = 12	Si = 28		? = 70	Sn = 118	
	N = 14	P = 31		As = 75	Sb = 122	Bi = 210?
	O = 16	S = 32		Se = 79.4	Te = 128?	
	F = 19	Cl = 35.5		Br = 80	I = 127	
Li = 7	Na = 23	K = 39		Rb = 85.4	Cs = 133	Tl = 204
		Ca = 40		Sr = 87.6	Ba = 137	Pb = 207
		? = 45		Ce = 92		
		?Er = 56		La = 94		
		?Yt = 60		Dy = 95		
		?In = 75.6		Th = 118?		

throughout which atomic weight steadily increases, read vertically; *groups* of presumably similar elements are shown in horizontal rows. His first period consists solely of the two elements hydrogen and lithium, with the former set off by itself to indicate lack of similarity to any other known element. (Helium, which falls between hydrogen and lithium in atomic weight, was not yet known.) His second period consists of seven elements, each the first member of a family group except for sodium, which is brought into line with lithium. The next seven elements fall neatly in place on the basis of their similarities with members of the second period, but with calcium Mendeleyev began an extension which brought his third period to a total of twelve elements. Although calcium resembles beryllium and magnesium, there are many elements which follow it in ascending order of atomic weight that do not resemble aluminum, silicon, phosphorus, sulfur, chlorine or potassium; it was thus impossible to begin a new period with calcium. In fact, the fourth period was difficult: the next elements showing resemblances to members of the third period were zinc, similar to magnesium, and arsenic, similar to phosphorus.* Accordingly, Mendeleyev not only lengthened his third period, but began his fourth as shown, proposing that all known elements between potassium and zinc are first members of new families.

Table 9-2, a museum piece, is reproduced here to illustrate Mendeleyev's method of attack on the problem of periodic classification. One of the most revealing features of the table consists of the question marks it contains. Question marks alongside atomic weight values indicate serious doubts, in Mendeleyev's mind, of their validity. Question marks adjacent to elemental symbols indicate elements then of recent and insufficiently confirmed discovery. And finally, question marks in the place of elemental symbols represent undiscovered elements; in constructing his periodic table Mendeleyev had to make allowance for elements whose very existence was unknown to him.

Uncertainties in atomic weights led to occasional serious misplacements in Mendeleyev's first periodic table. One need only compare the atomic weight given for thorium (Th) in Table 9-2 with that of Table 7-4 to appreciate how right Mendeleyev was in questioning it. The uncertainty indicated for the atomic weight of tellurium (Te) reveals some of the assurance with which he applied his ideas. If the elements tellurium and iodine had been arranged in order of increasing atomic weight, as his basic approach required, iodine would have come next to selenium and tellurium next to bromine, while their properties strongly suggest that they belong the other way around. Rather than construe this as a failure of his classification, Mendeleyev challenged the accuracy of the atomic weight data available to him. In the manuscript accompanying his first periodic table he asserted positively that careful redetermination of these two atomic weights should reveal that iodine atoms are heavier than tellurium atoms. While subsequent research has failed to confirm this prediction, Mendeleyev's relative placement of tellurium and iodine was quite correct. This pair of elements constitutes one of three *inversion* anomalies which persist in modern versions of the periodic table. [The others are argon (39.944), which precedes potassium (39.096) in the table, and cobalt (58.94), which precedes nickel (58.69).]

Nowhere was Mendeleyev's brilliance evinced more spectacularly than in his handling of the problem of missing elements. As shown in Table 9-2, he

---

*Calcium resembles magnesium much more strongly than does zinc, as Mendeleyev was aware; at the time, this grouping was the only way he could find to cope with the problem of *intervening* elements, Ti, V, Cr, etc. It did have the virtue of grouping Ca, Sr, and Ba together, and of placing Cd, which strongly resembles Zn, on the same horizontal line with that element. The similarity of As and P (in fact, the family character of the entire group N, P, As, Sb, and Bi) had been well established by 1869.

TABLE 9-3

PREDICTED AND OBSERVED PROPERTIES OF GERMANIUM

Mendeleyev's prediction (1871) for the undiscovered element he called eka-silicon (Es)	Observed properties of germanium, discovered by Winkler in 1885
1. Atomic weight = 72.	1. Atomic weight = 72.60.
2. Es a dark gray metal, with high melting point and density = 5.5.	2. Ge is dark gray; melting point = 958°C, density = 5.36.
3. Es only slightly attacked by acids, resistant to alkalies such as NaOH.	3. Ge not attacked by HCl, but dissolved by concentrated HNO_3; not attacked by NaOH.
4. Es will form oxide EsO_2 on heating; EsO_2 will have high melting point and density = 4.7.	4. Ge forms oxide GeO_2, with melting point 1100°C, density = 4.70.
5. Es will form a sulfide EsS_2 which is insoluble in water but soluble in ammonium sulfide.	5. Ge forms sulfide GeS_2, which is insoluble in water but soluble in ammonium sulfide.
6. Es will form a chloride $EsCl_4$, with boiling point a little less than 100°C and density = 1.9.	6. Ge forms chloride $GeCl_4$, with boiling point 83°C and density 1.88.
7. Es will be formed upon reaction of EsO_2 or K_2EsF_6 with sodium metal.	7. Ge is formed by reaction of K_2GeF_6 with sodium.

had concluded that there must be two undiscovered elements with atomic weights between those of zinc and arsenic. Certain of their existence, by 1871 he had made very detailed predictions of the properties of these two elements and of a third, immediately following calcium in atomic weight. His predictions were based on the group characters of the families he expected the new elements to join, observed gradations of properties within those families, and expected dissimilarities between neighboring elements within the periods involved. In direct consequence the element *gallium* was discovered in 1874, filling the gap immediately below zinc, *scandium* in 1879, fitting below calcium, and *germanium* in 1885, filling the second gap below zinc. In all three cases Mendeleyev's predicted properties were remarkably close to the observed properties of the newly discovered elements. Table 9–3 shows just how close, in the case of germanium. Mendeleyev's periodic table, of which we have seen only the first rather crude and imperfect version, underwent many revisions at his hands. In the course of improving it, he made bold predictions of the properties of several more undiscovered elements. None of his other predictions was quite so striking as that for germanium (Table 9–3), but nearly all were confirmed to a considerable extent. Mendeleyev's classification was not highly regarded in its early years, but the prescience of his predictions could not fail to impress the scientific community, and by 1900 the table had become an indispensable part of chemical science. It is not necessary for us to consider the various stages of evolution of this classification between 1869 and the present. The essential ideas underlying Mendeleyev's earliest work continue to underlie today's complete periodic table, which we shall now examine.

9–5 The modern periodic table

There are several forms of the periodic table of elements in current use, but we shall confine ourselves to the form shown in Fig. 9–3. Each element is represented by its symbol, and beneath the symbol of each element is shown its atomic weight, those few which are known only approximately being bracketed.* The order of increasing atomic weight, with the exception of the three inversions mentioned in the previous section, is from left to right in horizontal rows. The number placed over each elemental symbol, called the *atomic number*, indicates the order of appearance of that element in the periodic classification.

Each horizontal row in the periodic table is called a *period* of elements. The first of the seven periods consists solely of the elements hydrogen and helium. The second and third periods contain eight elements each, the fourth and fifth eighteen elements each. The sixth period contains thirty-two elements, fourteen of which, called the *lanthanide rare earths*, are set off by themselves for reasons of space, under the main part of the table. The positions these elements would occupy in a table of adequate width are indicated in the table, between the elements lanthanum (La) and hafnium (Hf). The seventh and final period is an incomplete one containing fifteen elements. Twelve of these, called *actinide rare earth elements*, belong in

---

*The eleven elements 43, 61, and 93–101 are those which have only "artificial" existence, i.e., their natural occurrence has not been detected in the earth's crust. Most of them occur in several forms (isotopes), and each bracketed number is an approximate atomic weight value for only one (the most prominent) of these forms. The same is true of elements 85 and 87, which are naturally occurring radioactive elements of very fleeting existence.

The periodic table of elements.

Periods / Groups →

	1a	2a	3b	4b	5b	6b	7b	8b			1b	2b	3a	4a	5a	6a	7a	0
1	1 H 1.0080																	2 He 4.003
2	3 Li 6.940	4 Be 9.013											5 B 10.82	6 C 12.010	7 N 14.008	8 O 16.0000	9 F 19.00	10 Ne 20.183
3	11 Na 22.991	12 Mg 24.32											13 Al 26.98	14 Si 28.09	15 P 30.975	16 S 32.066	17 Cl 35.457	18 A 39.944
4	19 K 39.100	20 Ca 40.08	21 Sc 44.96	22 Ti 47.90	23 V 50.95	24 Cr 52.01	25 Mn 54.93	26 Fe 55.85	27 Co 58.94	28 Ni 58.69	29 Cu 63.54	30 Zn 65.38	31 Ga 69.72	32 Ge 72.60	33 As 74.91	34 Se 78.96	35 Br 79.916	36 Kr 83.80
5	37 Rb 85.48	38 Sr 87.63	39 Y 88.92	40 Zr 91.22	41 Nb 92.91	42 Mo 95.95	43 Tc [99]	44 Ru 101.7	45 Rh 102.91	46 Pd 106.7	47 Ag 107.880	48 Cd 112.41	49 In 114.76	50 Sn 118.70	51 Sb 121.76	52 Te 127.61	53 I 126.91	54 Xe 131.3
6	55 Cs 132.91	56 Ba 137.36	57 La 138.92 (58–71 *)	72 Hf 178.6	73 Ta 180.88	74 W 183.92	75 Re 186.31	76 Os 190.2	77 Ir 193.1	78 Pt 195.23	79 Au 197.2	80 Hg 200.61	81 Tl 204.39	82 Pb 207.21	83 Bi 209.00	84 Po 210	85 At [210]	86 Rn 222
7	87 Fr [223]	88 Ra 226.05	89 Ac 227 (90–101 **)															

Transition Elements

*Lanthanide rare earth elements

58 Ce 140.13	59 Pr 140.92	60 Nd 144.27	61 Pm [145]	62 Sm 150.43	63 Eu 152.0	64 Gd 156.9	65 Tb 158.9	66 Dy 162.46	67 Ho 164.94	68 Er 167.2	69 Tm 168.9	70 Yb 173.04	71 Lu 174.99

**Actinide rare earth elements

90 Th 232.12	91 Pa 231	92 U 238.07	93 Np [237]	94 Pu [239]	95 Am [243]	96 Cm [243]	97 Bk [245]	98 Cf [246]	99 E [253]	100 Fm [255]	101 Mv [256]

FIG. 9–3. The periodic table of elements.

positions below the lanthanide rare earths for chemical reasons, and are shown in these positions beneath the main part of the table.

When the elements are arranged as shown in Fig. 9–3 it is found that elements with similar properties occur in vertical columns, called groups. Excluding the two series of rare earth elements, we see that sixteen distinct groups, or families of elements, are recognized in this classification. The groups we discussed in Section 9–3 are easily found: the alkali metals constitute group 1a, alkaline earth metals group 2a, oxygen group elements group 6a, halogens group 7a, and inert gases group 0. The eight groups designated 1a through 7a and 0 are known collectively as *main groups*. The second and third periods contain only elements in these groups. Elements in the groups designated 1b through 8b are known collectively as *transition* elements. Vertical resemblances, generally speaking, are less strong within b groups than within main groups. The group 8b, for historical reasons dating back to Mendeleyev, contains *three* elements from each of the 4th, 5th, and 6th periods, instead of the usual single entry per period.

The unique nature of the element hydrogen is emphasized, in Fig. 9–3, by its offset position. It does not fit into any of the groups of the periodic table, although because of its unit valence it is placed in some tables as a member of both 1a and 7a. Aside from the similarity of valence, however, it is unlike the halogens and alkali metals in nearly all respects.

Within *periods* there is systematic alteration of the properties of elements, as is shown clearly in Fig. 9–2 for the property atomic volume. It may be observed, for another example, that metals appear on the left-hand side of the table, nonmetals on the right. In following the 4th period from left to right, we find that the first element is a very active metal, potassium, the second a somewhat less active metal, calcium, after which there is a decrease in metallic activity from scandium to gallium. The elements germanium and arsenic, which follow gallium, are "borderline" cases, neither metallic nor nonmetallic, but intermediate. Then follow selenium, a mild nonmetal, and bromine, a relatively strong nonmetal. The final element of the period, krypton, is neither metal nor nonmetal, nor is it intermediate; it is an inert gas. Each complete period (except for the very first) exhibits steadily decreasing metallic activity, from left to right, similar to that of the 4th. Each begins with an active alkali metal, contains one or more "borderline" elements, and closes with a (nonmetallic) halogen followed by an inert gas. The characteristic "borderline" elements, lightly shaded in Fig. 9–3, constitute a rough line of demarkation between metals and nonmetals. This line shows both the preponderance of metals among the elements and the fact that metallic character shifts to the right in the periodic table with increasing atomic weight.

Similarities among elements in *groups*, as we have stated, are more pronounced among the main group than among the transitional elements. The latter also generally possess more complex chemical properties than the former, and we shall be concerned primarily with main group elements. It is of interest to note, however, that most of the *metallic* elements which exhibit more than one valence are to be found among the transitional elements. (Tin is a notable exception to this rule.) It may occur to the reader that the numbering of the *b* groups implies similarities between these and the corresponding main groups. There is *some* similarity between the elements of group 2*b* (Zn, Cd, and Hg) and those of group 2*a* (alkaline earth metals): it will be recalled that Mendeleyev recognized this in placing zinc and cadmium in the same row with magnesium in his first periodic table. There are also weakly discernible property analogies between the elements of groups 1*a* and 1*b*, 3*a* and 3*b*, etc., but the transition groups are best treated as unique families.

Within groups, as we have seen in Section 9–3, there are properties that are constant and others which exhibit uniform gradations. The properties density, melting point, boiling point, and atomic volume are among those that show gradations. Another is the property of metallic, or nonmetallic, activity. Lithium is the least active of the alkali metals; cesium, so far as we know by direct experiment, is the most active.* Similarly, there is steady increase in metallic activity among the alkaline earth metals of group 2*a*, from beryllium to radium. In group 4*a* carbon, a typical non-metal, is followed by the two "borderline" elements silicon and germanium, with the latter more metallic than the former; the two remaining elements of the group are typical metals. The halogens, group 7*a*, are all nonmetals, of which the most active is the first, fluorine, and the remainder progressively *less* active (as *non*metals, to be sure) with increasing atomic weight.

Just as valence was one of Mendeleyev's most valuable guides to construction of the earliest versions of the periodic table, valence relations are among the most important brought out by the modern table. Confining ourselves to the elements of main groups, we discern a definite relation between valences and group numbers. All elements of group 1*a* exhibit valence 1, all those of group 2*a* valence 2, exclusively. Within group 3*a*, 3 is the maximum and most common (though not exclusive) valence. For elements of group 4*a*, 4 is the maximum valence; it is also the most common valence for the first three elements of the group, while tin (frequently) and lead (predominantly) form compounds in which their valences are 2. Although the elements of group 5*a* show several valences, their maximum is 5 (for example, N_2O_5 and P_2O_5), and the valence most characteristic of the group is 3 (for example, NH_3 and PH_3). The most common valence for

---

*It is virtually certain, however, that the recently discovered element 87, francium, would prove more active than cesium if sufficient quantities of it could be made available to perform the appropriate experiment.

group 6a elements is 2, but again the maximum valence, exhibited by all but oxygen, is the same as the group number, 6. Finally, the characteristic halogen valence is 1, but the maximum valence exhibited by group 7a elements is 7. We may then generalize, for the main group elements: the *maximum* valence of an element is identical with the number of the (main) group in which it appears; the valences *most characteristic* of the main groups increase from 1 to 4 for groups 1a to 4a, and decrease from 3 to 1 for groups 5a to 7a. The valence of group 0, of course, is zero.

9–6 Value of the periodic classification

The historical importance of the periodic table, to chemistry, cannot be overestimated. We have seen how, in predictions such as Mendeleyev's, it served as a guide to the discovery of new elements. As successive discoveries were made, blank spaces in the table were waiting to receive the newcomers to the community of elements. In the case of the inert gases, of course, the periodic table itself had to be revised to provide the new spaces required. Today the table has virtually completed its function as a guide to discovery of new elements: all spaces are filled between 1 and 101, and it is as yet uncertain how many more elements can be added beyond 101. But the value of the periodic table is probably even greater now than before.

For those who practice chemistry, the periodic classification is indispensable to the task of systematizing the vast knowledge it embraces. Interrelations among the elements and gradations in their properties, both in periods and in groups, are all brought out by the table in a wonderfully clear and meaningful way. But it is not our purpose here to study the chemical behavior of the 101 elements in detail; for us, and in fact for science as a whole, there is a broader and more profound significance in the periodic table than its practical utility. Much of the remainder of this book will contribute to tracing the development of that significance.

We must bear in mind that Mendeleyev's discovery was *empirical*. In a search for regularity behind the profusion of properties of the many elements, he demonstrated that there is order by finding a way to *describe* it. We have noted that the inherent order among the elements is best described in terms of seven periods, of 2, 8, 8, 18, 18, 32, and 15 elements, comprising a total of 16 groups, each exhibiting internal chemical similarities. We cannot fail to admire the beauty and symmetry of this result in itself. But it is in the nature of science to go beyond mere recognition of striking natural phenomena, and find, if possible, a reasonable explanation for the phenomena.

We have already witnessed the manner in which Kepler's descriptions of the order he discerned in planetary motions became an integral part of

Newton's great synthesis, the Law of Universal Gravitation. We shall see that Mendeleyev's Periodic Law and periodic classification played a somewhat similar role in the more pervasive order that underlies the nature of matter. The properties of elements, after all, must be determined by the individual atoms that compose them, and a closer scrutiny of atoms might be expected to reveal reasons for the form of the periodic table. Means of examining the structures of individual atoms indirectly did become available to science in years subsequent to the time of Mendeleyev. To understand these methods and the discoveries to which they led, we must fortify ourselves with knowledge (important in itself) which may at first seem unrelated to Mendeleyev's problem. The mechanical concepts of work, energy, and momentum are fundamental to all science, and so, perhaps more surprisingly, are the phenomena electricity and light. Only when we have become acquainted with these subjects can we return profitably to the subject of atoms, and re-examine the periodic classification of the elements on a much deeper level.

9-7 Summary

The elements may be classified into the categories metal and nonmetal, but the division is not sharp, and there are differences of many kinds within the classes. The concept of valence, or relative atomic combining power, provides another means for grouping of the elements. Several families of elements, groups whose members have similar valences and display other strong similarities, had been recognized by mid-19th century. Mendeleyev was able to establish, in 1869, that the properties of the elements are in periodic dependence on their atomic weights, and succeeded in devising the first successful periodic classification of the elements. This was one of the great achievements of scientific history: the periodic table of elements reduced much of the complexity of chemistry to a relatively simple system, served as a guide to the discovery of new elements, and foreshadowed the beginnings of modern atomic theory. It was an empirical advance, however, and development of its further consequences required the application of concepts arising from other branches of science.

REFERENCES

FINDLAY, A., *A Hundred Years of Chemistry*, Chapters III and X.
JAFFE, B., *Crucibles, the Story of Chemistry*. Includes sketch of Mendeleyev's work.
LEICESTER, H. M., *The Historical Background of Chemistry*.
LEICESTER, H. M., and H. S. KLICKSTEIN, *A Source Book in Chemistry*, pp. 276–279 (Prout), 438–444 (Mendeleyev), 434–438 (Lothar Meyer).
PARTINGTON, J. R., *A Short History of Chemistry*, Chapter XV.
RAMSAY, W., *The Gases of the Atmosphere, the History of Their Discovery*.
SISLER, H. H., and others, *General Chemistry, a Systematic Approach*.
WEEKS, M. E., *The Discovery of the Elements*.

1. Classify the following elements according to the metal-nonmetal division: nitrogen, scandium, rubidium, astatine, osmium, palladium, radon, phosphorus, molybdenum, arsenic, lanthanum, helium, europium, niobium, bromine, uranium.

2. If the valence of oxygen is 2, of the halogens and hydrogen 1, and of nitrogen 3 wherever these elements occur in the following formulas, what are the valences of the other elements in the compounds represented?

AlN	SbH₃	BiO₂	B₂H₆

AlN   SbH₃   BiO₂   B₂H₆
C₂N₂   Ce₂O₃   CrO₃   Cu₃N   VF₅
Au₂O₂   InCl₃   PbI₂   PbO₂
MnF₃   Mn₂O₇   MoBr₄   U₃N₄   OsO₄

3. What are the names of the compounds listed in Exercise 2?

4. With the valence concept and appropriate knowledge of individual valences as guides, it is possible to write formulas for compounds, given only their names. Using specific valence information you have learned in this chapter, plus the information that the valence of ammonium and nitrate radicals is 1, sulfate radical 2, and phosphate radical 3, write what you consider the most probably correct formulas for the following compounds:

ammonium chloride gallium nitrate
stannic nitrate   ammonium sulfide
cuprous sulfide   radium bromide
cesium iodide   zinc oxide
silicon carbide   ferrous phosphate
calcium selenide   cupric phosphide

5. Assign valences to each of the elements (or radicals) in the following compounds:

AsI₅	BaCO₃	Bi₂Te₃	Ca₃As₂
Ca(ClO₄)₂	CS₂	CO	GeH
GeH₄	Au₂S	LiOH	KClO₃
MgSO₃	Au₂P₃	NiB	NiS
PCl₅	SiF₄	RbCN	Ag₃PO₄
WO₃			

6. The points in the atomic volume curve, Fig. 9–2, are based upon densities measured at the melting points of the elements. Can you think of a good reason for this? What would happen to the points for nitrogen, oxygen, and the halogens, for example, if the curve were based upon atomic volumes measured at the same temperature, say room temperature, throughout? Is the device, using melting point densities, defensible from the standpoint of establishing periodicity, or does it seem simply to "torture" the resultant curve into a desired, preconceived pattern?

7. No points for the inert gas elements are shown on Fig. 9–2, since these were unknown to Meyer and Mendeleyev. Densities of these elements measured at their melting points are not available, but their boiling points are all very near their melting points. Densities of four of the inert gases at their boiling points are as follows:

Neon	1.20 gm/cm³
Argon	1.40 gm/cm³
Krypton	2.16 gm/cm³
Xenon	3.06 gm/cm³

Find out whether these elements fit on the curve of Fig. 9–2 as you would expect. Had these densities been available to Mendeleyev, would they have assisted him in assigning positions for the inert gas elements in his periodic table?

8. Identify the element designated by X: A silvery metal, density 2.6 gm/cm^3. Liberates hydrogen from liquid water at ordinary temperatures, although less vigorously than potassium and barium. Forms an insoluble carbonate, formula XCO_3, formula weight approximately 148.

9. What properties would you expect of the elements astatine and francium?

10. The *Handbook of Chemistry and Physics* (Cleveland: Chemical Rubber Publishing Co.) is a compact gold mine of factual information. It contains a table of *Physical Constants of Inorganic*

Compounds, for example, listing many of the properties of the elements and their compounds. Using this table as a source of information, construct tables showing the characteristics of the elements in groups 4a, 5a, 1b, and 2b.

11. The elements of group 3a, with the exception of gallium, have the properties listed below.

Predict properties for the missing element, gallium, then compare your predictions with the observed properties, as presented in the *Handbook of Chemistry and Physics*. It is probable that you will find you have gone astray rather widely on the melting point of gallium; if so, the fact will serve to illustrate that there are many individual variations from the generalizations we have made in this chapter. These generalizations are very broad ones, indeed.

	Boron	Aluminum	Indium	Thallium
Color	Yellow	Silvery white	Silvery white	Bluish white
Luster	None	Lustrous	Lustrous	Lustrous
Density	2.3 gm/cm^3	2.70 gm/cm^3	7.31 gm/cm^3	11.85 gm/cm^3
Melting point	2300°C	659°C	155°C	303.5°C
Formula(s) of chloride(s)	BCl_3	$AlCl_3$	$InCl$, $InCl_2$, $InCl_3$	$TlCl$, $TlCl_3$
Density of trichloride	1.43 gm/cm^3	2.44 gm/cm^3	3.46 gm/cm^3	—
Solubility of trichloride	Decomposes in water	Moderately soluble	Very soluble	Very soluble
Formula(s) of oxide(s)	B_2O_3	Al_2O_3	InO, In_2O_3	Tl_2O, Tl_2O_3
Density of oxide	1.84 gm/cm^3	4.00 gm/cm^3	7.18 gm/cm^3 (In_2O_3)	10.19 gm/cm^3 (Tl_2O_3)

CHAPTER 10

MOMENTUM, WORK, AND MECHANICAL ENERGY

We have remarked that one of the most important ingredients of science is a set of valid concepts—abstractions formulated in the minds of scientists—in terms of which we may ask and, hopefully, answer meaningful questions. The usefulness of such concepts is greater the more general their applicability, and science has developed relatively few that can properly be called universal—that is, in terms of which meaningful questions can be asked and answered concerning *all* aspects of nature. Of those unifying concepts which are universal, perhaps the most important is that of *energy*. The *Principle of Conservation of Energy*, which we shall examine in this and subsequent chapters, is probably the most important single generalization in the whole of science.

The word *energy* is familiar to us all, and we use it constantly in everyday speech. While ordinary usage need not be restricted to any exact context, the usefulness to science and technology of the *concept*, not just the word, depends upon precise definition. The energy concept, in modern form, was slow to distill from the observations of science, partially because of lack of agreement among early scientists on the exact use of language. Many words, among them *force, impetus, momentum,* and *energy*, were used without proper differentiation. A deeper reason for the slow emergence of the energy concept is related to its very universality. Abstractions, after all, require intellectual recognition; only when these entities have appeared repeatedly in the thoughts and calculations attending scientists' observations of nature will their value to science be realized. A very large number of events, differing widely from one another, are interpretable in terms of energy, so that full recognition of the concept could only be accomplished slowly, over a long period of time.

The mechanical concept *work*, very much simpler than that of energy, was recognized long before the latter. But even this simpler concept became confused with an older one, *momentum*, during the 17th and early 18th centuries. Some of the questions that produced this confusion and contributed, ultimately, to its resolution, will prove helpful to us in understanding energy itself. Before posing these, then, we must turn our attention to *momentum*, a concept important in its own right and essential to the description of all mechanical systems, from the solar system to atoms and their constituents.

10-1 Momentum

The momentum of a body, by definition, is *the product of its mass and its velocity.* The idea of momentum was built into the science of mechanics early in the 17th century. Descartes had taken the mass times velocity of a body as a measure of its "quantity of motion," and Newton originally formulated his second law of motion in terms of the same product. Let us see whether we can reinterpret the version of Newton's second law already examined in Chapter 2, in terms of momentum as defined above.

Consider an object of mass m which is in motion with velocity v_0. Now let a constant force f act on this mass during a time interval t. Newton's second law of motion, we have seen, tells us that this force will impart to the object an acceleration a which is related to f and m by the equation

$$f = ma. \tag{10-1}$$

If we designate the velocity at the end of the time interval by v, we may write

$$a = \frac{v - v_0}{t}, \tag{10-2}$$

since acceleration is the change in velocity divided by the time during which the change occurs. Substituting Eq. (10-2) into Eq. (10-1), we obtain

$$f = \frac{m(v - v_0)}{t} = \frac{mv - mv_0}{t}. \tag{10-3}$$

This equation shows that the product of mass times velocity, the *momentum* of the object, was changed by action of the force f during time t. Thus the second law of motion could be stated in terms of momentum: *force equals time rate of change of momentum.* Whenever an unbalanced force acts on an object the momentum of that object is altered, and the rate at which momentum changes is a measure of the acting force. In the absence of force, momentum remains unchanged. We should note that momentum, like velocity, is a directed or *vector* quantity.

Now let us consider two bodies, of masses m_1 and m_2, with velocities v_1 and v_2, which are about to experience a head-on collision (Fig. 10-1). After this collision takes place both bodies will have new velocities, which we shall call v_1' and v_2'. During the time t that the impact lasts, the first body exerts a force on the second which, according to Eq. (10-3), will produce a change in momentum:

Fig. 10-1. Bodies about to collide head-on.

$$f_1 = \frac{m_2 v_2' - m_2 v_2}{t}. \qquad (10\text{–}4)$$

By Newton's third law of motion, however, we know that the second object will exert a force on the first,

$$f_2 = \frac{m_1 v_1' - m_1 v_1}{t}, \qquad (10\text{–}5)$$

which is equal in magnitude but opposite in direction to the force f_1. Hence, if we denote opposite directions by the signs $+$ and $-$ (see Section 3–1 on vector quantities), $f_1 = -f_2$, or

$$\frac{m_2 v_2' - m_2 v_2}{t} = -\frac{m_1 v_1' - m_1 v_1}{t}. \qquad (10\text{–}6)$$

Since t represents the same quantity on both sides of Eq. (10–6) (both forces act only during the instant of contact), it can be canceled out, and the equation may be rearranged to read

$$m_1 v_1' + m_2 v_2' = m_1 v_1 + m_2 v_2. \qquad (10\text{–}7)$$

Equation (10–7) may be stated in words: *the total momentum of the two bodies before collision is equal to their total momentum after collision.* Another way of putting the same result is to say that the momentum of the system (of two bodies) has been *conserved.*

The *principle of conservation of momentum,* derived above for the case of a simple head-on collision, is completely general, although care must be taken, in applying it, to account for all relevant forces. The sum of the momenta of any two bodies exerting forces on each other is maintained intact; the action of a third force, originating *outside* both bodies, could change this sum, however. The principle is particularly useful in studying the effects of large (internal) forces of brief duration. For example, an exploded shell may consist of many fragments, but the sum of the momenta of all its parts after explosion is the same as the momentum of the whole shell before explosion. The momenta of the fragments of a stationary shell add up to zero. If the shell is exploded near the earth's surface, gravitational force, acting on all fragments in the same direction, will quickly alter this sum, and strict conservation of momentum can be observed only at the instant of explosion. The example of an exploding shell should remind us vividly that the momenta must be added vectorially (see Fig. 10–2). Only when all motion is confined to a single straight line, as in a head-on collision, can we describe the directions by simply applying $+$ and $-$ signs.

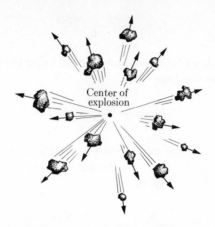

FIG. 10–2. Explosion fragments of a shell. The *vectorial* sum of individual momentum vectors is zero, if shell was at rest before explosion.

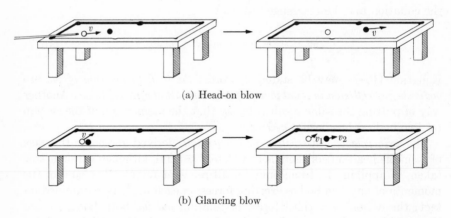

(a) Head-on blow

(b) Glancing blow

FIG. 10–3. Impacts between billiard balls: (a) head-on blow, (b) glancing blow.

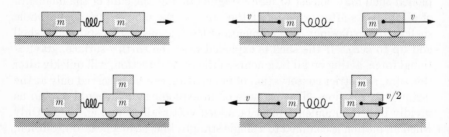

FIG. 10–4. Reaction carts.

Conservation of momentum is popularly illustrated by reference to the game of billiards. Let one billiard ball be propelled toward another (of equal mass) which is at rest (Fig. 10–3). If the ensuing collision is head-on, the first ball will come to rest during the impact, and the second will be set in motion with the same velocity (both speed and direction) that the first ball possessed initially. If the blow were a glancing one, both balls would be in motion after impact in such a way that the vector sum of their momenta would equal the initial momentum of the first ball.

For a more quantitative experiment let us consider two carts on a very smooth track, with a compressed spring between them (Fig. 10–4). Before the spring is released the total momentum of the carts, at rest, is zero. After the spring is released the carts move along the tracks in opposite directions, with equal velocities if their masses are equal. Their momenta are thus equal in magnitude but opposite in direction, and add up to zero. The equal velocities of the carts can be readily observed, with a distance scale marked on the track, by noting that they travel equal distances in equal times. If the mass of one cart is twice that of the other, however, its velocity after the spring is released will be only half that of the lighter cart, and it will be observed to traverse only half as much distance as the other in any given time interval. The total momentum of the two carts is then zero, just as in the case of carts with equal masses.

The principle of conservation of momentum, we may note, is inherent in Newton's three laws of motion. Applied to a single object, it amounts simply to the first law: in the absence of external forces the momentum (i.e., state of motion) of a body is constant. The principle is most useful when applied to systems of two or more bodies. Any changes in momentum produced by the mutual forces of bodies on each other (according to Newton's second law in terms of momentum) are equal and opposite, since these forces are reciprocal (Newton's third law). But explicit recognition of the conservation principle enables us to avoid consideration of the precise nature and duration of forces in many cases, providing a valuable shortcut to final results. The extent of recoil of a gun, for example, may be precisely predicted from the mass and velocity of the bullet, without detailed knowledge of the firing mechanism. A principle such as that of momentum conservation can be called "powerful" as well as universal: it possesses the virtue of transforming many difficult problems into easy ones!

10-2 Angular momentum

Next let us see whether the idea of momentum can contribute to the study of systems, such as that of the sun and planets, in which motions are *rotational*. The momentum conservation principle, as discussed in Section 10–1, applies only to the *linear* motions of bodies. Perhaps we have missed an analogously essential feature of rotational motion, some concept which could be used as a measure of quantity of rotation, and which is conserved in the absence of external influences. A thoroughgoing application of Newton's laws to all parts of a rotating system would aid us in the search for this concept, but we can take advantage of a law we already know, the law of equal areas, to achieve the same result.

Kepler discovered empirically that an imaginary line from the sun to any planet sweeps over equal areas in equal times. In Section 4–1 we arrived at a more general conclusion: for *any* object moving under the action of a *central* force, a line from the center to the object sweeps over equal areas in equal times. These equal areas are represented, for an object traveling in an elliptical orbit under the action of a force directed toward focus F, by the small sectors FPQ, FQR, etc., of Fig. 10–5. Now the distances traveled in equal times by the object of mass m (arcs PQ, QR, etc.) are proportional to its speed v, and therefore to its momentum mv. The area of each small triangle in Fig. 10–5 is equal to its base (chord PQ, or QR, etc.) multiplied by its altitude, the *component* of r (distance from object to center of force) perpendicular to the base. Since each chord, PQ, QR, etc., is proportional to its corresponding arc (for small arcs*), and each arc in turn is proportional to the momentum mv of the object, our triangular areas are proportional to the *product* of momentum and the component of r perpendicular to v. These areas are all equal, and we have therefore found a new quantity which *does remain constant* during orbital motion. Although mv changes continuously, due to the central force, and the distance r of the object from the center of force may change, the product of mv and the component of r at right angles to mv is *conserved* (in the

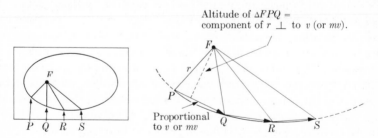

FIG. 10–5. The law of equal areas.

---

*We can make the triangles of Fig. 10–5 as small as we wish, and in the limit of vanishingly small time intervals the arcs PQ, QR, etc., become identical with their corresponding chords. The angular momentum of the moving object about the center F, as defined above, can then be given for *any instantaneous* position of its path, and will be found the same for all such instants.

absence of noncentral forces). This product is called the *angular momentum* of the object with respect to the center of its motion.

The concept of angular momentum is useful, and its definition particularly simple, when applied to objects in *circular* motion. For a circular orbit (Fig. 10–6) the distance r from the object to the center of force is simply the radius of the

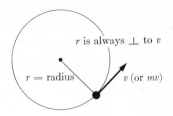

r is always $\perp$ to v

$r = $ radius

v (or mv)

Fig. 10–6. Angular momentum of object in circular orbit.

circle, and remains constant throughout the orbit. Furthermore, the radius is always perpendicular to a vector representing the velocity of the object at any instant. *The angular momentum of an object of mass m traveling in a circular path of radius r with speed v is thus given by the product mvr.*

An extended body may have angular momentum by virtue of rotation about an axis through its own center. A simple demonstration of the constancy of angular momentum in such a case is illustrated in Fig. 10–7. A man stands on a platform holding heavy weights in his outstretched hands; the platform is mounted on ball bearings so that it may rotate freely. If someone sets the man in slow rotation and he then brings his arms down he will rotate much more rapidly. Since the total mass of the system, man plus weights, remains constant, a decrease in the radius of rotation of the weights is offset by an increase in rotational speed, so that the angular momentum remains constant. This is strictly true only if there are no external influences; in practice, friction of the bearings will slowly bring the rotation to an end.

The concept of angular momentum and the principle of its conservation play an extremely useful and important role in the attack on many astronomical problems. The universe contains, for example, many "double

m m

(a)

m m

(b)

Fig. 10–7. Conservation of Angular Momentum.

stars," rotating systems far removed
from external forces, both members
of which rotate with respect to a
common center (Fig. 10–8). While
neither body coincides with the center of rotation unless one is very
much more massive than the other,
we can be sure that nothing they

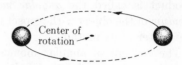

FIG. 10–8. Double-star system.

can do to each other (without influence from the outside) can change their
total angular momentum. This application of the constancy of angular momentum can be put to use in deducing important features of the double
star system from its observed motions. Similarly, in the solar system, in
which the mass of the sun is about 700 times the combined masses of all the
planets, so that for practical purposes the sun may be considered the center,
no matter how much the individual members may affect one another the
total angular momentum of the system can be changed only by outside
influences.   Any theory of the origin of planets must account for the
angular momentum they now possess, as well as all other features of the
solar system.   The angular momentum concept can be applied to careful
calculation of the "wobbling" the earth exhibits in its path around the sun,
which corresponds to the *mutual* rotation of the earth and moon about a
common center. (The earth is only about 80 times as massive as the moon.)

Since we have mentioned more astronomical applications of angular momentum conservation than others, perhaps we should stress again that the
concept is useful to the solution of *all* problems of rotational motion. One of
the most important connections in which we shall encounter it again will be
in our considerations of modern atomic theory. Meanwhile, however, let
us return to ordinary *linear* momentum *mv* and the confusion which developed in its interpretation during the 17th century.

10–3 "The proper measure of force"

We have seen that Newton conceived of *force* as any influence capable of
changing the quantity or direction of what we now call *momentum* of a
body. It was Descartes, earlier in the 17th century, who had first conceived
the use of the product *mv* as a measure of "quantity of motion." Descartes
held that the *total* quantity of motion (i.e., momentum) of the universe is
constant; thus, in his *Principia Philosophiae* (1644) he wrote:

"For though motion is only a condition of moving matter, there yet exists
in matter a definite quantity of it, which in the world at large never increases or diminishes, although in single portions it changes; . . . in the proportion as the motion of one part grows less, in the same proportion must
the motion of another equally large part grow greater."

It may be seen that this assumption of universal constancy of motion requires that any body which loses a given quantity of motion (mv) must impart an equal quantity to another body. It is implicit in Descartes' proposal, as it became explicit in Newton's laws, that the product mv is a measure of the force which a moving body can exert on another during the time in which it influences the second body.

Descartes' view was vigorously contested by the German mathematician Gottfried Wilhelm Leibnitz (1646–1716), who had also developed the mathematical methods of calculus independently of Newton. Leibnitz' initial paper (1686) bore the devastating title:

"A Short Demonstration of a Remarkable Error of Descartes and Others, Concerning the Natural Law by which they think that the Creator always preserves the same Quantity of Motion; by which, however, the Science of Mechanics is totally perverted."

It was Leibnitz' conviction that the "proper measure of force" of a moving body is the product of its mass and the *square* of its velocity (mv^2), a quantity to which he gave the name *vis viva* ("living force"). He arrived at this conclusion by assuming that the same effort or, as he called it, "force," is required to lift a mass m through a height d as to lift a mass $4m$ through a height $d/4$ (more generally, that the "force" required to lift a body is proportional to the product of the body's mass and the height through which it is lifted). Additionally, he remarked that ". . . a body falling from a certain height acquires a force [Leibnitz' usage] sufficient to raise it to the same height, if it is given the proper direction and no external forces interfere." This last statement means, for example, that if a hard ball is dropped on a rigid surface it will (ideally) rebound to its initial height; Leibnitz would assume that the rigid surface only gave the "proper direction" without lessening the "force."

With these definitions Leibnitz' conclusions follow readily. Let two hard balls, of mass m and $4m$, respectively, be dropped on a rigid surface (Fig. 10–9), with the heavier ball being dropped from a height only one-quarter as great as that from which the lighter ball is released. From the law of free fall it can be shown that the speed of a freely falling object is proportional to the square root of the distance it has fallen from rest; thus the speed of the light ball, just before striking the surface, is twice that of the heavier at the instant of rebound. Assuming, with

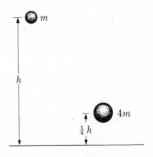

FIG. 10–9. Leibnitz' argument

Leibnitz, that both rebounds involve the same quantity of what he calls "force," and that this "force" resides in each ball by virtue of its motion just before impact with the surface, the "proper measure" of force must depend upon v^2 rather than v. If mass m has speed v and mass $4m$ has speed $v/2$ before striking, the product of mass and (speed)^2 for each is mv^2. On the other hand, their respective products of mass and speed are mv and $2mv$; Leibnitz argued that mass times velocity could not, therefore, be a "proper measure of force."

The controversy initiated by Leibnitz continued until the various concepts and ideas were at last properly sorted out by the French physicist d'Alembert, in a treatise published in 1743. D'Alembert pointed out that the battle had been largely one of words, that Newton's $f = ma$ is all that is needed for identifying force, and that the adherents of Descartes and Leibnitz had been talking about different things, in that Leibnitz' "force" is not the same as the "force" of Descartes and Newton. We have seen that Descartes was dealing with the quantity we now call momentum, and that the rate of change of momentum of a body *is* a "proper measure" of force exerted upon it. Descartes was also correct in asserting that the total quantity of motion (i.e., momentum) is strictly conserved. Leibnitz' deductions have proved equally fruitful, but his *vis viva* did not turn out to be a measure of force as we now define the term. Instead, it is related to a new concept of great importance.

Consider an object of mass m which is subject to the action of a constant force f. Newton's laws of motion tell us that the object will experience constant acceleration a. Galileo's law of uniform acceleration (free fall) gives the distance d traversed by the object in time t after starting from rest as

$$d = at^2/2. \tag{10-8}$$

If the two sides of Eq. (10–8) are multiplied respectively by those of Eq. (10–1) ($f = ma$), we obtain

$$fd = ma^2t^2/2. \tag{10-9}$$

But we also know, by the definition of uniform acceleration, that the final velocity attained by the object in the time interval t is

$$v = at. \tag{10-10}$$

The product a^2t^2, therefore, is equivalent to the square of this final velocity, v^2, and Eq. (10–9) becomes

$$fd = mv^2/2. \tag{10-11}$$

In words, the product of the magnitude of a force and the distance through which it acts on an object is equivalent to one-half the product of the mass of the object and the square of the final velocity it attains in that distance. The product of force and distance, fd, is thus proportional to the quantity Leibnitz called *vis viva*. Leibnitz' emphasis on the quantity mv^2 in relation to the heights to which objects will rebound constituted, essentially, the first recognition of the product fd as a conceptual quantity of independent importance, even though he confused it with force itself. The products mv and fd (and the latter's equivalent for some purposes, $mv^2/2$) are *both* necessary for the full description of motion, especially in simultaneous consideration of more than one moving object. The important concept that grew out of Leibnitz' considerations is now called *work*; its precise definition must precede our investigation of the more general concept, *energy*.

10–4 Work

Whenever a force external to a body acts on it to produce a displacement of its position, we say that *work* is done on the body. The acting force need not be a *net*, unbalanced force, such as is required to produce acceleration. When a trunk is being pushed steadily across a rough floor, for example, the net force acting on it is zero, as we have seen in Chapter 2; nevertheless, work is being done on the trunk. In this case work is necessary to overcome the frictional resistance offered by the floor, even though the force of pushing is balanced by the opposite force of friction and no acceleration is imparted to the trunk (once it has been set in steady motion). Similarly, work is done in carrying a suitcase upstairs, this time against its weight, even though it is carried slowly and steadily. On the other hand, in the process of accelerating a falling body, the force of gravity does work on it during the entire course of its fall. The concept *work* involves only the two quantities force and displacement, and other aspects of the motion produced need not be considered in its application.

Quantitatively, work is defined as *the force exerted on an object multiplied by the distance through which the force acts*. This definition may seem to imply that the force must act in the same direction in which the object moves. In practice, however, a push on a trunk need not be horizontal, but since the trunk is constrained by the floor to move horizontally, *only that component of the acting force parallel to the direction of motion is effective in performing work* (Fig. 10–10).

It will be immediately recognized that the above definition of work differs from the less demanding usage of the same word in everyday speech. A man who stands in one spot holding a heavy bundle is conscious of considerable effort and would be inclined to say that he is working. He is exerting a force, to be sure, but only to balance the downward gravitational pull

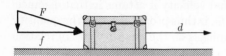

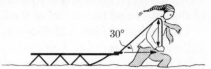

Fig. 10–10. Work done in pushing a trunk $= fd$. (Although force F exerted, only its horizontal component f is effective.)

Fig. 10–11. With the rope held at a 30° angle, the horizontal component is about 87% as large as the total force exerted.

on his bundle. By our definition we would say that he works only while lifting the bundle. Similarly, the mechanical work of understanding this chapter is limited to that expended in turning the pages, unless the reader is addicted to room pacing.

To compute the amount of work done on an object by a force we may use the simple formula

$$W \text{ (work)} = f \text{ (force)} \times d \text{ (distance)}, \tag{10–12}$$

if f is parallel to d. If f acts along some direction other than that in which the body is displaced, we must first find the component of f in the direction of displacement, then multiply that component by the distance to determine the quantity of work done. For example, if a sled is pulled horizontally by means of a rope held at an angle of 30° to the horizontal (Fig. 10–11), f in the product fd is only about 87% as large as the total force exerted ($\cos 30° = 0.866$).

Unlike momentum, work is *not* a directed (vector) quantity, but a simple *scalar*, requiring only one number for its specification. How big that number will be depends on the units in which force and distance are measured; any unit of force multiplied by a unit of distance will provide a unit of work. In the English system, for example, work may be measured in *foot·pounds*. In the cgs system, in which the unit of force is the dyne (defined in Chapter 2) and the unit of distance the centimeter, the unit of work is the product *dyne·centimeter* (see Appendix). This product is given a special name, the *erg*: one *erg* is the work done when a force of one dyne acts through a distance of one centimeter. Since the dyne is an extremely small unit of force, as we have seen, the erg is also a small unit for most practical purposes. For dealing with most mechanical problems a larger unit is more convenient, and that customarily used is the *joule*, defined as 10 million ergs of work:

$$1 \text{ joule} = 10^7 \text{ ergs.}$$

In the next chapter we shall learn why the name of James Prescott Joule deserves commemoration in the name of this unit.

It may not be clear at this point why scientists have elected to endow the particular product of the quantities force and distance with a special name and to regard it with especial seriousness. The answer is twofold. The product *fd* arises again and again, as we shall see, in the consideration of mechanical problems, and its treatment as a single entity, therefore, leads to simplification and economy of thought. Moreover, work itself is something quite different from the individual forces and distances involved in its performance. It is a measure of a change produced *in a body*, as a result of the action of a force originating outside the body, and is certainly not wholly describable in terms of mere change in the position of the body. From this point of view work is a *fruitful* concept: it leads to deeper understanding of the processes it is used to describe. Let us pursue its fruitfulness further.

10–5 Energy

How does work get done? *Any* force does work when acting through a distance. The forces that are most familiar to us are those of *contact* (pushing and pulling) and *gravitation*, which acts at a distance. For example, work is done by the force of gravity on any object allowed to fall freely. Upon reaching the ground, such an object exerts a contact force which can act through a distance on any displaceable object it may strike. We might say, then, that any object in a position such that it *might* fall possesses the *capacity* to do work, since if it did fall it would acquire motion, and when in motion it might strike and displace the position of another object.

Capacity to perform work (that is, to exert a force through a distance) is in general what is meant by the term *energy*. We can express the possibility that work may be performed, no matter how remote the accomplishment of that work may be, by using the word *energy*. A body in motion, by virtue of its *motion* alone, possesses energy, since it may collide with another body and, in losing some or all of its motion, do work on that body. A rock on a mountain top possesses energy by virtue of its *position* alone, since it may at some future time start rolling, acquire motion under the influence of gravitational force, and subsequently do work in displacing other bodies. A gallon of gasoline possesses energy (called chemical) since upon its combustion a sudden expansion occurs which can be used to do the work of pushing a piston in an engine. Heat (e.g., that given up by combustion of gasoline or coal) may be employed to transform liquid water to steam which can be used to do the work of propelling a locomotive. When light is absorbed by a dark surface the surface becomes warm; it is conceivable that the heat thus produced might also be used in a steam engine.

An obvious 20th-century reply to our question "how does work get done?" might have been "by machines." Machines are devices that perform work in response to work which is done *on* them. The energy source for work *input* can be one of a large number of possibilities, such as a man turning a crank, an internal combustion engine, or an electrical storage battery. The energy corresponding to this input is somehow transferred through the machine system so that work can be performed (the *output* of the machine) in some convenient way. The energy transfer may involve changes in the states of motion or in the positions, or both, of parts of the machine. Energies of motion and position, together, are called *mechanical energy*.

For an analysis of mechanical energy a machine called the *pile driver* affords an excellent illustrative example. The pile driver is a device used to drive heavy beams (piles) to great depths in the ground for the support of piers or buildings. It does this work by repeatedly raising a heavy weight (called a *ram*) to a fixed height and allowing it to fall freely onto the beam (see Fig. 10–12). The force exerted by the ram on the pile acts through a small distance each time it strikes and gradually drives the pile into the ground.

When the ram is poised at height h it possesses energy of position, since it may fall, acquire motion, strike the beam, and do work. Energy of position, in general, is called *potential energy*. When it is gravitational force which can, potentially, impart motion to an object (as in this case) the energy is called *gravitational potential energy*. The quantity of work that can be done on the ram by gravitational force depends on the distance h through which it is free to fall. The force acting, in accord with Newton's second law, is the product of the mass m of the ram, and the acceleration of gravity, g. The work that can be done on the weight as it falls, force times distance (since these are in the same direction), is then mgh. If allowed to fall, the ram will in some sense come to possess this work, and will transmit

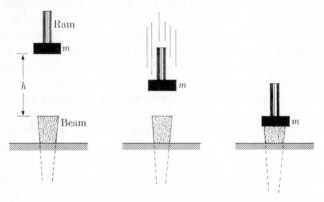

Fig. 10–12. Pile driver.

at least part of it to the beam. Let us therefore take the quantity mgh as a measure of the gravitational potential energy of the poised ram, i.e., its capacity for doing work by virtue of its position in space.

Let us next consider the condition of the ram at the instant it has completed its fall and is about to strike the beam. It has now lost all its potential energy, but has *motion* which it will lose when it strikes and does work on the beam. Its capacity to do work resides in its motion; energy of motion is called *kinetic energy*. How much kinetic energy does the ram possess at this instant? If we assume that the potential energy the ram possessed before its fall is completely transformed to kinetic energy during the fall, we can answer this question with the help of Eq. (10–11):

$$fd = mv^2/2. \qquad (10\text{–}11)$$

This equation was derived, it will be recalled, by considering the action of a constant force f on an object of mass m through time interval t, during which the object was displaced through distance d. In the case of the ram, $f = mg$, and d becomes h, since the body falls through that distance, and Eq. (10–11) becomes

$$mgh = \tfrac{1}{2}mv^2. \qquad (10\text{–}13)$$

In words, the work done on the body by the gravitational force mg acting through the vertical distance h is equivalent to the quantity $\tfrac{1}{2}mv^2$, now possessed by the ram instead of its original potential energy mgh. We may then say that the energy the ram possesses by virtue of its motion, its *kinetic energy*, at the instant before striking the beam, is given by the expression $\tfrac{1}{2}mv^2$.

While Eq. (10–13) applies specifically to energy of motion produced by the action of a gravitational force, Eq. (10–11) was derived quite generally for the action of *any constant net force*, through a distance d, in imparting motion to an object of mass m. Thus, in general, expenditure of the quantity of work fd solely to produce motion in a body imparts kinetic energy in the amount $\tfrac{1}{2}mv^2$ to the body. Any object of mass m traveling with velocity v, by virtue of its motion alone, possesses the capacity to perform work in this amount, and we may write as a general relation

$$\text{K.E. (kinetic energy)} = \tfrac{1}{2}mv^2. \qquad (10\text{–}14)$$

We are now in a position to understand the direction of Leibnitz' thought. His *vis viva*, mv^2, is not at all a measure of the force a moving body may exert, but a measure of the *work* it may perform, a concept not yet crystallized in Leibnitz' time. At that, it is *twice* the actual quantity of work ideally available in a moving body, since it lacks the factor $\frac{1}{2}$ that appears in our relation, Eq. (10–14). Despite this discrepancy, we can now see that Leibnitz was on the track of something important.

Let us return to the pile driver, which we left with the massive ram about to hit a beam. The beam will offer resistance, in an amount depending on the kind of soil into which it is being driven, that will stop the falling ram after it has traveled only a very short distance farther. Is the amount of work done here, the product of the force of resistance and the distance the beam is driven into the earth, equal to the ram's kinetic energy, $\frac{1}{2}mv^2$ (and thus to its original equivalent potential energy, mgh)? The answer is *yes, for the ideal case.* What this means is that *if* no work is expended in deforming either the beam or the ram, and *if* no heat is evolved during the collision between them, *then* the work done on the beam is equal to the work done by the force of gravity on the ram during its fall. For that matter, it is also equal to the work that must be done in lifting the ram, against gravitational force, to the height h in the first place.

10–6 Conservation of mechanical energy

The principle we have just stated, carefully hedged about with reservations, is that of the *conservation of mechanical energy.* It is a principle that was intuitively recognized, although of course not formulated in terms of the energy concept, at least as early as the time of Galileo. An example which approaches the ideal case much more closely than that of the pile driver, and which was considered by Galileo (and later by Leibnitz), is illustrated in Fig. 10–13. To quote Galileo's own description of the experiment:

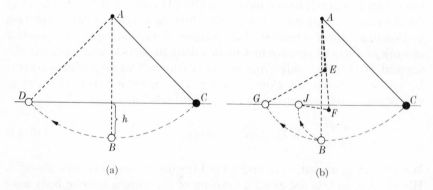

(a)   (b)

Fig. 10–13. Galileo's pendulum experiment: (a) without nail, (b) with nail, first at E, then at F.

"Suppose this sheet of paper to be a vertical wall, and from a nail driven in it a ball of lead weighing two or three ounces to hang by a very fine thread AB four or five feet long. On the wall mark a horizontal line DC perpendicular to the vertical AB, which latter ought to hang about two inches from the wall. If now the thread AB with the ball attached take the position AC and the ball be let go, you will see the ball first descend through the arc CB, to pass the point B, and to travel along the arc BD almost to the level of the line CD, being prevented from reaching it exactly by the resistance of the air and the thread."

When the pendulum bob is brought from B to C it is lifted through a vertical height h, thus gaining potential energy mgh, where m is its mass. On release, the force of gravity causes the bob to move downward, although the string constrains its motion to a circular arc. On arrival at point B the bob has lost all its potential energy, but now has energy of motion (kinetic energy) sufficient to do the work of carrying it to point D against the force of gravity. Since D is on the same horizontal level as C, this quantity of work is expended in lifting the bob through height h, thus restoring to it the quantity of potential energy mgh. On the ensuing backward swing the process is repeated; potential energy is converted to kinetic, and back to potential again at point C. (Note, however, that the bob will reach D in the forward swing, and C in the reverse, only in the ideal case, i.e., only if the "resistance of the air and the thread" can be neglected.)

To make the role of height h still clearer, Galileo proposed an extension of the experiment:

"[Next] let us drive in the wall, in the projection of the vertical AB, as at E or at F, a nail five or six inches long, so that the thread AC, carrying as before the ball through the arc CB, at the moment it reaches the position AB, shall strike the nail E, and the ball be thus compelled to move up the arc BG described about E as center . . . Now, gentlemen, you will be pleased to see the ball rise to the horizontal line at the point G, and the same thing also happen if the nail be placed lower as at F, in which case the ball would describe the arc BJ, always terminating its ascent precisely at the line CD."

When released at point C, the bob has just sufficient kinetic energy at B to raise it through height h, even though the interception of a nail at either E or F prevents it from pursuing its normal arc BD. In a final touch to the experiment, Galileo demonstrated that:

"If the nail be placed so low that the length of thread below it does not reach to the height of CD . . . then the thread will wind itself about the nail."

In this case the bob is restrained by the nail from rising through the entire height h, hence still possesses some kinetic energy when it reaches its highest position and continues its motion, wrapping the thread around the nail.

In modern language we would say of Galileo's experiment that the mechanical energy of the bob is *conserved*, meaning that the sum of its kinetic and potential energies remains constant as it swings. In every case (except the last) the kinetic energy possessed by the bob at point B is converted to the same amount of potential energy by the time the bob has lost its motion. At any intermediate stage of the swing the energy of the bob is part kinetic and part potential, always in such a way that the sum of the two is constant. As we have said, however, such constancy is only ideally obtained. Galileo's (idealized) experiment can be checked very well against observation for the first few swings of a pendulum, but if we wait long enough we find that the swinging dies out. The second swing is actually not *quite* as high as the first, although a well-constructed pendulum can execute many swings before a difference in height becomes noticeable. It is important to note that the endpoints of the swings *never get higher*, i.e., that mechanical energy is *never increased*, so long as the pendulum is not tampered with from the outside. In other words, the capacity of the pendulum for performing work is never greater than the initial potential energy imparted to it (work done *on* it) in lifting the bob to the height h.

Machines even simpler than the pile driver illustrate this limited energy conservation principle very clearly. Consider the *inclined plane*, for example, a machine of wide utility represented by the ramps which were used to raise stones for the ancient Egyptian pyramids. Figure 10–14 illustrates its operation. By the exertion of a very large force W, equivalent to the weight of the heavy stone, through the vertical height h, the stone could be lifted to its desired position directly. To exert such a force by human strength is impossible, however, and a much smaller force f applied through the greater distance L along the plane will achieve the same result. The work done *on* this machine, work input, is the product $f \times L$; the output work performed *by* the machine is given by the product $W \times h$. In accord with the mechanical energy conservation principle, we may say that the

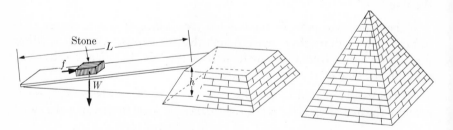

Fig. 10–14. Inclined plane as a machine.

very *most* we can expect of the work output is that it equal the work input. In other words, if the ramp and stone were both ideally smooth, we could expect that

$$W \times h = f \times L. \qquad (10\text{–}15)$$

For an actual ramp, the smoother its surface and that of the object moved along it, the more nearly will the ideal of Eq. (10–15) be met. Here, as in all other cases, *at least* as much work must be put into the machine as is derived from it.

In all human experience, attempts to get work done for nothing —that is, without expenditure of at least the equivalent energy—have failed. No successful "perpetual motion" machine, whose moving parts go on performing work indefinitely without an external energy supply, has ever been constructed. Mechanical work, as such, *can* be created, but only by some active electrical, chemical, or other agent. We may anticipate the next chapter by stating here the over-all principle that when all forms of energy are considered *the totality of energy is conserved*, although energy may be transformed from one kind to another. This important generalization did not become a part of science until mid-19th century; it was, in part, the multiplicity of possible energy forms which stood in the way of its earlier recognition. The principle *that energy can be neither created nor destroyed* cannot be arrived at by mechanical considerations alone. This is nowhere more clearly illustrated than in the mechanical study of impacts between various kinds of bodies.

10–7 Impact

We have seen (Section 10–1) that the total momentum of two bodies is strictly conserved when they collide. This principle does not suffice to determine their motions after collision, however. In the example of a billiard ball in head-on collision with another which is initially at rest, we tacitly assumed that both balls were ideally hard, or *elastic*. In that case the first ball is stopped by the collision, and the second becomes endowed with all the momentum mv and kinetic energy $\frac{1}{2}mv^2$ possessed by the first ball prior to collision. Suppose, however, that the balls were made of soft clay or putty, and that the table were of smooth glass on which the lumps could slide freely. If one lump, of mass m and velocity v, strikes another lump of equal mass and initially at rest, the two will stick together and the ensuing motion is that of an object of mass $2m$ (Fig. 10–15). Since momentum is conserved, the velocity of this compound body is $v/2$. Its kinetic energy is

$$\tfrac{1}{2}(2m)(v/2)^2 = \tfrac{1}{4}mv^2,$$

FIG. 10-15. Balls of putty collide on a glass surface.

just half the initial kinetic energy of the first ball. Such a collision is *inelastic*.

Impacts in which kinetic energy is conserved (in addition to momentum) are called *elastic collisions*. The redistribution of kinetic energy, even in the simple case of a head-on elastic collision, depends on the masses involved. Only when the masses are equal, as in the case of our two billiard balls, can *all* the kinetic energy of one object be transferred to another. If the masses are unequal, only a fraction of the kinetic energy can be transmitted from a moving object to one at rest, whether it is the heavier one that is initially in motion or the lighter.

It is interesting to consider a light elastic object, such as a tennis ball, dropped on a very smooth hard floor. The ball will bounce approximately to the height from which it was dropped (as in the Leibnitz example), which is equivalent to saying that it has as much kinetic energy after collision as before. Yet the force exerted by the floor has completely reversed the momentum, i.e., it has *destroyed mv* (of the ball) in the downward direction and *created* a similar amount of upward momentum, so that the *total change* in momentum of the ball is $2mv$ (mathematically: $+ mv - (-mv) = 2mv$). For conservation, an equal quantity of momentum, $2mv$, must have been imparted to the floor. But the floor, perhaps firmly attached to the earth, has so great a mass that the velocity it acquires, necessary to conserve momentum, is vanishingly small. Its kinetic energy, $\frac{1}{2}$ its mass times the *square* of this small velocity, is therefore for all practical purposes zero. Just because massive objects are good absorbers of momentum, then, they absorb practically no kinetic energy in elastic collisions.

While most of the collisions we see and experience are not perfectly elastic, it is rare that they are as perfectly inelastic as the extreme case of our two lumps of clay or putty. What do all inelastic collisions have in common? They differ from elastic collisions in that kinetic energy is lost during impact. (Note that no momentum is lost, however, although it is transferred from one body to the other.) Commonly, some of this kinetic energy is expended in performing the work of *deforming* the colliding bodies, as in an automobile accident. Equally commonly, *heat* makes its appearance; it can be readily observed, for example, that the temperature of an object may be raised by subjecting it to repeated blows.

10–8 Work and heat

In the practical performance of work, heat is always involved. When moving parts of a machine rub against each other heat is generated by friction, which may be minimized by lubrication and by use of smooth surfaces, but never entirely eliminated. We have defined a machine as a device that performs work as a consequence of having work done upon it, but all we could say of the work output was that it was *less than* the work input except in the "ideal case." The "ideal case" is most closely approached when friction is minimized, so that relatively little heat is generated. This suggests the existence of an intimate relation between work and heat. In order to establish such a relation we must be able to treat heat as quantitatively as we have now learned to treat mechanical work. This we shall do in the next chapter.

10–9 Summary

Descartes defined *momentum* of a body, the product of mass and velocity, as a measure of its motion, and Newton's second law of motion was originally formulated in terms of momentum: the net force acting on a body is equal to the rate of change of its momentum. The total momentum of a system of bodies remains strictly constant (is conserved) if the only forces which act are those the bodies exert on each other. Similarly, angular momentum is a measure of rotational motion, and is conserved in the absence of external influences. A force acting on a body also does *work*, in quantity corresponding to the product of the force and the distance through which it acts. A valuable concept for describing motion is *kinetic energy*, $\frac{1}{2}mv^2$, which may result from or be transformed into work. Energy generally is defined as the capacity to do work; a body which possesses a capacity to do work by virtue of its position is said to have *potential energy*. Mechanical energy is *not* strictly conserved; it may be dissipated as *heat*, for example.

REFERENCES

HOLTON, G., *Introduction to Concepts and Theories in Physical Science*, Chapters 16 and 17.

MACH, E., *The Science of Mechanics* (first published 1883). The Descartes-Leibnitz controversy is discussed in Chapter 3; the sense of the discussion can be readily followed even if the mathematical arguments are omitted.

MAGIE, W. F., *A Source Book in Physics*, pp. 50–51 (Descartes), 52–55 (Leibnitz), 55–58 (D'Alembert), and 5–6 (Galileo).

SEMAT, H., *Physics in the Modern World*.

TAYLOR, L. W., *Physics, the Pioneer Science*, Chapters 16 and 17.

1. To stop a train requires one million foot·pounds of work. If the train is stopped in 500 ft, what is the retarding force in pounds?

2. Find the work done in raising a 60-gm mass to a height of 25 cm. Give the answer in ergs. [Ans.: 1.47×10^6 ergs]

3. A mass of 100 gm falls freely from rest through a height of 20 m. Find the potential energy and the kinetic energy when the mass has fallen halfway, and compare with the total potential energy at the top and the total kinetic energy as the mass reaches the bottom. (Neglect air resistance.)

4. A uniform chain 1m long lies on a table with $\frac{1}{4}$ of the length hanging over the edge. The total mass of the chain is 400 gm. How much work would be required to put the rest of the chain on the table?

5. A mass of 60 gm, traveling with a velocity of 15 cm/sec, collides head-on with a 30-gm mass moving in the same direction with a velocity of 5 cm/sec. If, after impact, the 30-gm mass is found to have a velocity of 15 cm/sec, what is the velocity of the 60-gm mass? [Ans.: 10 cm/sec]

6. Find the total kinetic energy of the masses of Exercise 5 before and after impact, and compare. Is the collision elastic? Explain. [Ans.: Initial K.E. 7125 ergs; final K.E. 6375 ergs]

7. A 10-gm bullet is fired from a gun with a velocity of 200 m/sec (20,000 cm/sec). What is the recoil momentum of the gun? If the gun's mass is 2 kgm (2000 gm), with what speed will it begin its recoil?

(Note: The product of any unit of mass and another of velocity will constitute a proper unit of momentum, but the same units must be used on both sides of an equation.)

8. An ice-skater begins a pirouette with outstretched arms, shifts all his weight to one skate, draws his arms very close to his body, and while doing so spins faster and faster. Explain.

9. The earth may be considered to possess two kinds of angular momentum; one results from its orbital motion about the sun, the other from its spinning motion on its own axis. Approximate calculations may be made about the latter (spin) motion by treating the entire mass of the earth as though it were located at a point and rotating in a circular orbit about one-half the earth's known radius. The distance from the earth to the sun is about 93 million miles, and the earth's radius is about 4000 miles. The velocity of an object in circular motion can be computed by dividing the circumference of the orbit ($2\pi r$) by its period (365 days for revolution of earth about the sun, and 1 day for rotation about its own axis).

Assuming the earth's orbit to be circular, which of its angular momenta is greater, that of revolution with respect to the sun, or of self-rotation? By about what factor? [Ans.: The first, by a factor of nearly 6 million]

10. It is thought by some scientists that the moon may once have been a part of the earth. While there are serious reasons for doubting this theory, let us assume it for the purpose of mak-

ing an interesting deduction based on the principle of conservation of angular momentum. The moon's present orbit has a radius approximately 60 times the radius of the earth. Its period of revolution may be taken, roundly, to be 30 times that of the earth's rotation. The moon's mass is approximately 1/80 that of the earth.

(a) Using the same approximation as in Exercise 3 (that the earth's mass, located at a point, revolves in an orbit of radius $\frac{1}{2}$ that of the earth) as a guide to the earth's angular momentum, calculate the relative angular momenta of the earth and the moon at the present time.

(b) If the masses of the moon and earth had been combined in a single body at some remote time, what can you now say about the angular momentum of that body? Taking note of the fact that the mass of a combined earth-moon system would not be appreciably larger than that of the earth alone, find (approximately) what the length of a day would have been at that time.

(c) Suppose that the moon had split off the composite body of (b) with twice its actual mass, but that its motion were otherwise as we now find it (same orbit and period of revolution). Would the length of our day be longer or shorter than we find it? By about what factor? [*Ans.*: (a) The angular momentum of the moon is about 6 times that of the earth about the earth's axis; (b) the day was roughly 4 hours long]

11. Do you do work in the exact mechanical sense when walking on level ground? How? Do you do more work when walking on level ground carrying a 40-lb child on your shoulders? The answer to this question will involve an analysis of what happens when you take a step.

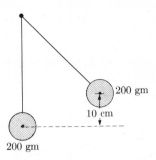

FIGURE 10–16.

12. A 200-gm mass is attached to a long string and suspended as a pendulum. The pendulum is set in motion by lifting the mass to the position shown in Fig. 10–16, 10 cm above its lowest point. What is its potential energy? If all this potential energy is converted to kinetic energy at the bottom of the swing, with what speed is it traveling at its lowest point? (The numbers have been selected so that square roots will be easy to take; note that $g = 980$ cm/sec^2 can be broken down as 20×49.)

13. Substitute a 100-gm mass for the 200-gm mass of Exercise 12. Would it have a different speed at the bottom of its swing, if allowed to swing from the same height? How is this speed related to the speed the mass would have after 10 cm of free fall?

14. Calculate the quantity of work, in foot-pounds, performed by a 175-lb man in climbing 20 stairs, each with a vertical rise of one foot. Can you convert this quantity to *joules* of work? To do so, you will need to know that 1 inch = 2.54 cm, 1 pound = 454 grams, and the weight of 1 gram is 980 dynes. (See Appendix for discussion of units.) [*Ans.*: 3500 ft·lb, 4750 joules]

15. What is the kinetic energy, in ergs, of the bullet in Exercise 7 (10 gm,

fired at 200 m/sec velocity) at the instant it leaves the barrel of the gun? Will it strike a distant target with the same, more, or less kinetic energy? The same, more, or less momentum? Explain.

FIGURE 10–17.

FIGURE 10–18.

16. If at least as much work must be put into a machine as is done by it, why are machines useful? Give specific answers for a single fixed pulley for lifting (Fig. 10–17) and a crowbar used for prying up heavy objects (Fig. 10–18).

17. The original treatment (due to Huygens) of impacts in which kinetic energy is conserved specified that the balls must be *hard*. In what sense are these balls *elastic*? Tennis balls also undergo almost perfectly elastic impacts, but they are not hard. Explain.

18. Let a lump of modeling clay of mass 10 gm slide on a very smooth surface with a velocity of 12 cm/sec. It collides head-on with another lump of mass 20 gm initially at rest, and the two stick together and continue to slide. With what velocity does the composite mass travel? What is the kinetic energy of the lumps before impact? After impact? (*Ans.*: $v = 4$ cm/sec; initial K.E. 720 ergs; final K.E. 240 ergs]

19. It is important to distinguish clearly between momentum and kinetic energy. What is the relation of each to the force that produces it? Can kinetic energy be a negative quantity? We have said that momentum is a directed quantity, and in any particular direction may be positive or negative. Is angular momentum also a directed quantity? (I.e., is any particular direction picked out by a rotating object?) The answer to this last question will require careful thought.

20. Our definition of gravitational potential energy depends upon the height through which an object may fall. Does this imply any universally defined reference point? Can you think of circumstances in which potential energy may be negative? For example, a building rises 500 ft from the ground. What is the potential energy of a 5-lb object on top of the building, with respect to the ground? But the building also contains basements and sub-basements extending 40 ft below the surface. What would the potential energy of the 5-lb object be, still with respect to the ground, if it were lying on the floor of the lowest basement? Note, then, that potential energies can be calculated only with respect to *arbitrarily* defined reference points.

21. Equation (10–3) may be rewritten

$$ft = mv - mv_0.$$

In words, the change in momentum which an object experiences as the result of action of a force f during time t is equal to the product of f and t.

If a 100-gm baseball, traveling initially at 500 cm/sec, is in contact with a bat for 0.2 sec, and leaves it traveling at 300 cm/sec in exactly the opposite direction, what is the average force exerted by the bat during the time of contact? [$Ans.$: 4×10^5 dynes]

22. Would you say that mechanical energy is conserved in the solar system? If not, what long-range result could be expected? For the elliptical orbit of a single planet, show (qualitatively) how the kinetic and potential energies of that body vary as it pursues its course around the sun.

CHAPTER 11

HEAT AND THE CONSERVATION OF ENERGY

We have said that the moving parts of a machine, rubbing against one another, generate heat. Just what does this statement mean? If we touch an object that has been rubbed vigorously against another we experience the sensation of warmth. Alternative ways of reporting the experience are to say either that *heat* has resulted from the rubbing of the objects or that their *temperature* has been raised. Are heat and temperature, then, the same thing, and are they valuable only for qualitative reporting of certain sensory responses of the nervous system? The answer, that they are distinct but inseparably related concepts, can be found only in terms of the operations which give them quantitative meaning. Let us examine some of these operations to increase our understanding of temperature and heat; only when we have done so can we formulate more fundamental questions in terms of these concepts.

11-1 Thermometry

It is a common observation that when a hot object is brought in contact with a cold one, the hot object cools, while the other warms up. We may say that the two objects, initially at *different temperatures*, tend to reach a *common temperature*. Measurement of temperature depends on this tendency, in conjunction with certain properties of substances which vary measurably with temperature. The property most frequently used for temperature indication is almost universal: substances *expand* as they are made hotter. The very few exceptions to this general behavior occur only within limited ranges of temperature.* Most solids and liquids expand only slightly with increasing temperature, while the expansion exhibited by gases is appreciably greater.

Galileo constructed one of the earliest *thermometers* (temperature measuring devices), using air as a temperature-indicating substance. This thermometer (Fig. 11-1), which was actually used by a contemporary physician for detection of fever, consists of a bulb of air communicating with a container of water via a long narrow stem. If the air in the bulb is

---

*E.g., liquid water, which contracts in volume as it is heated from 0°C to 4°C, but expands as its temperature rises above 4°C.

heated, its expansion forces water
downward, lowering the water level
in the stem; if cooled, its contraction
raises this level. With an arbitrary
scale laid alongside the stem it is
possible to measure the relative
temperatures of objects brought in
contact with the bulb.

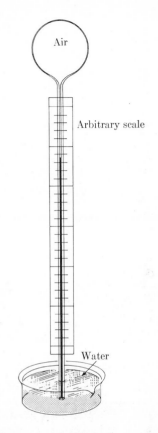

One serious drawback to Galileo's
thermometer is that the pressure of
the external atmosphere, acting on
the water in the container, can cause
fluctuations in the stem level which
are unrelated to the temperature of
the air bulb. It has become customary to seal the temperature-indicating substance in glass, so that it has
no contact with the atmosphere. If
the stem is made very narrow, it is
practical, and often advantageous,
to note the thermal expansion of
liquids instead of gases; mercury is
the most commonly used thermometric fluid today.

Thermometers must be calibrated
against fixed temperatures if the
relative measurements made with
them are to be meaningful. In the
earliest days of temperature meas-

FIG. 11–1. Galileo's thermometer.

urement, thermometers were exposed to such vaguely defined conditions as
"the greatest summer heat" and "the most severe winter cold" to obtain
"fixed" readings, all other measurements being referred to these points.
The need for more reproducible calibration temperatures gradually became
clear, and by the 18th century the practice of using the freezing and boiling temperatures of water for this purpose was firmly established.

A modern mercury thermometer (Fig. 11–2) consists of a mercury-
filled bulb in communication with a sealed stem of very small and uniform
diameter. For calibration, the bulb is first immersed in an ice-water mixture. As the mercury cools and contracts, its level in the stem is lowered;
when the position of this level becomes steady it is assumed that the
mercury and ice-water mixture are at the same temperature. The position
of mercury is then carefully marked on the glass. The bulb is next immersed in water, which is heated to its boiling point; this new, higher

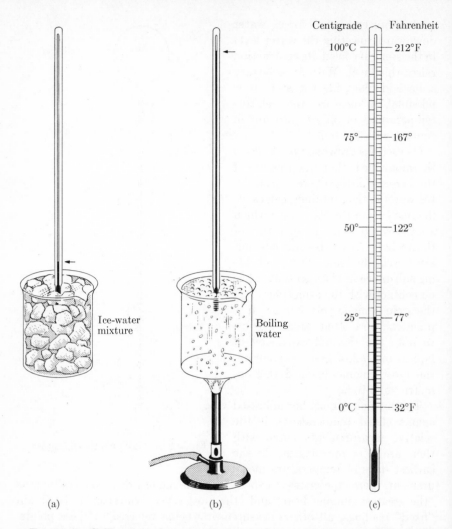

FIG. 11–2. Calibration of a mercury thermometer. (a) Marking off the lower fixed point, (b) marking off the higher fixed point, (c) marking off intermediate points, establishing a scale.

position of the mercury is now marked on the glass. A difference of temperature has been established by the two marks; it is found by experience that this difference, at fixed atmospheric pressure, is perfectly reproducible.

To establish a *scale* of temperature, the difference in height of the mercury column between the two fixed points must be suitably subdivided. In the *Centigrade* scale this distance is simply marked off into 100 equal divisions.* A Centigrade degree is thus 1/100 of the temperature interval between the freezing and boiling temperatures of water. For further convenience, the freezing point of water at normal atmospheric pressure is arbitrarily called 0°C, the boiling point 100°C; a temperature of 25°C thus represents just $\frac{1}{4}$ of the fixed calibration interval. In the *Fahrenheit* scale the lower fixed temperature is called 32°F, the higher 212°F, and the intervening linear distance on the thermometer is divided into 180 equal parts. A Centigrade degree is therefore larger than a Fahrenheit degree; interconversion between the two scales may be accomplished by means of the relation

$t°F$ (Fahrenheit temperature)
$$= 9/5 \ t°C \text{ (Centigrade temperature)} + 32. \qquad (11-1)$$

Both the Centigrade and Fahrenheit scales were developed during the 18th century. The latter was originally constructed with a certain ice-salt mixture as the lower calibration point, designated 0°F. While the Centigrade scale is used almost exclusively in the scientific community, there is nothing peculiarly "scientific" about it—it is simply convenient. The actual size of any temperature unit is arbitrary, since it is only difference in temperature that we are ordinarily able to measure.

It must not be thought that mercury is the only thermometric fluid currently in use, or, for that matter, that expansion is the only temperature-indicating property. The range of usefulness of mercury is limited by its freezing point (−39°C) and boiling point (357°C). At lower temperatures other fluids, e.g., hydrogen or helium gas, and at higher temperatures properties other than expansion, must be employed. The property of electrical resistance of platinum is commonly used for precise temperature measurement within the very wide range −190°C to 660°C.

11–2 Calorimetry and specific heat

Anyone who has sat before an open fire is aware that *something* is communicated from the fire to his body, and has learned to call that "something" *heat*. Similarly, the fact that bodies at initially different temperatures tend to reach a common temperature when in contact can be interpreted in terms of a flow of heat from the hotter to the colder body. We

---

*If these divisions are to be equal in temperature, as in length, the mercury must expand *uniformly* between the freezing and boiling temperatures of water. It doesn't, quite, and precise thermometry requires either intervening calibration temperatures or suitable corrections. The discrepancy is so slight that it need not worry us here, however.

make no hypothesis about the real nature of heat in choosing to think of it as something that flows, spontaneously, from bodies of higher temperature to others of lower temperature. That heat differs from temperature is clear from the fact that 10 kgm of water at 95°C in a radiator is much more effective in warming a cold room than a single gram at 95°C would be. Yet the distinction between temperature as the *intensity* of hotness of a given body and heat as a *quantity* of something which may flow from that body to a colder one was not firmly established before about 1750.

It is to Joseph Black, whom we have already met in Chapter 6, that we are most indebted for establishment of a science of heat. Black's quantitative measurements of heat depended on two methods that were developed by his predecessors. The first of these grew out of the observation of G. D. Fahrenheit (1668–1736) that equal volumes of cold and hot water, when mixed, attain a final temperature which is exactly midway between their initial temperatures. For example, if 100 cc of water at 20°C is mixed with an equal quantity of water at 80°C, the final common temperature is found to be 50°C. If we tentatively regard the change in temperature a body undergoes as a measure of the quantity of heat it has either gained or lost, the observation that the temperatures of the hot and cold water samples change by the same amount (30°) strongly implies that the heat lost by the former is equal to that gained by the latter. This implication can be (and was) checked by mixing unequal quantities of water, an experiment that we shall consider a little later. The assumption that, with proper insulation from the surroundings,

Heat gained (by colder body) = Heat lost (by hotter body)

became the basic principle of *calorimetry* (quantitative heat measurement) during the first half of the 18th century, and remains so today.

A second method of heat measurement, prominently employed by Black, was used earlier by George Martine (1702–1741). In this method an object is exposed to a source of heat, e.g., a stove or open fire, and its temperature observed at regular intervals of time. It is assumed that the source of heat is steady, and that the quantity of heat absorbed by the object is proportional to the elapsed time of its exposure, at least for small temperature intervals. This method is not so reliable, quantitatively, as the first, but Black found it useful, most fruitfully in connection with the phenomena to be discussed in Section 11–3. Note that the two methods involve different (but not contradictory) assumptions; reenforcement of the conclusions of any experiment by an independent method is always of great significance in science.

Black became concerned, early in his career, with the *relative capacities* of different substances for absorbing heat. Certain observations of Martine and of Fahrenheit had suggested that the amount of heat necessary to produce equal temperature changes in different kinds of bodies was not simply proportional to either the masses or the volumes of the bodies. As a result of more systematic experiments, using both techniques of measurement, Black came to the conclusion that the quantity of heat necessary to raise the temperature of a given mass of a substance through a given interval of temperature, a quantity he called *capacity for heat*, is unique for each substance. The quantity we now call *specific heat*, an outgrowth of Black's discovery, defined as *the quantity of heat required to raise the temperature of one gram of a substance through one Centigrade degree,* is an important intrinsic property of elements and compounds.

Let us see how specific heats may be measured and compared. A convenient unit for heat measurement grew out of Fahrenheit's experiment, as refined and extended by Black. We shall represent change of temperature by Δt, and quantity of heat (in units still to be defined) by H. (The Greek letter Δ, delta, designates "change of.") The quantity of heat required to raise the temperature of a body through Δt is proportional to Δt and to the mass m of the body, as may be expressed in the equation

$$H = sm\, \Delta t. \qquad (11\text{–}2)$$

Here s is a constant of proportionality. It was Black's conclusion that s depends on the substance heated, and we can see from Eq. (11–2) that it has the units of a quantity of heat per unit mass per degree of temperature change. A unit of heat may be defined by selecting some substance as a standard, and arbitrarily setting s for that substance equal to unity. The most convenient standard substance for this purpose is water: the metric unit of heat, the *calorie*, is defined in such a way that the value of $s_{H_2O} = 1$. *One calorie is that quantity of heat capable of raising the temperature of one gram of water through the temperature interval* 1°C.*

The water *calorimeter*, illustrated in Fig. 11–3, is used extensively for determining the specific heats of various substances. It consists of a

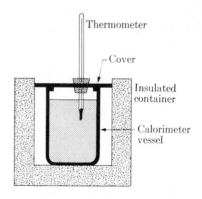

Thermometer

Cover

Insulated container

Calorimeter vessel

Fig. 11–3. Calorimeter.

---

*The Calorie used in dietetics is 1000 times that defined here, and is defined as the quantity of heat needed to raise the temperature of one kilogram of water by 1°C. This unit is also called a kilocalorie and a great calorie.

container, carefully insulated to minimize heat losses to its surroundings, equipped with an insulated cover and a thermometer. Let us imagine an experiment, as mentioned above, in which unequal quantities of water at different temperatures are mixed. First, suppose 100 gm of water is weighed in the calorimeter container, and that its temperature is observed to be 20°C. A second water sample, weighing 50 gm, has been brought to a temperature of 80°C in a separate container; this water is added to that in the calorimeter, mixed, and the final temperature noted. If the experiment is performed carefully this final temperature will be found to be almost exactly 40°C. Let us employ Eq. (11–2) to see whether this result is consistent with the assumption that heat gained by the cool water is equal to that lost by the hot water:

$$H_1 \text{ (gained by cold water)} = H_2 \text{ (lost by hot water)}.$$

H_1 = mass of cold water × specific heat of water × rise in temperature
    = $m_1 s_{H_2O} (\Delta t)_1$, and

H_2 = mass of hot water × specific heat of water × loss in temperature
    = $m_2 s_{H_2O} (\Delta t)_2$,

so that
$$m_1 s_{H_2O} (\Delta t)_1 = m_2 s_{H_2O} (\Delta t)_2.$$

If we represent the final temperature by t_f,

$$(\Delta t)_1 = t_f - 20°C,$$
and
$$(\Delta t)_2 = 80°C - t_f.$$

With numerical substitutions, the equation above, after canceling s_{H_2O}, becomes
$$100(t_f - 20°C) = 50(80°C - t_f),$$
hence
$$t_f = 40°C.$$

The temperature actually observed would be slightly less than 40°C; the container itself absorbs some heat, which we have neglected in the computation. Nevertheless, the assumptions are in good agreement with the observations.

Let us now use the calorimeter to determine the specific heat of a substance other than water, say aluminum. Start with 100 gm of water at 20°C in the calorimeter, as before, and add 250 gm of aluminum metal that has been brought to a temperature of 95°C. (The metal should be in small pieces, to facilitate exchange of heat with the water.) This time we may observe the final temperature and use it in Eq. (11–2) to determine s_{A1}. This final temperature, by *observation*, turns out to be 45°C. Equating the heat lost by the aluminum to that gained by the water, we obtain

$$s_{A1}\ 250\ (95°C\ -\ 45°C)\ =\ s_{H_2O}\ 100\ (45°C\ -\ 20°C).$$

Therefore

$$s_{A1}\ =\ \frac{100\times 25}{250\times 50}\ s_{H_2O}\ =\ 0.2\ s_{H_2O}.$$

Since s_{H_2O} is one calorie per gram per degree Centigrade, by the definition of a calorie, s_{A1} is 0.2 calorie per gram per degree Centigrade.

The utility of the water calorimeter makes clear the convenience of using water as a standard substance for defining a unit of heat, but the specific heat of water is relatively high. For most solid substances the specific heat is even lower than that of aluminum.

11–3 Latent heat and changes of state

From our discussion thus far it would seem that transfer of what we have agreed to call heat is invariably associated with changes of temperature. One of Joseph Black's most impressive achievements was his discovery that heat can be absorbed, under certain conditions, *without* producing a change in temperature. His first experimental demonstration of this phenomenon was carried out with two equal quantities of water in identical containers. One of these was placed in a mixture of snow and salt until frozen, the other cooled to within one degree of the freezing point (32°F) but not frozen. The two containers were then suspended side by side in a large room, in which the air temperature was observed to be 47°F. The temperature of the liquid water was recorded at intervals, and was found to have reached 40°F at the end of $\frac{1}{2}$ hour. The ice melted so slowly that $10\frac{1}{2}$ hours elapsed before it was found to be all liquid and its temperature had also risen to 40°F. Black's method in this experiment, it will be noted, is that of exposing the two samples to a steady heat source, in this case simply the relatively warm air of the room. If both absorbed heat at the same rate, 21 times as much heat was required to melt the ice and raise the temperature of the resulting water to 40°F as to raise the temperature of the same quantity of water through a similar interval. It could only be concluded that a large quantity of heat was absorbed by the melting ice which was not reflected in a change of temperature. This heat, absorbed in melting but inactive in producing temperature change, Black called the *latent heat of fusion* of ice.

Black's more precise measurement of the latent heat of fusion employed the calorimetric method of mixing; his best value, converted to the units we are using, was 82 calories per gram of ice; the value accepted today is 79.7 cal/gm. Black also showed that when water begins to freeze below its freezing point (supercooled water), its temperature immediately rises to the freezing point and remains there until all the water is frozen, although the snow and ice mixture surrounding the container may be considerably colder. This he took to mean that freezing, the reverse of melting, is accompanied by *evolution* of heat. Indeed it can be demonstrated that the same quantity of heat, 79.7 calories, *absorbed* by every gram of melting ice, is *given off* by every gram of freezing water.

On the hunch that absorption or evolution of heat accompanies all changes in state of matter, Black next turned his attention to the vaporization of water. He found that while the temperature of water rises steadily with constant addition of heat up to the boiling point, it remains constant during the period required for water to turn to steam. Further, he found that the temperature of steam rising from boiling water is the same as that of the water itself. But heat is being supplied continuously during this process, and thus there is *latent heat of vaporization*, necessary for change of state, but not effective in producing temperature change. Modern measurements have shown that one gram of water absorbs 539.6 calories of heat in passing from the liquid to the gaseous state at 100°C. One gram of steam, on condensing to liquid water, gives up this same quantity of heat.

The quantitative importance of latent heat is shown graphically in Fig. 11–4. Heat is supplied uniformly to a given sample of water, initially

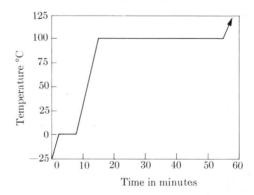

FIG. 11–4. Temperature plotted against time for a quantity of water exposed to a steady heat source.

ice at −25°C. The temperature of the sample is plotted on the vertical axis, time horizontally. A steady rise of temperature is observed until the freezing point, 0°C, is reached; temperature then remains constant with time until the entire sample has melted. A steady rise is again observed until the boiling temperature, 100°C, is attained, where another (longer) interval of constant temperature is observed. After all the liquid has vaporized the temperature of the resulting steam also exhibits a rise with the continuing application of heat. It is strikingly clear that much more time (and thus much more heat) is required for the melting and evaporation than for changing the temperature of liquid water from 0°C to 100°C. If the graph is read from right to left, the sequence of events accompanying uniform cooling of the same sample is obtained.

To illustrate a way of measuring the latent heat of fusion of ice, let us suppose that our calorimeter (Fig. 11–3) contains 100 gm of water at 80°C, that we add to it 20 gm of ice at 0°C, and observe that the mixture reaches a final temperature of 53.4°C. We know that the heat lost by the hot water is

$$H_1 = s_{H_2O} m \, \Delta t = 1 \text{ cal/gm-deg} \times 100 \text{ gm} \times (80° − 53.4°)$$

$$= 100 \times 26.6 = 2660 \text{ calories.}$$

We also know that the quantity of heat required to raise 20 gm of *liquid* water from 0°C to 53.4°C is

$$H_2 = 1 \text{ cal/gm-deg} \times 20 \text{ gm} \times (53.4° − 0°)$$

$$= 20 \times 53.4 = 1070 \text{ calories.}$$

We are then left with (2660 − 1070) = 1590 calories of heat which has been lost by the hot water, but has not produced a temperature rise in the cold water. This quantity of heat must have been absorbed by the ice, in the process of melting. Since 20 gm of ice are involved, the latent heat of fusion of ice from this experiment is (1590/20) = 79.5 cal/gm. Note that we are still assuming no heat has been gained or lost by the contents of the calorimeter *as a whole;* we must, however, take into account the heat involved in any changes of state that take place in the mixing.

All substances exhibit characteristic latent heats of fusion and vaporization, and a satisfactory theory of heat must somehow account for this phenomenon, discovered empirically by Black.

11–4 What is heat?

We have now learned something about the operations by which heat is measured, but we have gained no concrete idea of the *nature* of heat. We began by noting the "flow" of heat; if we take our cue from the convenience of this conception, the hypothesis that heat consists of a *fluid substance* suggests itself. This hypothesis can be traced back to Greek science (e.g., the Aristotelian element *fire*), and was widely held, in one form or another, until the 19th century. In Joseph Black's opinion it was the most probable hypothesis of the nature of heat, and Black's opinions were certainly to be respected.

The name *caloric* for the substance of heat was suggested by Lavoisier in 1787; his incorporation of this assumed substance into his system of chemistry was one stimulus for the construction of a detailed Caloric Theory. The basis of this theory was the assumption that heat, or the "caloric fluid," consists of minute material particles. Since no one had been able to demonstrate that a body is heavier when hot than when cold, it was thought that these particles might have vanishingly small mass. Since heat tends to distribute itself diffusely, the caloric particles were assumed to exert repulsive forces on one another. Wide variation among the specific heats of substances was accounted for in terms of varying attractions of substances for caloric. Caloric was thought to be conserved, i.e., neither created nor destroyed, and to occur in two interconvertible forms, *sensible* and *latent*. "Sensible" caloric was that form responsible for temperature changes, while latent caloric was assumed to enter into combination with matter. The assumption of latent caloric accounted for the evolution or absorption of "sensible" heat commonly observed to accompany chemical changes, as well as fusion and vaporization, i.e., changes of state.

While the concept of caloric provided the most successful theory of heat in the 18th century, not all scientists subscribed to it. An alternative idea was suggested by the observation that heat is produced by the action of frictional forces. Since these forces act only where there is motion, it may be that heat itself is simply motion of the particles of matter, motion which can be accelerated by friction. Newton entertained this view, and had written in 1704 that "Heat consists in a minute vibratory motion of the particles of bodies." Before him, in 1620, Francis Bacon had written a detailed treatise on heat and its production, and had reached a similar conclusion. But the first man who strove vigorously to justify the idea experimentally was the amazing Benjamin Thompson (1753–1814), better known as Count Rumford of Bavaria.

Benjamin Thompson was born in Woburn, Massachusetts. He entertained pro-royalist sympathies, entered British governmental service during the American revolution, and was later knighted by George III. Moving on to the European continent, he became Aide-de-Camp to the Elector Palatine Duke of Bavaria, then Inspector General of Bavarian Artillery and, later, Minister of War and Minister of Police. His service to Bavaria, which lasted until 1799, was rewarded in 1791 by elevation to the titled status of Count Rumford of the Holy Roman Empire. His last years were spent in France, where he married Lavoisier's widow. Although busy with varied practical concerns throughout his Bavarian years, Rumford somehow found time for active investigation in the science of heat, his most compelling intellectual interest.*

While to many of his contemporaries the apparently imponderable or "subtle" nature of caloric was no stumbling block to its acceptance, Rumford was unwilling to adopt the material view of heat without knowing that caloric has weight. Accordingly, he performed a series of experiments, with the greatest accuracy possible, on the weight of water before and after freezing. Aware of Black's discovery of latent heat, Rumford knew that a prodigious quantity of heat is given up by water as it turns into ice. If caloric is a substance, he argued, a given quantity of water should weigh less when frozen than when liquid. His careful experiments demonstrated, however, that there is no detectable change in the weight of water on freezing. Unable to establish ponderability in heat, Rumford became convinced that it is not a substance at all. He then sought other ways to discredit the caloric theory.

One of the most vulnerable aspects of the caloric theory was its assumption that heat is conserved. While it was known since ancient times that heat may be produced by friction, the caloricists assumed that frictional forces did not "create" caloric, but contrived somehow to "squeeze" it out of bodies in "sensible" form. Count Rumford's most celebrated experiment, designed to attack just this weak point in the caloric theory, was suggested to him in the following way:

"Being engaged lately in superintending the boring of cannon in the workshops of the military arsenal at Munich, I was struck with the very considerable degree of heat that a brass gun acquires in a short time in being bored, and with the still higher temperature (much higher than that

---

*Rumford was also well known as inventor, social reformer, and benefactor of scientific endeavor. He provided funds to establish the Royal Institution in London, for the purpose of "diffusing the knowledge . . . of new and useful mechanical inventions and improvements; and also for teaching, by regular courses of philosophical lectures and experiments, the applications of the new discoveries in science to the improvement of arts and manufactures." This institution has supported the careers of a long succession of scientists, beginning with Humphrey Davy and Michael Faraday. It justly remains one of the famous scientific centers of the world.

of boiling water, as I found by experiment) of the metallic chips separated from it by the borer.

"The more I meditated on these phenomena, the more they appeared to me to be curious and interesting. A thorough investigation of them seemed even to bid fair to give a farther insight into the hidden nature of heat; and to enable us to form some reasonable conjectures respecting the existence, or nonexistence, of an *igneous fluid* [i.e., caloric]—a subject on which the opinions of philosophers have in all ages been much divided."

If the caloricists' assumption that "sensible" heat is "squeezed" out of a body by friction were correct, then the capacity of the body for heat must be changed in the process. Accordingly, Rumford measured the specific heat of the brass chips formed in the boring of a cannon and that of the bulk brass constituting the main part of his cannon barrel, using the method of mixtures. He found the specific heat of brass completely unaltered by the action of his boring tool. Next he satisfied himself that the production of heat was unrelated to the *size* of brass chips produced. Finally, he devised a way of immersing the portion of the barrel to be bored and the boring tool itself in a fixed quantity of water. While the barrel was being bored continuously by horsepower Rumford measured the temperature of the water at regular intervals, and observed that it rose steadily until, after $2\frac{1}{2}$ hours, the water began to boil. He was delighted:

"It would be difficult to describe the surprise and astonishment expressed in the countenances of the bystanders on seeing so large a quantity of cold water heated, and actually made to boil, without any fire. Though there was, in fact, nothing that could justly be considered as surprising in this event, yet I acknowledged fairly that it afforded me a degree of childish pleasure, which, were I ambitious of the reputation of *grave philosopher*, I ought most certainly rather to hide than to discover."

Rumford performed several experiments of this sort, calculating in each case the total quantity of heat developed by friction. He laid primary emphasis on the impressive magnitude of these quantities, and on the fact that heat seemed to be continuously and inexhaustibly available so long as his horses were performing work. Rumford felt he had dealt a blow to the caloric theory from which it could not recover, as is shown in his conclusion:

". . .anything which any insulated body, or system of bodies, can continue to furnish without limitation, cannot possibly be a material substance; and it appears to me to be extremely difficult, if not quite impossible, to form any distinct idea of anything capable of being excited and communicated in the manner in which heat was excited and communicated in these experiments, except it be MOTION."

11-5 The mechanical equivalent of heat

While there was nothing in Count Rumford's experiments constituting a proof that heat is motion, his arguments did severely weaken the alternative caloric hypothesis. Where there is motion, it will be recalled from Chapter 10, there is *energy*, and the heat-is-motion hypothesis could be made to read: *heat is a form of energy*. The energy concept, in terms of the older concept of mechanical work, was becoming increasingly clear. By 1800 there was ample evidence, including Rumford's experiments, to suggest a possible equivalence between heat and work. The improved steam engine of James Watt* (1736–1819), after all, with its relatively enormous capacity for conversion of heat to mechanical work, had been one of the principal factors in the transformation of England from an agricultural to an industrial nation. While Rumford was convinced that the heat produced in his experiment depended only on the work done by his horses, he did not attempt to calculate *how much* heat was produced by expenditure of a *measured* quantity of work. It was not until the decade of the 1840's that the equivalence of heat and work was fully explored, most significantly by the German physician Julius Robert Mayer (1814–1889) and the English brewer and amateur physicist James Prescott Joule (1818–1889).

As ship's surgeon during a tropical voyage, Mayer observed that the color of venous blood is a more vivid red than when observed in the cooler climate of Germany. This single circumstance, he reported, touched off a train of thought: tropical heat (somehow, presumably, the cause of altered color of blood) led him to heat as a form of energy, and in turn to many other energy forms manifested by nature. In a long paper (1842) filled almost equally with brilliant insight and questionable logic, Mayer became the first to enunciate publicly the completely general form of the Principle of Conservation of Energy: "... Energies are ... indestructible, convertible entities."

Mayer's approach was to begin with a theoretical formulation of the broadest possible kind, for which he offered no convincing quantitative

---

*Watt, as instrument maker at Glasgow University, was associated with Joseph Black, who explained to him some of the phenomena Watt observed in his early studies of the steam engine. The success of a technologic invention, we should note, often does not depend on the "correctness" of its inventor's conceptual scientific frame of reference. Watt, like Black, preferred to regard heat as a material substance. Moreover, the theory of the (ideal) heat engine that originally utilized the concept of caloric is still valid. Sadi Carnot (1796–1832), who devised this theory, later came to regard heat as particle motion, with heat and mechanical energy interconvertible and equivalent. Carnot died in a cholera epidemic, and his notebooks containing these views remained unknown for nearly half a century.

proof. His paper was largely ignored, appearing to his contemporaries as an entirely speculative work unsupported by fact. Yet Mayer recognized the most crucial question of fact posed by his great generalization: is there a definite quantity of heat which corresponds to a given quantity of mechanical energy? If so, how great a quantity? Not possessing either the equipment or the inclination for experiments of his own, he attempted to answer this question on the basis of existing data in the scientific literature.

Joule, in England, began with this more limited question, and set out to demonstrate the equivalence of heat and mechanical energy by experimental means. The contrast between the two men has been ascribed* to the difference in their national scientific traditions: "True to the speculative instinct of his country, Mayer drew large and weighty conclusions from slender premises, while the Englishman aimed, above all things, at the firm establishment of facts. And he did establish them." Joule's first results, published in 1843, consisted of measurements of the mechanical work required to drive an electric generator and the heat simultaneously produced by the electric current of the generator. Subsequently he turned his attention to the measurement of heat generated by friction. In all, he devoted a period of ten years to intensive quantitative experimentation, designed to show that whenever a quantity of mechanical work is expended in the production of heat, a quantity of heat is produced such that the ratio

$$J = \frac{\text{Quantity of work done}}{\text{Quantity of heat produced}}$$

has always the same value.†

Of the various kinds of experiments Joule performed to measure J, a typical one is illustrated in Fig. 11–5. Mechanical work is done by gravity on the weight W as it falls through height h. Weight W, in turn, does work on the paddlewheel, causing it to rotate. There is friction between the blades of the paddlewheel and the water in the calorimeter vessel, which produces heat. The quantity of heat produced can be measured by determining the rise in temperature of the water, for after many repeated falls a readily measurable temperature increase is observed. The mechani-

---

*By John Tyndall, himself a famous scientist and the successor of Michael Faraday at the Royal Institution, London.

†Joule's precision and thoroughness overshadowed the similar work of Colding, a Danish engineer. The energy principle was "in the air" just before the middle of the 19th century, and a number of scientists grasped it independently. See, e.g., Carl B. Boyer, "History of the Measurement of Heat, II, The Conservation of Energy," *Scientific Monthly*, **LVII** (1943), pp. 546–554.

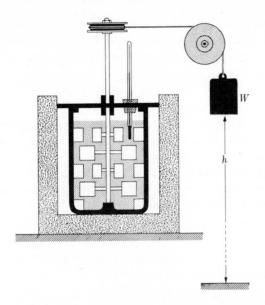

Fig. 11–5. Apparatus for measuring the mechanical equivalent of heat.

cal work done on the weight by gravity, and by the weight on the paddle-wheel, is equivalent to its potential energy at height h; therefore, for a single fall,

$$\text{Quantity of work done} = m_W g h.$$

If the mass of the weight, m_W, is in grams, the height h in centimeters, and g in cm/sec², this quantity of work will be expressed in ergs. The amount of heat imparted to the water is

$$\text{Quantity of heat produced} = s_{H_2O} \times m_{H_2O} \times \Delta t,$$

which will be in calories if s_{H_2O} is taken to be 1 cal/gm-deg, m_{H_2O} is in grams, and the interval Δt is in Centigrade degrees. The ratio J, determined by allowing the weight to drop N times, is then given by

$$J = \frac{N \times m_W \times g \times h}{m_{H_2O} \times \Delta t} \text{ ergs/cal.}$$

By 1849 Joule had obtained the same value of J, within reasonable experimental error, for hundreds of separate measurements employing a variety of modes of heat production. From his most careful measurements he assigned the value 4.15×10^7 ergs/cal to this ratio, which is called the *mechanical equivalent of heat*. Measurements made with modern techniques give

$$J = 4.1855 \times 10^7 \text{ ergs/cal.}$$

If we recall that the energy unit of one *joule* is defined as 10^7 ergs, we may express the mechanical equivalent of heat (also known as Joule's equivalent) more simply: $J = 4.19$ joules/cal.

Joule's prodigious efforts, so justly commemorated in the names of both the mechanical equivalent and the energy unit, eventually had great effect in convincing his contemporaries that:

"We shall be obliged to admit that Count Rumford was right in attributing the heat evolved by boring cannon to friction . . . [I am] satisfied that the grand agents of nature are, by the Creator's fiat, *indestructible*; and that whenever mechanical force [i.e., work] is expended, an exact equivalent of heat is *always* obtained."

11–6 The principle of conservation of energy

Around 1840 the time was so ripe for emergence of the principle that energy can be transformed but not created or destroyed, and that heat is only one form of energy, that several scientists in different countries came upon the idea independently. Yet the principle was not widely accepted or even widely known until after 1850. The individual who proved most influential in bringing about general recognition of the principle was the brilliant and versatile Hermann von Helmholtz (1821–1894). Helmholtz, a physiologist as well as a physicist, sought to discredit the hypothesis of "vital force" then popular in biological science, and argued that living creatures would be perpetual motion machines if they derived energy from any source other than their food. The impossibility of perpetual motion had long been recognized in mechanics, and it was on this principle and Newton's third law that Helmholtz based his belief in the equivalence of all forms of energy. Thus he extended (1847) the energy conservation principle to include life processes as well as those described by chemistry and physics. He demonstrated the universality of the principle by elaborate mathematical calculations and rigorous logic applied to scientific observations. Within a very few years his arguments, combined with Joule's irrefutable experiments, convinced the scientific world that energy is *indestructible*, although *interconvertible*. Confidence in the principle has become so great that it is frequently stated in the single grand generalization: *the energy of the universe is constant.*

About 1860, when it had received general recognition, the energy conservation law became a cornerstone of all natural science. Every new theory is tested to see whether it is consistent with energy conservation, and every empirical discovery is interpreted in the light of it. Throughout the remainder of this book we shall encounter the principle in many different contexts, especially as we begin to learn about energy forms other than those we have studied thus far. For the time being, however, we shall continue to focus our attention on heat. The equivalence of heat and mechanical energy may have convinced us that heat is a form of energy, rather than a material substance, but it has shed no further light on the hypothesis that heat is motion. In Chapter 13 we shall learn something of the fundamental nature of heat.

11-7 Summary

It is necessary to distinguish between *temperature* and *quantity* of heat. Temperature, the level or intensity of heat, is measured in degrees on an arbitrary, reproducible scale. Quantity of heat is measured in units called calories, defined in terms of the specific substance water and the Centigrade temperature scale. Gain or loss of heat implies rise or fall of temperature except during change of state, during which heat is absorbed or released without change of temperature. Heat was once thought to be a "subtle fluid," but Count Rumford concluded from his experiments that heat is a "mode of [internal] motion." In the first half of the 19th century it became clear that heat is a form of energy; Joule and others showed that if work is done to produce heat the quantitative ratio of work input to heat produced always has the same value. This led to one of the most far-reaching of all scientific principles, that of conservation of energy: *the energy of the universe is constant*, although energy may be transformed in a great variety of ways. To understand just how heat is a "mode of motion" requires a further study of matter, primarily of gases.

REFERENCES

HOLTON, G., *Introduction to Concepts and Theories in Physical Science*, pp. 345–357, 376–383.

MACH, E., *History and Root of the Principle of the Conservation of Energy*. Difficult but rewarding.

MAGIE, W. F., *A Sourcebook in Physics*, pp. 134–145 (Black), 146–161 (Rumford), 197–203 (Mayer), 203, 211 (Joule).

McKIE, D., and N. H. HEATHCOTE, *The Discovery of Specific and Latent Heats*.

ROLLER, D. *The Early Development of the Concepts of Temperature and Heat— The Rise and Decline of the Caloric Theory* (Number 3 of the Harvard Case Histories in Experimental Science). Contains a detailed treatment of the work of Black and Rumford, plus some important work of Sir Humphrey Davy not described in this chapter.

SEMAT, H., *Physics in the Modern World*.

TAYLOR, L. W., *Physics, the Pioneer Science*, Chapters 19–22.

TYNDALL, J., *Heat, a Mode of Motion*.

For more detail on particular contributors to the early science and technology of heat, see:

DICKINSON, H. W., and H. P. VOWLES, *James Watt and the Industrial Revolution*.

RAMSAY, W., *The Life and Letters of Joseph Black*.

THOMPSON, J. A., *Count Rumford of Massachusetts*.

EXERCISES — CHAPTER 11

1. (a) Ethyl alcohol boils at 78°C. What is this temperature on the Fahrenheit scale? (b) The "normal" temperature of the human body is 98.6°F. What is this temperature on the Centigrade scale? [*Ans.*: (a) 172°F; (b) 37.0°C]

2. How many calories of heat must be supplied to 2 kgm (2000 gm) of water to raise its temperature from 17°C to the boiling point? How many additional calories would be required to make one-fifth of the water vaporize?

3. What final temperature would you expect to observe in a calorimetric experiment in which 70 gm of water at 15°C are mixed with 25 gm of water at 97°C? [*Ans.*: 36.6°C]

4. A 100-gm mass of ice at 0°C is added to 100 gm of water at 80°C in a calorimeter. What final temperature do you predict?

5. The specific heat of iron is 0.113 cal/gm/°C, and its density is 7.86 gm/cm^3. If *equal volumes* of iron and water are set side by side before a steady heat source, which will show the greater rate of temperature rise? By about what factor? [*Ans.*: Iron, by about 10 to 9]

6. The Law of Dulong and Petit (see footnote, Section 7–6), which was very useful in the assignment of atomic weights to solid elements during the 19th century, states that the products of the atomic weights and specific heats of the elements all have approximately the same value.

(a) Find whether this law is valid for the several elements whose specific heats are listed below.

Element	Specific heat (cal/gm/°C)
Aluminum	0.217
Copper	0.093
Iron	0.113
Lead	0.031
Silver	0.056

(b) Use the average value of your results in (a) to calculate the approximate specific heat of the element manganese.

(c) The element rhenium (Re) forms an oxide which contains 85.4% rhenium by weight. What would you predict for its atomic weight if this compound were assigned the formula Re_2O? ReO? ReO_2? Re_2O_3? The specific heat of rhenium is found to be 0.035 cal/gm/°C. With this information, can you settle the question of its atomic weight and assign an appropriate formula to its oxide without peeking at the table of atomic weights? This is an example of the way in which the law of Dulong and Petit, despite its highly approximate nature, was valuable to 19th-century chemistry.

7. A 200-gm mass of cadmium metal at 20°C is added to 40 gm of water at 40°C in a calorimeter. The observed final temperature is 35.6°C. What is the specific heat of cadmium? [*Ans.*: 0.056 cal/gm/°C]

8. (a) A common practice in past generations was to place large tubs of

239

water in fruit cellars on very cold nights, to protect the fruit against freezing. Explain. (b) A burn inflicted by a small quantity of steam is very much more severe than one inflicted by a much larger quantity of liquid water near its boiling point. Explain.

9. Assume that the quantity of water referred to in Fig. 11–4 is one gram. At what rate is heat then being supplied to result in the points shown in the graph?

10. Acetic acid freezes at 16.7°C with a latent heat of 44.7 cal/gm; the specific heat of this substance is 0.47 cal/gm/°C. What final temperature would result from mixing 10 gm of solid acetic acid at 15°C with 50 gm of water at 50°C? [*Ans.*: 38.8°C]

11. A pendulum with a 200-gm bob is set to swinging from a height of 10 cm. After 20 minutes the height of its swing is only 5 cm. Why? Calculate the average *rate* at which the pendulum bob has lost energy during the 20-minute period.

12. In a certain machine it is found that a force of 5×10^7 dynes must be exerted through 100 cm in order that the machine may exert a force of 4×10^9 dynes through only 1 cm. What quantity of heat, in calories, is developed by friction between the moving parts of the machine during this operation? [*Ans.*: 24 cal]

13. A 10-kgm block of iron (specific heat 0.113 cal/gm/°C) falls from a height of 10 m and is then stopped suddenly by collision with a massive rigid surface. What has become of its kinetic energy? If its temperature at the start of its fall was 20°C, what is the *maximum* temperature it could exhibit on being brought to rest? Why is this a maximum?

14. Joule predicted, in 1845, that the temperature of water at the bottom of a waterfall should be higher than that at the top; he later verified this prediction in Switzerland (while on his honeymoon!). What is the basis of Joule's prediction? Niagara Falls is about 50 m high. What is the maximum difference in temperature you might expect to observe between water at the top and at the bottom of Niagara Falls? [*Ans.*: About 0.12°C]

15. How much external energy, in calories, must a 150-lb man expend in climbing a ramp with a vertical lift of 50 ft? What is the source of this energy? (1 lb = 454 gm, 1 in. = 2.54 cm.) [*Ans.*: About 2400 cal]

CHAPTER 12

THE GASEOUS STATE OF MATTER

A circumstance which attended acceptance in the 19th century of the idea that heat is a form of energy was development of a theory that made possible the *quantitative* identification of heat and molecular motion. We shall study some of the details of this theory, the *Kinetic Theory of Matter*, in the next chapter. The theory was initially devised to explain the behavior of matter in its gaseous state. To understand its success and its importance we must be acquainted with some of the empirical knowledge of gases that preceded its construction. In a sense, the subject matter of the present chapter constitutes a digression from the developing train of thought between the past two chapters and Chapter 13. It is an essential digression, however; without it that train of thought could not be pursued further.

12-1 The concept of pressure

Gases and liquids, together, are known as the *fluid* states of matter; in contrast to solids, which are rigid, they possess ability to assume the shape of any container. Gases are unlike liquids, however, in their ability to fill a container *completely*. The rate at which water flows out of a hole of given size in a barrel is greatest when the hole is at the bottom, and progressively less at higher positions on the sides, as shown in Fig. 12–1(a). (The top of the barrel must be open to the atmosphere, as shown, for appreciable flow to take place.) A single hole in a closed container of compressed gas, however, will permit the gas to escape at a rate which does not depend upon position, for a hole of fixed size (Fig. 12–1b).

In the necessity for using the word "compressed" in the last sentence we have found it impossible to avoid allusion to the extremely useful concept of *pressure*. It is clear that our contained gas must exert a force on the walls of its container that results in its tendency to escape. (When we say that the gas is *compressed* we mean that the force it exerts on the inside of its container must be greater than that exerted on the outside by atmospheric air; if it were not, air would leak *into* the container.) As indicated in Fig. 12–1(b), the force exerted by the gas on any small portion of its container wall must be uniform, since it is the same for all holes of equal area, regardless of position. It is just this kind of consideration that makes

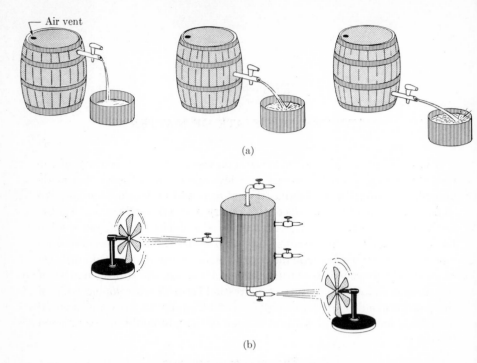

FIG. 12–1. (a) Rate of flow of water from a barrel increases as position of spigot is lowered. (b) Compressed gas will turn the fan at the same rate when permitted to escape from any one of the similar valves at the positions shown.

it convenient to define, as a new quantity, the ratio of a force to the area over which it is distributed (see Fig. 12–2). That quantity, force per unit area, is called *pressure*:

$$P \text{ (pressure)} = \frac{f \text{ (force)}}{A \text{ (area)}}.$$

The considerations of the preceding paragraph may now be summarized by saying that a contained gas exerts the same pressure on all parts of its container, while the pressure exerted by a liquid (Fig. 12–1a) increases with depth.

The increase in liquid pressure with depth is not limited to the walls of the container; anyone who dives is aware that the pressure inside the water itself similarly increases. It is also true that at any given point in the interior of a fluid the same pressure is exerted in all directions. Although this statement is central to the study of liquids at rest (*hydrostatics*, a

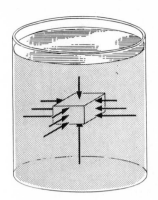

Fig. 12–2.   Pressure exerted by a
boulder on the earth: 500 lb/300 in²
= 1.43 lb/in².

Fig. 12–3.   Pressures exerted on an
immersed object.

science highly developed as long ago as the time of Archimedes), it is not
possible to point to single simple observations which "prove" it. Perhaps
it will be sufficient for us to argue, as did Stevinus of Bruges, that if there
were *un*equal pressures acting at any point in a stationary fluid, motion
(currents) would result, and the fluid would not be static at all.

An object which is wholly immersed in water experiences pressures from
above and below and from all sides. The absence of sideward motion shows
that pressures from opposite horizontal directions, at any level, are equal
(Fig. 12–3), but in general the object will either sink or rise. In either case,
the total force exerted by water on the body is greater upward than
downward, since the upward force is exerted on the lower surface, at
greater depth in the liquid. If the density of the object is less than that of
water, so that it displaces more than its own weight of water, the lack of
balance between the pressures on its upper and lower surfaces will be sufficient to cause it to float. Even if its density is greater than that of water,
and the object sinks, its weight is opposed by an upward force, dependent
on this pressure difference.*   Blaise Pascal (1623–1662) devised a simple
way of demonstrating the effect of removing pressure from one side of an
immersed object, illustrated in Fig. 12–4. If a disk of copper is placed
tightly against a funnel, so that there is no water in contact with its upper
surface, it will not sink. By similarly protecting the under surface of a
block of wood, it can be made to rest under water without rising to the
surface.

---

*This will be recognized as the basis of the famous principle of Archimedes: an
object immersed in a fluid is buoyed up by a force equal to the weight of a volume of fluid that is equal to its own volume.

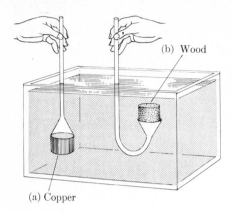

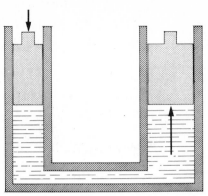

FIG. 12–4. Pascal's experiments: (a) "floating" copper, (b) "sinking" wood. (After an illustration in his *Traité de l'Équilibre Des Liqueurs*, 1663.)

FIG. 12–5. Principle of the hydraulic press. Force exerted on small piston is multiplied for large piston, because pressures are equal.

Pressures exerted on any portion of a confined mass of fluid (liquid or gas) are communicated throughout the mass. This is very clearly illustrated by a machine called the hydraulic press (Fig. 12–5), one of the practical fruits of hydrostatics. This machine consists of a container filled completely with fluid and having two openings fitted with pistons, one larger in diameter than the other. If downward pressure is applied to the small piston, an equal upward pressure is communicated to the large one. Although these *pressures* are equal, there is a large difference in the areas to which they are applied; therefore the total *force* exerted on the piston of larger diameter is much greater than that applied to the smaller one. If the area of one piston is 100 times that of the other, then, in Pascal's words, ". . . one man pressing on the smaller piston will exert a force equal to that of one hundred men pressing on the larger . . ."

12–2 Barometry and "the sea of the air"

That "water seeks its own level" is an old and valid saying. The water levels in two open vessels connected by rubber tubing (Fig. 12–6), for example, will come to the same height no matter how much the vessels are displaced with respect to each other, and regardless of the shapes of the vessels. Any modern explanation of this fact would include a statement that the *pressure of the atmosphere* acts equally on the two open water surfaces. But in Fig. 12–6(d) one vessel is filled with water and tightly closed; it may then be lifted well above the open water surface in the other, and

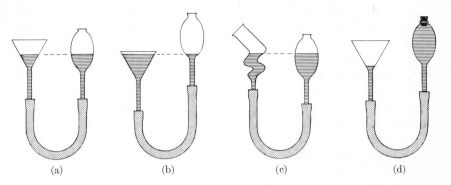

(a)   (b)   (c)   (d)

FIG. 12–6. "Water seeks its own level" if surface is open to the atmosphere; in (d) the right-hand vessel is closed at the top.

remains filled despite the connecting tube. (Similarly, the air vent in Fig. 12–1(a) is necessary if water is to flow freely from the barrel.) Again we familiarly invoke atmospheric pressure on the open surface, greater than that of the extra height of water on the right, to account for the observation. As late as the time of Galileo, however, explanations of these and similar observations were offered in entirely different terms. The Aristotelian doctrine that "nature abhors a vacuum" was almost universally held by men of learning prior to 1644. According to this principle, for example, water cannot emerge from a barrel unless air is simultaneously permitted to enter because otherwise a vacuum, which cannot exist, would be created.

It was a student of Galileo, Evangelista Torricelli (1608–1647), who first performed the experiment that led to the present conception of atmospheric pressure. It was well known to artisans that no suction pump was capable of lifting water through a height greater than about 34 ft. Torricelli, unwilling to believe that nature is so capricious as to impose an arbitrary 34-ft limit on her abhorrence of vacuum, conceived the idea that the atmosphere presses down on the earth's surface with a pressure just sufficient to support a 34-ft column of water. Knowing that mercury is about 13.5 times denser than water, he realized that this same pressure should not be capable of supporting a column of that liquid more than about 1/13.5 as high as 34 ft, i.e., 30 in. Accordingly, he performed (in 1644) the experiment shown in Fig. 12–7. A glass tube of length greater than 30 in. was filled to the top with mercury, the open end was covered by his finger, then the tube was inverted into a bowl of mercury. When he removed his finger from the end of the tube the mercury level dropped to about 30 in. above the surface of the mercury in the bowl, leaving an empty space in the upper part of the tube. A bulb sealed to the end of a tube could be similarly evacuated. Torricelli then felt that he had, in this very simple manner, created the vacuum which nature was supposed to abhor.

We must note that Torricelli was led to performance of his historic experiment by a line of theoretical reasoning. It was his prior conviction that "we live immersed at the bottom of a sea of elemental air, which by experiment undoubtedly has weight.* . . ." According to Torricelli's scheme, the atmosphere consists of layer upon layer of air, each layer pressing on those below. The cumulative weight of all layers, at the bottom of this "sea," exerts pressure on the surface of the mercury in his bowl (Fig. 12–7) sufficient to support a column of mercury 30 in. high in a tube which contains no air to exert opposing pressure.

The idea of "abhorrence" of vacuum did not die easily, and few of Torricelli's contemporaries would concede that he had created one. His cause was soon taken up with great enthusiasm, however, by the genius Blaise Pascal. Pascal was intimately familiar with the science of hydrostatics (treating of liquids at rest), and he proceeded to apply the same principles to the new idea of a "sea of air." His work was largely theoretical, but he felt the need for experimental verification of a single point: if the atmosphere is a "sea," then, like a sea of water, it should exert progressively lower pressures with increasing height. An invalid himself, Pascal obtained the services of his brother-in-law, F. Perier, who performed Torricelli's experiment with great care at the foot and again at the summit of the Puy-de-Dôme, a mountain in the Auvergne. Perier observed a substantial difference in the height of the mercury columns obtained at the two altitudes, the lower value being that at the summit.

It was a technological invention, the vacuum pump, which finally led to observations capable of persuading the entire scientific community of the validity of Torricelli's and Pascal's views. Otto von Guericke (1602–1686) constructed the first such device, a pump capable of forcing water out of a container without allowing air to enter. Robert Boyle, in 1660, built the first pump capable of removing air directly from a vessel. Boyle's earliest pump, shown in the diagram of Fig. 12–8, operates in the following manner: with the piston in its highest position the stopcock to vessel V is opened. The piston is then lowered, permitting the air from V to expand into cylinder C. The stopcock is then closed and the piston raised, causing air in C to escape through the brass valve B. The cycle is repeated, and with each repetition the quantity of air remaining in vessel V becomes smaller.

---

*The experiment referred to, demonstrating that air has weight, had been devised by Galileo. Galileo pointed out that even Aristotle affirmed the weight of air: "As evidence of this he [Aristotle] cited the fact that a leather bottle weighs more when inflated than when collapsed."

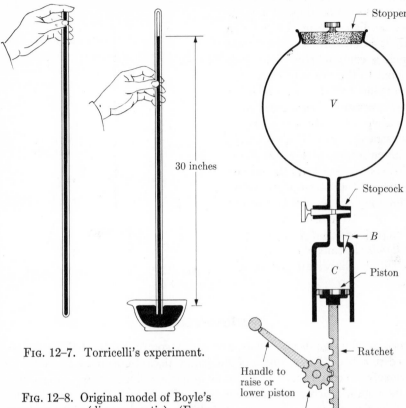

FIG. 12–7. Torricelli's experiment.

FIG. 12–8. Original model of Boyle's vacuum pump (diagrammatic). (From *Robert Boyle's Experiments in Pneumatics*, by J. B. Conant; Harvard University Press.)

Boyle's vacuum pump permitted him to perform many significant experiments, among them demonstrations that a coin and a feather fall at the same rate *in vacuo* and that a bell cannot be heard if struck in the absence of air. His experiment of greatest consequence to the "sea of air" theory consisted of pumping air from a space enclosing the mercury bowl of Torricelli's device (Fig. 12–9). As air was removed the mercury level in the tube fell, until, with the best vacuum Boyle's pump could produce, it was nearly as low as the level in the bowl. Thus it was proved that the pressure of external air on the surface of mercury in the bowl was responsible for supporting the column of liquid in the tube.

The device that resulted from Torricelli's experiment is called a *barometer*. The mercury column of 30 in., or approximately 76 cm, which at-

mospheric pressure at sea level will
support, does not depend on the
shape or diameter of the tube in
which it is measured. The height
of such a column, since it is proportional to the pressure sustaining
it, may thus be taken as a measure
of that pressure. Barometric pressure varies with altitude, as Perier
demonstrated, and it also varies,
in a given locale, with atmospheric
conditions. At sea level the *average*
pressure of the atmosphere corresponds roughly to the barometric
height of 76.0 cm. This height,
for convenience, is *defined* to represent *standard* atmospheric pressure,
often simply abbreviated *one atmosphere.*

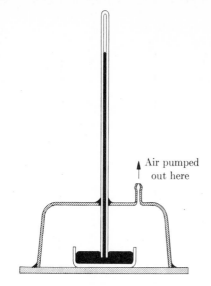

Fig. 12–9. Mercury falls as air is
pumped out.

12–3 Boyle's law

Gases, unlike liquids and solids, are readily compressible; slight pressure
applied to any confined sample of gas will noticeably decrease its volume.
Conversely, when pressure on a sample of gas is reduced, the gas expands,
i.e., its volume increases. Another way of phrasing the remark made
earlier in this chapter, that a gas will fill completely any container into
which it is introduced, is to say that gases possess *unlimited expansibility.*
As pressure applied to a sample of gas becomes progressively smaller, the
volume that sample occupies becomes progressively larger, without apparent limit. Robert Boyle's vivid phrase for these complementary properties of gases, compressibility and expansibility, was "the spring of the
air." It was in an appendix to the second edition of his book *New Experiments, Physico-Mechanicall, Touching the Spring of the Air,* published in
1662, that he first divulged his discovery of a quantitative relation between
pressure applied to, and volume occupied by, a sample of gas.

The apparatus used by Boyle for his experiment is shown in Fig. 12–10.
A J-shaped tube is sealed at the end of its shorter leg, which has a scale
marked on it. Boyle first trapped a quantity of air in the shorter (sealed)
leg, by means of mercury that stood at the same height in both legs. Under
these conditions the pressure exerted by the trapped air on the mercury
below it was obviously equal to that exerted by the atmosphere on mercury
at the open end. Atmospheric pressure as measured with a separate Torri-

celli barometer was 29.13 in. of mercury. After noting the level of mercury in the shorter leg (48 on the arbitrary scale), Boyle added more mercury at the open end of the J-tube, producing a *difference* in the height of the mercury in the two legs. With successive additions of mercury, i.e., increasing difference in the heights of the two columns, the level of mercury in the shorter leg became progressively higher. When that level reached 24 on the scale, half the original reading, the mercury in the longer leg had risen to a position 29.69 in. higher than that in the shorter leg. The addition of more mercury finally reduced the short-leg reading to 12; a corresponding difference in mercury levels was observed as 88.43 in.

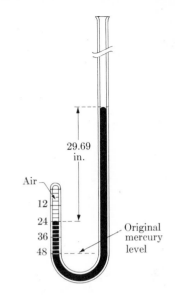

Fig. 12–10. Boyle's J-tube experiment.

Boyle had constructed his J-tube with care, so that its diameter at the shorter end was as uniform as possible. In these circumstances, his readings of the *length* of the column of trapped air, on the scale, were proportional to its *volume*. (The volume of a cylinder is proportional to its height.) The *total* pressure exerted on the air sample, for any mercury level, is given by the *sum* of the barometric height, 29.13 in., and the difference in heights of the two J-tube columns. Thus between the first and second measurements cited in the last paragraph the *volume* of air was halved (cylindrical container reduced in length from 48 to 24) while the *pressure* was approximately doubled (29.13 in. of mercury increased to 29.13 + 29.69 = 58.82 in.). Between the first and third measurements, the volume was quartered (48 to 12) while pressure was quadrupled (29.13 in. to 29.13 + 88.43 = 117.56 in.). These results strongly suggest an *inverse proportionality* between volume and pressure for an enclosed quantity of gas. Representing volume by V and pressure by P, we may express such a relation algebraically as

$$V = \frac{k}{P}, \qquad (12\text{–}1)$$

where k is a constant of proportionality. If this is so, then

$$P \times V = k, \qquad (12\text{–}2)$$

TABLE 12–1*

ROBERT BOYLE'S MEASUREMENTS ON THE COMPRESSIBILITY OF THE AIR

1 Arbitrary scale readings at shorter leg of J-tube: proportional to volumes of enclosed air.	2 Differences in heights of mercury in short and long legs of J-tube.	3 Pressure applied to air in inches of mercury: barometric height (29.13 in) added to values in col. 2	4 Products of values in cols. 1 and 3, proportional to $P \times V$.
48	0 inches	29.13 inches	1398
40	6.19 "	35.32 "	1413
32	15.06 "	44.19 "	1414
24	29.69 "	58.82 "	1412
16	58.13 "	87.26 "	1396
12	88.43 "	117.56 "	1411

*From "*New Experiments, Physico-Mechanicall, etc* . . .", 1662. Boyle's observations are recorded to sixteenths of inches, here converted to decimal equivalents for convenience. Column 4 has been computed from Boyle's measurements.

i.e., the product of pressure and volume, or of quantities proportional to them, should remain constant no matter how P and V themselves may vary. Table 12–1 shows several of Boyle's original results, the final column containing values of his arbitrary scale readings (proportional to air volumes) multiplied by applied pressures (in inches of mercury). The constancy of the values in this column within the (rather large) experimental error of Boyle's measurements verified Eq. (12–2), and hence the relation of inverse proportionality between the volume and pressure of an enclosed sample of air.

The relation set forth in Eqs. (12–1) and (12–2), appropriately known as *Boyle's law*, is an important empirical law of gas behavior. Although we have shown only Boyle's original data, the relation has been found at least approximately correct (see Section 12–5) for all gases at pressures both above and below that of the atmosphere. We must add the important proviso, however, that it is valid only for measurements performed at constant temperature. A full statement of Boyle's law, then, is that *the volume of any fixed quantity of gas, at constant temperature, varies inversely with pressure*. Does the word "pressure" in this statement mean pressure exerted *on* or *by* the gas? The answer is *either;* any measurements employing Boyle's J-tube, for example, are taken with the mercury at rest, so that pressures applied on and by the gas must be at equilibrium, the pressure of gas in the shorter leg being equal to that of the atmosphere and additional mercury in the longer leg.

Boyle's law is useful for predicting the volume of a gas sample at a given pressure (or vice versa) if both pressure and volume are known for a particular case. If a sample of gas occupies volume V_1 at pressure P_1, and occupies a volume V_2 at the same temperature but at a different pressure P_2, then from Eq. (12–2),

$$P_1 V_1 = k$$

and

$$P_2 V_2 = k,$$

hence

$$P_1 V_1 = P_2 V_2. \qquad (12\text{–}3)$$

We learned in Chapter 8 that a 32-gm sample of oxygen occupies 22.4 liters at 0°C and one atmosphere (76.0 cm of mercury) pressure. Let us compute the volume occupied by the same quantity of this gas at 0°C and a pressure of 56.0 cm of mercury. Substituting in Eq. (12–3), we obtain

$$22.4 \text{ liters} \times 76.0 \text{ cm} = V_2 \times 56.0 \text{ cm};$$

hence

$$V_2 = 22.4 \text{ liters} \times 76.0 \text{ cm}/56.0 \text{ cm} = 30.4 \text{ liters},$$

the answer sought.

12–4 Charles' law and the Kelvin temperature scale

In Chapter 11 we remarked that a nearly universal property of matter is expansion with increasing temperature. The extent of *thermal* expansibility (expansion with temperature) is generally rather small in solids and liquids. Ice, for example, expands its volume by only about 1/10,000 for each Centigrade degree its temperature is raised, and liquid water by only about 1/2800.* Thermal expansibilities of solids and liquids vary widely, more-over, from substance to substance. The thermal expansibilities of gases had long been known to be greater than those of other states of matter,

---

*I.e., a sample of ice which occupies 1.0000 cm^3 at −2°C will occupy 1.0001 cm^3 at −1°C; a 1.0000 cm^3 volume of water at 20°C increases to 1.0004 cm^3 at 21°C.

and in 1787 Jacques Charles (1746–1823) discovered that *all* gases expand to the same uniform extent with temperature, if the pressure is held constant. (Similar observations were made later, but independently, by Dalton and by Gay-Lussac.) If the volume of an enclosed sample of gas is measured at 0°C and 1 atm pressure, and the sample is then heated to 1°C and its pressure readjusted to 1 atm, the volume will be found to have increased by almost exactly the fraction 1/273. If heated to 2°C the gas volume becomes 2/273 greater than at 0°C, and so on uniformly; at 273°C it has increased by the fraction 273/273 or, in other words, has doubled.

Algebraically, we may represent the thermal expansion of gases described in the last paragraph by the equation

$$V = V_{0°C} + \frac{t°C}{273} \times V_{0°C}. \tag{12–4}$$

That is, the volume of a fixed quantity of gas at temperature $t°C$ is equal to the volume it occupies at 0°C plus that volume multiplied by the fraction $t°C/273$. When $t°C = 273$, for example, the fraction becomes unity, and $V_{273°C} = 2V_{0°C}$. For temperatures below 0°C, the uniform contraction to be expected of the gas sample can be treated similarly. If $t°C = -27.3$, for example, $V_{-27.3°C} = V_{0°C} - V_{0°C}/10$, or 0.9 $V_{0°C}$; the volume occupied by a gas sample at this temperature is only 9/10 that occupied at 0°C, if both volumes are measured at the same pressure.

If a graph is constructed according to Eq. (12–4), a straight line is obtained, as shown in Fig. 12–11. *If* a gas could be found for which this

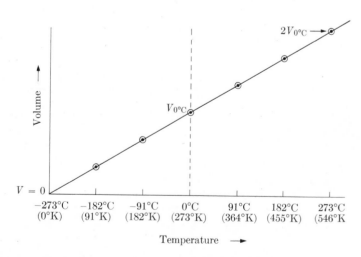

Fig. 12–11. Graphical representation of Eq. (12–4).

relation is valid at all temperatures, no matter how low, we see from the graph that its volume would vanish entirely at −273°C; algebraically, at that temperature $V_{-273°C} = V_{0°C} - (273/273)V_{0°C} = 0$. This seems absurd, of course, and we must concede that no such gas exists; all known gases condense to the liquid state at temperatures higher than −273°C, and the uniform expansion or contraction with increasing or decreasing temperature expressed by Eq. (12–4) may be applied only to gases. Nevertheless, the concept of a gas that would obey Eq. (12–4) at all possible temperatures is useful. Let us define a new temperature scale in such a way that the temperature −273°C, at which the (imaginary) gas has contracted to nothing, is called zero. Any temperature T on the new scale will be given by adding 273 to the corresponding Centigrade temperature. For example, when $t°C = -273$, $T = 0$; when $t°C = 0$, $T = 273$; when $t°C = 273$, $T = 546$; etc. Since $T = t°C + 273$, $t°C = T - 273$; with this substitution in Eq. (12–4), we have

$$V = V_{0°C} + \frac{(T - 273)}{273} V_{0°C} = \left(\frac{T}{273}\right) \times V_{0°C}.$$

Since $V_{0°C}$ is a fixed quantity for any given sample of gas at fixed pressure, it may be combined with the fraction 1/273 to give a single constant of proportionality, and we obtain

$$V = kT. \tag{12–5}$$

The simplicity of Eq. (12–5), in comparison with Eq. (12–4), stems from our newly defined temperature scale. This scale is known as the *absolute* scale of temperature or, alternatively, as the *Kelvin* scale, after the eminent 19th-century physicist Lord Kelvin (born William Thomson, 1824–1907). We shall designate Kelvin temperatures by the symbol °K. The size of the Kelvin degree is the same as that of the Centigrade degree, since Kelvin temperatures are obtained simply by adding the constant 273 (more accurately, 273.16) to Centigrade temperatures.

Equation (12–5) is an algebraic representation of a second empirical law of gas behavior, known as *Charles' law*. In words, *the volume of a fixed quantity of gas is directly proportional to its Kelvin temperature, if the pressure remains constant.* If a given quantity of gas occupies volume V_1 at temperature T_1 and a certain pressure, and volume V_2 at temperature T_2 and the same pressure, then $V_1/T_1 = k = V_2/T_2$, or

$$\frac{V_1}{T_1} = \frac{V_2}{T_2}. \tag{12–6}$$

As an example, consider 32 gm of oxygen, which occupies 22.4 liters at 0°C and 1 atm pressure; what volume will the same quantity of oxygen occupy at 25°C and 1 atm? If we substitute in Eq. (12–6), we obtain

$$\frac{22.4 \text{ liters}}{273°\text{K}} = \frac{V_2}{298°\text{K}},$$

and hence

$$V_2 = 298 \times \frac{22.4 \text{ liters}}{273} = 24.4 \text{ liters.}$$

12–5 Ideal gases

The laws of gas behavior presented in the last two sections will prove indispensable to our considerations of the next chapter; they are also extraordinarily useful practical relations. Before taking temporary leave of them, however, we must note that they are, at best, approximations: *there is no known gas which obeys Boyle's and Charles' laws at all temperatures and pressures.* These laws come very close to exact description of the behavior of a gas, however, within certain ranges of temperature and pressure. The conformity of a given gaseous substance to Boyle's and Charles' laws is closest at low and moderate pressures, and at temperatures considerably above the highest temperatures at which the gas may be liquefied. Under extreme conditions of either temperature or pressure, a real gas may deviate very widely from the behavior described by these laws. The substance which conforms most closely over the widest range of conditions is helium, which, significantly, liquefies at a lower temperature (4°K) than any other substance.

We have previously noted that a device frequently employed in science is *idealization*, i.e., imagining some approximate relation to be the real one for the sake of initial argument, then later taking its approximate nature into account. We may imagine, for example, that there exists a gas which conforms exactly to Boyle's and Charles' laws under all conditions of temperature and pressure, and call this wonderful substance an *ideal gas.* In the next chapter we shall see what arguments can be constructed to account for the behavior of such a gas, and how, with modifications, the ideal gas model helps us to understand the behavior of *real* gases, and indeed of all matter.

12–6 Summary

Gases exert pressure, although they are indefinitely expansible; barometric pressure, for example, is the pressure of the "sea of air" that constitutes the atmosphere. Boyle discovered that at constant temperature the pressure exerted by a gas varies inversely with volume. Gases expand if temperature is increased while constant pressure is maintained; Charles discovered that the percentage of expansion accompanying a certain temperature change is the same for all gases. The volume of any gas is proportional to its temperature, measured on what is called the absolute (or Kelvin) scale. The laws of Boyle and Charles are limited in accuracy, although they are valid for many gases over wide ranges of temperature and pressure.

REFERENCES

CONANT, J. B., *Robert Boyle's Experiments in Pneumatics* (Number 1 of the Harvard Case Histories in Experimental Science). Contains an abundance of material from Boyle's writings concerning his development of a vacuum pump, his experiments in evacuated vessels, and his discovery of the relation between the pressure and volume of a gas.

CONANT, J. B., *Science and Common Sense*, Chapter 4 (on the concept of atmospheric pressure), parts of Chapter 5 (on Boyle's experiments) and 6 (on hydrostatics and on Boyle's law).

HOLTON, G., *Introduction to Concepts and Theories in Physical Science*, pp. 367–373.

MAGIE, W. F. ,*A Source Book in Physics*, pp 70–73 (Torricelli), 73–80 (Pascal), 80–84 (von Guericke), 84–87 (Boyle), 88–92 (Mariotte's independent discovery of Boyle's law). For Galileo's discussion of the weight of air it is necessary to refer to *Two New Sciences*, late in the First Day.

PASCAL, B., *Physical Treatises*. This book begins with Pascal's very entertaining and informative treatment of hydrostatics, an important subject to which we have hardly more than alluded. Subsequent pages contain his extension of these principles to the "sea of air" theory, and include Perier's account of the Puy-de-Dôme experiment.

PAULING, L., *General Chemistry*, Chapter 14. Properties of gases are also treated in other standard chemistry texts, such as that by Sisler et al.

1. (a) A cube of iron (density 7.86 gm/cm³) of side 10 cm rests on a table. What pressure does it exert? (b) What would be the apparent weight of this cube when wholly immersed in water (density 1.00 gm/cm³)? [*Ans.:* (a) 78.6 gm/cm²; (b) 6860 gm]

2. (a) A certain object, when placed in water, neither floats nor sinks, but remains at whatever depth it is introduced. What must be its density? Why? (b) What is the smallest density a liquid may have and be capable of floating aluminum (density 2.7 gm/cm³)?

3. Otto von Guericke constructed a barometer using water, rather than mercury, as the barometric fluid. Describe the probable dimensions of his device, and the operations which must have gone into its construction.

4. (a) If in a hydraulic press (Fig. 12–4) the diameters of the small and large pistons are 1 and 10 in., respectively, what is the ratio of the force applied (to the small one) to that exerted (by the large one)? (b) What is the *minimum* distance through which the smaller piston must be moved to raise the larger ½ in.? What principle enables you to answer this question? Is the hydraulic press a machine?

5. (a) The density of water is about 62.5 lb/ft³ in English units. As we have learned, the atmosphere is capable of supporting a column of water (at sea level) about 34 ft in height. What pressure, in pounds per square foot, does the atmosphere exert upon any portion of the earth's surface at sea level? (b) The radius of the earth is

about 4000 mi, and the surface area of a sphere may be calculated from the relation $S = 4\pi r^2$. Assuming the earth to be a sphere and the pressure to be uniform over its entire surface, estimate the *total weight* of the atmosphere, in tons.

[*Ans.:* (a) About 2100 lb/ft²; (b) about 6×10^{15} tons]

6. Before the vacuum pump made possible Boyle's experiment on the behavior of a barometer in a vacuum (Fig. 12–9), Pascal had proposed that an apparatus of the design shown in Fig. 12–12 would accomplish a similar purpose. It consists of two straight tubes AB and CD, each about 36 in. long. The tube AB is sealed at its upper end and communicates with tube CD via an intervening reservoir at B, whose volume is several times that of either tube. The lower end of tube CD is open, and the upper end may be opened to the atmosphere by removing the stopper at C. The entire apparatus is inverted, then carefully filled with mercury through opening D. When the apparatus is completely filled and air pockets have been eliminated, the opening is covered with a finger and the assembly is placed in the position shown in the diagram, with opening D below the surface of mercury in vessel E.

(a) Indicate where you would expect to find all the mercury levels (in AB, BC, and CD) after the finger has been removed.

(b) Now the stopper at C is carefully removed. What would you expect to happen to each of the mercury levels?

Pressure (cm of Hg)	Volume (liters)
10	15.2
20	7.60
30	5.17
40	3.80
50	3.04
60	2.54
70	2.18
76	2.00
80	1.90
90	1.69

FIG. 12–12. Pascal's "double barometer."

Give thoughtful reasons for your answers to (a) and (b), and state what this experiment shows about the behavior of a barometer in a vacuum.

7. Suppose that in Boyle's vacuum pump (Fig. 12–8) the volume of vessel V is ten times that of cylinder C. If the pressure in V is initially 76 cm of mercury, what would it be after a single downward stroke of the piston?

8. A 1.6-gm sample of nitrogen, at 0°C, occupies the volumes indicated at the several pressures given below:

(a) Plot the values of P against those of V. What kind of curve results? (b) Examine Eq. (12–1) with care, to determine what variable, when plotted against volume, should produce a straight line. Construct a graph accordingly, and determine from its form whether the above data conform to Boyle's law.

9. Is it possible to define an absolute temperature scale which is different from the Kelvin scale? Devise one if you can.

10. (a) A sample of gas occupies 24 milliliters at 27°C and 1 atm pressure. What will be its volume at 27°C and a pressure of 40.0 cm of mercury? (b) What volume will the same sample occupy at 52°C and 1 atm pressure? (c) What volume will the same sample occupy at 52°C and 40.0 cm pressure? [Ans.: (a) 45.6 ml; (b) 26 ml; (c) 49.4 ml]

11. Magnesium reacts with hydrochloric acid to liberate hydrogen:

$$Mg + 2HCl \rightarrow H_2 \uparrow + MgCl_2.$$

What volume of hydrogen, measured at 64.0 cm of mercury pressure and 25°C, may be obtained from the reaction of 1.2 gm of magnesium with hydrochloric acid?

12. The calculations for Exercises 10(c) and 11 may be facilitated by use of the following *combined* form of Boyle's and Charles' laws:

$$\frac{P_1 V_1}{T_1} = \frac{P_2 V_2}{T_2}.$$

Using the fact that a quantity which is proportional to two different quantities is also proportional to their product, deduce this relation from Eqs. (12–1) and (12–5). (Do not confuse the k's in these two equations; remember that they represent different constants of proportionality.)

13. Use the relation of Exercise 12 to compute the volume occupied by a certain gas sample at 300°C and 2 atm pressure, if it is known to occupy 5 liters at −23°C and a pressure of 38 cm of mercury. [*Ans.*: 2.86 liters]

14. (a) A simple apparatus for demonstrating Boyle's law is shown in Fig. 12–13. It consists of a fine capillary tube in which mercury encloses a volume of gas. With the device in the horizontal position shown, the pressure on the trapped gas is exactly equal to that of the atmosphere. Why? (b) If atmospheric pressure, measured on a separate barometer, were 75.0 cm, what should be the length of the gas column when the tube is held vertically, closed end down? (c) What would be the length of the gas column when the tube is held vertically, open end down? (The mercury does not run out; why?)

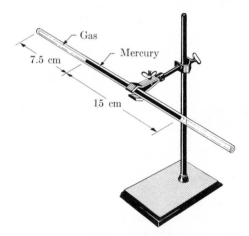

FIGURE 12–13.

CHAPTER 13

THE KINETIC THEORY OF MATTER

A major feature of scientific enterprise has been the construction of theoretical *models*, i.e., mental constructs representing some aspects of nature, designed to explain known phenomena and to predict new ones. Those whose explanatory and predictive values have survived the test of detailed scrutiny form the main framework of present-day science; many more, of course, have been discarded. Even those models that survive rarely do so in the original form proposed for them. We have seen how thoroughly the *details* of Copernicus' heliocentric model of the solar system were revised by the generations of astronomers who followed him; it is the all-important premise of heliocentricity that has survived. Similarly, although atomicity is an indispensable ingredient of today's science, we shall see how profoundly some aspects of Dalton's original atomic model of matter have been altered since his time. The alteration with time that attends a successful model is not merely the result of new and improved data, it is often the growth and development of the model itself. A "good" model is often found applicable to a much wider range of phenomena than could possibly have been envisioned at its inception, and it is made to reflect this breadth more and more adequately.

We have now sufficient background for exploring one of the major models of science, the *Kinetic Theory of Matter*. The theory was initially constructed to account for the behavior of gases, but it provided a key to fundamental interpretation of heat energy. In a sense, kinetic theory reduced the problem of heat to one of mechanics, the mechanics of very many particles. But in doing so it added features mechanics had never known, and it paved the way for a modern atomic theory of matter that Dalton would have had great difficulty in recognizing.

13–1 History of the kinetic theory

The small discrete particles of which a gas presumably consists may be either in motion or at rest. If they are at rest they must be in contact, for the earth's gravitational attraction would pull them together like marbles in a bag. If not in contact they must be in motion—very rapid motion, in fact—if the gas as a whole is to escape the collapsing influence of gravity.

These alternative models of gas structure were considered by Robert Boyle in his discussions of the "spring of the air." Torricelli, before him, had given some detailed expression to the idea of gas particles in contact. The alternative hypothesis of particles in motion, called the *kinetic* model, originated in early Greek atomistic philosophy.

Two striking features of gas behavior require immediate attention in any theory of gas structure: one is the ease with which gases may be compressed, the other the indefinite undirected extent to which they can expand. On the particles-in-contact model, the former property may be accounted for by imagining particles composed of soft springy material, easily deformed and capable of confinement in a very small volume. If this material is truly springy, the particles will expand with reduction of the pressure applied to them. It is hard to imagine a material capable of self-expansion *without limit*, however. Aware of this difficulty, Boyle preferred the kinetic gas model. If the particles of a gas are relatively far apart, compression of the gas as a whole would simply entail pushing them closer together, i.e., reducing the volume of empty space, not of the particles themselves. And if in continual rapid motion, the particles would certainly tend to wander into any space offered to them; indefinite expansibility of a gas as a whole would be an expected consequence of the kinetic model. Newton, in the *Principia*, demonstrated that this property could also be expected of particles in contact, *if* they are assumed to repel each other with a special kind of force unobserved elsewhere in nature. Newton presented this result only speculatively and, like Boyle, apparently preferred the kinetic model.

In 1738, Daniel Bernoulli (1700–1782) published the first quantitative treatment of the kinetic theory of gases. Imagining a gas as composed of very many minute spherical particles in continuous random motion, Bernoulli made a mathematical analysis of the cumulative effect of their impacts on a movable piston (Fig. 13–1) enclosing a volume of gas. The piston is supported by the gas; at equilibrium, the pressure (force per unit area) exerted downward by the piston must be equaled by an upward pressure exerted by the gas. (Fluids exert equal forces in all directions, as we know, but here the only direction of interest is that

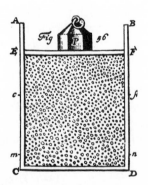

FIG. 13–1. Downward pressure exerted on the piston by weight P is balanced by upward pressure due to impacts of many molecules in rapid motion. (From Bernoulli's *Hydrodynamica*, 1738)

along which the piston may move.) The exertion of pressure by the gas, Bernoulli argued, is made possible by innumerable impacts of the tiny gas particles on the piston. If greater weight is applied to the piston it moves downward to a new equilibrium position corresponding to a compressed volume of gas. In Bernoulli's view, the pressure of the gas is increased because the gas particles, now separated by smaller average distance than before, collide with the piston more frequently and thus exert a greater total force.

Bernoulli was able, mathematically, to demonstrate that his assumptions concerning the origin of gas pressure led to Boyle's law *as a deductive consequence*; i.e., it followed from his model that the volume and pressure of a gas should be inversely proportional. The empirical validity of Boyle's law was well established at the time, but Bernoulli's derivation of it failed to impress his contemporaries, and the theory was neglected. He also deduced from his kinetic theory that gas volumes should increase with temperature at constant pressure, thus anticipating the empirical discovery of Charles' law. As a basis for this deduction Bernoulli stated. ". . . it is admitted that heat may be considered as an increasing internal motion of the particles," an "admission" not generally conceded until more than a century later.

The problem of deciding between the alternative models of gas structure was intimately linked to the similar question as to the nature of heat. If heat is motion, gas particles must be in motion; if heat is a substance, it seems more probable that they are at rest. We have seen that most 18th- and early 19th-century scientists adopted the material view of heat; consequently, the particles-in-contact theory of gases prevailed. In Chapter 7, for example, we spoke of John Dalton's mental image of a gas containing particles at rest, each surrounded by a "sphere of caloric," with neighboring "caloric spheres" in mutual contact. This was one variation of the prevailing view. Curiously, Dalton cited as authoritative support for his own ideas the *Principia* demonstration mentioned above, overlooking Newton's preference for the kinetic model.

The discovery of the equivalence between heat and mechanical energy, and hence the confirmation that heat is a form of energy, was directly responsible for a revival of interest in the kinetic theory of gases. Joule himself was among the first to revive and extend the kinetic model. A truly comprehensive version of the kinetic theory was published in 1857 by the German physicist Rudolph Clausius (1822–1888). With further elaboration and refinement by James Clerk Maxwell (1831–1879), Ludwig Boltzmann (1844–1906), and others, it became one of the most impressive theoretical edifices of the 19th century. Let us examine its principal features in an elementary way.

13-2 Kinetic model of an ideal gas

The problem is to devise a mental image of gases that will prove consistent with their known properties. The approach is to propose a model, apply known mechanical laws to deduce its logical consequences, and finally compare these consequences with observational experience. Our empirical knowledge of gases includes the facts that they are highly compressible, indefinitely expansible, and, more quantitatively, that they conform (within limits) to Boyle's law,

$$PV = \text{constant, at constant temperature,}$$

and to Charles' law,

$$\frac{V}{T} = \text{constant, at constant pressure.}$$

For simplicity we shall first consider only *ideal* gases, which by definition obey the laws of Boyle and Charles in all circumstances. The model, essentially that of Bernoulli and of Joule, can be described by means of four *assumptions*.

ASSUMPTION 1: *a pure gaseous substance consists of identical molecules which do not exert forces on one another except during collision.* This assumption draws a sharp distinction between gases and the other states of matter. Solids are rigid, presumably because of strong attractive forces acting between the particles composing them. Liquids, while not rigid, have well-fixed volumes; their particles are somehow held together. On the other hand, gases are able to expand indefinitely, so that it is reasonable to suppose that no mutual forces tend to hold the particles together.

ASSUMPTION 2: *the size of an individual molecule of a gas is negligible in comparison with the average distance between molecules.* Compressing a gas, if this idea is correct, consists of decreasing the space between molecules, not of squeezing the molecules themselves.

ASSUMPTION 3: *the molecules of a gas are constantly in random motion, at an average speed that does not change with time in the absence of external influences.* The randomness assumed here is consistent with what we should expect if there is molecular motion: the directions of travel of individual molecules will be altered frequently and unsystematically by collisions with one another and with the container walls. The significance of assuming that the average particle speed does not change of itself will appear in the development of the theory, but we need the assurance of a final requirement:

ASSUMPTION 4: *all collisions between molecules and between molecules and the walls of their container are perfectly elastic.* As we have come to understand the meaning of the term *elastic* in Chapter 10, this assumption simply states that the kinetic energy of a gas is conserved throughout its internal collisions. The kinetic energies of individual molecules may change, but always in such a way that no kinetic energy is lost. On this assumption we may not expect molecules to deform one another, or to produce dents in the container walls, since in such *inelastic* impacts work would be done at the expense of kinetic energy.

We shall find that comparison of the theory with Charles' law will necessitate the addition of a fifth assumption, but let us first see how pressure is understood quantitatively on the basis of the model as described thus far.

13-3 Exertion of pressure by an ideal gas

According to our assumptions, individual gas molecules must collide frequently with their container walls. Each such impact will impart a small force to the wall, and the sum total of all such small forces exerted repeatedly over any sizable area is presumably the source of gas pressure. The quantitative expression for pressure follows readily from the model, particularly if we restrict ourselves to *average* behavior of the molecules. Our derivation will parallel that given originally by Joule.

Imagine a sample of gas confined to a cubical container of side l (Fig. 13-2), consisting of N molecules, each of mass m, all moving with the same speed v. Now the complete randomness of the motion produces the same pressure on all the walls; this effect could be equally achieved in a cubical box if the molecules were divided into three equal groups, each of which bounces back and forth perpendicular to two opposite walls. (This argu-

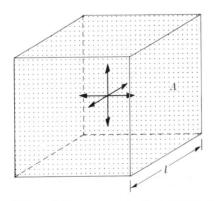

FIG. 13-2. Diagram for kinetic theory.

ment may sound naive, but it is actually justified by sophisticated mathematical arguments.) We shall suppose, then, that one-third of the molecules are entirely responsible for the pressure on a given wall, and that the other molecules never strike it.

Consider one of the molecules in motion perpendicular to face A (Fig. 13–3), repeatedly striking A and the opposite face at regular intervals of time. Each impact of the molecule at A will exactly reverse its direction without altering its speed; the force it exerts on wall A will be given by the

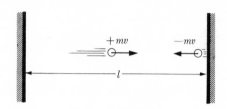

FIG. 13–3. Momentum transfer at a wall.

change in momentum per unit time, and its momentum change at each impact is $2mv$.* Let the time interval between impacts on face A be t; during this time the molecule will have made a journey to the opposite face and back, a distance $2l$. Since speed v is distance traversed divided by time required,

$$v = \frac{2l}{t}, \tag{13-1}$$

or t, the interval between impacts on A, is

$$t = \frac{2l}{v}. \tag{13-2}$$

We may now write an expression for the force f which our single molecule exerts on A:

$$f = \frac{\text{change in momentum}}{\text{time}} = \frac{2mv}{2l/v} = \frac{mv^2}{l}. \tag{13-3}$$

But there are $N/3$ molecules behaving in this way, and the total force F

---

*If the molecule approaches the wall with momentum $+mv$ and leaves, after head-on elastic impact, with momentum $-mv$, its total change in momentum must be $+mv - (-mv) = 2mv$. The collision is exactly analogous to that between a tennis ball and a concrete floor; see discussion in Section 10–7 on impacts between light and massive bodies.

on wall A, due to the cumulative effect of all impacts, will be simply $N/3$ multiplied by f, the force exerted by a single molecule. Therefore

$$F = \frac{N}{3} \times \frac{mv^2}{l}. \tag{13–4}$$

Pressure, by definition, is force per unit area, and the area of face A is l^2. Hence

$$P = \frac{F}{l^2} = \frac{N}{3} \times \frac{mv^2}{l^3} = \frac{N}{3} \times \frac{mv^2}{V}, \tag{13–5}$$

since $l^3 = V$, the volume of the cubical container. Equation (13–5) is the relation we have sought, but it may be written in a more interesting way:

$$P = \frac{2N}{3V}(\tfrac{1}{2}mv^2). \tag{13–6}$$

According to Eq. (13–6) the pressure exerted by a gas is directly proportional to the number of molecules and the kinetic energy per molecule, and inversely proportional to the volume occupied.

A formula identical with Eq. (13–6) is obtained by a more elaborate derivation in which it is not assumed that all the gas particles are moving at the same speed. In that case the average is taken over all speeds, and $\tfrac{1}{2}mv^2$ represents the *average* kinetic energy per molecule. We have neglected collisions between molecules, but they have been found to make no difference in the final result. In other words, the highly simplified model of this section leads to the same expression for gas pressure as the more general model outlined in Section 13–2.

13–4 Kinetic theory and the gas laws

Equation (13–6) may be rearranged to the form

$$PV = \tfrac{2}{3}N(\tfrac{1}{2}mv^2), \tag{13–7}$$

which is highly suggestive of Boyle's law, $PV = $ constant. According to Eq. (13–7) the product of gas pressure and volume will remain constant for a given number of molecules so long as the average kinetic energy per particle remains unchanged. The condition under which Boyle's law is valid, it will be recalled, is that the temperature must remain unchanged. This suggests that constant temperature may be associated with constant molecular kinetic energy, although it does not uniquely define a relation between temperature and the kinetic energy of the gas model.

But we also have Charles' law, that the volume of a gas sample is proportional to its Kelvin (absolute) temperature at constant pressure. The combination of Charles' law with that of Boyle, as we have already seen in Exercise 12, Chapter 12, yields the result that the combination PV/T is constant for a fixed mass of gas, or

$$PV = kT, \qquad (13\text{–}8)$$

where T is the temperature on the absolute scale, and k is simply a constant of proportionality. The similarity of Eqs. (13–7) and (13–8) is too striking to be overlooked; if theory and experiment are to be in accord, it follows that the absolute temperature of a gas must be a measure of its kinetic energy. Formally and quantitatively we may add to the list of assumptions underlying the kinetic theory:

ASSUMPTION 5: *the temperature of a gas, on the Kelvin scale, is directly proportional to the average kinetic energy of its molecules.*

It may appear that introduction of this new assumption to the main structure of the kinetic theory artificially "twists" the theory into conformity with a known empirical relation. But the purpose of a theory is to conform to observation, and the insight given by the kinetic theory of gases extends far beyond the fundamental gas law as given by Eq. (13–8). We shall examine some of the successes of this theory.

13–5 Further verification of the kinetic theory

Simple though Eqs. (13–7) and (13–8) may appear to be, these relations, taken together, formulate the main substance of the kinetic theory. The agreement between the assumptions of this theory and the empirical evidence of the gas laws is certainly arresting, but it does not begin to represent the actual achievement of the kinetic model. There are few physical theories in which so many quantitative consequences can be traced with only the most elementary mathematics. Let us consider some examples of laws and observations correlated by the kinetic theory.

1. *Avogadro's hypothesis.* Consider two separate samples of unlike gases which occupy equal volumes at the same pressure. Then, since $P_1 = P_2$ and $V_1 = V_2$,

$$P_1 V_1 = P_2 V_2,$$

and it follows from Eq. (13–7) that

$$N_1(\tfrac{1}{2}m_1 v_1^2) = N_2(\tfrac{1}{2}m_2 v_2^2). \qquad (13\text{–}9)$$

But according to Assumption 5, which was adopted to meet the requirement of Charles' law, the temperature of a gas on the absolute scale and the average kinetic energy of its individual molecules are directly proportional to each other. This means that if our two gas samples are at the same temperature,

$$\tfrac{1}{2}m_1v_1^2 = \tfrac{1}{2}m_2v_2^2,$$

and hence, under these conditions, Eq. (13–9) is equivalent to

$$N_1 = N_2.$$

This is just Avogadro's hypothesis: equal volumes of gases at the same pressure and temperature contain equal numbers of molecules.

2. *Diffusion of gases.* If gases of different molecular weights at the same temperature have identical average kinetic energies, the average speeds of their molecules must differ. Consider two gases, with molecular masses m_1 and m_2 and average molecular speeds v_1 and v_2. At the same temperatures,

$$\tfrac{1}{2}m_1v_1^2 = \tfrac{1}{2}m_2v_2^2,$$

from which

$$\frac{v_1^2}{v_2^2} = \frac{m_2}{m_1},$$

or

$$\frac{v_1}{v_2} = \sqrt{\frac{m_2}{m_1}}. \tag{13–10}$$

In words, the ratio of the average molecular speeds of two gases at the same temperature is given by the square root of the inverse ratio of their molecular masses. Monatomic helium, atomic weight 4, and diatomic hydrogen, molecular weight 2, possess molecules whose mass ratio is 2:1. By Eq. (13–10),

$$\frac{v_{\text{H}_2}}{v_{\text{He}}} = \sqrt{\frac{2}{1}} = 1.414,$$

or

$$v_{\text{H}_2} = 1.414\, v_{\text{He}}.$$

The kinetic theory thus predicts that hydrogen molecules travel at an average speed 1.414 times that of helium atoms at the same temperature. Similarly, it predicts that O_2 molecules (32) travel 1.414 times faster than SO_2 molecules (64), and hydrogen molecules $\sqrt{64/2} = 5.66$ times faster than SO_2 molecules at similar temperatures.

Experimental verification of Eq. (13–10) has been accomplished in a variety of ways, most of which involve measurement of the rates at which

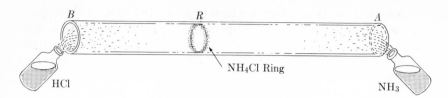

FIG. 13–4. Diffusion of gases.

gases *diffuse* through one another or through the walls of a porous container, or escape from confinement through a single small opening. A quantitative *law of diffusion of gases*, of the same form as Eq. (13–10), was discovered empirically by Thomas Graham (1805–1869) in 1829, but was not related to other features of gas behavior until the kinetic theory was developed.

An especially simple verification of Eq. (13–10) is illustrated in Fig. 13–4. If ammonia and hydrogen chloride vapors are simultaneously introduced at the two ends of the long straight tube AB, they will diffuse toward each other through the tube. The position at which the advance echelons of NH_3 molecules meet those of HCl will be clearly marked by formation of a white ring at point R, produced by the reaction

$$NH_3 + HCl \rightarrow NH_4Cl.$$

(NH_4Cl, ammonium chloride, is a white solid.) According to Eq. (13–10),

$$\frac{v_{NH_3}}{v_{HCl}} = \sqrt{\frac{36.5}{17.0}} = \sqrt{2.14},$$

and hence

$$v_{NH_3} = 1.46 \, v_{HCl}.$$

If ammonia molecules travel 1.46 times faster than HCl molecules on the average, they should travel 1.46 times farther in any given time. This prediction may be compared with the ratio of the measured lengths AR and BR, which is indeed very nearly 1.46.

In this experiment there is a measurable lapse of time between the introduction of NH_3 and HCl vapors to the tube and the appearance of a white ring. The tube is initially filled with air, and in consequence no single HCl or NH_3 molecule is likely to travel down the tube in a straight path. Molecules of each kind undergo countless collisions with one another and with air molecules *en route*, and it is only because both are struggling against similar odds that the white ring appears where predicted in accord with Eq. (13–10). Gas molecules would be able to travel in long uninterrupted straight paths only in a vacuum, and rates of diffusion of gases through one another represent *average* molecular progress in a given direction.

3. *Specific heats of gases.* Without examining the subject in detail we may readily arrive at a feature of gas specific heats pointed out by Joule in his elementary paper on kinetic theory. If temperature is proportional to average molecular kinetic energy, then increasing the temperature of any gas from 0°C to 1°C, say, means simply increasing the average kinetic energy per molecule by the fraction 1/273, the same for all gases. But specific heat is conventionally defined as heat *per unit mass* per degree change of temperature; therefore it follows that the specific heats of gases are inversely proportional to their molecular weights. This law was well known experimentally before Joule's derivation of it, but the theory shows its consistency with other aspects of gas behavior.

The inverse proportionality between specific heat and molecular weight is strictly applicable only to gases of similar molecular structure. Temperature is identified with average *translational* kinetic energy, i.e., energy of motion of a molecule as a whole. In our simple model of point molecules, representing a monatomic gas, this is the only kinetic energy possible. Molecules made up of two or more atoms can possess kinetic energy of rotation or interatomic vibration as well, and heat supplied is partly used to increase this nontranslational energy. For this reason the specific heats of polyatomic gases are greater than those of monatomic gases of equal molecular weight.

---

4. *Changes of temperature upon expansion and compression.* Anyone who has inflated a bicycle tire is aware that a gas is warmed by compression. Conversely, it can be readily demonstrated that the temperature of a gas falls as it expands against a piston. To interpret these facts in terms of our model of an ideal gas, let us imagine such a gas confined in a cylinder fitted with a piston (Fig. 13-5). If the weight on the piston is removed the gas will expand, pushing the piston upward to a new position. *Work* must be

FIG. 13-5. The temperature of a gas falls as its molecules perform the work of lifting a piston.

done to move the piston through a distance against gravitational force; therefore, by the conservation principle, energy of some form must be expended. If the force applied to the piston arises from impacts of molecules, collisions with a *displaceable* object (the piston) must be *inelastic*. Individual molecules rebound from the under surface of the piston with *less* than their initial kinetic energy, and many such impacts impart upward motion to the piston. Since so many molecules will have lost kinetic energy in the performance of work, the average kinetic energy of all gas molecules present is lowered. But temperature has been assumed proportional to average molecular kinetic energy: therefore the temperature of the gas will have fallen.

Quantitatively, the difference in temperature of the gas before and after expansion may be used to calculate the quantity (in calories) of heat it has lost, if its specific heat under these conditions is known, and the mechanical work done may be computed from the weight of the piston and the distance it rises. Expansion of an ideal gas might thus be used to measure the mechanical equivalent of heat. Only approximate agreement with the accepted value, 4.19 joules/cal, is obtained with most real gases, for reasons to be explained in Section 13–7.

The reverse effect, heating of a gas on compression, is readily understood: again inelastic collisions occur between molecules and piston, but this time in such a way that the molecules *gain* kinetic energy. The external work of pushing the piston downward, in increasing the average molecular kinetic energy, produces a rise in temperature.

5. *Brownian movement.* Our last example is one which almost directly verifies the fundamental assumption of molecular motion, but which requires detailed investigation of *departures* from average molecular behavior for quantitative description. In 1827 the English botanist Robert Brown (1773–1858) discovered that tiny grains of pollen, suspended in water and observed microscopically, execute rapid and erratic motions. Some typical observed paths of particles exhibiting what is now called *Brownian* motion are shown

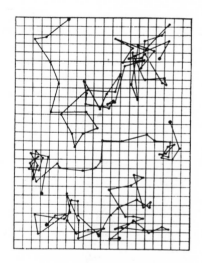

FIG. 13–6.   Brownian movement. Changing positions of three minute solid particles suspended in water, as seen through the microscope at 30-sec intervals. (After J. Perrin.)

in Fig. 13–6. Brown at first thought the phenomenon unique to products of life (e.g., pollen), but later experiments convinced him that *any* material dances about when finely divided and suspended in water. Similar observations may be made of tiny particles suspended in a gas. Qualitatively, the kinetic theory suggests an explanation: on so small a particle the effect of random molecular impacts does not average out to produce uniform pressure in all directions, and as a result the particle is pushed first one way and then another. Quantitative calculations have confirmed that such paths as those shown in Fig. 13–6 should be expected, but their detailed nature depends on the probable number of molecular collisions and thus on the number of molecules in a gas. It was on the basis of such calculations that the first numerical estimates of Avogadro's number (the number of molecules in one gram-molecular weight of a substance, modern value 6.02×10^{23}) were obtained. Observation of Brownian movement in liquids, as well as gases, justifies the extension of kinetic theory to the liquid state, an extension we shall consider in a later section.

13–6 The mechanical theory of heat

It should now be clear why abandonment of the caloric theory of heat and acceptance of the kinetic theory of gases were simultaneous episodes of scientific history. The successes of the kinetic theory, of which we have considered only a sampling in Section 13–5, inspire great confidence in the idea that heat is molecular energy. It was actually temperature (on an absolute scale) that we identified in Assumption 5 with average kinetic energy of the gas molecules, but for an ideal gas temperature and heat content are strictly proportional to each other; all energy added to an ideal monatomic gas increases the speed and thus the kinetic energy of its molecules. On this interpretation, as Joule first pointed out, absolute zero is the temperature at which molecular motion has ceased altogether. This is somewhat more meaningful than the identification of absolute zero with zero volume which arose from examination of the empirical law of Charles.

But the real world is made up of solids and liquids as well as gases, and there are no real gases at very low temperatures—even helium can be liquefied. Moreover, there is a more significant distinction between heat and temperature than the ideal gas model would imply—witness the heats absorbed in melting and vaporization without producing temperature changes. Can the mechanical view of heat be generalized to include all matter?

The answer is yes, even though there is no simple kinetic theory for liquids or solids. Let us first consider extending the concept of temperature to substances other than gases. Two bodies are at the same temperature if their individual temperatures remain unchanged when the bodies are in contact with each other; there is then no net exchange of heat between them. (This definition is not in contradiction with the existence of heats of fusion and vaporization; in a warm room the temperature of an ice-water mixture remains constant throughout the melting, but the air is cooled during the process. If the air were at 0°C no melting would take place.) Let us examine the collisions between gas molecules and the walls of a real container. The solid walls are made up of molecules as truly as is the gas, although they are obviously not so free as gas molecules. Individual collisions must be between molecules. Suppose for a moment that the molecules of the solid were stationary; impact of a gas molecule on any one of them would cause it to vibrate, even if it were not free to move very far. But this would absorb energy. The only condition under which there would be no net exchange of energy, in the average of many molecular collisions between the walls of the container and the gas, is that both kinds of molecules already have the same average energy of motion. In other words, once we admit that solids are made up of particles, acceptance of the kinetic theory of gases implies that temperature must be identified with the average kinetic energy of these particles. Note that temperature is a *macroscopic* concept, and can be applied only to the average of an assembly of many particles. The same argument can be applied to a liquid, for it too can be in contact with a gas at the same temperature.

In order to arrive at a thoroughly consistent mechanical interpretation of heat we must understand the role of energy in changes of state. During freezing or melting, say, heat is absorbed or released without change in the average kinetic energy of the molecules, if our interpretation of temperature is correct. At this point we must remember that there would be no solids or liquids, and thus no changes of state, if molecules were actually those of the perfect (ideal) gas model. We shall begin, then, by finding how real gases differ from the idealization described by the five assumptions above.

13-7 Revision of the ideal model for real gases

The imaginary *ideal* gas must obey Boyle's law under all circumstances, so that a plot of the product PV versus P, at any constant temperature, should be a straight horizontal line, as shown in Fig. 13-7(a). While most gases do conform rather closely at moderate and low pressures, at very high pressures they do not. Figures 13-7(b) and (c) show how nitrogen behaves at two different temperatures and a range of high pressures. As pressure increases both curves first dip below the line representing ideal behavior, then, at very high pressures, rise above it. The amount of dip below the line, it will be noted, is greater at the lower temperature of −70°C. Similar graphs are obtained for other gases; in every case the amount of dip below

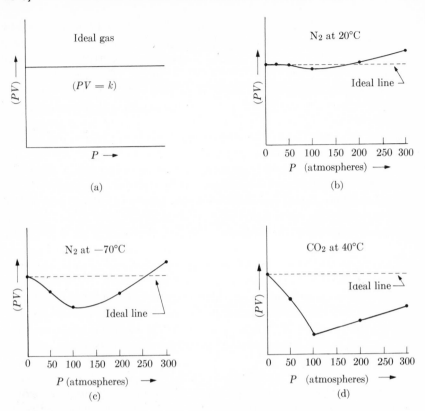

FIG. 13–7. Departures of real gases from Boyle's law. (The curve in part (d), for CO_2 at 40°C, rises above the ideal line at pressures higher than those shown.)

the straight line is greatest for temperatures near that at which the gas can be liquefied. The corresponding curve for CO_2 at 40°C, Fig. 13–7(d), dips much farther than that for N_2 at −70°C; CO_2 may be liquefied at 31°C, by application of 73 atm pressure, but nitrogen cannot be liquefied at temperatures above −147°C no matter how high the pressure.   Thus at ordinary temperatures CO_2, unlike nitrogen, deviates markedly from Boyle's law, even at moderate and low pressures.

The graphs of Fig. 13–7 reveal that there are two kinds of deviation from Boyle's law.   Dips below the ideal line may be described by saying that a real gas is more compressible than Boyle's law would predict. (I.e., the applied pressure required to compress the gas to a given volume is smaller than predicted, hence the product PV is also smaller.)   Deviations at the highest pressures, which carry the curve above the ideal line, indicate that under these conditions a real gas is more difficult to compress than an ideal gas. (I.e., greater than predicted pressure must be applied for compression to a given volume, hence PV is greater than predicted by Boyle's law.) The first effect would be expected if, contrary to Assumption 1 of the ideal gas model, gas molecules *do* exert attractive forces on one another, noticeably so at rather small distances. The second requires modification of Assumption 2: we must concede that when gas molecules are brought very close together at very high pressures their sizes may become appreciable with respect to the average distance between them. As a result the gas tends to resist further compression more than would an ideal gas in which the molecules occupy no space.

A modified kinetic model, assuming the action of intermolecular forces and taking account of molecular sizes, was first successfully employed in a detailed analysis of real gas behavior by Johannes van der Waals (1837–1923) in 1873. His explanation of excess compressibility (dips below the ideal line in Figs. 13–7) in real gases is illustrated qualitatively in Fig. 13–8. A molecule in the interior of the gas is surrounded, on the average, by equal numbers of similar molecules on all sides; the average net force of attraction acting on such a molecule by its neighbors is zero. As a molecule is about to strike a wall, however, there is an unbalanced attractive force *away* from the wall, and it therefore strikes with somewhat smaller momentum than it would in the absence of intermolecular attractions. The mutual attractions, appropriately called *van der Waals forces*, of most molecules are relatively weak, and have negligible effect at low pressures, when the molecules are far apart. For any gas their effect is enhanced by increased pressure and also by lower temperature, since with slower molecular motion the intermolecular forces have a longer time to act as the molecules move past one another. The van der Waals forces between CO_2 molecules are stronger than those between N_2 molecules, as indicated by the greater deviation from Boyle's law when the two are compared at similar temperatures. In general, we may say that the forces of attraction between gaseous molecules are greater the higher the temperature at which the gas may be liquefied. It should be noted that the rise in the curves of Fig. 13–7 above the ideal line at very high pressures does not mean that intermolecular attractive forces cease to act under these conditions. The effect of molecular size, negligible at lower pressures, becomes greater than the opposite effect of van der Waals forces at very high pressures.

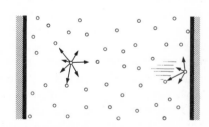

FIG. 13–8. Effects of van der Waals forces: attractions in different directions on a molecule in the interior of gas balance one another, on the average, but an unbalanced net force acts on a molecule which is about to strike a wall.

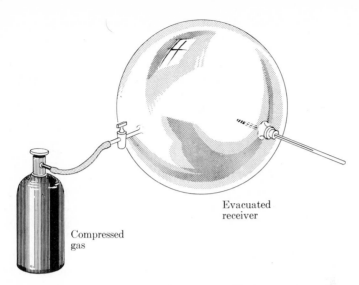

Evacuated
receiver

Compressed
gas

FIG. 13-9. Expansion of a gas into a vacuum. No temperature change should be observed if the gas is ideal.

The action of van der Waals forces between gas molecules is strikingly illustrated in the phenomenon known as the *Joule-Thomson effect*, after its discoverers James Prescott Joule and William Thomson (Lord Kelvin). As we have seen in Section 13-5, the expansion of an ideal gas leads to a drop in its temperature if it performs work in the process. If an ideal gas were permitted to expand into a vacuum, however, no temperature drop could be expected, since the molecules do no work (Fig. 13-9). But it is observed that the temperatures of most real gases *are* lowered by simple expansion into a vacuum, or from a region of high pressure to another of low pressure; this is the Joule-Thomson effect. The effect is particularly striking in CO_2: when the valve on a tank of compressed CO_2 is suddenly opened, permitting expansion into the surrounding atmosphere, the gas undergoes so great a temperature drop that solid CO_2 ("dry ice") is formed. The Joule-Thomson effect is applied industrially in the production of "dry ice," liquid air, and other liquefied gases.

Falling temperature in a gas means reduction of average molecular kinetic energy. But since no external work is done by gas molecules in Joule-Thomson expansion we must look inside the gas itself to find the source of this reduction. The answer is found in the van der Waals forces: work must be done against intermolecular attractive forces simply to increase the separation of the molecules. This work is done by the gas molecules at the expense of their own kinetic energy, hence the temperature of the gas as a whole falls.

13–8 Kinetic interpretation of changes in state

When a gas is either cooled or compressed its molecules are, on the average, closer together than before. Since real gases are more compressible than Boyle's law predicts at low temperatures and high pressures it is clear that the van der Waals forces must increase in strength as molecules are brought together. If a gas is placed under sufficiently high pressure, at suitably low temperature, it loses its gaseous character altogether, and becomes liquid. Since the densities of liquids are very much greater than those of their corresponding vapors, the molecules of a liquid must be so close together that their mutual attractive forces are, relatively, very strong. Condensation to the liquid state may be considered to result from the action of these forces. We note that molecules of a liquid cannot be rigidly attached, and must be free to move about very nearly at random; otherwise liquids would not flow, and two mutually soluble liquids (e.g., alcohol and water) would not diffuse into each other freely, as they are observed to do. Forces acting between molecules in a liquid do prevent them from separating to great distances, however.

Solids are rigid, and do not tend to assume the shape of their container; obviously the forces between particles in a solid are much stronger than those in liquids. These are actually van der Waals (intermolecular) forces only for one restricted class of solids (as we shall see in Chapter 20), of which "dry ice" is an example. But whatever the forces acting in a solid, they must prevent its particles from traveling freely. We may assume that each particle has a nearly fixed permanent population of nearest neighbors whose attractions confine it to a very limited portion of space (Fig. 13–10). The motion which particles of a solid must have in keeping with the kinetic interpretation of temperature could then be only oscillatory. The particles

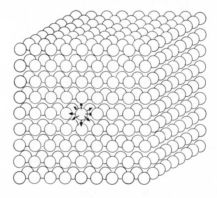

Fig. 13–10.   Schematic representation of a solid and possible directions of vibration.

may move back and forth, up and down, or perhaps rotate, but always within the small space permitted them by the action of cohesive forces. If the temperature becomes high enough the oscillatory motion is so great that individual particles are able to break away and move about; when this has happened to the whole mass the solid has melted.

In terms of the above discussion, how may we interpret the large energy changes that accompany changes in state? We recall that to drive the molecules of one gram of water into the vapor state at 100°C, 539.6 calories of heat must be supplied. Since this quantity of heat does not produce a change in temperature, the average kinetic energies of water and steam molecules at 100°C must be identical. The molecules are separated by vaporization, however: 1 gram of liquid water at 100°C occupies only about 1 milliliter, while 1 gram of steam at the same temperature occupies nearly 1700 milliliters. The 539.6 calories of heat energy supplied is expended in doing the *work* of separation of molecules against intermolecular forces. Since the most fundamental part of the change we call vaporization is change of the *positions* of molecules with respect to each other, we can say that their *potential* energies are increased in the process. Conversely, when 1 gram of steam condenses to the liquid state at 100°C the *loss* of potential energy by its molecules is reflected by evolution of 539.6 calories of heat energy.

When a solid melts, it absorbs latent heat of fusion in the process, similarly increasing the potential energies of its particles. The densities of liquids at their freezing points are rarely very much larger than those of the corresponding solids at the same temperature,* so that average distances of separation are not markedly increased on melting. The relative positions of molecules *are* profoundly altered, however; the regular ordered array of particles in the solid structure becomes the relatively unordered liquid, whose molecules are in nearly random motion.

If solid iodine is heated in a closed container, violet iodine vapor is observed even though no liquid forms. Wet clothes may be dried on a line even at temperatures below the freezing point of water. These are two examples of the change in state called *sublimation*—direct passage of matter from the solid to the gaseous state. Just as in the cases of fusion and vaporization, sublimation at constant temperature is accompanied by the absorption of heat, which supplies large changes in molecular potential energy even though the molecular kinetic energy remains constant. The quantity of heat required for sublimation must supply the energy needed for melting and for vaporizing at the same time.

---

*In the unusual case of water the solid occupies an even greater volume than the liquid at 0°C; this is related to an unusual structural feature of ice.

13–9 Vapor pressure

It is a common observation that liquids tend to evaporate when left standing in open containers, even at temperatures far below their boiling points. Let us consider a single water molecule moving toward the air-water surface in the container shown in Fig. 13–11. At the instant this molecule reaches the surface it will be exposed to a region where there are no water molecules exerting attractive forces above it, and in consequence will be subjected to a strong downward pull by the molecules below. The chance that it will continue in the upward direction and break away from the body of liquid is therefore slight. Only if its initial kinetic energy were exceptionally high would it be able to pass off into the atmosphere above the liquid surface. Molecules that do escape, then, must have kinetic energies greater than the average; with their departure the average kinetic energy, and hence temperature, of the remaining body of liquid is lowered. The cooling effect of evaporating water when one emerges from a swimming pool into open air is an example of this effect. A further example is provided by the "cryophorous," Fig. 13–12. In this device a quantity of water is enclosed in a sealed container; a portion of the container's surface, not in contact with the water, is cooled to low temperature with "dry ice." Water molecules from the vapor tend to freeze out on this cold surface, and more leave the liquid to take their place in the vapor. The resulting continuous and rapid evaporation causes the main body of liquid to cool to its freezing point, and all the water becomes frozen.

Most of the molecules that leave a liquid surface in an open container escape to the atmosphere; in the "cryophorous" most are removed by freezing on a cold surface. In an ordinary closed container, however, molecules that attain the vapor state have restricted space in which to move about (Fig. 13–13). The requirements of random motion are such that some of these molecules must be moving toward the liquid surface at any instant, and upon reaching it will probably be held in the liquid by in-

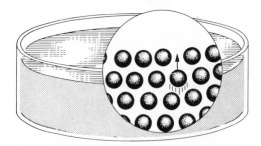

Fig. 13–11. A molecule must have high energy to escape from a liquid surface.

Dry ice

Water vapor
freezes here

Air-free
space

Liquid water
freezes here

FIG. 13–12. The cryophorous.

FIG. 13–13. Liquid in a closed container. Dynamic equilibrium is attained when equal numbers of molecules leave and return to the surface in unit time.

termolecular forces. Accurate measurements have shown that, at a given temperature, a definite unvarying pressure is exerted by vapor in an enclosed space adjacent to a liquid surface. The constancy of this pressure, called the *vapor pressure* of the liquid, can be explained by assuming a constant number of vapor molecules present in the enclosed space. In terms of our kinetic model, a fixed number of vapor molecules may be maintained only if there are equal numbers of molecules leaving and returning to the liquid surface per unit of time, a condition known as *dynamic equilibrium* between the liquid and its vapor.

With increasing temperature average molecular kinetic energy increases, hence the number of molecules of a liquid with sufficient energy to break through to the vapor state should be increased. We should therefore expect the vapor pressures of liquids to increase with rising temperatures as, indeed, they are observed to do. The change of the vapor pressure of water with temperature is shown in the graph of Fig. 13–14. It will be noted that the vapor pressure of water is one atmosphere, i.e., 76.0 cm of mercury, at the temperature (100°C) we have called the *boiling point* of that substance. We must now refine our definition, and will call 100°C the *normal* boiling point of water. Liquids boil when their vapor pressures become equal to the pressure of the surrounding atmosphere; the normal boiling temperature of a liquid is that at which its vapor pressure is one standard atmosphere. Anyone who has cooked food at high altitudes is aware that the boiling point of water is lowered by decreasing atmospheric pressure. At an altitude of 13,000 ft, for example, atmospheric pressure is

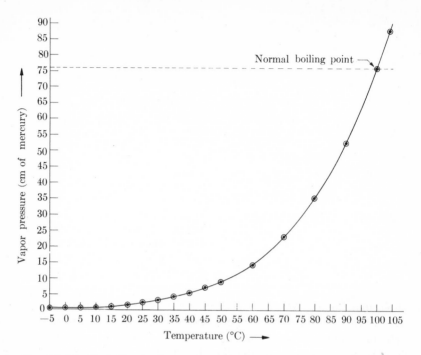

FIG. 13–14. Variation in the vapor pressure of water with temperature.

such that water boils at approximately 87°C; the temperature of water in an open container at this altitude cannot be increased further by heating alone.

13–10 Degradation of energy

If heat is molecular motion, any substance whose temperature is greater than 0°K (absolute zero) must possess heat energy. The oceans which cover three-fourths of the earth's surface may thus be considered an enormous reservoir of heat. Let us imagine a device for conversion of the heat energy of the ocean to useful mechanical work. If we were to cool a ship to a temperature lower than that of the ocean, then launch it, heat would flow spontaneously from the ocean to the ship (Fig. 13–15). Suppose that an engine aboard the ship is capable of collecting all the heat as it arrives from the ocean and converting it *completely* to the mechanical work of driving a propeller. In the performance of this work there will be frictional forces acting between the propeller blades and the ocean water which will create heat, thus returning heat to the ocean. The temperature difference between the ocean and the ship would therefore be maintained,

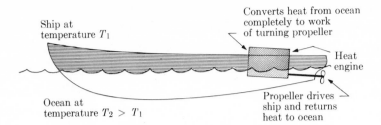

FIG. 13-15. Perpetual motion of the second kind.

and our wonderful ship could be kept indefinitely in motion without carrying a fuel supply of its own.

The device we have imagined sounds suspiciously like a perpetual motion machine, but it does not violate the principle of conservation of
energy: it would operate by interconversion of exactly *equivalent* quantities
of heat and mechanical energy. It *is* an unattainable device, however,
representative of what is called *perpetual motion of the second kind*. Perpetual motion machines "of the first kind" are ruled out by the conservation of energy, but those of the second kind involve a cycle in which work
is continuously performed by complete conversion of equivalent heat
energy. It is possible to convert only a fraction of the heat supplied to any
heat engine, such as that imagined for the ship, into useful work. The
initial temperature difference between the ocean and our ship would
diminish until both reached a common temperature and flow of heat to the
ship ceased. The principle of impossibility of complete conversion of heat
to work in any cyclic process is known as the *Second Law of Thermodynamics.** The principle was implicit in the work of Carnot on heat
engines, and its full significance was recognized independently by Clausius
and Kelvin about the middle of the 19th century.

An equivalent way of phrasing the Second Law of Thermodynamics is to
say that whenever heat is converted to work, some heat is transferred from
a warmer to a colder region. In the case of our ship, this means that
permanent transfer of some heat from the ocean to the cooler ship un-
avoidably accompanies transformation of other heat to work; the ship
cannot remain at its original temperature. In a sense, the law is only an application of the observed fact that heat flows spontaneously from a warm
to a cool body, but not the other way round.

It will aid understanding of these statements to consider the operation of

---

*The principle of conservation of energy is often referred to as the *First Law of
Thermodynamics.*

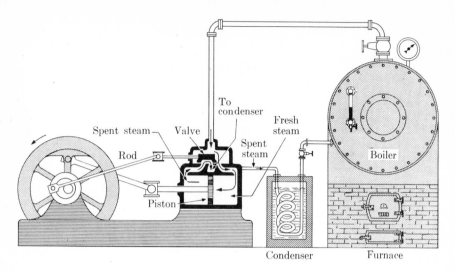

FIG. 13–16. Schematic representation of Watt steam engine.

a steam engine, typical of all devices which convert heat to mechanical energy. In the steam engine, as shown schematically in Fig. 13–16, heat given up by combustion of a fuel is used to heat water in a boiler, forming steam under pressure. High-pressure steam is allowed to expand against a piston via the route shown, and the consequent motion of the piston is imparted to a wheel. In the performance of this work the steam temperature falls. A rod is attached to the wheel in such a way that as the piston moves to the left a special valve moves to the right; at the end of the forward piston stroke the position of this valve denies the incoming steam access to the right-hand side of the piston but allows it to expand against the left-hand side. The return stroke, also forced by high-pressure steam, is thus begun. At the same time, the position of the valve is such that the "spent" steam at the right of the piston is passed through an exhaust channel to a low temperature *condenser* cooled with cold water. From the condenser, steam recovered as liquid water is returned to the boiler. Both forward and reverse thrusts of the piston are forced by steam, owing to the action of the special valve, an invention of James Watt; as steam expands against one side, the "spent" steam on the other side is exhausted to the condenser. In Fig. 13–16, the positions of piston and valve are such that fresh steam is expanding against the right-hand side of the piston while "spent" steam on the other side is passing off to the condenser.

In the cycle of operation of the steam engine just described some of the heat supplied to water in the boiler is used to perform the work of pushing a piston and to overcome frictional resistances between moving parts of the engine. The remainder, and in fact the major part, however, is simply transferred from the high-temperature region of the boiler to the relatively low-temperature region of the condenser. If no condenser were used, but the "spent" steam simply exhausted to the surrounding atmosphere, the situation would be unchanged.* Most of the heat supplied to the boiler would then be transferred to the atmosphere. The important point is that exhaust is necessary, and it can only take place at a lower temperature than that of the "live" steam.

Note that it *is* possible to convert mechanical energy completely into heat—a simple method is to expend work against friction. This difference between heat and mechanical energy, despite the mechanical interpretation of heat, is a consequence of the randomness of heat motions. The high-pressure steam, in the steam engine, pushes the piston at the expense of the kinetic energies of its molecules. Since the motions of steam molecules are random, only a fraction of them lose significant amounts of kinetic energy in colliding with the piston, and the tendency is for the gas to regain within itself any randomness lost in performing ordered (singly directed) work on the piston. This is a general trend observed in nature. All ordered motions tend to die out, and their energy is converted into heat; for example, liquid in a bowl may be set into rotation by stirring, but the flow pattern subsides quickly when the stirring has ceased. Another example of the general tendency to randomness is that toward mixing. Suppose we have two adjacent containers of different gases, say O_2 and N_2, and remove a partition between them; the diffusion that follows until the gases are uniformly mixed takes place spontaneously, but it would cost considerable effort and ingenuity to "undo" the diffusion.

All of these matters and other spontaneous thermal processes can be treated quantitatively in terms of a concept called *entropy*. Increase in entropy can be compared with the shuffling of an initially ordered pack of cards, and entropy can be said to measure the amount of disorder. Clausius, who introduced the concept, stated the second law in terms of it: *the entropy of the world tends to a maximum*. A comparable statement of the first law of thermodynamics is *the energy of the world is constant*.

Taken at face value, the Second Law of Thermodynamics suggests long-range implications which found their way into the philosophy and literature

---

*While not necessary in principle, it is more efficient to operate a steam engine with a condenser than without, since rapid condensation of "spent" steam, which the condenser provides, partially evacuates the space adjacent to one side of the piston. In this way there is a greater difference in pressure on the two sides of the piston than could otherwise be achieved, hence a greater net force acts on the piston in the direction of its thrust.

of the late 19th and early 20th centuries. In the universe heat energy is continuously being produced from other energy forms in spontaneous processes. Now we have seen that heat can be only partially converted into work, and that existing temperature *differences* tend to be leveled out. The most obvious conclusion is that the *availability* of the energy of the universe is constantly decreasing, i.e., that energy is continuously being *degraded* to heat energy at uniform temperature and that the supply of energy which can be converted into useful work is simultaneously diminishing. If this conclusion is correct the universe, at some time in the vastly distant future, will have have reached the "heat death," a state in which all matter is at uniform temperature and there is no further possibility of performing mechanical work. Actually, modern developments have cast much doubt on the validity of extending the Second Law of Thermodynamics to the universe as a whole, and the idea that everything everywhere will inevitably "run down" cannot be taken for granted. Neither can this idea be categorically denied on the basis of knowledge now at hand. We shall see, however, that there is much evidence for historical development of the universe; as our information increases the simple process of "running down" seems less compelling for the future.

13-11 Summary

The unlimited expansibility of gases may be understood if it is assumed that they consist of particles in random motion, and that only negligible forces act between the particles. A quantitative kinetic theory of gases, initiated by Daniel Bernoulli and by Joule, was developed in full detail by Maxwell, Boltzmann, and others during the second half of the 19th century. What appears macroscopically as uniform pressure is interpreted as the net effect of a multitude of individual molecular collisions. Boyle's law, originally an empirical discovery, follows as a theoretical consequence of the kinetic model of an ideal gas, as does Charles' law if absolute temperature is identified with the average kinetic energy of gas molecules. The kinetic model also yields Avogadro's hypothesis, describes gaseous diffusion quantitatively, and explains the dependence of specific heats on molecular weight. The effects of molecular collisions produce visible random motions in particles large enough to be viewed microscopically, the so-called Brownian motion. Heat is interpreted in the kinetic theory as mechanical energy of molecules. Refinements of the ideal gas model are necessary to describe the behavior of real gases and to account for changes of state, which involve changes in molecular potential energy.

References

BORN, M., *The Restless Universe*, Chapter 1.

COWLING, T. G., *Molecules in Motion*.

CREW, H., *The Rise of Modern Physics*, pp. 212–220.

HOLTON, G., *Introduction to Concepts and Theories in Physical Science*, Chapter 20, pp. 432–469.

MAGIE, W. F., *A Source Book in Physics*, pp. 172–174 (Joule and Thomson on expansion of gases), 228–236 (Clausius), 247–250 (Bernoulli), 251–255 (Brown), 255–257 (Joule on the velocity of gas molecules).

MOTT-SMITH, M., *The Story of Energy*, Chapters VII through XV.

SISLER, H. H., and others, *General Chemistry, a Systematic Approach*, Chapter 3.

1. Interpret in terms of the kinetic theory: (a) the compressibility of gases; (b) the unlimited expansibility of gases; (c) expansion of gases with increasing temperature at constant pressure; (d) rising temperature of an ideal gas during compression.

2. (a) According to the pressure equation of the kinetic theory, Eq. (13–6), how does the pressure exerted by a gas at fixed volume and temperature vary with the number of molecules present? If 0.2 gm of hydrogen at 27°C, confined to a volume of 1.0 liter, exerts a pressure of 187 cm of mercury, what pressure would 0.05 gm of hydrogen exert if present in the same volume at the same temperature? (b) Interpret your result in (a) in terms of the assumptions of the kinetic theory.

3. The combined form of Boyle's and Charles' laws, known as the general gas law equation, is written $PV = RT$, as applied to one gram-molecular weight of an ideal gas. Since one gram-molecular weight occupies 22.4 liters at 0°C and one atmosphere pressure, we may use the relation to compute a value for R. If P is in atmospheres, V in liters, and T in Kelvin degrees, R is found to be 0.082. Check this result. Use the value of R obtained above to compute the pressure which would be exerted by one gram-molecular weight of an ideal gas confined to a volume of 50 liters at 227°C. [*Ans.*: 0.82 atm or 62.3 cm of Hg]

4. The value for the gram-molecular volume of gases we have used in previous chapters, 22.4 liters or, more accurately, 22.414 liters, is an ideal one. It has been determined by measurements on various gases at extremely low pressures, where their behavior is almost exactly that of an ideal gas, and the ideal gas laws have been used to obtain the value corresponding to standard temperature and pressure. The measured volume occupied by one gram-molecular weight of nitrogen (28.016 gm) at standard conditions is actually 22.394 liters. The gram-molecular volume of ethylene (C_2H_4, molecular weight 28.054) has been found to be 22.179 liters. What percentages of error are incurred in calculations involving these gases at standard conditions when they are assumed to behave ideally?

5. Values for the volumes occupied by gram-molecular quantities of nitrogen (boiling point −196°C) at 16°C and ethylene (boiling point −104°C) at 25°C and at various pressures, based on actual measurements, are shown below:

Pressure (atmospheres)	Volume of 28.016 gm N_2 at 16°C in liters	Volume of 28.054 gm C_2H_4 at 25°C in liters
1	23.677	24.170
2	11.837	———
5	4.7290	4.7108
10	2.3635	2.2824
15	1.5716	1.4814
20	1.1774	1.0657
25	0.9407	0.8213

An ideal gas would occupy 23.698 liters at 1 atm and 16°C, 24.436 liters at 1 atm and 25°C.

(a) Make appropriate calculations to find how closely nitrogen and ethylene conform to Boyle's law under the conditions shown.

(b) What can you say about the relative magnitude of van der Waals forces acting in nitrogen and in ethylene? What would their boiling points have led you to expect about the relative sizes of these forces?

(c) Interpret the deviations of these gases from ideal behavior, as revealed by your calculations, in terms of van der Waals forces and the kinetic theory.

(d) For what kinds of gases, and under what conditions, may the ideal gas laws be applied with least chance of error?

6. Since Nm is simply the total mass of a sample of gas, Eq. (13-7) may be used to calculate the velocity corresponding to average molecular kinetic energy of a known quantity of gas if the pressure is expressed in dynes/cm^2. For ammonia at 25°C this velocity is about 6.6×10^4 cm/sec. What period of time would be required for ammonia molecules to travel 10 m in a direct path? When an ammonia bottle is opened at one end of a room a period of the order of minutes elapses before its odor may be detected at the other end of the room. Why?

7. What are the relative speeds of diffusion of the gases nitrogen and hydrogen?

8. When a gas is heated in a closed container the pressure it exerts on the walls increases. Why?

9. Which molecules have greater average kinetic energy, those of ice, liquid water, or water vapor at 0°C? Explain.

10. Arrange the following in order of decreasing average molecular speed at 100°C: N_2, H_2O, CO, NH_3, UF_6, SF_6, F_2, He, Xe, SO_2, SO_3, NO_2, H_2.

11. Liquid ethyl chloride, normal boiling point 12.2°C, is used in medical practice for local anesthesia. It has no specific physiological action, but when applied to a small area of the body that area becomes numb because it is cooled to a temperature considerably below 12.2°C. Explain.

12. Vapor pressures of acetone at various temperatures are shown in the table below:

Temperature (°C)	Vapor pressure of acetone (cm of mercury)
−30	1.12
−10	3.87
5	8.91
10	11.56
20	18.48
30	28.27
40	42.15
50	61.26
60	86.64
70	120.1

Construct a graph for acetone vapor pressure against temperature, similar to that of Fig. 13-14 for water, and find the normal boiling point of this substance.

13. On top of Mt. Everest (elevation 29,000 ft) the external atmospheric pressure is approximately 24 cm of mercury. Use Fig. 13-14 to find the approximate boiling point of water at this altitude.

14. The vapor pressure of water at 0°C is 0.46 cm of mercury; since ice and

liquid water coexist at this temperature, this vapor pressure is common to water in the solid and liquid states. At —5°C the pressure of water vapor in equilibrium with ice *alone* is 0.30 cm of mercury. At 100°C, solid gold chloride ($AuCl_3$) and iodine (I_2) have vapor pressures of 0.70 and 4.6 cm of mercury, respectively. In terms of the kinetic theory, discuss the probable mechanism of establishing such fixed vapor pressures by a solid.

15. When the pressure of water vapor in the atmosphere at a given temperature is equal to the vapor pressure of water at that temperature the atmosphere is said to be *saturated* with water vapor. The *relative humidity* of the atmosphere is defined as the ratio of the observed pressure of water vapor at any given time to the vapor pressure of water at the same temperature. When this ratio is multiplied by 100, *per-* *centage* relative humidity is obtained, giving the percentage of saturation of the atmosphere with water vapor.

(a) What is the percentage relative humidity of a saturated atmosphere?

(b) What, roughly, is the percentage relative humidity at 77°F (25°C) if the pressure of water vapor in the atmosphere is 1.0 cm of mercury? (See Fig. 13–14.)

(c) When the relative humidity is 50% at 104°F (40°C) does the atmosphere contain more or less moisture than it does when the relative humidity is 100% at 77°F (25°C)?

16. The fall in temperature of the "live" steam in expanding against the piston in Fig. 13–16 is accompanied by the production of small water droplets. What is the effect of the formation of these droplets on the pressure of the "spent" steam that results at the end of the stroke?

CHAPTER 14

ELECTRIC FORCES AND ELECTRIC CURRENTS

In some respects we have now become acquainted with more mechanics than Newton ever knew. In particular, we have surveyed its extension to those individual parts of matter called molecules, and have achieved a mechanical explanation of heat. The 19th-century clarification of the concept of energy, and the identification of the energy of molecular motion with heat, signified a tremendous advance both in pure and applied science. But concerning the nature of forces, we have considered no advances beyond the knowledge of Newton and his 17th-century contemporaries. In the kinetic theory of heat we spoke only of molecular impact, the microscopic analogy of a tennis ball bouncing against a rigid wall. In Dalton's atomic theory the subject of forces was avoided altogether. Yet what holds atoms together when they form a molecule? If atoms themselves have structure, if they are composite, what holds the parts together? The masses involved are so small that gravitation could play no perceptible role, but as yet the only conceivable alternative we have considered is the kind of force described by van der Waals, which is assumed to act between molecules but is probably too weak to hold the component parts of either molecules or atoms together. Even here, all we know is that if van der Waals forces are *assumed* to exist certain properties of real gases are conveniently explained; we know nothing of the nature of the forces themselves.

By far the most important part in binding the components of atoms and molecules together is played by *electric* forces, whose elementary macroscopic manifestations we shall consider in this chapter. Questions of atomic and molecular structure have no simple answer, however, and we shall need to consider other forces and other manifestations of energy before we can attempt to answer them. Even in the 20th century the answers remain incomplete, though they are far-reaching. The study of atomic structure will eventually lead us back to astronomy and some consideration of the whole universe, but not until we have made a thorough investigation of many microscopic (actually *sub*microscopic) phenomena. At almost every step we shall find a knowledge of electricity of strategic importance to our understanding.

14–1 Electric charge

The very word *electricity* betrays the most primitive manifestations of electric phenomena. Many substances, such as hard rubber, glass, sealing wax, and lucite, when rubbed with wool, fur, or silk, may acquire the ability to attract light bodies of any kind, bits of chaff or paper, for example. *Amber* was the naturally occurring substance known to the ancients which possessed this property most prominently, and the word *electricity* derives from the Greek word for amber, *elektron*. A body which has been rubbed and possesses the property of attraction is said to have an *electric charge*. Amber is a rare and costly material and hardly need be used to demonstrate the essential facts of static electricity in these times, with hard rubber and plastic objects readily available. If an ordinary comb or fountain pen is rubbed briskly with wool or fur, it can attract tiny bits of paper or lint, and glass, rubbed with silk, will behave similarly.

Historically, not even the qualitative laws of static electricity were formulated clearly until well into the 18th century. Much useful experimentation was carried on in England during the 17th century, and further, more systematic experiments with charged bodies were conducted in France by the young scientist Charles Francois de Cisternay Dufay (1698–1739). A comprehensive summary of Dufay's work was published in 1734. The essential features of static electricity can readily be demonstrated by a set of experiments analogous to those of Dufay.

Let us suspend an inflated rubber balloon by means of a dry thread, as indicated in Fig. 14–1. If the balloon is rubbed with fur it is thereafter found to be attracted by the fur, or even by an empty hand. This attraction, easily noticeable because the balloon is light in weight, is a manifestation of its charge. If a hard rubber rod which has also been rubbed with fur is now brought near, the balloon is found to be repelled (Fig. 14–1b). On the other hand, a glass rod, newly rubbed with silk, attracts the charged balloon. However, if the glass rod is wrapped tightly in the silk and is then brought near the balloon, very little, if any, movement of the latter is observed.

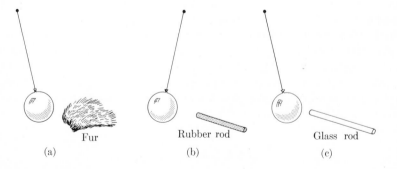

Fur   Rubber rod   Glass rod
(a)   (b)   (c)

Fig. 14–1. Behavior of a suspended rubber balloon which has been rubbed with fur.

From experiments of this sort Dufay concluded that "there are two distinct electricities, very different from one another." If rubber is rubbed with fur, both become "electrified," i.e., charged, and the two are thereafter *attracted* to each other (Fig. 14–1a). But another piece of rubber, the rod, *repels* the balloon (Fig. 14–1b) after it has been rubbed with fur. It would seem safe to assume that whatever happens to the rubber of the balloon when it is rubbed with fur, also happens to the rubber of the rod. We can conclude that two bodies, electrified in the same way, repel each other. The charge on the fur and on the glass rod (Fig. 14–1c) must be of another kind, which attracts that on the rubber. In this way Dufay was led to the principle that *like electrical charges repel, unlike charges attract.*

Let us consider a second kind of experiment. If the expanded balloon is covered with aluminum paint it becomes, effectively, a very light aluminum sphere instead of a rubber one. Such a balloon, suspended by a dry thread, is shown in Fig. 14–2. This sphere, without rubbing, will now be attracted to an electrified (silk-rubbed) glass rod (Fig. 14–2a). If the glass rod and balloon once touch, however, the balloon thereafter moves violently away, as shown in Fig. 14–2(b). If the glass is then removed from the vicinity and the balloon is touched with a finger it becomes "neutralized," and is again attracted by the rod until the two are brought in contact. This sequence of observations may be repeated with a hard rubber rod that has been rubbed with fur. Although the charges on rubber and glass are different, according to the experiments illustrated in Fig. 14–1, here they behave similarly: the aluminized balloon is first attracted by either glass or rubber, and is repelled by either after touching.

Dufay carried out experiments similar to our second set as well as the first. Understanding of them was greatly facilitated by Benjamin Franklin (1706–1790). It was he who named the two kinds of electricity *positive* and *negative*, algebraic terms which at least *imply* that charge should be quantitatively measurable and that its two kinds are capable of canceling each other's effects. In the uncharged (or electrically *neutral*) aluminum-covered balloon there are equal quantities of both kinds. A charged glass rod, brought near, separates the two kinds, as indicated by the plus and minus signs of Fig. 14–2(a); charge *like* that on the rod is repelled, charge unlike it is attracted. In accord with present conventional usage, as proposed by Franklin, the charge on the glass rod is called *positive*, and in the separation of charge on the sphere it is positive charge that is repelled and negative charge that is attracted. During the instant of contact, one of two things must happen: either some of the positive charge on the glass is communicated to the balloon, or some of the negative charge on the balloon is attracted onto the glass. After touching, in either case, the sphere has greater positive charge than before and is no longer neutral; it is then repelled by the similarly (positively) charged glass. The analogous situation,

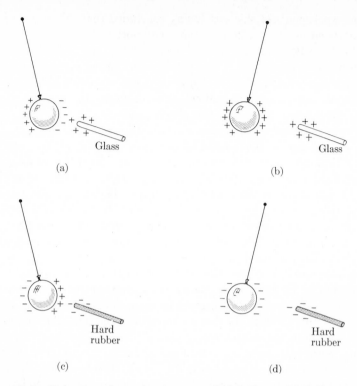

FIG. 14–2.   Behavior of an aluminum-covered balloon: (a) balloon neutral, attracted to charged glass rod, (b) balloon is repelled after contact, (c) neutral balloon attracted to charged rubber rod, (d) balloon repelled after contact with rod.

with the roles of the two kinds of charge reversed, occurs when a rubber rod is brought near the neutral sphere, as indicated in Figs. 14–2(c) and 14–2(d).

Franklin's assignment of "negative" to the kind of charge produced by fur on rubber and "positive" to that on glass which has been rubbed with silk was quite arbitrary, although we should have no good reason to interchange the terms today. The use of plus and minus for the two kinds of charge began to constitute a *theory* of electricity; it shows insight into one of the most important features of electric charge, namely, that the two kinds *can* cancel, and together may amount to no charge at all. Electric charge is in this respect entirely different from mass. One mass can never "cancel" another, but can only add to it. There is, in this sense, but one kind of gravitational force, hence only one kind of mass. Electricity was long considered a member of the family of "subtle fluids." More commonly there were thought to be *two* electric fluids, since there are two kinds of electric charge. In terms of the two-fluid view, an uncharged body has equal quantities of both fluids, and charging consists of extracting one kind of fluid, leaving an excess of the other. Franklin held that there was only one kind of fluid, the total amount of which is conserved: a body with a "normal" amount of this fluid is neutral; charging consists of a transfer of fluid from one body to another, leaving one with a deficiency (−), the other with an excess (+). We shall see in a later chapter that *no* fluid is required, and that charge is now known to be associated with particles of small mass, although just why this should be so is not yet understood. Modern views of electricity contain some features of both the two-fluid and one-fluid hypotheses: there are two kinds of charge, but only negatively charged particles flow readily in bulk solid matter, and it is either excess or deficiency of these particles (electrons) that constitutes the kind of charge we are considering here. Although Franklin's view was incorrect, we shall find his description not altogether inappropriate: "The electrical matter consists of particles extremely subtile, since it can permeate common matter, even the densest metals, with such ease and freedom as not to receive any perceptible resistance."

For the experiments we have described above the materials have been chosen carefully. If a metal rod is held in the hand, for example, attempts to electrify it by rubbing are not likely to succeed. For this reason metals were first classed as "nonelectrical" substances, but we now call them *conductors* of electricity, since they permit the ready *flow* of charge. For *insulators*, defined as substances on which charge does *not* readily flow, contact with the experimenter's hand makes very little difference. Amber, rubber, glass, and lucite are all insulating materials. They share some charge with an aluminized balloon (Fig. 14–2) on contact with it, but only a small part of their total charge. The classification of materials into conductors and insulators is not entirely strict; there are poor conductors and poor insulators, and even the best of insulating materials permit some flow of charge.

Metallic objects will maintain a charge if they are carefully insulated, i.e., if they are isolated from contact with other conducting materials. Just because they permit the flow of electricity, movable insulated conductors also make good indicators of the presence of electric charge. We have referred to the use of an aluminum-covered balloon for this purpose. An instrument designed to detect the presence of electric charge is called an *electroscope*. Probably the earliest version of an electroscope was invented by Sir William Gilbert (1540–1603), a physician to Queen Elizabeth I. Although Gilbert's positive contributions to the knowledge of electricity are dwarfed by his work on magnetism, to be considered in the next chapter, he did perform many experiments to show that *all* substances are in some measure affected by electricity. His electroscope, similar in design to the magnetic compass, consisted of a pivoted metallic needle that was free to

turn. In the presence of a charged
body this needle would turn for reasons entirely analogous to the motion of our balloon, in Fig. 14–2.

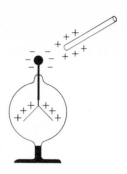

Nearly two centuries elapsed before the vastly superior *gold-leaf
electroscope* (Fig. 14–3) was invented. The model illustrated consists of two leaves of delicate gold
foil attached to a metal rod. The
rod itself is insulated at its position
of support. When a charge is
brought near the top of the rod,
the gold leaves become similarly
charged, repel each other, and stand
apart. Note that in this use of the

FIG. 14–3. Gold-leaf electroscope in
presence of a positive charge. The
leaves will also diverge if the conductor
which supports them has a net charge.

electroscope the conducting gold leaves and rod have no *net* charge; the
presence of a charged object simply causes separation of the two kinds of
charge, as indicated in Fig. 14–3. If the charged object is taken from the
vicinity of the instrument the leaves will fall. If the charged object is
momentarily brought in contact with the electroscope rod, however,
some positive charge will remain, and the leaves will remain diverged
after the external charge has been removed. The similarity between
this behavior and that of the aluminized balloon (Fig. 14–2) is clear.
The gold-leaf electroscope is superior to both the balloon and Gilbert's
needle, as an instrument, because it can be made much more sensitive
and can be used for quantitative measurements.

14–2 Coulomb's law

Dufay's fundamental discovery, that like charges repel and unlike
charges attract, was a qualitative one. "Attraction" and "repulsion" are
words which describe forces, and the behavior of bodies under the action of
forces should be subject to the quantitative laws of mechanics. To apply
the principles of mechanics to electricity, however, it would first be necessary to find what law governs the force between charges.

The manner of dependence of electrostatic force on the distance between
two charges was discovered experimentally by Charles Augustin Coulomb
(1736–1806) and reported in 1785. The discovery was probably anticipated by Cavendish, but he failed to publish much of his work, which therefore was of little value to the science of his time. For both Coulomb and
Cavendish success depended on the construction of a delicate torsion
balance, much like that used by Cavendish for determining the gravita-

tional constant. Since the latter experiment has been described in
Chapter 4, the details of the method
need not be repeated here. The laws
of a spring balance and a torsion balance are esssntially the same, it will
be recalled: the amount of twist (or
stretch, for a spring balance) is proportional to the force producing it.
The torsion balance can be made
very sensitive, and with such a
balance, carefully shielded from outside influences, Coulomb compared
the forces between charged spheres
at various distances of separation
(Fig. 14–4).

FIG. 14–4. Principle of Coulomb's
demonstration of the inverse square
law.

Coulomb first tested spheres with like charge, and reached the conclusion that "the repulsive force between two small spheres charged with the
same sort of electricity is in the inverse ratio of the squares of the distances
between the centers of the spheres." The experiments were somewhat more
difficult in the case of attraction between spheres of unlike charge, but
Coulomb was also able to conclude that "the mutual attraction of the
electric fluid [charge] called positive on the electric fluid which is ordinarily
called negative is in the inverse ratio of the square of the distances." This
particular dependence of electric force on distance had been assumed to be
the correct one for some time. The similarity between this relation and
that exhibited by gravitational forces will be recognized at once.

Coulomb's experiments did not yield a complete law for electrostatic
forces, for he measured only the dependence of these forces on distance.
Comparison with the law of gravitation, however, suggested that *quantity
of charge* might play a role analogous to *mass*. With no further justification,
Coulomb assumed the analogy valid—rightly, as we shall shortly show.
His statement of the complete law, now known as Coulomb's law, may be
paraphrased: *Like charges repel, and unlike charges attract, with a force
which varies directly with the product of the charges and inversely with the
square of the distance between them.* If we represent one quantity of charge
by q and the other by Q we may express the law algebraically:

$$F = K \frac{qQ}{r^2}, \qquad (14\text{–}1)$$

where F is the mutual force, r is the distance between charges q and Q, and
K is a constant depending on the units employed for charge, distance, and
force. This equation describes forces of either attraction or repulsion; if q

and Q are both positive or both negative (like) the sign of F is positive, which is interpreted as repulsion; if only one of the charges is negative F is also negative, which represents attraction.

The gold-leaf electroscope may be used to verify Coulomb's assumption that electric force is proportional to the product of the quantities of charge involved. *Relative* quantities of charge can be determined by noting the extent of deflection of the gold leaves. Two equal charges will produce the same amount of deflection when brought to the same position near the electroscope. The deflection produced by the two together may also be noted, and repetition of this process may be used to *calibrate* the instrument, i.e., to correlate amount of deflection with quantity of charge. Torsion balance measurements may be made using charges whose sizes have been compared on a calibrated electroscope, to show that electric force is indeed proportional to the product qQ, as assumed in Eq. (14–1).

As yet we have not specified a value for K, the proportionality constant in Coulomb's law. In order to do this, we must decide on a unit of measurement for electric charge. There are various units employed for charge, and that in most common use is appropriately named the *coulomb*. For electrostatic phenomena the coulomb is a large and unwieldy unit, but it is of convenient size to describe the charge that flows in ordinary *currents* (which we must soon consider), and to introduce more than one unit for charge might prove confusing. If force is measured in dynes, charge in coulombs, and distance in centimeters, the proportionality constant has the value

$$K = 9 \times 10^{18}$$

Thus two objects bearing equal charges of one coulomb each, when placed one centimeter apart, would exert a mutual force of 9×10^{18} dynes, which corresponds to about ten billion tons. The coulomb *is* a very large unit for electric charges at rest, then, but we shall shortly witness its convenience in application to other electric phenomena.

14–3 Electrostatic discharge

One reason that a torsion balance of great delicacy was needed in the experiments of Coulomb and Cavendish is that, in practice, there is a limit to the amount of electric charge that can be accumulated on an object like a small sphere. In the first place, net charge resides only on the surface of a body, a fact that was noted early in the 18th century and rediscovered in 1767 by Joseph Priestley.* Moreover, if one attempts to build up a very

---

*Newton had proved that as a consequence of the inverse square law of force, a spherical *shell* would exert no gravitational forces on masses within it. Priestley, finding no electric forces exerted on charges placed inside a hollow charged body, concluded by analogy that electric forces must also obey an inverse square law. Coulomb, with his experiments, demonstrated this inverse square dependence explicitly.

high charge on the surface of an object, the charge tends to "leak off," especially at sharp points. "St. Elmo's fire," the glow observed by sailors since ancient times at the points of masts and spars during storms, can be understood in this way. The phenomenon was recognized by Franklin as a basis for his famous invention, the lightning rod. He had been the first to prove, with his celebrated kite experiment, that atmospheric electricity has properties identical to those of electricity produced by rubbing. Having noticed in his experiments that electricity tends to discharge at points, Franklin concluded that a pointed rod would "probably draw the electrical fire silently out of a cloud before it came nigh enough to strike, and thereby secure us from that most sudden and terrible mischief."

The laboratory observations of Franklin and others on electric discharge were made possible by two technical developments. One was the electrostatic generator, a device which produces charge by rubbing an insulating material (glass, for instance) mechanically instead of by hand. The other, the "Leyden jar," resulted from the discovery that charge can be held, or "condensed" on a conductor by the presence of another, oppositely charged conductor. Consider two metal plates, as in Fig. 14–5, separated by dry air, glass, or another good insulator. It is certain that the like charges on one plate repel each other. Their mutual repulsions are somewhat overcome by the attractions of opposite charges on the other plate, however, and as a result both kinds of charge are held in place. A device such as that shown in Fig. 14–5 is called an electric *condenser* or *capacitor*. Leyden jars, named in honor of the place where they were first widely used, consisted of glass jars covered with conducting material inside and out. When a charge was placed inside the conductor by contact (at point *A*, Fig. 14–6) with a body

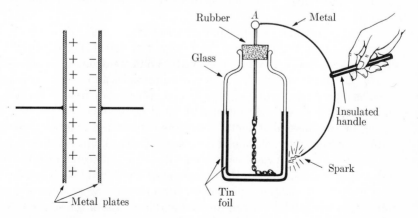

Fig. 14–5. Parallel plate condenser, showing distribution of charge.   Fig. 14–6. A Leyden jar being discharged.

that had been electrified by rubbing, the outside conductor also became charged. Sufficient charge could be accumulated, especially with the aid of a mechanical electrostatic generator, to produce a severe electric shock, or a visible electric spark, as indicated in Fig. 14–6. The parallel plate condenser, an improvement on the Leyden jar, was introduced by Franklin.

After a spark has passed between the two plates of a condenser the plates are no longer charged; it is for this reason that the spark is called an electric *discharge*. A condenser may also be discharged without sparking, by simply connecting the two plates by a metallic wire. The plates of a charged condenser contain a static charge, but during the process of discharge, charge moves, or "flows," from one plate to another through the wire. Any movement of charge constitutes what we call an electric *current*. It is difficult to study moving charge in a condenser, since during the process of charging the flow is extremely slow, and the discharge is completed in an almost infinitesimally short time. The study and practical utilization of electric current did not become possible until a means of producing and maintaining steady currents had been discovered.

14–4 Current electricity

Luigi Galvani (1737–1798), a biology professor in Bologna, noticed by chance in 1786 that in certain circumstances convulsions were set up in frogs' legs placed near an electric spark. On further investigation, he found that the spark was unnecessary; spasms occurred when the frog was suspended from a metallic hook and a rod made of a different metal was brought in simultaneous contact with the hook and the frog's leg muscle. Although Galvani thought that the disturbance was a manifestation of "animal electricity," he had discovered the principle of the electric battery.

It was Galvani's countryman Alessandro Volta (1745–1827) who ascertained that animal nerve tissue served to detect, not to initiate, the electric effect the former had observed. Volta went on (in 1800) to construct "an apparatus which . . . in a word provides an unlimited charge or imposes a perpetual action of impulsion on the electric fluid." He had discovered that a steady electric current could be produced by a source consisting of two dissimilar metals, such as copper and zinc, separated by water or, better, by a solution of lye or salt. One of Volta's earliest *batteries* consisted of a series of cups, each filled with brine, connected by alternating pieces of zinc and copper in the manner shown in Fig. 14–7. The effects of electric current—sparks and shocks, for example—were observed when connection was made between the first and last cups of the series, as could easily be done with a metallic wire. Thirty or more cups, arranged in this way, were found sufficient to produce the same kind of electric shock as that

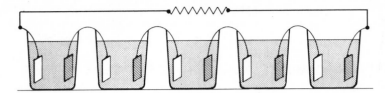

FIG. 14–7. Early version of Volta's battery.

given by a Leyden jar or electrostatic generator. But these devices could provide only instantaneous, intermittent discharges, and Volta's battery gave a continuous effect. In his clarification of Galvani's discovery Volta had made an invention of great practical importance.

It will not be feasible for us to follow the further historical growth of electrical science in detail, because electrical concepts and terminology remained confused for some years. The whole subject of current electricity is easier for the most unscientific of us today than it was for the intellectual giants of a century and a half ago because of the clarification of concepts that has taken place gradually since Volta's momentous discovery. Let us examine those concepts which will facilitate our task of describing current electricity.

The first of the important electrical concepts, *charge*, has been discussed in connection with Coulomb's law; we have defined the coulomb as a unit of charge. The discharge of a condenser, we have noted, results in the neutralization of the opposite charges which have accumulated on its two plates; charge flows between them at the instant of discharge. Any flow of electric charge is called *current*. If a metal wire is connected between the terminals of a battery (e.g., the first and last cups of Fig. 14–7), there will be a current in the wire. It is as though the two dissimilar metals bear opposite charges, and charge flows between them, tending to neutralize the two. As shown in Fig. 14–8, a diagram of a single cell from a Voltaic battery, copper is positive with respect to zinc, and current in the external wire can be considered to consist of

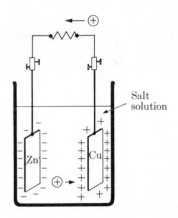

FIG. 14–8. Representing a single cell from a Voltaic battery. Copper is found positive with respect to zinc, so that current can be considered a cyclic flow of positive charge in the direction indicated.

a flow of positive charge from copper to zinc. The battery has the ability to impel continuous flow of charge in the wire without altering the quantity of charge on either terminal. For this to be the case, charge must also flow in the salt solution, and the entire assembly, battery plus external wire, constitutes a *cyclic* path for electric current. Any such cyclic conducting path is called a *circuit*. Even with the most powerful battery or other source, charge cannot flow unless the circuit is closed, i.e., complete.

In the presence of a steady current, the amount of charge passing is the same at all points of its circuit, i.e., charge does not accumulate anywhere. Quantitatively, then, current may be defined as the amount of charge passing a given point in a conductor per unit time:

$$I \text{ (current)} = \frac{Q \text{ (charge)}}{t \text{ (seconds)}}. \tag{14-2}$$

If Q is measured in coulombs and t in seconds, the resultant unit is *one coulomb per second*, which is called the *ampere*. Several kinds of instruments have been devised for insertion into a circuit to measure electric current; they are called *ammeters* (ampere measurers), whatever their principle of operation.

Charge will not flow around a circuit of itself. If a battery (or other source, such as the generator of a modern power plant) is not present there can be no current. What is it that the battery supplies? To aid understanding of the answer to this question we may draw an analogy to the flow of water in a stream or pipe, for which a pressure "head" is necessary The water above a waterfall, for example, possesses a certain gravitational potential for doing work. We could express this potential by measuring the difference in energy content of the water above and below the waterfall in terms of a number of joules of energy per gallon of water. This would be equal to the work which must be done to lift one gallon of water through the height of the fall, and would obviously increase proportionately with height. We may say that there is a *difference of gravitational potential* between points at the top and bottom of the waterfall. By analogy, there must be a *difference of electric potential* between two points in a circuit if charge is to flow between them. The forces in this case are electrical, not gravitational, and electric forces are those involved in the performance of electrical work: a flow of charge, like a flow of water, is capable of doing work.

Electric *potential difference* between any two points is defined as *the quantity of work done in transferring a unit of charge from one point to the other*. Potential difference can exist whether current is present or not, just as the pressure "head" in a water system is present whether or not water is flowing from an open faucet. Since difference of potential is defined as work *per unit* of charge, it is independent of the actual quantity of charge transferred. Algebraically,

$$V \text{ (potential difference)} = \frac{W \text{ (work)}}{Q \text{ (charge)}}.$$ (14–3)

If work is measured in joules and charge in coulombs, the unit of potential difference is one *joule per coulomb*, called one *volt*. Difference of potential is often called simply *voltage*. A device whose terminals may be connected at two points of a circuit to measure the potential difference between them is called a *voltmeter*.

It is potential difference, or voltage, between the terminals of a battery which has the ability to impel current through an external circuit attached to those terminals. Just why the particular arrangement of component parts Volta selected for his device has the effect of establishing a potential difference is a chemical question, and will be answered in a later chapter. The magnitude of electric current in a circuit depends on the electric potential difference applied. The larger the quantities of charge accumulated on the plates of a condenser (Fig. 14–5), the greater the spark that will be observed when the condenser is discharged. Each cell in Volta's battery (Fig. 14–7) has a certain small voltage across its terminals, and as more and more identical cells are placed in the series arrangement shown, the device becomes capable of producing greater currents in an external circuit.

Charge, current, and potential difference are the fundamental concepts necessary for analyzing a simple circuit. Consider the circuit diagram of Fig. 14–9, which might represent any lighting or heating circuit, a flashlight or a toaster, for example. The symbols are defined in the diagram; note the essentials: a source of potential difference, a circuit and, for practical use, a "load" in which energy is expended, for example, the filament of a flashlight bulb or the heating element of a toaster. (When a circuit containing no load is closed, the result is called a "short circuit," accompanied by sparking and intense heating effects.) So long as the switch is open there is no current and no work is done; when the switch is closed the potential difference produces a current in the entire circuit. The filament of a bulb has properties such that some of the work done by charge moving through it is converted to heat but most of it to light; in a circuit devised for heating, the reverse must be true.

The *total* electric energy expended

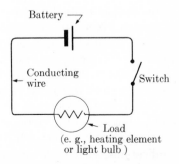

Fig. 14–9. Simple circuit diagram.

(work done) in a circuit may be obtained by multiplying the voltage (work per unit charge) by the total charge that flows, and depends on the length of time the switch is closed. If the potential difference and current are both known, the *rate* at which work is done can be computed at once, however, for

$$V \text{ (volts)} \times I \text{ (amperes)} = \frac{W \text{ (joules)}}{Q \text{ (coulombs)}} \times \frac{Q \text{ (coulombs)}}{t \text{ (seconds)}}$$

$$= \frac{W}{t} \text{ joules/sec.} \tag{14-4}$$

Rate of doing work is called *power*:

$$P \text{ (power)} = \frac{W \text{ (work)}}{t \text{ (time)}}, \tag{14-5}$$

and the unit, one *joule per second*, is called one *watt* of power. From the relation (14-4) we see that potential difference in volts, multiplied by current in amperes, yields power in watts:

$$P \text{ (watts)} = V \text{ (volts)} \times I \text{ (amperes)}. \tag{14-6}$$

Thus a 60–watt bulb, between the terminals of a 120-volt source of potential difference, would draw a current I of 0.5 amp. To find the total energy supplied to the bulb in a given time we could simply multiply its power in watts by the number of seconds it is kept lighted, and would obtain an answer in joules. In either domestic or commercial circuits, a power station furnishes V, a difference of potential, which, by the closing of switches, is allowed to produce currents in various loads. Work is done in these loads at rates which can be measured in watts or kilowatts (1000 watts). The monthly electric bill is based not on V, I, Q, or P alone, but on W, the total energy expended. A *kilowatt-hour*, the unit usually used for this purpose, is a unit of energy, as a moment's reflection will confirm.

We are now in a position to see that most of the electrical concepts which prove so useful to us today could not have been easy to formulate in 1800, the date of Volta's discovery. Potential difference—truly the key concept of all—is defined in terms of the much broader concept *energy*, and the latter was not clarified until the middle of the 19th century. The new concepts developed gradually as further investigation revealed new empirical generalizations, such as the one we shall now consider.

14-5 Ohm's law

The magnitude of the current actually observed in a given load depends on the load itself as well as on the potential difference applied. If a 40-watt lamp bulb and a 1000-watt laundry iron are attached between the same 120-volt terminals (Fig. 14–10), the lamp can draw only 1/25 as much current as the iron, since V is the same for both, and the product VI (power) for the lamp is only 1/25 as great as for the iron. In practice, an ordinary 40-watt lamp bulb will dissipate power at the rate of 40 watts only when the voltage across its terminals is 120 volts, approximately that of the standard house circuit. At this voltage the current in its filament is $I = P/V = \frac{1}{3}$ amp. and that of the iron, rated at 1000 watts for 120 volts, is $8\frac{1}{3}$ amp. At lesser voltages, say 115 or 110, each appliance will draw a current which is smaller than these values.

The relation between voltage applied and current produced in a conductor was first thoroughly studied by Georg Ohm (1789–1854), a German schoolmaster; he published his results in 1827. The best known of his discoveries was that current is *proportional* to the applied difference of potential for metallic conductors. This can be demonstrated by applying various voltages to the terminals of a coil of wire (Fig. 14–11). It is found

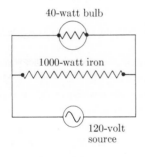

FIG. 14–10. Two devices connected "in parallel" across the same voltage source.

FIG. 14–11. Ohm's law. (a) Diagram of circuit used for obtaining results plotted in (b). For a given conductor, V is proportional to I.

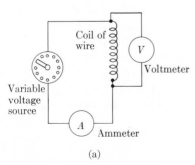

(a)

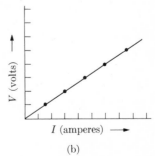

(b)

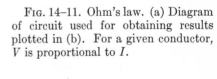

that when potential difference is doubled, current doubles; when potential difference is trebled, current trebles, and so on. This observation, the substance of *Ohm's law*, may be stated

$$V = RI, \qquad (14\text{-}7)$$

where R, a constant of proportionality for a given conductor, is called the *resistance* of that conductor. Ohm investigated the dependence of resistance on such factors as length and cross section of a uniform conductor, and on the material of which it is made. In his honor the unit of resistance is called the *ohm*. If one volt applied across the terminals of a conductor produces a current of one ampere, the conductor is said to have a resistance of one ohm.

Ohm also discovered at least one of the limitations of the law that bears his name: the resistance of a given conductor is not absolutely constant, but depends on temperature. In other words, the ratio V/I remains the same for a given wire, no matter what the voltage across it, only so long as the temperature of the wire is fixed. The resistances of most conductors increase as their temperatures are raised. The ratio V/I is considerably higher for an ordinary light bulb attached to 120-volt terminals than for the same light bulb attached to the terminals of a 6-volt dry cell, for example. This fact in no way impairs the validity and usefulness of the concept of electrical resistance, however, since practical conductors (often called resistors) are designed for that temperature or range of temperatures at which they are to be used.

Ohm's law and the concept of resistance are of great value in practical electricity. Actually, however, Volta's invention of a device capable of furnishing appreciable steady currents over extended times made possible discoveries of much greater consequence than this law. In the hands of such men as Davy and Faraday, it brought chemical discoveries of fundamental significance, and our present state of understanding of the structure of matter would certainly not have been possible without it. We must not ignore the fact that the development of the entire electrical industry can be traced to the same beginnings; Galvani's chance observation led, although not directly, to the age of electrical devices in which we live. The relations between electricity and magnetism, which could be detected and studied only when steady sources of current became available, provided keys both to the question of atomic structure and the development of electrical technology. We shall trace these relations in the next chapter, after first examining the phenomena designated by the term *magnetism*.

14–6 Summary

Electric charge is of two kinds, called positive and negative; like charges repel each other, unlike charges attract, with forces that vary inversely as the square of the distance between them. Static charge was first produced by rubbing together two dissimilar substances; the discoveries of Galvani and Volta led to the production of electric *currents* by means of chemical "batteries." An electrical conductor carries current if a *difference of potential* exists between the ends of the conductor. For measuring these quantities the unit of charge is the coulomb, the unit of current is the ampere (coulomb/sec), and potential difference is measured in volts (joules/coulomb). Ohm discovered that in any conductor the current is proportional to the potential difference across it; the ratio of potential difference to current is called the *resistance* of the conductor. Electrical energy is expended as heat in a conductor at a rate which is directly proportional to the product of the current and the potential difference across the conductor.

REFERENCES

BRAGG, W. L., *Electricity*, Chapter I.

MAGIE, W. F., *A Source Book in Physics*, pp. 390–393 (Gilbert), 398–400 (Dufay), 400–403 (Franklin), 408–417 (Coulomb), 421–427 (Galvani), 427–431 (Volta), 465–472 (Ohm), and others.

ROLLER, D., and D. H. D. ROLLER, *The Development of the Concept of Electric Charge: Electricity from the Greeks to Coulomb* (Number 8 of the Harvard Case Histories in Experimental Science). Traces the development in detail.

TAYLOR, L. W., *Physics, the Pioneer Science*. Contains a historical account with more emphasis on scientific content itself than in the Roller and Roller treatment.

The laws and principles contained in this chapter (and also those in Chapters 15, 16, and 17) may be found in standard textbooks of elementary physics. See, for example, H. E. White, *Classical and Modern Physics: A Descriptive Account*.

1. Can you say why a negatively charged comb or fountain pen picks up small bits of lint or paper? Remember that a positively charged glass rod will also attract such light objects.

2. We shall see that a hydrogen atom consists of two particles, called the proton and the electron, which have equal charges of opposite sign. Their masses and charges are

mass of proton $(M) = 1.67 \times 10^{-24}$ gm,

mass of electron $(m) = 9.1 \times 10^{-28}$ gm,

charge on each $(q) = 1.6 \times 10^{-19}$ coul.

It will be instructive to compare the magnitude of the electrostatic attraction between these particles with their gravitational attraction. If distance (r) is measured in cm and force in dynes,

F (electrical) $= 9 \times 10^{18} \, (q^2/r^2)$,

F (gravitational)

$= 6.7 \times 10^{-8} \, (mM/r^2)$.

How do these forces compare? Can the effects of gravitational force be expected to make any noticeable contribution to the cohesion between a proton and an electron? (Results of accuracy sufficient for illustrative purposes may be obtained by rounding off all numbers to the nearest integer.)

3. Find the current through a 40-watt lamp when 120 volts are applied to its terminals. What is the resistance of the lamp in ohms? What would be the current through the lamp if only 110 volts were applied, assuming that its resistance is not appreciably affected by temperature?

4. Devices connected in the manner shown in Fig. 14–10 are said to be connected "in parallel"; in this kind of circuit the same potential difference is applied across all branches. Devices connected one after another, as in Fig. 14–12, are said to be "in series." This kind of circuit may be understood by analogy to a series of cascades in a stream; there is equal current in all, for there is but one path. The total hydrostatic potential of the stream is the sum of the potentials of its individual cascades. Similarly, the potential difference across an entire series circuit is the sum of the individual voltages across its individual component conductors.

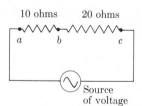

FIG. 14–12. Series circuit.

Suppose that 120 volts are supplied by the source, and that the resistances of the two conductors are 10 and 20 ohms, respectively. How much current is there? What is the difference of potential across each conductor? [$Ans.: I = 4$ amp; $V_{ab} = 40$ volts; $V_{bc} = 80$ volts]

5. Show that for a wire that obeys Ohm's law the rate at which work is done in heating the wire, by passing a current through it, is proportional to the square of the current. (This relation was discovered experimentally by Joule, and is sometimes called Joule's law.)

6. It was mentioned, in Chapter 11, that Joule measured the *electrical* as well as the mechanical equivalent of heat. Would you expect these equivalents to have the same or different values? Why? Suppose a current of 0.25 amp is steadily supplied for 10 min, at a potential difference of 120 volts, to a heating element immersed in a calorimeter containing 100 gm of water. If the initial temperature of the water were 20°C, what should it be at the end of the interval, under ideal conditions? What is the resistance of the heating element?

7. Two electrically charged bodies, at a distance of 10 cm, repel each other with a force of 50 dynes. What will this force become if

(a) the sign of charge on one body is changed,

(b) the bodies are placed 2 cm apart,

(c) the charge on one body is doubled

and that on the other is reduced by a factor of 4,

(d) the bodies are placed 50 cm apart,

(e) the bodies are placed 20 cm apart and the charge on each is doubled,

(f) the bodies are placed 5 cm apart and the charge on one is quadrupled.

8. If a negatively charged body is brought near a gold-leaf electroscope, the latter's leaves diverge. If, with the charged body still held near, the electroscope rod is touched by a finger, the leaves fall. When the charged body is removed, however, the leaves diverge again, and the electroscope is found to bear a net positive charge. Can you explain this sequence of events? A series of diagrams will help.

9. After walking across a carpet one frequently gets a shock on touching a metallic object, such as a radiator, or even when shaking hands with another person. Rapid movement of moist air masses produces lightning discharges. Gasoline trucks often drag chains. Automobiles are usually brushed by metal strips before their drivers are permitted to offer money to the toll-takers on a bridge. Explain in terms of electrostatics.

CHAPTER 15

MAGNETISM AND ELECTROMAGNETISM

15–1 Lodestone and magnets

Knowledge of magnetism, as a curiosity, is as old as that of electrostatics. The mineral magnetite, an iron oxide (Fe_3O_4) that is traditionally called lodestone, was found to have the ability to pick up and hold pieces of iron, even one below the other, as in Fig. 15–1. Unlike amber, which, when rubbed, attracts light objects of all kinds, lodestone appreciably influences only iron. Iron which has recently been in contact with lodestone possesses a slight ability to attract other pieces of iron. Although the magnetic property of lodestone is long lasting, the effect on iron is quite temporary. A magnet tends to orient itself along a north-south line; the early magnetic compass, which came into nautical use about a thousand years ago, consisted of a magnetized iron needle supported on a cork floating in water. A piece of lodestone had to be carried aboard ship for the purpose of magnetizing the needle at frequent intervals. Only much later was it discovered that steel could be made to retain its magnetic strength, so that nearly permanent magnetic needles could be constructed.

With iron filings it is easy to show that the influence of a piece of lodestone extends beyond its own surface; even when separated from the lodestone by glass or paper, bits of iron are clearly affected by its presence. Historically, this observation was the first clear evidence of "action at a distance," i.e., force exerted by one body on another in the absence of physical contact between them. The fact that after a needle has been touched to lodestone it tends to point north also suggests the presence of some intangible force. During the 16th century it was discovered that if such a needle is suspended so that it is free to turn in a vertical as well as a horizontal plane (Fig. 15–2), the north end "dips" toward the earth (in the northern hemisphere). Knowledge of this phenomenon, together with experiments on the behavior of magnetic needles in the vicinity of a spherical lodestone (Fig. 15–3), led Sir William Gilbert to the correct conclusion that the earth itself is a magnet. It also led him to the belief, unsupported by evidence, that gravity is a manifestation of magnetism, although he was rather vague as to details. Nevertheless, this hypothesis influenced Kepler, and in general suggested the assumption that gravitational force is also an "action at a distance," an idea that reached its full growth in Newton's law

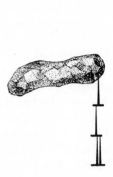

FIG. 15–1.   Lodestone supporting
iron nails.

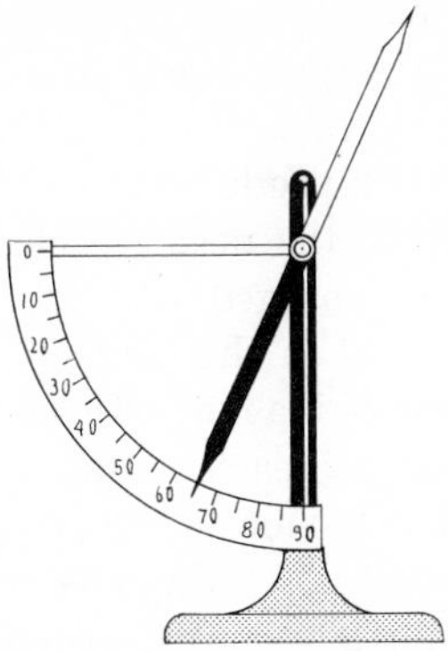

FIG. 15–2.   A dip needle.

of gravitation. The origin of the earth's magnetism is not yet understood, and any connection between magnetism and gravitation is still an unsolved problem in the 20th century.

The phenomenon of magnetism has been vastly illuminated since 1600, when Gilbert's book on the subject, *De Magnete*, was published. Yet Gilbert recorded many of the essential facts. It was important to distinguish clearly between the effects of static electricity and of magnetism, and this Gilbert did. Different kinds of matter are involved in the two cases, since iron was the only substance known to Gilbert to be subject to magnetic forces. But there is a more fundamental distinction, easily illustrated by experiment. Suppose we float a magnetized needle on a cork, then mark with N that end, or "pole," which points north, the other with S. If this is done with two magnets and one of them is brought near the other, it is

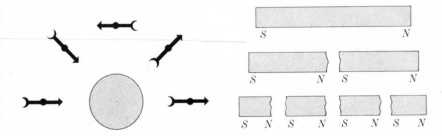

FIG. 15–3.   Behavior of compass
needles near a spherical lodestone,
which led Gilbert to conclude that the
earth is a magnet.

FIG. 15–4. New poles appear when a
magnet is broken.

found that N repels N, S repels S, while N and S attract each other. So far the story sounds like that of electrostatics, i.e., like charges repel and unlike charges attract. In the electric case, however, rubbing neutral glass with neutral silk produces a positive charge on the glass which is entirely separated from the negative charge on the silk. The glass rod as a whole is positively charged, and if broken in two there are two positively charged pieces. But in the magnetic case it proves impossible to separate pole N from pole S; if a magnetic needle or a piece of lodestone is broken it becomes two magnets, each complete with N and S poles, each capable of the same kind of behavior as the original magnet (Fig. 15–4). This aspect of magnetism, that "... the self-same part of [lodestone] may by division become either north or south," seemed astonishing to Gilbert. The process of division may be indefinitely repeated, always with the same result: N and S poles appear, so that each new piece is complete with both kinds of poles. From this it can be concluded that there is nothing in magnetism truly comparable to electric charge. Charge is of two separable kinds, which we have called positive and negative. Magnetic poles are also of two distinct kinds N and S, but they are not separable. This is the most important single characteristic of magnetism.

Since other magnets and iron filings are affected at a distance from a magnetic pole, it can be said that a *magnetic field* of force is produced in the neighborhood of a magnet; any magnetic pole in this region experiences a force which is proportional to the *field strength*. The direction of the field at any point is taken as the direction of the force on an N pole at that point. This direction can be ascertained by means of a small compass. The entire pattern of the field can be determined by placing a piece of glass or paper over the magnet and sprinkling the top with iron filings. The filings become

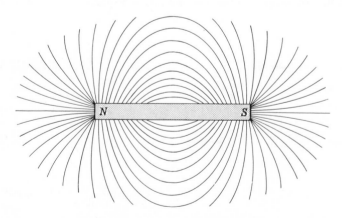

Fig. 15–5. Magnetic field of a bar magnet.

tiny magnets and tend to form little chains from pole to pole. Figure 15–5 represents the field of a bar magnet. Variations in field strength are apparent as a falling off of the tendency for the filings to line up, and it is clear that the field strength diminishes with increasing distance from the magnetic poles producing the field.

Determination of the law of force between magnetic poles is complicated by the presence of opposite poles on the same magnet, by the earth's magnetic field, and by the fact that poles are not often well localized. Coulomb, experimenting with a magnetized steel needle 25 inches long, assumed that the pole strength is "condensed" within two or three inches near the ends of the needle, and showed that the force between poles is proportional to the inverse square of the distance between them. This law is useful, but it contributed nothing to the essential understanding of magnetic phenomena. The first fundamental contribution to this subject after the work reported by Gilbert was the discovery that electricity and magnetism are very closely related after all, although there is no connection between magnetism and static electric charges. *Moving* charges, which constitute currents, were ultimately found to be entirely responsible for magnetism, as far as is known even today.

15–2 The magnetic effects of currents. Oersted and Ampère

The Danish physicist Hans Christian Oersted (1777–1851), during a lecture demonstration performed in the year 1819–1820, caused a strong current to flow in a north-south line above a magnetic compass needle. He was (at least in the eyes of one of his students) "quite struck with perplexity" to see the needle deviate toward an east-west direction, as indicated in Fig. 15–6. According to the student's account, Oersted had the immediate presence of mind to reverse the direction of the current in the wire, "and the needle deviated in the contrary direction." Thus was made one of the most momentous scientific discoveries of any age. The whole subject of electromagnetism was opened for investigation, a subject which within half a century was to embrace the phenomenon of light as well. Some discoveries are greater than their own mere factual content, and mark a revolutionary change in man's intellectual outlook on the world as a whole. Oersted's discovery was such a one. It initiated the decline of the Laplacian "mechanical view" of the universe which we have discussed briefly in Chapter 4, and signified the rise of a much richer, more comprehensive view.

Even though its full consequence could not have been recognized at once, Oersted's observation aroused the excited interest of scientists and even of popular audiences all over Europe. At least a part of this interest may be ascribed to the fact that the behavior of Oersted's compass needle was not

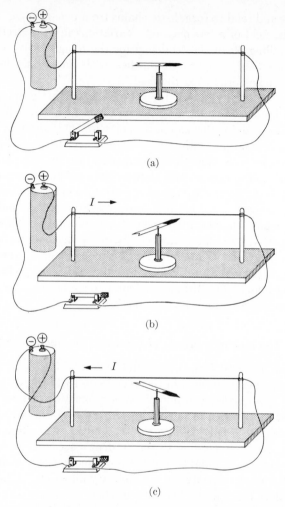

(a)

(b)

(c)

Fig. 15–6. Behavior of a compass needle placed below a north-south wire, (a) in the absence of current, and (b), (c), when the current is in the directions shown.

consistent with the mechanistic philosophy then in vogue. Gravitational forces, electrical forces, even the forces between magnetic poles, all fitted into a simple picture of forces of attraction or repulsion acting along the line joining the two bodies involved. But the compass needle in Oersted's experiment was neither attracted nor repelled by the wire. If small compasses or, better, iron filings are free to turn in the neighborhood of a wire carrying a current, each bit of iron places itself at a right angle to the line joining it to the wire, with the result shown in Fig. 15–7. Mechanics as constituted in 1820, and previously thought to be complete, failed to account for such behavior.

Let us note carefully the directions of the forces involved. Oersted's observation that reversing the direction of current caused a "contrary" deflection of the magnetic compass needle makes it significant for the first time to specify the direction of an electric current. Arbitrarily, since nothing can actually be seen to flow in a circuit, the convention was adopted that current in an external wire flows from the positive terminal of a battery to the negative terminal. This convention is generally applied; in the discharge of a condenser, for example, current is said to flow from the positively charged plate to the negative one.

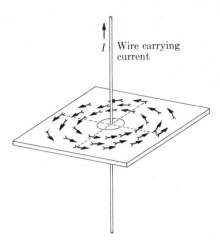

FIG. 15–7. Small compasses, or iron filings, set themselves at right angles to a wire carrying a current and to lines drawn from each to the wire.

The arrows along the wires of Figs. 15–6, 15–7, etc., represent the direction of the current in this sense. The arrow representing a compass needle is directed from S to N, where N represents the end that "seeks" the earth's north pole, and shows the orientation of the magnetic needle. In the neighborhood of a current the relative orientations of current and compasses must be *observed*, and can then be *described* in terms of this conventional assignment of directions. The most convenient way of describing the behavior of a compass needle near a current-carrying wire is to use what is called the right-hand rule: grasp the wire with the right hand so that the thumb points in the direction of the current, whereupon the fingers take the direction of the N pole of a magnetic needle. In the various illustrations of this section the arrows can be seen to be drawn in accord with this empirical rule, i.e., they represent the observed phenomena consistently.

Many scientists contributed to further knowledge of the magnetic effects of currents, but it was Andre Marie Ampère (1775–1836) who, in a beautiful synthesis of experiment and theory, discovered the full set of laws governing these effects. Ampere noticed that two parallel wires attract each other if they carry currents in the same direction, and repel each other if their currents are opposite (Fig. 15–8). (This observation had been made by others, but its significance could hardly be recognized until its connection with magnetism was known, and the earlier reports attracted no attention.) As early as 1820, soon after the announcement of Oersted's

discovery, Ampère "further deduced
from this by analogy the consequence that the attractive and
repulsive properties of magnets depend on electric currents which cir-
culate about the molecules of iron
and steel in a direction perpendicular to a line which joins the two
poles." These words of the important French scientist Dominique
Francois Jean Arago (1786–1853),
who first reported Oersted's discovery to the French Academy, take
us a little ahead of our story, but are
reproduced here to show the interlocking roles of theory and experiment. Arago goes on: "These theoretical views suggested to him
[Ampère] at once the thought that
one might obtain a stronger mag-
netization by substituting for the
straight connecting wire which I had
used a wire wound into a helix coil,
in the middle of which a steel needle
is placed . . . " Thus was invented
the *electromagnet* (Fig. 15–9) a device
of great importance in electrical ma-
chinery applications of all kinds. (A
practical electromagnet for lifting,
employing a soft iron core, was made
in 1823 by Sturgeon, who is usually
credited with the invention.) Arago
further pointed out that the observed position of the N and S poles
of the coil "conforms perfectly to the
result that M. Ampère had deduced," as though he were a little
surprised.

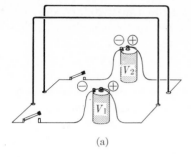

(a)

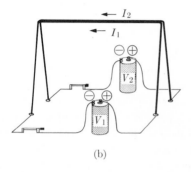

(b)

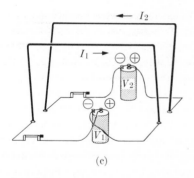

(c)

Fig. 15–8. Parallel currents attract,
opposite currents repel.

In addition to performing careful and exhaustive experiments to ascertain just how all the forces involved in electromagnetism depend on
distance, direction, and magnitude of currents, Ampère brought the
full weight of his mathematical training to bear on the quantitative
description of the new phenomenon. Of the mathematical details essen-

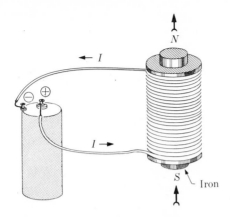

FIG. 15–9. A simple electromagnet, as devised by Ampère. The coil of wire, when there is a current, behaves like a bar magnet, with N and S poles as shown. The core of iron (or steel, as in Ampère's original design) is not an essential component, but serves to strengthen the magnetic effect.

tial to the rigorous development of the subject we shall employ virtually none in this account. We can readily follow, however, the qualitative line of reasoning which leads to Ampère's hypothesis of the equivalence between "molecular" current circuits and magnets, cited by Arago.

We have seen that small magnetic compass needles or iron filings tend to orient themselves in circles about a straight wire which carries electric current (Fig. 15–7). If the wire is bent into a loop these circles would thread the loop, as shown in Fig. 15–10 (a). On one side the face of the loop is found to attract the N poles of small test compasses, while the face on the other side of the loop attracts the S poles (Fig. 15–10b). But this is just what would happen if the wire loop were replaced by a disk of permanently magnetic material of the same diameter, one of whose faces would be N and the other S, as in Fig. 15–10(c). The loop in this way is equivalent to a magnetic disk, and by comparison of their action in orienting iron filings it is impossible to distinguish between the two. A large number of such disks, placed one on top of another N to S, are held together by attraction and form a single magnet of more conventional shape, a bar magnet. Similarly, Ampère reasoned, the parallel loops of a coiled wire carrying current would attract each other, and the coil as a whole would behave much like a bar magnet (Fig. 15–9). Note that our concern is with the outside rather than the interior of the coil. Moreover, the magnetic effect of the coil would be enhanced by adding an iron core, which when magnetized by the coil would act like an additional bar magnet. The similarity in behavior between an electromagnetic coil and a bar of magnetized iron was so strong that

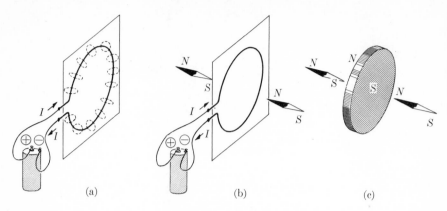

(a)   (b)   (c)

FIG. 15–10. (a) Imaginary iron filings "threading" a single wire loop in circles. (b) Faces of the single loop attract opposite ends of a compass. (c) Thin magnetic disk, with N and S poles, equivalent to single wire loop in (a) and (b).

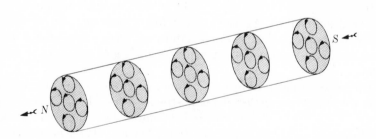

FIG. 15–11. Schematic representation of Ampère's "current loop" hypothesis of magnetism. Entire magnet is assumed to contain tiny loops of electric current, all oriented parallel to one another, as in the cross-sectional planes shown.

Ampère was led to believe that there must be electric currents in the iron, as he knew there were in the coil. He therefore postulated that the magnetism of iron is due to the total effect of many tiny whirls of current within the iron itself, all lined up parallel to one another (Fig. 15–11).

The basis for Ampère's belief that magnetism consists of little current whirls was put very directly in his own statement: "The proof on which I rely follows altogether from this, that my theory reduces to a single principle three sorts of actions which the totality of the phenomena proves to result from a common cause and which cannot be reduced to one principle in any other way." The "three sorts of actions" to which Ampère refers are those of N poles, S poles, and electric currents. We see that he was motivated by that universal striving in science to express various kinds of phenomena in terms of the simplest possible kind of *inter*relation.

If N and S poles are only manifestations of circular loops of current, the reason why they cannot be separated is clear: any loop must have two faces, and the separation of a coil of loops into two coils simply creates two new faces, one of each kind. Ampere's hypothesis was a feat of great scientific imagination. He could not possibly have established the physical reality of his current whirls on an atomic or molecular level. It was nearly a century later, well after the discovery of the subatomic charged particle called the electron, that the possibility of cyclic currents in individual atoms was confirmed. The problem is much more complicated than Ampère imagined, but it is now known that electrons in atoms and molecules can behave like submicroscopic current loops. In iron and other magnetic materials many of the individual whirls can be so oriented that their effects reenforce each other strongly, rather like the successive loops of an electromagnet. In most substances the individual loops are oriented at random and cancel each other's effect almost entirely. Although some aspects of magnetism are still not entirely understood, all magnetic effects are now confidently attributed to electric currents of some kind, in essential agreement with Ampère's hypothesis.

15–3 The role of the magnetic field

Quantitative description of the magnetic interaction between currents is somewhat more complicated than that of any we have hitherto encountered. Only in the case of parallel current-carrying wires are electromagnetic forces those of attraction or repulsion along the line joining two interacting elements. Depending on the relative orientation of two portions of electric circuits, the magnetic force between them may assume literally any direction. Its magnitude may be made to vary from zero to some definite maximum simply by changing the orientation of one of the wires while keeping its distance from the other unchanged. A formula giving both magnitude and direction of this force may be written mathematically, but is difficult to visualize physically. A much easier approach is to think of the interaction as taking place in two steps. Let us follow these steps.

Oersted's original discovery was that a current in a circuit affects a compass needle at some distance; in other words, the current sets up a magnetic field in the sense discussed in Section 15–1. Let us consider the field set up by the circuit on the left of Fig. 15–12(a). We have already seen that the orientation of a compass at a point near a long straight wire is perpendicular to the direction of current in the wire, and also perpendicular to a line drawn from the point to the wire. The small arrows of Fig. 15–12(a) indicate the direction from S to N of tiny compass needles placed at various

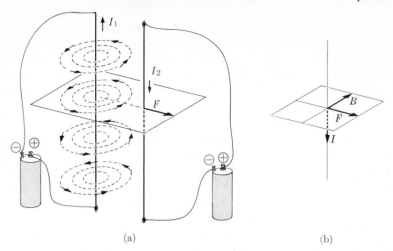

(a)   (b)

Fig. 15–12. A magnetic field B, with directions as indicated at various points, is set up by current I_1. Another conductor carrying current I_2 will experience a force F at right angles to the directions of both I_2 and B. In the case shown, B is perpendicular to the second conductor at all points along the latter's path. Force exerted on a current by a magnetic field is always perpendicular to the directions of both the current and the field, as shown in (b).

points. This plot represents the magnetic field produced by the current, as do the arrows of Fig. 15–7. The strength of the field is proportional to the current that produces it, and also depends on the geometric configuration of the circuit. For a long straight wire the field strength at a point varies inversely as the distance (not the square of the distance) of that point from the wire; for more complicated circuits the dependence of field strength on distance is less simple.

Now for step 2 in our visualization of electromagnetic interaction: let us consider the effect of the magnetic field of a straight wire (that on the left, Fig. 15–12) on a straight portion of a second circuit (that on the right) which is also carrying current. The second wire is found to experience a force in all of its orientations but one: if it is held parallel to the field, i.e., parallel to the direction taken by a compass needle near the first wire, the force vanishes. The maximum force on the right-hand wire is observed when it is held perpendicular to the field of the first wire, i. e., parallel to the wire itself. In these circumstances the *magnitude* of the force F is proportional to the current I flowing in the second wire and the length L of the second wire in the field; its *direction* is at right angles *both* to the field and to the wire carrying the current, as shown. Algebraically, the maximum value for F may be represented by

$$F = B \times I \times L, \qquad (15\text{–}1)$$

where B represents the magnetic field strength at the particular distance from the first wire. The source of B is the current in the left-hand circuit or, for more general application of Eq. (15–1), *any* electric circuit or permanent magnet. We have not given a quantitative definition of magnetic field strength, yet Eq. (15–1) may serve just that purpose; B may be defined so that the quantity BIL corresponds to the *observed* force F on the wire.

The concept of magnetic field has been emphasized here, as an intermediary in visualizing the interaction between electric currents, in order to simplify a description which is necessarily complicated when expressed simply as "action at a distance." We have no valid reason for attributing physical reality to magnetic fields in the sense that something actually happens to the properties of space in the presence of currents. Yet progress in understanding electromagnetic phenomena depended on the introduction of this concept, especially when the subject was generalized to include *non-steady* currents. Modern electromagnetic theory relies almost entirely on the field concept.

Before proceeding to the next great discovery in electromagnetism, let us note that the electric motor is a practical application of the work of Oersted and Ampère. To see that this is true, we need only remember that if one current circuit exerts a force on another, and that if one of them is free to move, the possibility of doing mechanical work as a result of sending currents through wires is at once established. To illustrate the motor principle, a permanent magnet may be substituted for one of the circuits, as in Fig. 15–13, and a long wire passed between its poles to complete a circuit in a

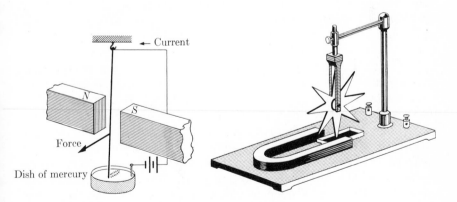

Fig. 15–13. Force on a wire carrying a current between the poles of a magnet will produce motion if the wire is free to move.

Fig. 15–14. Rotational motion in a star-shaped conductor.

dish of mercury. When current is passed through the wire it will move outward in the direction of the resultant force, since it is not rigidly attached at the bottom. If a star-shaped conductor is used (Fig. 15–14), as each of its points swings out of the mercury the circuit is re-established by a neighboring point moving in, so that rotational motion can be made to continue indefinitely. These two devices are mere toys, as was another rotating device exhibited by Faraday as early as 1821. The practical electric motor, similar in its essential features to the motors in use today, was invented independently by Davenport in the United States and by Jacobi in Russia during the year 1834.

15–4 The law of induction

The concept of field was particularly useful to Michael Faraday (1791–1867) in his important series of discoveries and predictions, which eventually brought the phenomenon of light into the realm of electromagnetism and led to the discovery of radio waves. Faraday was unquestionably one of the greatest scientists of all time. In electricity and magnetism alone his achievements would have ensured him rank comparable to that of Galileo and of Newton in mechanics, yet he also made important contributions to chemistry. Faraday was untutored in higher mathematics and his great theoretical work was all performed in terms of models, mental constructs which he endowed with crude, almost primitive, mechanical properties. He was a man of limited interests and without general cultural achievement, but his capacity for original thought in the field of science has hardly been surpassed. Another great British scientist, James Clerk Maxwell (1831–1879), to whom the electromagnetic theory of light is justifiably attributed, remarked that to devise this theory he had simply reduced to mathematical form what Faraday had perceived physically.

The list of fundamental laws of electricity was made logically complete by Faraday's discovery in 1831 of the phenomenon now called electromagnetic *induction*. Here again is a discovery that was not made singly: equal claim for priority must go to an American, Joseph Henry (1797–1878), then teaching at a boys' school in Albany, N. Y., and H. F. E. Lenz (1804–1865), then in St. Petersburg, Russia, was only a step behind. The discovery was this: *if a conductor is moved in a magnetic field, or a magnetic field is changed with respect to a conductor, a potential difference is established across the conductor.* One way of changing a magnetic field with respect to a conductor is to thrust a bar magnet into a coil of wire, as indicated in Fig. 15–15; the difference of potential across the coil during the motion may be detected by means of a sensitive voltmeter connected across its terminals. A small surge of current in the coil activates the voltmeter whether it is the coil or the magnet that is moved. Another way of producing the same effect

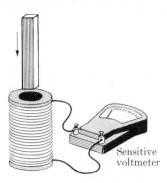

Fig. 15–15. A deflection may be produced on a sensitive voltmeter attached to a coil of wire by thrusting a bar magnet into the coil.

Fig. 15–16. Momentary potential differences are established in the coil on the right at the instants of opening and closing the switch in the circuit on the left.

is to place two coils side by side (Fig. 15–16). If one is connected to a battery through a circuit containing a switch, the other to a current-detecting instrument, small surges of current are detected in the second coil when the switch is closed, and again when it is opened. There is no magnetic field associated with the first coil when it carries no current, but there is a change in field from zero to full strength when the switch is closed, and the reverse when it is opened. Note that it is *change* in magnetic field that is essential; no voltage is induced in the second coil by a steady current in the first. Quantitatively, the amount of potential difference induced is proportional to the *rate* of change of the field.

In a sense, Oersted had discovered that "electricity may be converted to magnetism," and the search for a method to achieve the inverse, i.e., "converting magnetism into electricity," had been widespread. Although the work of Henry and Lenz contributed uniquely to our over-all knowledge of electromagnetic induction, Faraday's work was more comprehensive and thorough than either. He followed the consequences of his discovery untiringly. We shall here be interested primarily in the meaning of this discovery to the subsequent growth of science, but can hardly fail to note its great practical value.* It is potential difference that is needed to produce currents and do work. To produce the motion of a conductor in a magnetic field, mechanical work is required. According to the law of induction, then, by moving a coil of wire in a magnetic field mechanical energy may be transformed into electrical energy! This is the principle which has made our modern electrical industry possible.

One great advantage of electrical energy is that it can be easily transported from one place to another, by the simple agency of wires. The generator (or dynamo) which produces potential differences on the principle of electromagnetic induction makes possible an energy cycle: mechanical energy from a waterfall or a steam engine can be transformed into electrical energy, carried by wires to any desired location, and there used to operate heating devices (including light bulbs), or, perhaps more significantly, it may be transformed back into mechanical energy by motors operating in accord with the discovery of Oersted. Some of the initial energy is inevitably lost during transmission, through heating the wires and through mechanical friction, but the gain in convenience is almost incalculable. Small electric motors can also be run by currents from batteries, utilizing the chemical energy available in certain spontaneous chemical changes, but the electromagnetic generator is for most purposes a much more economical source of electrical energy. Although the principle of the motor was discovered before that of the generator, its commercial development did not proceed alone; the practical use of electric power depended as much on generators as on motors.

15–5 Other aspects of electromagnetic fields

We shall not discuss other practical consequences of the relation between electricity and magnetism, such as the transformer and the telephone, whose development required ingenuity but nothing new in principle. Another great scientific step was required, however, for the transmission of electrical energy *without* wires—at least for man to gain control over such transmission. For like M. Jourdain's famous discovery that he had been speaking prose all his life, it has turned out that nature has been sending out electromagnetic waves all along.

The imagined occurrences in the space surrounding electric currents were vividly real to Faraday. Stresses (figuratively like those produced in a

---

*Faraday himself was not explicitly interested in pursuing the technological applications of his discovery, but neither was he entirely unconscious of the possibilities. When asked by Prime Minister Gladstone what useful purpose electromagnetic induction might serve, he replied, "Sir, you may be able to tax it."

block of jelly when it is twisted, although visualized by Faraday as resembling the pressure inside tubes of fluid) may be said to be set up in the neighborhood of a current. These stresses represent what we have called the magnetic field. But according to the law of induction, a *change* in these stresses, caused either by motion or by the opening and/or closing of circuits, sets up a difference of potential. The potential difference established in this way may be considered the manifestation of a new set of stresses, which we may call an electric field.* Space is now getting rather full of stresses, but there is more to come. This same space transmits light. Following a venerable hypothesis, by no means original with Faraday, the latter believed that there is no such thing as "empty" space, but that the entire universe is filled with a subtle, undetectable fluid called the *ether* (*vide* Aristotle's "quintessence"). It occurred to him that since light must also involve stresses in the ether (and we shall see in the next two chapters that this indeed seemed the only reasonable basis for understanding some of the properties of light), electric and magnetic stresses (fields) might affect the transmission of light. If this were so, Ampère's motive, the desirability of substituting one principle for three, would lead logically to the conclusion that light, electricity, and magnetism are all, in some way, aspects of the same thing.

It has been said, probably first by a covetous university man, that Faraday's originality had never been hampered by a university education. He performed countless experiments, some of which appear almost ridiculous today, but ultimately he did find a relation between light and a magnetic field. He observed that the transmission of light through glass is changed, in a way we shall describe later, when the glass is situated between the poles of a strong electromagnet. Thus Faraday's suspicion of a connection between light and magnetism, at least, was confirmed.

Faraday's lack of the tools of mathematics made it impossible for him to go much beyond the qualitative conviction that light is electromagnetic. The utilization of this idea, both for further scientific discovery and for practical application, was made possible by James Clerk Maxwell's elegant mathematical treatment of the subject and the subsequent experimental confirmation by others of his predictions. The sense of this significant development can now be followed without recourse to mathematical detail.

---

*An electric field manifests itself as a force on an electric charge, and could have been introduced in connection with static charges; in electrostatics, however, the field concept has no advantage over the idea of "action at a distance." It becomes important only when the force on a given charge cannot be easily traced to another charge, as in the case of induction due to a change in magnetic field. Similarly, the concept of *gravitational field* could have been introduced in connection with the considerations of Chapter 4, but no advantageous purpose would have been served by doing so.

But to do so and to be led in consequence to deeper understanding of atoms and molecules, rocks and galaxies, we must first turn our attention to some aspects of mechanics we have hitherto neglected.

15–6 Summary

An iron oxide mineral called lodestone was found to attract iron, even at a distance, and the phenomenon was called *magnetism*. The effect on pure iron is temporary, but permanent magnets may be made of steel. A magnet exhibits poles of two kinds, called N and S because of the tendency of any magnet to orient itself along the earth's meridian. In contrast to electric charge, these poles cannot be separated. In 1820, Oersted discovered that a magnet is affected by an electric current; in other words, the current sets up a *magnetic field*. Ampère investigated this behavior quantitatively, described the magnetic interaction of currents in two separate circuits, and also concluded that *all* magnetism can be traced to currents, including currents on a molecular scale. The electromagnet and the electric motor were practical consequences of Oersted's and Ampère's work. In 1831, Faraday discovered that a current is set up in a conductor that is moved in a magnetic field—the principle of the dynamo, or electric generator. Faraday also believed that light is related to electromagnetism, but he was unable to trace the connection in a systematic way.

References

Einstein, A., and L. Infeld, *The Evolution of Physics*. A book for the layman, emphasizing the concept of *field*.

Faraday, M., *Experimental Researches in Electricity*. Makes interesting reading, as does his *Story of the Candle*, although the latter is not altogether appropriate to the subject matter of this chapter. A good brief biography of Faraday will be found in *British Scientists of the Nineteenth Century*, Part I, by J. G. Crowther.

Magie, W. F., *A Source Book in Physics*. Extracts from the original papers of Oersted (pp. 436–441), Ampère (pp. 447–460), Faraday (pp. 473–489), Lenz (pp. 511–513), and Henry (pp. 514–519).

Taylor, L. W., *Physics, the Pioneer Science*. Includes a historical account of the development of the applications, as well as the principles, of electromagnetism.

Tyndall, J., *Michael Faraday as a Discoverer*.

1. The earth, as Gilbert concluded, is a magnet. Is the magnetism of its north magnetic pole like that of the N pole of a magnetic compass needle or that of the S pole? Remember that the N pole is that which points north if the needle is free to turn.

2. In order to repeat Oersted's experiment with a north-south wire and a magnetic compass, it is necessary to pass a very strong current in the wire to make the compass needle assume a true east-west direction. Ordinarily the needle deviates toward this direction, but takes up a final position at some intermediate angle. Why should this be so, if the magnetic field of the current is at right angles to the wire?

3. One of Gilbert's achievements was a clear distinction between electricity and magnetism, attained by showing that electrostatic charges and lodestone do not affect each other. Yet Joseph Henry, in reporting the results of his experiments on electromagnetic induction, said "We have thus as it were electricity converted into magnetism and this magnetism converted again into electricity." How may these statements be reconciled?

4. The current produced by the potential difference of a battery flows steadily in a single direction, and is called direct current (DC). The usual form of commercial electric power is not direct but *alternating current* (AC), in which the direction of flow of charge is reversed at regular intervals. In common 60-*cycle* AC current, for in-

stance, this reversal takes place 120 times in each second. Using the law of induction, explain how AC power may be transmitted from one coil of wire to another, even though there is no electrical connection between the two. (A device of this sort is called a *transformer*.)

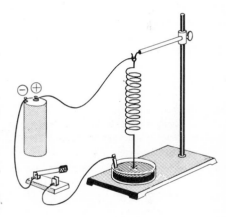

FIGURE 15–17.

5. The loose, springy coil of wire shown in Fig. 15–17 is attached to the terminals of a battery. When the switch is closed, current flows in the coil. What is the relation between the directions of the current in any two adjacent loops of the coil? What effect would you expect to observe in the coil as a whole when the switch is closed? What would be the effect of intermittent opening and closing of the switch? Explain. (This device is called "Roget's spiral.")

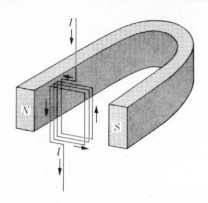

FIG. 15–18. The principle of the galvanometer.

6. Figure 15–18 is a diagrammatic representation of an important practical device called a *galvanometer;* it is the prototype of most current and voltage measuring instruments. A coil of wire, whose ends lead off to an external circuit, is suspended between the poles of a horseshoe magnet. The directions of current and magnetic field are shown. When there is current in the external circuit, and hence in the coil, in what direction is force exerted on the horizontal segments of the wire loops in the coil, if at all? On the vertical segments on the left? Vertical segments on the right? If the coil is pivoted so that it may move, what effect should be observed when the current is in the direction indicated? If the direction of current is reversed? In both cases, what would happen to a needle attached to the coil? How should motion of the needle depend on the size of I, the current in this coil?

7. Can you imagine ways in which the device discussed in Exercise 6 could be adapted to the production of rotary motion, hence mechanical work? To the production of potential difference, hence electrical energy? You may wish to consult a reference, e.g., L. W. Taylor, *Physics, the Pioneer Science,* that describes the operations of motors and generators.

8. Coal consists of the fossil remains of prehistoric plant life. Whether it is a steam plant or a hydroelectric plant that operates the generator which provides electrical energy to our homes, the ultimate source of this energy is the sun. Can you explain why this statement is valid?

9. In our discussion of the exertion of magnetic force by one current-carrying wire on another, illustrated by Fig. 15–12, we spoke only of the field associated with the left-hand circuit. Does the circuit on the right have no magnetic field? Could there be a force exerted on it if there were no magnetic field? Is there no force exerted on the left-hand wire? What principle must you employ to answer this last question? Does the force F on a wire of length L, carrying current I in the presence of a magnetic field B, depend in general only on the magnitudes of B, I, and L? Explain.

CHAPTER 16

WAVE MOTION

A great part of our evidence concerning the world in which we live comes to us through our sense of sight. The observations which gave rise to the oldest branch of science, astronomy, were entirely visual. Information concerning terrestrial objects may reach us through the sense of hearing as well as that of sight. About the nature of light, the name given to that which produces sight, the ancients could do no more than speculate. Sound, more obviously, is related to motion in some way, and Aristotle was able to remark: "All sounds arise either from bodies falling on bodies or from air falling on bodies. It is due to air . . . being moved by expansion, contraction and compression."

One early speculative view of the nature of light was the "tentacular" theory, according to which the eye puts forth invisible tentacles, and sees much as a blind man "sees" with his fingers, or a stick. There was a variety of additional opinion, including two views which, with modification, have persisted to modern times. One was that light consists of particles, infinitesimal projectiles dispatched from a viewed object to the eye. The other was that light consists of "action" of some sort in an all-pervading medium. The latter view, which had been held by Aristotle, became, in the time of Huygens, the basis of a detailed model of light, in which the "action" was specified to be rapid vibration of the medium. Both particle and "action" views were initially *mechanical*, in the sense that they stem from analogies to visible events, mathematically describable in terms of the laws of motion.

The science of mechanics did not develop until the 17th century, and it is perhaps not surprising that wave theories of both sound and light were worked out almost simultaneously. Although the science of sound is simply a branch of mechanics, it is not possible to describe light satisfactorily within the framework of Newtonian mechanics alone, as we shall see. Some of the general characteristics of wave motion were first recognized in connection with sound, others in connection with light, so that it is almost impossible to disentangle the two subjects. In one sense, light and sound have nothing to do with each other. The wave theory of light was not generally accepted in the 17th century for the basic reason that light is *not* properly a mechanical subject. Nevertheless, the ideas necessary for understanding the nature of light are derived from mechanical concepts, and for this reason we must return to mechanics.

16–1 Mechanical waves

The wave theory of light, developed by Huygens late in the 17th century, was initially based on analogy with the behavior of a row of elastic balls. An impulse imparted at one end of such a row is transmitted along the entire row by a succession of mechanical impacts, and an observer watching the sequence of events would say that a *wave* has passed through the row. Similarly, a deformation of one end of a rope or spring is propagated along its entire length in the form of a wave. Any disturbance of a quiet water surface produces waves. All of these, and many others, may be called *mechanical* waves, since they involve motions of tangible masses of material. What features are common to all mechanical waves?

For all mechanical waves there must be a medium, something to support their transmission. The medium does not move as a whole, but its parts transmit an impulse imparted to it. A simple case is that of the row of suspended steel balls pictured in Fig. 16–1. Any shock, such as the sharp blow that would result from lifting the ball on the right and allowing it to strike its neighbor, ultimately results in motion of the last ball of the row, even though the intermediate spheres may not move perceptibly. Both momentum and energy are transmitted along the row, as evidenced by the motion of the end ball on the left. Each intermediate sphere receives the impulse only to transfer it at once to its next neighbor, rather like a member of a very efficient bucket brigade passing a pail of water. Time is required for this process, and the interval that elapses between the first impact on the right and the beginning of motion in the last ball at the left can be measured. If the distance between the two ends is also measured, the *speed* with which the impulse travels can be computed.

Surface waves on water are more complicated, but the same general conditions prevail. Toss a pebble into a quiet pool, and waves will spread out gradually in every direction, describing circles of ever-increasing radius (Fig. 16–2). Still, no currents are established in the water itself: a small piece of cork on the surface will simply bob up and down as the waves reach it, and will not travel with the impulse. Ordinary water waves consist of a succession of motions, not just a single impulse; the cork indicates that each portion of the surface moves up and

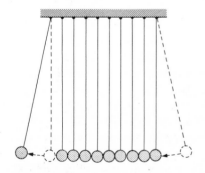

Fig. 16–1. Showing the transmission of an impulse by a series of suspended balls. The release of the right-hand ball from its dotted position results in the displacement of the ball on the left.

FIG. 16–2. Surface waves.

down with each succeeding wave, but does not essentially change its horizontal position. When a pebble is tossed into a pool, a small part of the water surface is slightly depressed; on return it rises slightly above its original level. Oscillations continue, at least for a little while, at this portion of the surface. The vibrations are transmitted to neighboring portions of the surface, and the result is an ever-widening succession of circular waves as the disturbance moves away from its center of origin. In the example of a single pebble striking a water surface, the oscillations soon die out; a mechanical oscillator, vibrating continuously, may be used to send out waves whose strength remains constant with time.

In addition to a medium for transmitting waves, there must obviously also be a source to initiate them. By this we mean any mechanical device which can impart to the medium the energy which is carried away by waves. A simple continuous source is one in which vibrations occur at a steady rate. The number of vibrations executed per second is called the *frequency* of the source. When waves are produced in water by a steady mechanical vibrator, a cork floating on the surface is observed to bob up and down as many times per second as the oscillator producing the waves. The *frequency of the wave*, i.e., the number of oscillations occurring per second in its transmitting medium, is thus the same as the frequency of the source. But the source stays in one place, while the waves travel away at some definite speed v. The speed of a wave depends on the nature of the medium, al-

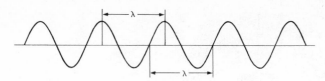

FIG. 16–3. Diagram of a simple wave, showing the wavelength λ.

though, within a given medium, it does not vary with distance from the source. It may also depend upon the frequency of both wave and source, but before we can explore the nature of this dependence, we must consider another useful characteristic of waves.

A mechanical wave may be represented by a diagram similar to that shown in Fig. 16–3. The surface of a body of water which is transmitting waves is marked by successive elevations and depressions, or "crests" and "troughs." At any one position of the surface, crests and troughs alternate at intervals, but at a single instant, a diagram of the surface configuration along any direction from the center of disturbance would resemble Fig. 16–3. Similarly, if one end of a long taut rope is rapidly and steadily moved up and down, it can be made to look like the diagram at individual instants of time. Figure 16–3 may thus be considered a "frozen" wave profile, since it provides unmoving representation of a situation that is constantly changing. For a wave of given frequency and speed, it is found that the distance from one crest to the next, or between any adjacent pair of crests or troughs, is constant. Since the pattern of a wave constantly repeats itself, the distance from any position on its profile to the next equivalent position is equal to the distance between crests. This distance, truly characteristic for a wave in any given medium, is called the *wavelength*, and is customarily designated by the Greek letter λ (lambda).

A relation between wavelength, frequency, and speed may be derived very simply. Consider a source vibrating n times per second, so that n wave crests are sent out into the medium in each second. During one second the first crest will travel a distance numerically equal to the speed v, since v is the distance traversed (by any point on the wave) per second. But this distance is just equal to n wavelengths, since there are n crests, one wavelength apart, sent out per second. Algebraically, then,

$$v = n \, \lambda. \qquad (16\text{–}1)$$

Equation (16–1) is valid for all types of waves that can be specified in terms of a particular frequency and a particular medium. Simple as it is, this is perhaps the most useful equation involved in the description of wave motion, especially for determining an unknown frequency for a wave whose wavelength and speed can be measured.

FIG. 16–4. Reflection of surface waves. (Composite photograph.)

Other general attributes of wave motion can be explored by the observation of ripples on the surface of water. Water waves are *reflected*, for example, by the wall of a pool or any other solid barrier, as indicated in Fig. 16–4. They are also *refracted*, or bent, on passing from one region to another in which the wave speed is different. The speed with which surface waves are transmitted in a shallow pool depends on the depth of the pool, for example. Figure 16–5 is a photograph of ripples undergoing refraction at the dark horizontal line that marks a change in depth. The waves travel diagonally toward the right, in a direction perpendicular to the wave crests photographed. Reflection and refraction phenomena are exhibited by waves of all kinds.

Surface waves, which we can see so easily, actually constitute a very special wave type. Since they spread outward from a point of disturbance in ever-widening circles, their propagation may be said to be two-dimensional. The impulse transmitted along the line of balls in Fig. 16–1, on the other hand, is restrained to a single direction, i.e., this medium will support wave motion in only one dimension. Similarly, the waves that can be sent along a rope or helical spring are one-dimensional. In other cases, of which sound is an example we shall consider later, a disturbance may be propagated in all directions from its source, establishing wave motion in three dimensions. Each crest on such a wave spreads out in an ever-growing sphere, the surface of which remains perpendicular to its direction from the center. Such a spherical surface is called a *wave front*. As a wave front re-

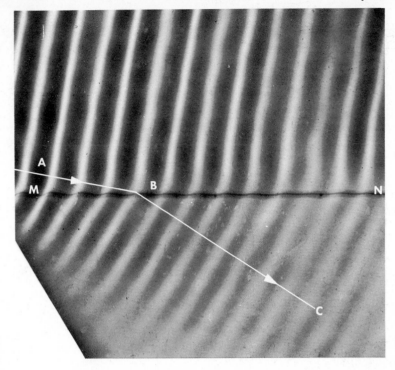

FIG. 16–5. Photograph showing refraction of water wave along line MN. Waves moving in the direction from A to B, in the region of deeper water, correspond to waves moving from B to C, in the region of more shallow water. (By permission, from Webster, Farwell, and Drew's *General Physics for Colleges*, Appleton-Century-Crofts, Inc., 1923.)

cedes from the center of wave propagation, its curvature, of course, diminishes. A portion of a wave front *very* far from its source, where the curvature is negligible, is called a *plane wave*.

The transmission of any mechanical wave is made possible by the interactions of neighboring portions of a medium on one another. In the one-dimensional example of a set of suspended steel balls, each sphere moves slightly in the direction of propagation of the impulse, and collides with its neighbor as a result. A wave transmitted in this way is called a *pressure wave*. Because the motions of the component parts of the medium and the propagation of the wave take place in the same direction, waves of this sort are also called *longitudinal*. All kinds of matter, whether solid, liquid, or gaseous, are capable of transmitting pressure in this way, and can thus carry longitudinal waves.

Because they are rigid, solids are capable of carrying another sort of mechanical wave, called *transverse*. In transverse waves, the motion of a particular part of the medium is perpendicular to the direction of propagation of the impulse (Fig. 16-6). In order to transmit such waves, a medium must offer resistance to changes in its shape, as is characteristic of the solid state of matter. A wave moving along a rope or string is an example of a transverse wave. The motion of the rope, at any point, is up and down, yet the wave moves along its length. Surface waves on water are also approximately transverse, since the motion of any particular part of a water surface is at right angles to the direction of propagation of the impulse. (This is only approximately so; there is some horizontal motion combined with the vertical motion of a water surface, and water waves are actually a complex combination of the longitudinal and transverse types.) Although only longitudinal waves can be transmitted *through* liquids, and thus only waves of this sort can ever reach the bottom of a pool or ocean from above, liquid *surfaces* can transmit transverse waves. The surface of a liquid, because of strong interactions between its component molecules, resists changes in shape and thus has some of the properties of a solid membrane, e.g., a drumhead.

The diagram of Fig. 16-3, we have said, may be used to represent mechanical waves in general, yet it is obvious that only waves of the transverse type can conform to it in a literal sense. Still, longitudinal waves may be represented by similar curves, as illustrated in Fig. 16-7. If impulses are imparted to the sphere on the right at regular intervals, they are passed along the line by impacts between individual spheres and their neighbors. After each impact one sphere moves forward to collide with its neighbor, the other moves backward into the path of a new impulse which is moving along the row. At any instant, therefore, positions in which the balls are close together alternate with others in which they are relatively far apart. Since impacts on the right are imparted at regular intervals, the spacing of these positions along the row are also regular. Positions in which the balls are close together correspond to the *crests* of the wave, those of greatest separation the *troughs*. Impact *pressure*, of course, is greatest where the balls are closest together; a wave crest

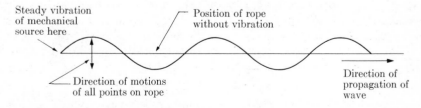

Steady vibration of mechanical source here

Position of rope without vibration

Direction of motions of all points on rope

Direction of propagation of wave

Fig. 16-6. Transverse wave in a stretched rope; the motion of any part of the rope is in a direction perpendicular to the direction of wave propagation.

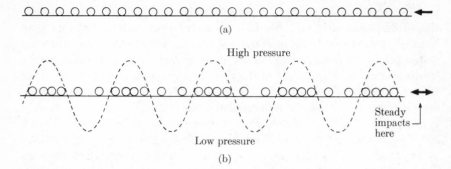

Fig. 16-7. Longitudinal wave in a row of spheres subjected to steady, repeated impacts at one end. The spheres at rest are assumed bound by invisible elastic threads to the positions shown in (a). After repeated impacts there will be alternation of close and separated positions, as in (b).

therefore corresponds to a region of highest pressure in a longitudinal wave, a trough to a region of least pressure.

16-2 Huygens' principle

We have said that transmission of a wave depends on the effects of neighboring portions of a medium on each other. Now each atom or molecule of matter has neighbors all around it; how does it happen that an impulse is transmitted in straight lines from its source, instead of being dispersed in a confused and random way? The answer, given by Huygens, was first published in 1690. First,

"Each particle of matter in which a wave spreads ought not to communicate its motion only to the next particle which is in the straight line drawn from the [source], but it also imparts some of it necessarily to all the others which touch it and which oppose themselves to its movement. So it arises that *around each particle there is made a wave of which that particle is the center.*"

Huygens' idea was illustrated with a diagram, which has been redrawn in Fig. 16-8. A wave originating at point A, has progressed outward until a portion of its wave front lies along the arc BG. From each point on this wave front, according to Huygens, new wavelets proceed outward, forming wave fronts of their own. Portions of wave fronts originating from B, G, and points b are shown reaching the further arc $DCEF$. Then, in Huygens' words,

". . . each of these waves can be only infinitely feeble compared to the wave $DCEF$, to the composition of which all the others contribute by that part of their surface which is the most distant from the center A."

In other words, the wavelets from
arc *BG reenforce* each other in such a
way that their net effect is a large,
unimpeded wave proceeding away
from the source. In all other directions, these wavelets effectively cancel, and their net effect is zero except
in the direction of a straight line
drawn from the source. The new
wave front *DCEF* is called the *enve-*
lope of all the wavelets originating
on the previous front *BG*. The statement that *every point on a wave front*
may be considered a source of second-
ary wavelets which spread outward in
all directions, together with the method for finding a new primary wave
front as the envelope of secondary fronts, is known as *Huygens' Principle*.

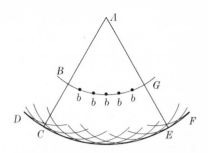

Fig. 16–8. Huygens' drawing showing the propagation of a wave front by
means of secondary wavelets.

It was Huygens' belief that light is wavelike, and he applied his principle
to the reflection and refraction of light. Yet his reasoning should apply to
waves of all kinds. Let us consider refraction, the bending of a surface
ripple as shown in Fig. 16–5 or, assuming the application to be legitimate,
that of light as it passes from one transparent medium to another, e.g., air
to glass. For our description, we shall, in part, paraphrase that originally
proposed by Huygens.

Imagine two media which transmit the same kind of wave at different
speeds, and separated from each other by a plane surface. One edge of this
surface is represented by the straight line *AB* in Fig. 16–9. Let the line *AC*
represent part of a wave front, "of which the center is so far away that this
part can be considered a straight line." The part of the wave proceeding

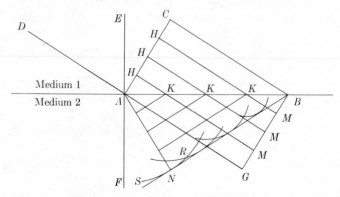

Fig. 16–9. Huygens' interpretation of refraction in accord with his principle.

from point C will reach the plane AB, at point B, in a certain time. In the same interval of time, the part proceeding from A would reach G, if the medium below AB were the same as that above. Let us suppose, however, that the second medium transmits the wave less rapidly, say by one-third. The wave will then move outward from A only two-thirds of the distance CB, in the time that it takes to move from C to B. In accordance with Huygens' principle, each point on AC can be considered the source of a new wave front: SNR represents an arc on a circle, centered at A, whose radius is just two-thirds of distance CB, that is, the position of the front for a wavelet originating at A after the time interval under consideration. "Now if we consider further the other parts H of the wave AC, it appears that, in the time taken by the part C to come to B, they will not only have reached the surface AB by the lines HK parallel to CB, but that further they will have set up at the centers K . . . [wavelets] whose radii are equal to two-thirds of the lines KM." The envelope of these wavelets is a plane whose edge is the line BN, which thus represents the new wave front. The direction of the wave, given by any perpendicular from AB to the new envelope, is that of the line AN in the new medium. Since its direction was DA in the first medium, its path has been "bent." This construction satisfactorily represents the refraction of water waves as shown in Fig. 16–5, and Huygens demonstrated that it represents the observed behavior of light rays on passing from air to glass, as well.

Huygens applied his principle in many other ways, always assuming that light behaves like any mechanical wave. We shall return to some of these applications when we consider light more explicitly. Although Huygens' attention was focused primarily on the properties of light, his importance to us resides in the fact that he established a theoretical basis for the treatment of waves of all kinds. The most significant triumph of Huygens' principle, as applied to light, came more than one hundred years after his death. He himself only partially appreciated the significance of *interference*, a wave attribute so characteristic that it may be used to define wave motion in the absence of other criteria. Let us now consider this important property in terms of mechanical waves, and see how Huygens' principle may be applied in its description.

16–3 Interference

Since they are readily seen and photographed, let us return to consideration of surface water waves. Waves can bend around corners, at least to some extent. It is true that if one drops a pebble on one side of a large ship, he would hardly expect to see ripples on the other side of the ship, no matter how still the water. But the photograph of Fig. 16–10 shows what happens at a small opening in a barrier. When all waves are cut off except those at one point, it is as though that part of the wave front able to come through

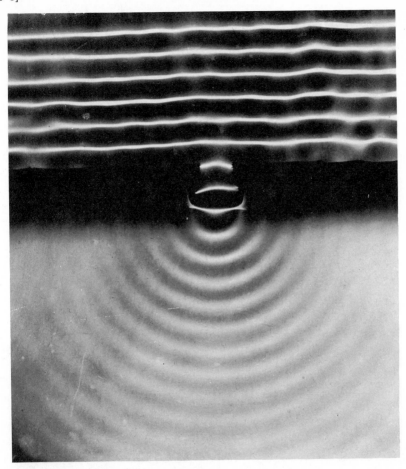

Fig. 16–10. Photograph of ripples emerging through a single opening. (By permission, from Webster, Farwell, and Drew's *General Physics for Colleges*, Appleton-Century-Crofts, Inc., 1923.)

the aperture constitutes a small source for circular waves. We have here a pictorial justification for Huygens' principle; in the absence of wavelets from other portions of the wave front, a secondary wave is free to spread in all directions, with no cancellation from neighboring wavelets.

In Fig. 16–11 we see what happens as a result of waves from two neighboring sources vibrating with the same frequency. Only very near the sources are there two distinct sets of crests. Elsewhere there are segments of waves where the two sources reenforce each other, separated by blurred areas where there are no distinct waves at all. At the latter places a crest from one source has arrived simultaneously with a trough from the other, and the two have effectively neutralized each other. It is just this phe-

Fig. 16–11. Interference of ripples that are set up by two neighboring sources. (By permission, from Webster, Farwell, and Drew's *General Physics for Colleges,* Appleton-Century-Crofts, 1923.)

nomenon of reenforcement and cancellation that is called *interference.* The net result of the interference is that only in certain directions is a regular wave propagated away from the sources A and B; each radial line of blurring indicates a direction in which the wave motion is not effectively carried. Interference is a most important property of all wave motion.

The determination of the effect of two waves by simple algebraic additions of the simultaneous separate effects makes use of what is often called the "principle of superposition." Figure 16–12 shows how to find the pattern produced by two superposed waves at a given instant. The heavy line is the displacement that results from the simultaneous displacements of the dotted and dashed waves. This graphical superposition enables us to understand the kind of interference pattern called a "standing wave," most familiar and most easily exhibited with a stretched string or rope. Let us see how a vibrating string illustrates wave superposition.

If a vibrator were attached to an indefinitely long string one would see a wave propagated along the string, something like a one-dimensional ripple. But in a finite string, under tension because the other end is firmly fixed, a pattern such as that shown in Fig. 16–13 is set up. This result does not look like a traveling wave at all; most points on the string vibrate up and down, but the form of the wave is stationary, or "standing." The forced immobility of the fixed end of the string is responsible for the behavior illustrated in Fig. 16–13. Impulses cannot be transmitted farther from the vibrator, but they may be reflected back along the string, and the reflection is constrained to take place in such a way that the original and reflected waves cancel each other at the endpoint for all times. The transverse motion of any point of the string may thus be considered as the combined effect of two oppositely directed waves which are, of course, alike in wavelength and frequency. A series of such waves is shown in Fig. 16–14. In (a) a crest from the vibrator and a reflected trough satisfy the necessary condition at A, the end of the string. Note that the dashed wave moves to the right, the dotted one to the left. At this instant, the cancellation is complete for all points, and the string is straight. But both waves are moving so that a

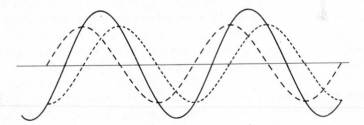

Fig. 16–12. Superposition of two waves.

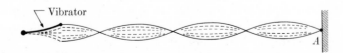

Fig. 16–13. Standing waves set up by a vibrator in a string fixed at A.

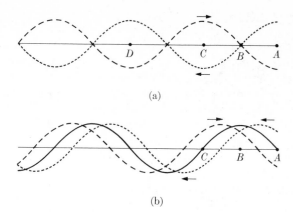

(a)

(b)

FIG. 16–14. Showing the formation of a standing wave.

point near A, say B, will in the next instant be displaced upward. Figure 16–14(b) shows the situation when both waves have moved a distance equal to one-sixth wavelength; the solid line indicates the actual instantaneous shape of the string. At C, one-half wavelength from A, the waves continue to cancel as they move in opposite directions and, just as at A, there is no resultant displacement. The same is continuously true of D and all other points a whole number of half-wavelengths from A, but between these points the string vibrates up and down as the original and reflected waves progress. The points of no motion are called *nodes* and those between are called *loops*; the pattern of nodes and loops for a particular wavelength is shown in Fig. 16–15. Note that each of the progressive waves into which we have resolved the observed motion is impossible singly, because of the fixed point A, and that the actual motion is the combination. By resolving this motion into the two waves, however, we have traced its relation to the vibrator responsible for the whole disturbance.

Similar standing waves can be initiated in a string fastened at both ends by plucking, striking, or bowing the string. The velocity of the wave depends on the mass of the string and the tension with which it is strung. Waves of a variety of frequencies can be set in motion simultaneously, so that the total motion may be rather complicated, but in every case the condition that the ends do not move must be satisfied. This restricts the possible frequencies to those for which the total length of the string is an integral number of half-wavelengths, as indicated in Fig. 16–15; waves corresponding to other frequencies are incapable of composing standing patterns in the string.

Standing waves can also be set up in a tube of air, and the vibrations of the air can be made evident for demonstration purposes by disturbances

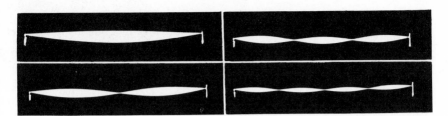

FIG. 16–15. Standing waves in a stretched string (time exposure).

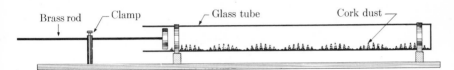

FIG. 16–16. Standing waves in an air column, set up by the longitudinally vibrating rod, make a pattern in cork dust. The device is known as Kundt's tube.

of chalk or cork dust in the tube. This device is called *Kundt's tube*, after its inventor. Note that the nodes (points of no disturbance) are a half-wavelength apart, as in the case of a string. The pattern indicated in Fig. 16–16 corresponds to a single frequency, but all frequencies are possible which satisfy the condition that superposition gives completely destructive interference at the closed end of the tube, whatever the pattern between the ends.

There are many different manifestations of interference, all of which depend on the ability of waves to cancel and reenforce each other. The property of interference traditionally serves to distinguish between wave motion and unorganized motions of particles. Two particles simultaneously arriving at the same place are still two particles, but two waves received at a given point will tend to undo each other unless their crests arrive at the same time. This criterion has been especially important for distinction between those waves and particles which cannot be viewed directly; the demonstration of any sort of *interference pattern* is evidence of wave motion.

16–4 Sound

Sound, in ordinary parlance, consists of just those mechanical vibrations and waves whose frequencies the human ear can detect. This was recognized by the Roman Vitruvius (ca. 10 A.D.), who gave the first known account of architectural acoustics. Pythagorus had experimented with sound as related to music, and proved that the lengths of strings which gave a tone, its fifth, and its octave, were in the ratios 6:4:3, but his discovery served to bolster his scheme of philosophic numerology rather than science. No systematic scientific treatment of sound was undertaken until the 17th century, when Père Marin Mersenne (1588–1648), follower of Galileo, friend of Descartes, and indefatigable correspondent on scientific matters, made the subject his own. Among his discoveries were the laws of vibrating strings, i.e., how the frequency of an emitted tone depends not only on the length but on the tension and mass of a string. Beginning with Mersenne, the whole subject of mechanical vibrations and mechanical waves was developed rapidly.

We live in an atmosphere of air, and therefore the most familiar medium for the transmission of sound is air. Light is also transmitted through air, but much more rapidly than sound; anyone watching a distant man use an axe, for example, finds that the sounds of the blows arrive perceptibly later than the sight of the impacts which produce them. Mersenne used this fact to measure the speed of sound in air. In his day some philosophers held that sight is instantaneous, and others that time (although very short) is required for light to travel from any object to the eye. It was necessary for Mersenne to assume that the time, if any, for transmission of light is negligible in comparison with that required by sound. His method of measuring the speed of sound was to time the interval between the flash and sound of a gun fired at known distance. We shall see that the speed of light, while finite, is so very much greater than that of sound that Mersenne's assumption is justified. The speed of sound in air depends to some extent on temperature, but its value is about 1100 ft/sec (331.36 m/sec at 0°C). In media more dense than air, the speed of sound is greater; in water, for example, sound waves (not surface waves!) travel more than four times as fast as in air. The speed of sound in various metals is of the order of ten times that in air, with considerable variation depending on the density and elasticity of the metal.

All substances transmit sound, but *some* kind of material medium is indispensable; sound cannot travel through empty space. This statement, in accord with our definition of mechanical waves, was first proved by Robert Boyle, as mentioned in Chapter 12. Note that sound, since it may be transmitted by gases and liquids, must consist of pressure, or longitudinal, waves. If the spheres of Fig. 16–7 are imagined to be air molecules, that diagram may be considered to represent crudely a sound wave traveling in air; the air at any one point is alternately compressed and rarefied as the wave is transmitted.

The attributes of wave motion described in this chapter, including reflection, refraction, and interference, are all exhibited by sound. Sound may be reflected sharply, as in the production of echoes, or diffusely to produce confused reverberation. Interference between direct and reflected waves may produce "dead spots" for certain frequencies in auditoriums. The most familiar consequence of the principle of superposition in sound waves, however, is the phenomenon of *beats*. The word interference is usually reserved for effects produced by waves of the same frequency, whereas beats result from two vibrations of slightly different frequencies. The effect produced is a regular variation of sound intensity, brought about by regular alternation of reenforcement and cancellation of the two wave crests. The intensity waxes and wanes at a rate called the beat frequency, which is exactly the difference in frequency between the two original waves. For example, two frequencies of 40 and 41 vibrations per second would reenforce each other once each second; crests of waves of 40 and 42 vib/sec would arrive simultaneously twice each second, and tend to cancel in between. Beats are easily detected in those notes of a piano for which the hammer strikes more than one string if the strings are not perfectly in unison. The detection and elimination of beats is, in fact, very useful in tuning piano strings.

The abstract properties of waves, notably those involving interference and beats, are defined without respect to any particular mechanism, but we should note that sound is simply a branch of mechanics. A vibrating body, such as a tuning fork, a stretched string, or the vocal chords, sets up vibrations in the medium with which it is in contact. These secondary disturbances are propagated away from the source by the influence of one part of the medium on another, with a velocity that depends on the nature of the medium. Mechanical energy is transmitted from the source to a receiver (e.g., the ear) at some distance by means of the intermediate vibrations of the transmitting medium. The amount of energy involved in sound transmission is ordinarily small in comparison with that expended in other activities; the importance of sound lies primarily in its facilitation of communication and aesthetic pleasure. The general theory of sound forms the physical basis of music and musical instruments, and finds utilitarian application in construction engineering and architecture. We shall not dwell on the many interesting aspects of these subjects, but references for further reading are included at the end of the chapter. Later we shall return to the subject of mechanical waves in connection with earthquake shocks and the information they give us about the interior of the earth.

Now that we have examined the general properties of wave motion, we shall be able to pursue the consequences of Huygens' hypothesis that light is wavelike. As we compare and contrast the behavior of light and mechanical waves, we shall come to understand some of the hazards as well as the usefulness of what is called "reasoning by analogy."

16–5 Summary

Mechanical energy may be transmitted through a material medium, without the transport of matter, by means of waves. A vibrating body, for example, may set up vibratory disturbances in the surrounding medium which spread away from the source with a speed which depends on the elastic properties of the medium. A fluid is able to transmit only longitudinal or pressure waves, while a solid, by virtue of its rigidity, is capable of sustaining transverse waves, i.e., vibrations at right angles to the direction of propagation. Waves are *reflected* at a boundary, *refracted* in passing from one medium to another. A theoretical basis for treatment of the properties of waves of all kinds was established by Huygens in his principle that every point on a wave front may be considered a source of secondary wavelets which spread outward in all directions. This principle, together with Huygens' method for finding a new primary wave front as the envelope of secondary fronts, was employed by Huygens in the description of reflection, refraction, and other properties of waves, and is especially helpful in understanding the important phenomenon of *interference*, a property so characteristic of wave motion that it may be used as a criterion for the existence of waves. Mechanical waves are most familiar as sound, but the analogies between sound and light are so pronounced that many properties of mechanical waves were worked out by Huygens as the basis for his wave theory of light.

REFERENCES

JEANS, J. H., *Science and Music.* In addition to being well known as a scientist and writer, the author of this nontechnical book was an accomplished organist.

MAGIE, W. F., *A Source Book in Physics,* pp. 115–117 (Mersenne), 283–287 (Huygens).

MILLER, D. C., *The Science of Musical Sounds.* Remarkably well illustrated and informative.

TAYLOR, L. W., *Physics, the Pioneer Science,* Chapters 24 through 28.

WOOD, A., *The Physics of Music.*

1. What is the wavelength of a tone whose frequency is 440 vib/sec if the speed of sound is 1100 ft/sec? [Ans.: 2.5 ft]

2. Suppose that a stone dropped into a pond produces waves that travel with a speed of 125 cm/sec. How far do the waves travel in 8 sec? If the wavelength of the waves is 80 cm, what is their frequency?

3. How could you tell your distance from a cliff by timing the interval between a shout and its echo? Assume some reasonable values and give a quantitative answer.

4. How far away is a thunderstorm if a flash of lightning is seen 6 sec before a clap of thunder is heard?

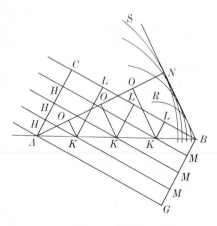

Figure 16–17.

5. Figure 16–17 is Huygens' original drawing showing that an incident wave in the direction CB, having the plane wave front AC and falling on a reflecting surface AB, gives rise to a wave front BN traveling in the direction AN according to his principle. Analyze the diagram, and prove that the angle between the direction of incidence and a perpendicular to the surface AB is equal to the angle between the same perpendicular and the direction of the reflected wave. Is the behavior of a wave different, in this respect, from that of a particle reflected elastically from a massive wall?

6. With reference to Fig. 16–9, prove that angle ABN = angle FAN, and angle CAB = angle DAE. The *sine* of an angle, in terms of a right triangle, is the side opposite the angle divided by the hypotenuse. Therefore, sine angle ABN = AN/AB, and sine angle CAB = CB/AB. If v_1 is the velocity of the wave above AB and v_2 is the velocity below AB, prove that

$$\frac{\text{sine angle } DAE}{\text{sine angle } NAF} = \frac{v_1}{v_2}.$$

7. Consider the "dead spot" (wave cancellation) on either side of the central reinforcement at the bottom of Fig. 16–11. How much farther is this point from one source than the other? How much farther is the next dead spot from one source than the other? Can you make a general statement about the condition for cancellation in terms of distances from the sources?

8. Auditoriums constructed without due reference to acoustical principles

often have areas in which sounds from the stage are almost inaudible or greatly distorted. How could such spots be accounted for?

9. Can you think of any scientific justification for the saying "he is a man who has his ear to the ground," as used to describe a person sensitive to preliminary indications of future trends?

10. Are the standing waves set up in stringed musical instruments transverse or longitudinal? Is a transverse standing wave in a string capable of setting up longitudinal pressure waves in its surrounding medium?

11. Two tuning forks are rated at 440 and 435 vib/sec, respectively. What is the beat frequency when the two are sounded simultaneously?

CHAPTER 17

LIGHT AS WAVE MOTION; ELECTROMAGNETIC WAVES

The practical design of optical instruments, devices for manipulating light, developed very slowly prior to the 17th century. Even so, these techniques ran far ahead of fundamental understanding of light. Plane mirrors were used in prehistoric times; the use of a concave mirror, or a concave arrangement of plane mirrors, to set fire to a Roman fleet is described in legend, at least. Allusions to "burning glasses," and even a story of a glass by which distant ships could be discerned, are found in Greek literature. Greek astronomy depended entirely on unaided vision, however, although this was not its only limitation. It is probable that Aristarchus' heliocentric hypothesis would have been confirmed long before the time of Copernicus if the Greeks had invented optical glass. But it was left to the Arabs, well over a thousand years after Aristarchus, to learn the magnifying properties of lenses, and we have seen that the telescope was not invented until the time of Galileo.

Relatively little progress toward understanding the properties of light could be made until the question of its speed was settled. The earliest known attempt to measure this speed was made by Galileo, who tried to time the transmission of a lantern signal from one hill to another. His method failed, and he could only conclude that if the velocity of light is not infinitely great it is at least greater than he was equipped to determine. Galileo's difficulty lay in the measurement of very short time intervals. To determine a very great speed, one of two sets of conditions must be satisfied: either the investigator must be able to measure extremely short times, or he must use such great distances that readily measurable time intervals become involved. We have already noted that Galileo had trouble with the short times incurred in the study of free fall. The speed of light is vastly greater than that of a falling body, and there is no known device, analogous to his inclined plane, for slowing light down by a significant factor. The first proof that the speed of light is finite made use of the relatively vast distances between members of the solar system.

17-1 The velocity of light

"For a long time philosophers have been endeavoring to decide by some experiment whether the action of light is transmitted in an instant to any distance whatever, or requires time. M. Roemer . . . has thought out a way

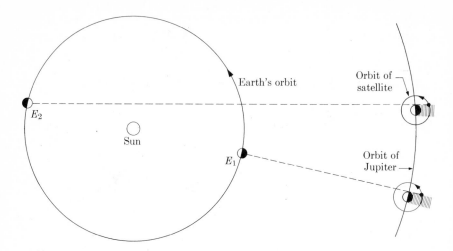

FIG. 17-1. Roemer's determination of the speed of light.

of doing this . . ." Thus begins a memoir presented to the French Academy, describing results obtained in 1675. Ole Roemer (1644–1710) was a Danish astronomer who spent ten years in Paris, where his most famous achievement was first announced. His method, illustrated in Fig. 17–1, depended on observation of one of the moons of Jupiter, which had been the subjects of very careful investigation since their discovery by Galileo. The period (time required to complete its orbit) of any one satellite could be accurately timed by noting its successive emergences from the shadow of Jupiter. For the particular satellite studied, this time was about $42\frac{1}{2}$ hours, and could be measured well within a minute. Presumably, this period is constant, i.e., the orbital motion is repeated without variation. If a particular instant of emergence is noted when the earth is at E_1, it should therefore be possible to predict later times of emergence, including those to be observed approximately six months later when the earth is at E_2, and a year later when the earth has returned to E_1. (Remember that Jupiter requires nearly 12 years to complete its own orbit about the sun, and has thus moved relatively little during a terrestrial year.) Assuming that emergences of the satellite from Jupiter's shadow are seen from earth at the instant they actually occur, Roemer found that his predictions for roughly a year ahead were accurate, but those for six months were not. The satellite seemed to slow down during the time the earth was moving away from Jupiter, so that it was behind its predicted time when observed from E_2; on the return to E_1 it appeared to speed up again, and emergence came at the predicted time when the earth and Jupiter were on the same side of the sun.

Roemer's observations were exactly those to be expected if time is required for light to traverse the earth's orbit. The light should be received at E_2 later than expected by just the time needed for it to travel the extra distance. Roemer's original analysis of the data available at the Paris observatory indicated that predictions were about 22 minutes off for the six-month period between earth positions E_1 and E_2. More accurate data have shown that this time, just that required for light to travel a distance equal to the diameter of the earth's orbit, is a little more than 16 minutes, or about 1000 seconds. Since the distance of the earth from the sun is 93,000,000 miles, the speed of light is given by

$$v = \frac{d}{t} = 186,000,000 \text{ mi}/1000 \text{ sec}$$

$$= 186,000 \text{ mi/sec.}$$

In the metric system of units this velocity is very nearly 3×10^{10} cm/sec. The most accurate modern values of the velocity of light are determined by terrestrial methods similar to that attempted by Galileo, employing devices for measuring very short time intervals. Despite its relative lack of precision, however, Roemer's method demolished the "philosophical" view that light is transmitted instantaneously. Every serious attempt to describe the fundamental nature of light, thereafter, had to be consistent with a very great but finite speed of transmission.

17–2 Light: wave motion or particles?

Leonardo da Vinci (1452–1519) studied water waves and sound waves as well as light, and recognized so many analogies that he thought light might be some form of wave motion. This suggestion, like his other scientific work, lay buried in undeciphered notebooks, however, and it was not until the properties of waves became generally evident in the 17th century that Huygens was able to begin working out the analogies in a systematic way. Robert Hooke (1635–1703) had suggested the idea of light as wave motion, but Newton was not convinced, partly because light "travels in a straight line" while waves can bend around corners. (We shall find that there was another reason for being skeptical of the wave theory of light, one which seemed unanswerable at the time.) Huygens was able to show with his little wavelets that straight line propagation is normal for waves in the absence of obstacles, as we have seen.

When a considerable portion of a wave front is allowed through an aperture, it is difficult to say whether waves bend around corners or not. A large ship casts a very effective "shadow" for small ripples, for example. Huygens' argument for light was that secondary waves from all parts of an

advancing wave front would tend to
cancel each other well inside the
boundary of a shadow, so that no
illumination beyond those boundaries was to be expected. It is clear
from Fig. 16–10 that mechanical
waves do bend around corners under
some conditions, however, and we
should expect *some* bending of all
waves at obstacle edges. A cone of
light entering through a fairly small
aperture extends farther than it
should if propagated purely in
straight lines. This fact was discovered by Francesco Maria Grimaldi (1618–1663), an Italian math-

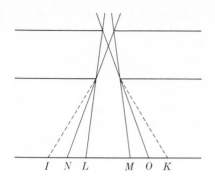

FIG. 17–2. Grimaldi's experiment
showing the extent of light beyond the
limits of geometrical illumination.

ematics professor, and Fig. 17–2 is taken from his book on light. He observed that "as often as the experiment is tried" light extends from I to
K instead of terminating at N and O, the geometrical straight line limits,
but that at the extremities the illumination was colored "partly reddish,
partly also strongly bluish." The patterns formed at the edge of what
should, by geometrical considerations, be a very sharp shadow are very
complicated when white light is used, and the phenomenon was not understood in detail until early in the 19th century.

Huygens' arguments for the wave theory of light did not hinge on the
complicated patterns observed by Grimaldi and others, but on his own
ability to understand such common phenomena as transmission, reflection,
and refraction of light in terms of waves. Later we shall see that he found
one of his discoveries, concerning the transmission of light in transparent
crystals, only partially explainable in terms of waves. Huygens started with
the idea, Aristotelian in origin, that the medium which transmits light is the
ether, which fills all space and passes freely through all ordinary matter. In
the ether, he thought, pressure waves would travel by the vibration of contiguous portions, just as sound is propagated in air. He did not understand
the key role of interference phenomena in wave motion, however, and his
ideas concerning light were largely disregarded in favor of those attributed
to Newton.

Grimaldi, we have said, observed bands of color at the edge of a shadow,
whereas the light used was initially white. It was Newton who, through
experiment, concluded that white light is *composite*, "a confused Aggregate
of Rays indued with all sorts of Colours." Newton's many experimental
discoveries in optics were so impressive and so important, and his scientific
prestige was so great, that his opinions on the nature of light were generally

accepted without question. Because Newton inclined to the hypothesis that light consists of minute particles, that view came to be considered as securely founded as Newtonian mechanics. Scientists of the 18th century were more sure of its validity, in fact, than Newton himself had ever been, and progress in the understanding of light was regrettably inhibited by the abiding authority of the great man. Newton's experimental contributions to optics, among the many lasting monuments to his genius, were so important that we must examine some of them before we find out how the particle hypothesis of light came to be discarded.

17–3 The visible spectrum

Newton's study of color was apparently prompted by efforts to avoid a defect of all early telescopes which, today, we would call *chromatic aberration*: telescopic images were blurred by colored fringes, especially in instruments designed for high magnification. Although Newton himself did not succeed in making any practical improvement in telescope lenses, his findings were of much greater significance than the problem he set out to solve. The essence of his proof that white light is composite, i.e., compounded of all colors, lay in the two experiments illustrated in Figs. 17–3 and 17–4. It had long been known that triangular glass prisms could produce color effects. Newton allowed sunlight from a small aperture to pass through a prism, as in Fig. 17–3, and showed that a single color, say yellow,

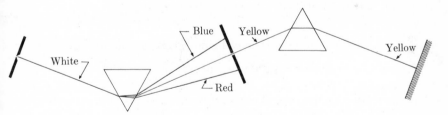

Fig. 17–3. Decomposition of white light.

Fig. 17–4. Recombination of white light.

is not further broken down by a second prism—it remains pure yellow, and its behavior is thus very different from that of white sunlight. Figure 17–4 shows that the colors separated by the first prism can be recomposed into white light by a prism set in opposition to the first. White light is thus a mixture of colors.

Newton coined the word *spectrum* for an array of color such as that produced by the first prism. Literally, the word means "image"; a spectrum consists of a series of images of the original source opening (usually a slit) spread out in a regular sequence of colors. All light is bent, or refracted, in going from one transparent medium to another, such as from water to air, or from air to glass, as we have noted in Chapter 16. But blue or violet light is bent more than other colors, and red light least of all. The rainbow is a spectrum, produced by unequal bending of light entering droplets of water, and consists of the invariable array red, orange, yellow, green, blue, indigo, and violet. White light contains all these colors, which must differ from each other in some physical respect.

We know now that light is wavelike, and that the colors of the spectrum differ from each other according to wavelength: the visible rays of longest wavelength are red, those of shortest wavelength violet. (Newton suspected this, but other considerations prevented his acceptance of the idea.) Spectrum colors are all "pure" colors, each associated with a single band of wavelengths, but the divisions into conventional color descriptions are arbitrary: orange yellow shades into red, and greenish yellow might just as well be called yellowish green. For an accurate description of any portion of the spectrum, a numerical specification of wavelength must be given.

17–4 The interference of light: Young's experiment

Treatises on history and literature generally deal at some length with the 18th-century "Enlightenment," and the "Age of Reason." Many efforts were made, during that century, to apply the methods of science to wider realms of thought. With very few exceptions, however, the first half of the century was relatively barren of accomplishment in the physical sciences themselves. Later in the 18th century Lavoisier, Priestley, and others laid foundations for rational chemistry, and important experiments were performed in electricity. But the central ideas of Newtonian mechanics occupied the minds of most workers in science almost too exclusively, and there was a general tendency to reject ideas that could not be made to fit into a scheme of mechanical determinism.

It is against this background that we must view Young's crucial experiment of 1803. There have been men of greater genius in science, but there has never been one of wider diversity of great talent than Thomas Young (1773–1829). He was a London physician, whose theory of color vision remains the basis of modern theories. He was a remarkable linguist, still known to Egyptologists for his deciphering of certain hieroglyphics. His discovery of present interest emerged almost naturally, given Young's scientific imagination, from his previous discoveries concerning the mechanics of vibrating bodies and the interference of sound waves; it may not be entirely irrelevant, in this connection, to add that he was an accomplished musician. The publication of his results on the interference of light aroused so much opposition and disbelief among confirmed followers of Newton that he temporarily gave up the subject. Some brilliant French scientists who pursued the question were later able to revive his interest, but with difficulty.

In Young's most famous experiment light from a "source slit," S_1 in Fig. 17-5, is allowed to fall on two narrow parallel slits, S_2 and S_3. All three slits are perpendicular to the plane of the diagram. If light traveled in truly straight lines, we should see two bright lines of light, images of S_2 and S_3, on the screen at the right. What is actually observed is shown in Fig. 17-6. Young was quick to see the explanation:

"Supposing the light of any given colour to consist of undulations [waves], of a given breadth [wavelength], or of a given frequency, it follows that these undulations must be liable to those effects which we have already examined in the case of the waves of water, and the pulses of sound. It has been shown that two equal series of waves, proceeding from centres near each other, may be seen to destroy each other's effects at certain points, and at other points to redouble them; and the beating of two sounds has been explained from a similar interference. We are now able to apply the same principles to the alternate union and extinction of colours."

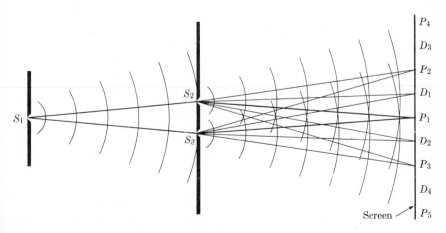

Fig. 17-5. Young's experiment.

There is an obvious similarity between Young's experimental arrangement (Fig. 17-5) and that well
known to produce interference in
water waves (Fig. 16-11). It was on
the basis of this analogy that Young
explained the new phenomenon in
terms of light waves.

Let us examine the pattern of Fig.
17-6, which Young assumed to be an
interference pattern, more closely.

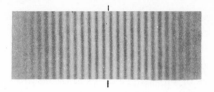

FIG. 17-6. Photograph of interfer-
ence pattern produced by two slits.
(By permission, from *Fundamentals of
Optics*, by Jenkins and White, Mc-
Graw-Hill Book Company, Inc., 1950.)

Down the center of the screen is a
bright band, shading off to darkness on both sides. On either side of this
band, dark and light bands alternate at regular intervals. Now it is found
that the central bright band occurs at just those points which are equidistant from slits S_2 and S_3; i.e., point P_1, Fig. 17-5, occurs on this band, and
distances S_2P_1 and S_3P_1 are equal. In accordance with Huygens' principle,
slits S_2 and S_3 act as individual centers of wave propagation, each sending
out a wave front. At P_1, points on both wave fronts will have traveled
equal distances from their respective sources. Since the two wave fronts
have a common origin (slit S_1) they must have the same wavelength and
phase, and distances S_2P_1 and S_3P_1 correspond to equal numbers of wavelengths for both sources. Waves which have traveled an equal number of
wavelengths will meet crest on crest, and reenforce one another—hence the
bright spot at P_1.

There is another bright band, one point on which is designated P_2,
Fig. 17-5. Distance S_3P_2, obviously, is greater than distance S_2P_2.
If the observed pattern is interpreted as one of wave interference, reenforcement (brightness) at P_2 can be accounted for if the *difference* between these distances is one whole wavelength; if that is the case, points
on the two wave fronts will meet crest on crest at P_2. By the same argument, the brightness observed at point P_3, as far below P_1 as P_2 is above
it, may be explained. The darkness at point D_1 is accounted for if S_3D_1
is greater than S_2D_1 by exactly one-half the wavelength of the light,
since crests of one wave would then meet troughs of the other at that point.
Continuing brightness at P_4 and P_5 must mean that the paths to those
points from the two source slits differ by *two* whole wavelengths, and darkness at D_3 and D_4 that there is a path difference of one and one-half wavelengths. In general, at all those points on the screen for which the path
difference from the slits is a whole number of wavelengths there is reenforcement of light, and at all those for which the path difference is an odd
number of half wavelengths there is destructive interference which produces
darkness.

Note that Young specified, in the quotation given above, that "light of any given colour" may be used. If white light is used in his experiment, color fringes appear on both sides of the central band. With the exception of the central one, each band is edged with red on the outside and with blue or blue-green toward the center; the dark bands are not completely without light. The photograph of Fig. 17-6 has been taken with so-called monochromatic light, i.e., light of a single color. Young, having demonstrated the wave nature of light with his conclusive interference experiment, identified different colors with different wavelengths. He recognized that the colors so commonly seen in thin films of oil, or in soap bubbles, are due to constructive interference (reenforcement) of some wavelengths and destructive interference of others.* Later he was even able to measure the wavelengths which correspond to light of various colors. The simplest method of measuring wavelengths, however, employs a device, called a "diffraction grating," which was beyond the technical facilities of Young's day.

17-5 The diffraction grating spectrum

We have seen that Young explained his interference experiment by applying Huygens' principle: each of the two small apertures is taken to be a source of secondary wavelets which reenforce each other in some directions and cancel in others, like the water ripples of Fig. 16-11. Suppose now that Young's experiment is performed, but with a very large number of narrow slits, equally spaced, instead of the two slits originally used. Such an assembly of slits, called a *grating*, is represented schematically in Fig. 17-7; although only five slits are shown in this diagram, actual gratings may contain thousands. If a plane wave is incident on the left, as shown, all the slits in the grating can be considered to be simultaneous sources of the light which emerges on the right. Most of the incident light is stopped by the opaque portions of the grating, but points on all secondary wave fronts from the various slits reenforce to form a beam which proceeds in the same direction as the incident beam. On a screen placed at any distance

---

*Some of the light incident on an oil or soap film is reflected by its outer surface, and some may be transmitted through the film and reflected from its under surface. The latter, on reaching the outer surface, may interfere with the light which is simply reflected there: for some wavelengths the two waves reenforce each other, while for others there is a cancellation. Variations in the color of light leaving a film are due to variations in film thickness. As the path difference between the two interfering waves varies, the conditions appropriate for reenforcement or cancellation are met for light of different wavelengths. Seen in white light, the colors of a film are not "pure," because, for a given film thickness, more than one wavelength may fulfill the conditions for constructive interference, or fail to satisfy those for destructive interference.

from the grating, in line with the incident light, a bright image of the source slit will therefore be seen. Of more interest, however, is what may be observed at various angles to the incident beam. At any angle such that the path difference for light emerging from consecutive slits is a whole wavelength, the wavelets reenforce to form a secondary plane wave, as shown in Fig. 17–7. In other words, if a source slit, as in Fig. 17–8, is illuminated by light of a single wavelength, its image can be seen by looking straight toward the grating and also by looking along the line BG. The reenforcement condition is also fulfilled along direction CG, as well as at even larger angles, such that path differences from adjacent slits differ by two or more whole wavelengths. These observations may all be made by the unaided eye, although it is more customary to use a lens which brings all light to a focus on a screen parallel to the grating, e.g., along line AB.

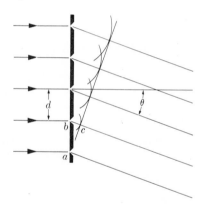

FIG. 17–7. Close-up of a diffraction grating, showing the reenforcement of monochromatic light in a particular direction at angle θ to the incident direction.

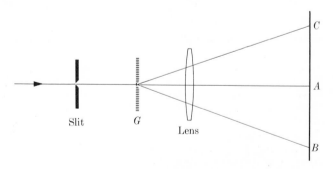

FIG. 17–8. Diffraction grating mounted with slit and screen. The purpose of the lens is to make sharp images of the slit on the screen at the right.

On such a screen, for light of a single wavelength, we observe an image of the source slit at A, and secondary images which are regularly spaced on both sides of that point. The whole process described here is an example of what is called *diffraction*.

To use the grating for quantitative measurement of light wavelengths we must take advantage of a modest application of trigonometry. Note that abc, Fig. 17–7, and ABG, Fig. 17–8, are similar triangles. The length ab is just d, the distance between successive slits of the grating; the length bc, if the condition for wave reenforcement is to be fulfilled, must be equal to one whole wavelength λ of the incident light. Since the triangles are similar,

$$\frac{\lambda}{d} = \frac{AB}{BG}. \qquad (17\text{–}1)$$

Since the lengths AB and BG are large enough to be measured by ordinary meter sticks, λ may thus be determined if d is known. It is simpler, however, to make use of the fact that the opposite side over the hypotenuse of either right triangle is a characteristic constant for angle AGB, its sine (see Appendix). If the grating is mounted in such a way that it is convenient to measure angle AGB (which we shall call θ), the sine of θ may be found in a table, and wavelength determined by the relation

$$\lambda = d \sin \theta. \qquad (17\text{–}2)$$

Note that it remains necessary to know d, the distance between slits in the grating.

As we have noted, it is possible for wavelets to combine and form a single wave front with a difference in path of *two* full wavelengths between contributions from consecutive slits. In this case, Eq. (17–2) becomes

$$2\lambda = d \sin \theta, \qquad (17\text{–}3)$$

where θ is greater than the angle AGB of Fig. 17–8, if light of the same wavelength is involved. For lines observed at still greater angles, other integers must be substituted for the 2 of Eq. (17–3). The real importance of the grating, however, is that it sharply separates lines of particular wavelengths from one another, since the direction along which the reenforcement condition is met varies with wavelength itself. It is this property of gratings which makes them excellent devices for the measurement of wavelengths.

The wavelengths of light are so small that great technical skill and care are needed for the construction of gratings. The spectrum of visible light extends from about 7.5×10^{-5} cm, in the red, to 3.5×10^{-5} cm, in the violet. Light wavelengths are usually expressed in units smaller than the cm, to avoid the negative powers of 10. The *Angstrom unit*, designated A and defined as 10^{-8} cm, is the unit most commonly used for this purpose. In these terms the wavelength of red light is about 7500 A, that of violet light about 3500 A. Since light wavelengths are so very small, the slits in a diffraction grating designed to measure them must be very close together. The earliest diffraction gratings, constructed by Joseph Fraunhofer (1787–1826), consisted of very fine wires spaced at intervals as small as 0.05 mm. Modern gratings are made by precise ruling of fine equidistant lines on opaque glass or metal surfaces. A grating of high quality may have 15,000 lines ruled per inch on such a surface, for example.

Very few light sources emit a single color; the most nearly pure common source is that produced by applying a burner flame to common sodium chloride, resulting in a yellow light that is characteristic of the element sodium. When white light is passed through a diffraction grating a *continuous spectrum*, similar to that observed by Newton with his prism, is observed. Many other sources, such as that produced by passing an electric discharge through mercury vapor (the mercury arc), consist of light of several discrete wavelengths. When light from such a source is passed through a grating, a *line spectrum* is obtained on the observation screen, since each of its component colors forms an image of the source slit at an angle characteristic for its particular wavelength. The wavelengths of light producing these various lines can then be readily determined by angular measurement and the use of Eq. (17–2). Various types of spectra are shown in the frontispiece.

17–6 Polarization of light

Although the polarization of light is a familiar phenomenon today, it remained a novelty long after its discovery, late in the 17th century, by Huygens. A Danish observer, Bartholinus (1625–1692), noted that objects viewed through a transparent crystal of the mineral Iceland spar (calcite) appear double: a black dot on white paper becomes two dots, a small beam of light two beams, for example. Huygens, convinced that light is wavelike, could explain this observation on the basis of two sets of secondary wavelets, one spherical, as in ordinary wave propagation, the other *spheroidal*, progressing more rapidly along one direction than in any other (Fig. 17–9). Although the supposed existence of two sets of waves was puzzling, Huygens thought that it might have something to do with the very regularity of structure of the crystal involved. This guess has since been confirmed: unlike air or glass, whose properties are the same along all directions, a crystal may have different properties in different directions. Iceland spar is an outstanding example of a crystal exhibiting such differences.

Huygens made a further observation on the effects of Iceland spar which he could not understand: he proved that the two rays of light which produce

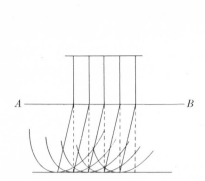

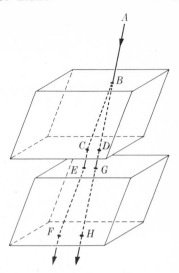

Fig. 17–9. Huygens' diagram accounting for two wave directions in a crystal. One wave goes in the direction of the dotted lines, as it would in glass. The other gives rise to the spheroidal wavelets shown, each of which expands most rapidly in one particular direction determined by the crystal structure.

Fig. 17–10. Huygens' experiment with two calcite crystals.

a double image are unlike each other even after they have emerged from the crystal. An experiment to demonstrate this requires two crystals. Let a calcite crystal divide a beam of light in two, as first observed by Bartholinus, then let these two beams fall on a second crystal, as in Fig. 17–10. Usually four beams result, each of the original two being divided again. But for one particular orientation of the second crystal with respect to the first no further division occurs, and only two beams are seen. Huygens was struck by this result: "Now it is wonderful that the rays CE and DG, coming from air to the lower crystal, do not divide in the same way that the first ray AB does." The two beams CE and DG must certainly differ from each other, yet they are divided at other orientations of the second crystal.

With the material called polaroid so commonly available today, an experiment demonstrating the property that puzzled Huygens can be performed very simply. Two sheets of polaroid will transmit almost as much light as one if they are "parallel." The requirement is not just that their *planes* be parallel. If one sheet is kept stationary and the other rotated about an axis at right angles to its plane all variations of light intensity, from darkness to maximum brightness, are observed. At their most opaque orientation we say that the polaroids are "crossed." This experiment differs from Huygens' in that polaroid does not give rise to double images; it stops one of the two beams that calcite transmits. When two polaroids are crossed, the beam coming from the first has properties which, somehow, prevent its transmission through the second in this particular orientation.

The difficulty in understanding Huygens' discovery lay in the analogy between light and mechanical waves. Pressure waves, capable of transmission in all media, involve small motions of the parts of the transmitting medium back and forth along the line of propagation. There is only one direction of vibration for a longitudinal wave, and hence no physical basis for distinguishing any direction except that of propagation. In a transverse wave the vibrations are at right angles to the direction in which the wave travels. For complete description of a single transverse wave the direction of vibration must be specified. The one-dimensional waves in a rope may be vertical, for example, or horizontal; only vertical vibrations could be transmitted along a rope through the vertical slot of Fig. 17–11, while horizontal vibrations would be destroyed. This suggests that if light waves were transverse, Huygens' experiment might be explained. Now we have seen in Chapter 16 that in three dimensions only a solid, the state of matter that tends to retain its *shape*, can support transverse waves. Whatever transmits light, supposedly the ether, is so tenuous that it is undetectable; presumably it fills all space and it certainly offers no measurable resistance to the motion of material bodies. An imponderable *solid* ether, which would be needed on the mechanical model for transverse light waves, was quite beyond the powers of the imagination. It is easy to see why neither Newton nor Huygens entertained any such idea, and thus why Newton rejected wave character altogether and Huygens could think only in terms of longitudinal waves.

Extensive and irrefutable evidence of the wave nature of light, sufficient to convince scientists who had doubted Young's conclusions, was furnished by the work of Augustin Jean Fresnel (1788–1827). It was also Fresnel, in collaboration with Arago, who provided conclusive proof that light waves

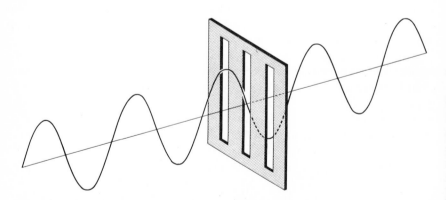

Fig. 17–11. Only vertical waves can be transmitted along a rope passing through a vertical slot.

are transverse. The crucial experiment showed that the two beams of light from Huygens' calcite crystal are incapable of interfering with each other; they cannot combine either to reenforce or to cancel. The same fact may be demonstrated by using two slits, as in Young's experiment, and covering each with a piece of polaroid. If one polaroid is oriented at right angles to the other, i.e., in such a direction that light would be extinguished if both were inserted in the same beam, the interference pattern indicated on the screen in Fig. 17–6 is not observed. Now mechanical vibrations at right angles to one another are independent, incapable of reenforcing or canceling. Since the two beams of light emerging from a calcite crystal do not interfere with each other, it can be concluded that the vibrations in one must be perpendicular to those in the other. And since no such directional difference could be possible in a longitudinal wave, it must follow that light waves are transverse.

Light in which vibrations take place in a particular direction at right angles to the direction of propagation is called *polarized* light. Ordinary unpolarized light consists of vibrations in all directions perpendicular to that of wave propagation (Fig. 17–12). A calcite crystal or a sheet of polaroid imposes its own polarity ("directedness") on unpolarized light. Polaroid transmits vibrations in the direction of its own axis, and stops (absorbs) those perpendicular to this axis. Any intermediate direction of vibration is partly transmitted and partly absorbed; the vibration, like any other directed quantity, is equivalent to a component along the transmission axis

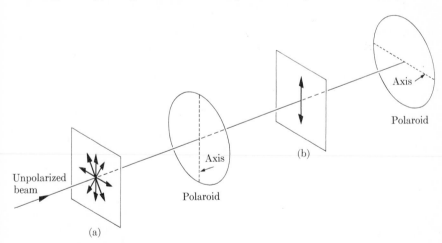

Fig. 17–12. Unpolarized light contains vibrations in all directions within any plane (a) perpendicular to the direction of propagation. A single sheet of polaroid transmits vibrations only along its own axis, as indicated in plane (b). A second sheet of polaroid, oriented so that its axis is at right angles to the axis of the first, absorbs the polarized beam entirely.

and another at right angles. Calcite transmits both kinds of vibrations, but refracts them differently, so that it divides one unpolarized ray of light into two rays with vibrations at right angles. Huygens' paradox disappears in terms of this interpretation, for a beam polarized along the calcite axis will not be divided by passage through the crystal.

As we have said, Huygens could hardly have entertained any explanation of light polarization which implies that light waves are transverse, because of the mechanical difficulties involved in imagining a medium capable of transmitting such vibrations across the vast reaches of the universe. Arago and Fresnel wisely refrained from speculation on questions of medium. Just as Young had drawn the logical conclusion from his experiments that light is wavelike, despite the existence of widespread contrary prejudice, interpretation of their experiments with integrity led them to the belief that light waves are transverse, even though the result seemed unacceptable to most of their contemporaries. In his mathematical treatment of light vibrations, Fresnel actually found the assumed ether a very useful concept, but he could not have taken its mechanical properties literally. For him, as for Faraday, the concept of ether was an aid to comprehension, but by no means its master.

17–7 Light and electromagnetism

Faraday, as we have said earlier, endowed the ether with just those properties needed to visualize the results of his own and Ampère's experiments in electromagnetism. Faraday's model of the ether contained mechanical inconsistencies, but these did not hamper the free play of his intellect; the electromagnetic ether "stresses" which he imagined led to great scientific progress. He felt sure that there must be some connection between these "stresses" and light, as has been discussed in Chapter 15. It was in 1845 that he discovered the phenomenon now known as the *Faraday effect*, the first of several *magneto-optic* effects to be detected.

Faraday found that a block of glass, when placed between the poles of an electromagnet, becomes capable of rotating the plane of vibrations in a beam of polarized light. The Faraday effect may be demonstrated by passing a beam of light first through a sheet of polaroid, then through glass placed between the poles of a strong electromagnet, and finally through a second sheet of polaroid. When no current is supplied to the coils of the electromagnet, there is no magnetic field at the position of the glass. If the bottom polaroid is rotated until it absorbs all the light from the glass with the current shut off, it is observed to transmit some light when the current is turned on. To absorb all the polarized light again, it is necessary to turn the bottom polaroid to a new position; if the current is shut off, extinction of the light can be achieved only if this polaroid is returned to its initial position. Some natural crystals, e.g., quartz, have the property of rotating the plane of vibration of polarized light even in the absence of a magnetic field. Glass ordinarily transmits a polarized beam without altering it, however, and it is only in a region of great magnetic "stress" that it possesses rotating ability.

It was impossible to interpret the Faraday effect in detail at the time of its discovery. Its chief value was to strengthen Faraday's conviction that electromagnetic "stresses" should be capable of propagation, as waves, through his imagined ether, and that light itself may be similar to an electromagnetic "stress." Faraday was not equipped to transform this qualitative speculation into a detailed, quantitative electromagnetic theory of light. It was James Clerk Maxwell who first developed such a theory, in a paper proposing that "we have strong reason to conclude that light itself (including radiant heat, and other radiations if any) is an electromagnetic disturbance in the form of waves . . ." Maxwell was generous in recognition of his debt to Faraday: "The conception of the propagation of transverse magnetic disturbances . . . is distinctly set forth by Professor Faraday in his 'Thoughts on Ray Vibrations.' The electromagnetic theory of light, as proposed by him, is the same in substance as that which I have begun to develop in this paper, except that in 1846 there were no data to calculate the velocity of propagation."

Maxwell's famous paper was published in 1865. Its strongest argument was a mathematical proof that *if* electromagnetic disturbances could be established, they would be propagated with a speed, deduced from electrical measurements, equal to the independently measured speed of light. These disturbances would be transverse waves, according to Maxwell's theory, as is consistent with the phenomena associated with light polarization. But they are not mechanical waves in any sense; no vibratory motion of *any* medium is required for their propagation, but rather periodic variations, at any given point in space, of electric and magnetic stresses, or fields. The transverse character of electromagnetic waves results from the directions of these fields, which are perpendicular to the direction of wave propagation. Maxwell and his contemporaries continued to speak of the "ether" as the medium carrying these waves, and scientists continued to worry about its properties, but the mechanical necessity for its assumption was removed by Maxwell's theory. The purely mechanical universe of Laplace became an outmoded remnant of the past.

17–8 The electromagnetic spectrum

Maxwell could give no instructions for setting up electromagnetic waves, and it was not until 1887 that such waves, in accord with the theory, were actually demonstrated. Heinrich Hertz (1857–1894) carried Maxwell's mathematical analysis further, and proved that any electric charge, when accelerated, should produce waves of a predictable kind. An oscillating charge should send out waves of its own frequency and of a wavelength determined by that frequency and the velocity of light. Hertz produced such waves—the first manmade radio waves—with an oscillatory spark discharge, and showed that they exhibit interference and other wave properties. Frequencies as high as those of visible light cannot be produced by macroscopic electric circuits, but Hertz' demonstration of longer waves of the same general properties served to establish the electromagnetic theory of light; it was concluded that visible light must result from very rapid vibrations of microscopic or submicroscopic charges.

Hertz' experiment also began the extension of our experience to electromagnetic waves of all frequencies. The light and radiant heat known to Maxwell form only a small part of the whole gamut of radiation, although a very important part in everyday life. There is no theoretical limitation on the wavelength of electromagnetic waves. The phrase *electromagnetic spectrum* has been extended to embrace all vibrations which have the same general character as light and travel through empty space with the same velocity. Different names are used to designate various wavelength ranges for convenience, but as indicated in Fig. 17–13, there are no sharp demarcations between the sections of the spectrum. The longest waves, down to a few meters, are radio waves; shorter waves, used for radar communication, are often called microwaves, and may be as short as a few millimeters. Radiant heat, or infrared radiation, comes next in order of decreasing wavelength or increasing frequency, and breaks off at the beginning of the visible spectrum. Visible light is comparatively well defined, and consists of electromagnetic radiation ranging in wavelength from about 7.5×10^{-5} cm at the beginning of the red to 3.5×10^{-5} cm at the end of the violet (7500 A to 3500 A). Beyond the violet, the still shorter waves include ultraviolet and x-rays. All waves shorter than about 10^{-9} cm are called gamma rays whatever their origin, although the name was first adopted to describe certain radiations from radioactive substances. Different methods of detection are required for the various ranges of the electromagnetic spectrum, but one of the most useful is the photographic plate. Photographic emulsions may be prepared which are sensitive to infrared rays as well as visible and ultraviolet light, and can record all vibrations of higher frequency as well. Macroscopic circuits are designed to detect waves in the radio and radar bands.

Except for the long waves which can be produced by macroscopic electrical circuits, electromagnetic vibrations (including visible light) must originate in nonuniform motions of the component charges of atoms and molecules. The detection and study of these radiations has been the single tool of greatest importance in probing the detailed constitution of matter.

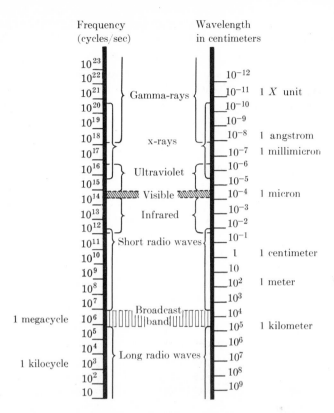

FIG. 17–13. Chart of the electromagnetic spectrum.

At the time Hertz first demonstrated electromagnetic waves, the existence of most parts of the electromagnetic spectrum had not even been guessed. But the stage was set for their recognition, and for their interpretation as signals bearing information on the structures of atoms.

17–9 Summary

In 1675 Roemer showed from astronomical observations that light travels with a velocity which, although large, is finite. About the same time Newton showed that white light is composite, i.e., consists of colors that may be separated and recomposed. The wave nature of light was proved by Young's interference experiment at the beginning of the 19th century. Young also found that the colors differ in wavelength, with violet waves shortest and red longest in the visible spectrum. The *polarization* of light on being passed through a calcite crystal posed difficulties that were resolved by Fresnel and Arago on the assumption that light waves are *transverse*. In 1865 Maxwell, following the ideas of Faraday, concluded from a theoretical study that electromagnetic disturbances would be propagated with the speed of light, and that the direction of the electric and magnetic fields in this disturbance would be transverse to the direction of propagation; from this he reasoned that light consists of electromagnetic vibrations. The first manmade electromagnetic waves were produced by Hertz in 1887. Visible light occupies a very small portion of the electromagnetic spectrum, which ranges from the longest radio waves to the shortest of what are called gamma rays.

REFERENCES

BRAGG, W., *The Universe of Light*. A popular account by a famous British physicist.

MAGIE, W. F., *A Source Book in Physics*, pp. 335–337 (Roemer), 298–308 (Newton), 294–298 (Grimaldi), 308–315 (Young), 289–294 (Huygens), 325–334 (Arago and Fresnel), and 528–538 (Maxwell).

MICHELSON, A. A., *Light Waves and Their Uses*, especially Lectures I and IV.

TAYLOR, L. W., *Physics, the Pioneer Science*. Chapters 29 through 38 deal with light and the historical development of its study.

1. A radio station lists as its wavelength 600 m, and announces that it broadcasts at a frequency of 500 kc. Find the velocity of the radio waves from these two pieces of information. [*Ans.*: 3 × 10⁸ m/sec]

2. Radar waves have now been sent to the moon and detected on their return. Remembering that the moon is 240,000 mi away, determine how much time elapses between sending the radar signal and receiving its echo. [*Ans.*: Somewhat more than 2½ sec]

3. When an electric discharge is produced in hydrogen gas, it emits red light of wavelength 6560 A and blue light of wavelength 4860 A. What are the frequencies of these light waves? [*Ans.*: 4.56 × 10¹⁴ and 6.17 × 10¹⁴ vib/sec, respectively]

4. Light travels more slowly in glass than in air; does the wavelength or frequency of light change as it passes from one to the other?

5. According to a principle proposed by Pierre de Fermat (1601–1665), the actual path along which light travels from one point to another is that which takes the least time. How does the path shown in Fig. 17–14 conform to this principle, i.e., why should the dotted straight line path take longer than the solid line showing bending? (Remember that light travels more slowly in glass than in air.) What does Fermat's principle predict as the path of light within a given homogeneous medium?

6. One diffraction grating has 6000 lines (slits) per centimeter, while another has only 4000 lines per centimeter. Find d in centimeters for each grating. Which grating diffracts light of a given wavelength through the greater angle?

7. Which is bent more by a grating giving a pattern according to the formula $\lambda = d \sin \theta$, red or blue light? Compare and contrast the spectrum produced by a prism with one produced by a diffraction grating.

8. As a soap film grows thin enough to appeared colored, the first color to appear is blue, although not a "pure" blue. Why?

9. Hold a handkerchief close to your eye and look at an unshaded light. Rotate the handkerchief a little. Can you suggest a qualitative explanation for the effect you observe, by analogy with the diffraction grating?

10. Sky light is partially polarized, as is much of reflected light. How could you determine this fact with a single piece of polaroid?

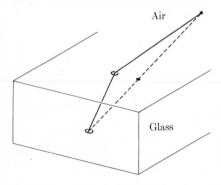

Air

Glass

FIGURE 17–14.

CHAPTER 18

ELECTRONS AND ATOMS—EVIDENCE FOR ATOMIC STRUCTURE

The foundations for the discovery that electricity is not a continuous fluid were laid, in the first part of the 19th century, with the development of electrochemistry. Soon after Volta's invention of the battery, water was decomposed by an electric current: if wires from the two terminals of a battery are dipped into water (or, preferably, a dilute salt solution), hydrogen is produced at one wire and oxygen at the other. Electroplating techniques developed from the observation that metals, e.g., silver and copper, are deposited from solutions of their salts by the action of electric current. Sir Humphrey Davy decomposed molten potash and soda by electrical means, thus preparing the elements potassium and sodium for the first time. Although it was obvious that there is some connection between electrical and chemical forces, early electrochemical observations seemed too complicated to admit of ready explanation. Berzelius postulated that *all* compounds are made up of two oppositely charged parts, hence held together by electrical forces. This purely qualitative conclusion was much too far-reaching to be justifiable. Elucidation of the actual relation between electric charge and atomic and molecular structure depended on many parallel lines of scientific progress, and has thus been largely an achievement of the 20th century. An important first step toward our present-day understanding was taken by Faraday, who demonstrated two simple empirical laws of electrochemistry, in 1834.

18-1 Faraday's laws of electrolysis

In the experiment illustrated in Fig. 18–1 the quantities of gases liberated can be measured. Similarly, in the experiment of Fig. 18–2 the quantities of metal deposited on the negative electrode from a solution of metal salt can be determined. In either case, the current through the apparatus can be measured by inserting an ammeter in the circuit. The first of Faraday's laws of electrolysis states that the mass of any given substance liberated or deposited by an electric current is directly proportional to the total quantity of electrical charge which has passed. Quantity of charge, in coulombs, may be obtained by multiplying the strength of the current, in amperes, by the

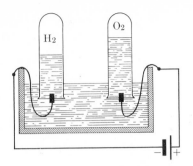

FIG. 18–1. Electrolytic decomposition of water. Pure water is a poor conductor of electricity, and a dilute
solution of sulfuric acid is used for an
electrolyte.

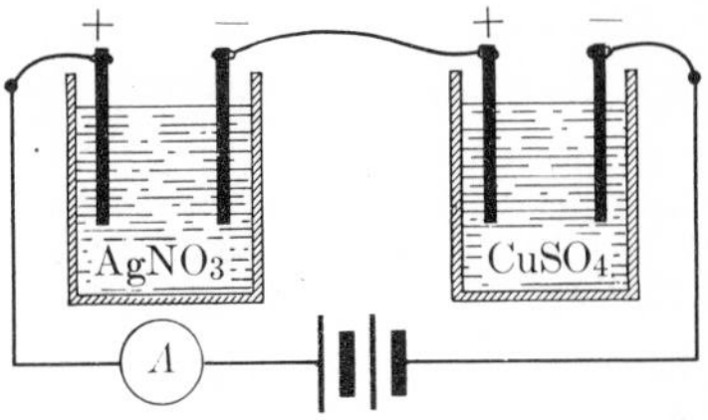

FIG. 18–2. Deposition of silver and
copper simultaneously.   The same
quantity of electric charge, 96,500 coul,
deposits 108 gm of silver and 31.8 gm
of copper (one-half of 63.6 gm).

time of its flow in seconds. It is found, for example, that passage of 96,500
coulombs (coul) liberates 1 gm of hydrogen, and that 193,000 coul produce
2 gm.

Now let us consider the results shown in Table 18–1, on weights of various
elements liberated by passage of the fixed quantity 96,500 coul of charge.
Each of these weights, it will be observed, is either equal to the gram-atomic
weight of the element involved (H, Cl, Na), to half the atomic weight (O,
Mg), or to one-third the atomic weight (Al). We may state the general result more concisely than was possible for Faraday if we recognize that the
denominator of the fraction of the atomic weight liberated is in every case
just the chemical valence of the element. Faraday's second law, often called

TABLE 18–1

QUANTITIES OF SEVERAL ELEMENTS LIBERATED BY PASSAGE OF 96,500
COULOMBS OF CHARGE

Element	Atomic weight	Weight liberated by 96,500 coul
Oxygen	16.00	8.00 gm
Hydrogen	1.01	1.01
Chlorine	35.5	35.5
Sodium	23.0	23.0
Magnesium	24.3	12.2
Aluminum	27.0	9.0

the law of electrolysis, then may be stated: *the mass of an element liberated by a given quantity of electricity is proportional to the atomic weight of the element divided by its valence.* Algebraically, the mass liberated is given by

$$M = \frac{It}{96,500} \times \frac{\text{Atomic weight}}{\text{Valence}}, \qquad (18\text{--}1)$$

where I is the current in amperes and t is the time in seconds. The quantity 96,500 coul, which liberates 1 gram-atomic weight of an element of unit valence, has been named the *faraday*. The terms *electrolyte* for a conducting solution, *electrode* for the terminal at which chemical liberation may take place, and *electrolysis* for the process were introduced by Faraday himself.

Many years after Faraday's electrochemical discoveries, in 1881, the great German physician-physicist Helmholtz commented: "Now the most startling result of Faraday's laws is perhaps this: if we accept the hypothesis that the elementary substances are composed of atoms, we cannot avoid concluding that electricity also, positive as well as negative, is divided into elementary portions which behave like atoms of electricity." This idea had indeed occurred to Faraday, but he was not sufficiently convinced of the existence of atoms to regard it as justified. The logical implication of Faraday's laws, in combination with the atomic hypothesis, is that electrolytic solutions contain charged atoms, or perhaps groups of atoms, which are free to move under the action of electrical forces. These charged particles are called *ions*. At a positive electrode, negative ions can become electrically neutral atoms; positive ions may lose charge and be liberated at a negative electrode. There must be some *smallest quantity of charge* that can be carried by any ion, the same for all ions of the same valence, since the fixed quantity of charge, 96,500 coul, deposits 1 gram-atom of any univalent element. If we call the magnitude of this elementary charge e, then

$$Ne = 96,500 \text{ coul}, \qquad (18\text{--}2)$$

where N is Avogadro's number, the number of atoms in 1 gram-atom of an element. Ions of elements of valence 2 (for example, oxygen and magnesium) would be required to carry charge $2e$, while aluminum ions would carry charge $3e$, on this scheme. The number of elementary charges associated with each atom deposited by electrolysis is thus identical with the valence of the element involved, according to this interpretation. The *charge per unit mass* for hydrogen ions is obviously 96,500 coul/gm, for sodium ions 1/23 this amount, and so forth.

Despite the clear implications of Faraday's discovery, the idea of discontinuity, or "atomicity" of electricity was not generally accepted until near the end of the 19th century. To trace the manner in which it gained acceptance, we must turn to a different aspect of science.

18–2 Gaseous discharge tubes

Science and technology have always interacted reciprocally. We are so accustomed to the applications of fundamental scientific discoveries, such as electrical generators and motors, that it is easy to forget the debt of science to technology. As an example of this debt, we have noted that important 17th-century studies of gases were made possible by the invention of the air pump. A further advance in vacuum pump design, achieved by a remarkably skillful German glass blower, Heinrich Geissler, opened the way for the atomic researches of the late 19th century. Certain elaborate glass tubes of glowing gas, ornate forerunners of modern fluorescent lights, are still called "Geissler tubes."

A gas discharge tube is simply a glass tube into which a pair of metal electrodes has been sealed (Fig. 18–3). When a large potential difference is applied across the electrodes of a tube containing air or another gas at reduced pressure, the interior of the tube exhibits a steady glow of light. With the improvement of vacuum techniques, it became possible to make a systematic study of the behavior of discharge tubes at very low pressures. It was noted that the color of the discharge depends on the nature of the gas present in the tube as well as on pressure, a subject to which we shall return. Whatever the gas originally present or the metal composing the electrodes, however, the internal luminosity of the tube was observed to diminish, and a green fluorescent glow in the tube walls to appear, at *very* low pressures. Careful examination revealed that this glow was produced by something emanating from the negative electrode, called the *cathode*. Although invisible, these rays cause light emission (fluorescence) when they strike glass or other objects inside the tube.

The new discharge tube rays, which came to be called *cathode rays*, are capable of producing sharp shadows (Fig. 18–4), indicating that they travel in straight lines. But Professors Plücker and Hittorf at Bonn (where Geissler had developed his vacuum pump) soon noticed that the fluorescent

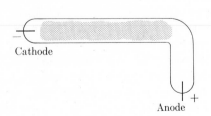

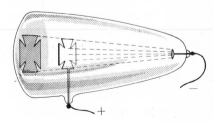

Fig. 18–3. One form of discharge used to show the origin of cathode rays; a glow was observed in the long arm, but did not appear near the anode.

Fig. 18–4. A sharp dark shadow (absence of luminescence on the glass) shows that cathode rays travel in straight lines.

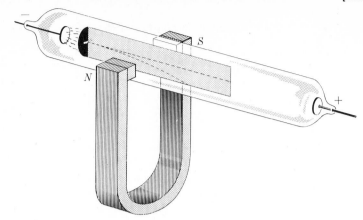

FIG. 18–5. The fluorescent screen in the tube makes the path of the cathode rays visible. When a magnet is brought up the previously straight path is deflected as shown.

cathode-ray glow is shifted in the presence of a magnet, indicating that the rays are deflected by a magnetic field (Fig. 18–5). Later it was shown that they are also deflected by an electric field and the idea began to gain ground that cathode rays consist of charged particles. The electric and magnetic deflections correspond to those to be expected of particles bearing negative charge, although there was considerable diversity of opinion on the subject. Hertz, who had so brilliantly confirmed Maxwell's electromagnetic theory of light, maintained that cathode rays are *longitudinal* ether waves, for example! This opinion was not frivolous; it was based on his failure to observe the magnetic field which should accompany cathode rays if they constitute an electric current, and by his inability to detect their deflectability by an electric field. Hertz' difficulty was that his vacuum technique was not sufficiently good to enable him to observe the effects he sought.

Meanwhile the idea of elementary subatomic particles of equal charge began to have fruitful theoretical consequences in the study of the optical and electrical properties of matter. Designation of these particles by the word *electron* was proposed by Johnstone Stoney (1826–1911). Whether such hypothetical particles, the logical consequence of Faraday's laws in the light of atomic theory, bore any relation to the phenomena exhibited in discharge tubes was something that could be determined only by quantitative measurement of the properties of cathode rays.

18–3 The "discovery of the electron"

A quantitative determination of cathode-ray properties was first successfully achieved in 1897 by J. J. Thomson (1856–1940) at Cambridge Uni-

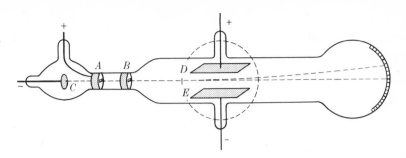

FIG. 18–6. Apparatus used to measure e/m. The dotted circle shows the region in which a magnetic field can be set up.

versity. He made what would be considered today a very primitive cathode-ray tube, as shown in Fig. 18–6. Note that the anode has a hole through which a narrow beam of rays may pass into the main body of the evacuated container. This beam could be deflected by the auxiliary electrodes shown, metal plates built into the tube. The dotted path shows the deflection produced by a difference of potential across these electrodes; with positive charge on the upper plate, as shown, upward deflection is consistent with the assumption of negative charge on the cathode ray. (It is not the path of the beam which is directly observed, but the position of the fluorescent spot the beam produces on the screen at the end of its path.) Alternatively, an electromagnet (not shown, since it would obstruct the view) could be slipped over the tube to produce a magnetic field at right angles to the plane of the diagram in the region between the auxiliary electrodes. We shall present the principles of the experiment Thomson performed with this tube, although we shall not work out the details of his quantitative measurement.

In Chapter 15 we noted that a small length of wire carrying a current at right angles to a magnetic field B is subject to a force BIl, where I is the magnitude of the current and l is the length of circuit considered. Let us measure I in amperes (coulombs/second), and length in centimeters, so that Il is a certain number of coul-cm/sec. A current consists of moving charge, and a charge of e coulombs moving with a velocity v cm/sec gives us the equivalent of a small length of current Il equal simply to ev coul-cm/sec. The consequent force on a moving charge when B is perpendicular to v is then Bev, directed at right angles to both B and v. Now if a force acts on a moving particle at right angles to its velocity, the particle will move in the arc of a circle at unchanging speed; according to Huygens and Newton the acting force must be equal to mv^2/r, where m is the mass of the particle and r is the radius of the circle (Eq. 3–10). Thus in the presence of the field B,

$$Bev = \frac{mv^2}{r} \qquad (18\text{-}3)$$

or

$$Br = \frac{vm}{e}. \qquad (18\text{-}4)$$

The magnetic field strength B can be measured by the force exerted on a known current, and r can be ascertained by measuring the deflection produced on the cathode-ray beam, but there are three unknown quantities on the right side of Eq. (18-4). Two of the unknowns, e and m, are characteristic of the rays if these consist of particles of unique charge and mass. Therefore, valuable information would be obtained if v could be determined independently. This is where Thomson's plate electrodes came in. An electrical force can be applied to the cathode rays by putting a difference of potential across these plates, and in a direction opposite to that applied by the magnet. By adjusting the magnitude of this potential difference, the beam can be returned to its undeflected position. If we denote by E the applied electrical force *per unit of charge*, then the total electrical force is Ee, which is balanced by the magnetic force Bev. In other words, Thomson adjusted E until the conditions were such that

$$Bev = Ee, \qquad (18\text{-}5)$$

hence

$$v = \frac{E}{B}, \qquad (18\text{-}6)$$

a ratio that he was able to measure. By substituting this value in Eq. (18-4), he was able to get a numerical value for the ratio m/e, more commonly expressed as its reciprocal, e/m.

It must be realized that in our consideration of Thomson's experiment we have *assumed* that cathode rays consist of identical material particles of definite mass and charge, hence are subject to known mechanical and electrical laws. Thomson was able to demonstrate, indeed, that there is a *unique* value for the charge-to-mass ratio, e/m, that is, that all cathode rays apparently have the same properties. He obtained the same measured value of e/m for cathode rays traveling at a wide range of speeds, and using tubes initially filled with a variety of different gases. These results could hardly be interpreted in any way other than that cathode rays must be composed of identical particles. The success of Thomson's experimental measurements of e/m is often said to constitute the "discovery" of the electron, although the existence of this subatomic particle had previously been inferred, and had already begun to take its place in physical theory.

The numerical value of e/m for electrons is about 1.76×10^8 coul/gm. This quantity is about 1840 times larger than the value of 96,500 coul/gm found for charged hydrogen atoms (ions) in electrolysis. Since hydrogen consists of the lightest atoms known, electrons must be vastly smaller in mass than any atom. Specifically, if the electron and the hydrogen ion are assumed to bear the same quantity of charge, the mass of the former must be only 1/1840 that of the latter.

18-4 Determination of the electronic charge

It still remained to be proved that charge is truly *discrete*, occurring only in integral multiples of some smallest, indivisible amount. The experiment described above gave only the ratio e/m, but no direct evaluation of the electronic charge e and no proof that it has a unique value. J. J. Thomson proceeded to outline the basic method for a determination of elementary charge, but the experiment was difficult to perform in practice, and self-consistent, reproducible results were not obtained for some years. Notable success was first achieved by the American physicist Robert A. Millikan (1868–1953), who undertook work on the problem in 1909.

Millikan's method was to measure the force on a very small charged body in an electric field, and to determine the least amount of charge a body can possess. Individual electrons or ions are invisible, but tiny droplets of liquid visible through a short-range telescope may acquire charge if they are sprayed into the air. A diagram of the apparatus is shown in Fig. 18–7. A pair of metal plates connected to a battery produces a constant uniform electric field in the region between them. A fog of oil droplets is sprayed above the upper plate and as they settle one may fall through a small hole in this plate. If this drop has no charge, it will continue to settle; if it has a charge q, it will be affected by the electric field. The field may be adjusted until the drop remains stationary, which would mean that the downward force of its own weight and the upward electric force are balanced. Under these equilibrium conditions

$$Eq = mg, \qquad (18\text{-}7)$$

where mg is the weight of the droplet. The strength of the electric field, E, is measurable, so that q can be computed if the drop can be weighed.

Just as the charges involved here are too small to be determined by ordinary electroscopes or galvanometers, so the mass of an oil drop is too small to be weighed by ordinary methods. But earlier in the 19th century Stokes had worked out the formula for the air resistance on a spherical drop, and had shown how it is related to the constant "terminal" or drift velocity with which the sphere falls in still air. By means of this formula the

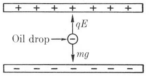

Fig. 18–7. Millikan's experiment for determining the electronic charge.

weight can be computed from known properties of the material of which the sphere is composed if the terminal velocity of its fall is known. For each drop this drift velocity can be found by timing its rate of fall when there is no electric field between the plates. Equation (18–7) may then be solved for q. Note that it is not assumed that q is equal to e, or even that there is any smallest division of charge at all.

The smallest charge measured in this way is 1.6×10^{-19} coul, and all other charges were found to be integral multiples of this amount. No smaller quantity of charge, either positive or negative, has ever been observed. Millikan's experiment proved the existence of elementary indivisible charges, although it did not directly identify these charges with e, the charge on Thomson's electron. Indirect evidence, as well as further direct evidence, confirms the identity of Millikan's elementary charge with e, however, and his experiment is commonly referred to as the measurement of the *electronic* charge.

18–5 X-rays

The discovery of x-rays, by Wilhelm Konrad Roentgen (1845–1923) late in 1895, caught the popular as well as the scientific imagination. Roentgen observed that a fluorescent screen glows brightly when placed near a gas

discharge tube which is operating at
high voltage and low pressure. The
effect persisted even when the entire discharge tube was wrapped
in black paper, and when wood was
placed between the tube and the
screen. A heavy metal plate was
found capable of cutting off the
glow, however. Something with
remarkable power to penetrate air
and light materials was escaping
from the tube. Roentgen quickly

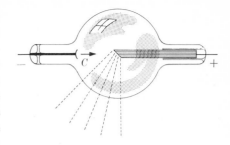

Fig. 18–8. Early x-ray tube.

established that the new rays were not cathode rays, by demonstrating
that their paths were unaffected by a magnet. He found them capable
of discharging an electroscope, and of blackening a photographic plate.
He observed that the rays come from that part of a discharge tube on
which cathode rays impinge. By constructing a tube of special design,
containing a "target" to stop cathode rays (Fig. 18–8), Roentgen was able
to produce the new rays with greatly enhanced intensity. Although they
were called x-rays because their nature was not understood, the new
phenomenon itself became widely known at once. Within a few weeks of
Roentgen's announcement of his discovery, the unique penetrating power
of x-rays was being used to obtain shadow photographs of various parts
of the body, of metal objects within wooden boxes, etc., wherever there
were discharge tubes.

Since x-rays affect photographic plates, it was natural (although not
mandatory) to suppose that they consist of electromagnetic waves similar
to visible light. If so, they must exhibit interference and diffraction effects,
and the search for such effects was unsuccessful for several years. Roentgen
tried to apply Young's experiment with extremely fine slits, but was unable
to obtain an interference pattern in this way. The reason for his failure is
that the wavelengths of x-rays are extremely short; using mechanical slits
for x-rays would be like trying to observe interference of ordinary light
from two adjacent classroom windows. Despite the failure of experiments
like Roentgen's, the conviction grew that x-rays consist of very short
electromagnetic waves. Finally, Max von Laue suggested that the regular
spacing between layers of atoms in crystals should be of about the right
size to produce interference effects in x-rays; his prediction was confirmed
experimentally in 1911. Since that time x-rays and crystal structure
have remained intimately related; crystals are used to measure the wavelengths of the radiation, and x-rays are employed to determine the structural details of crystals.

18-6 Radioactivity and the discovery of the nucleus

Another great discovery followed hard on the heels of Roentgen's announcement of x-rays. Henri Becquerel (1852–1909), in Paris, had devoted years to the study of fluorescence—the visible glow produced in many materials by exposure to light or other radiation. Cathode rays cause fluorescent materials to glow, it will be remembered, and among Roentgen's earliest results was the observation that x-rays seemed to emerge at greatest intensity from the spot on a discharge tube showing the greatest fluorescence of glass. To Becquerel this suggested a possible association between fluorescence and the emission of x-rays. He therefore set out at once to find out whether fluorescent substances, after exposure to light, are capable of fogging photographic plates and discharging electroscopes, i.e., of producing effects similar to those of x-rays. Now one common fluorescent material is the double sulfate of potassium and uranium. Becquerel found that this compound *does* blacken photographic plates, unlike most of the materials he tried, but that it does so whether it has been previously irradiated or not. What Becquerel found through his interest in fluorescence, then, turned out to be quite unrelated to fluorescence! Early in 1896 he was able to show that the ability to darken photographic plates observed in potassium uranium sulfate was ascribable to the presence of uranium, and that all compounds of this element emit penetrating radiation. This result constituted the discovery of the phenomenon which came to be called *radioactivity*; uranium was thus the first element known to be radioactive.

Marie Sklodowska Curie (1867–1934) and her husband Pierre Curie (1859–1906), who had followed Becquerel's work with great interest since its inception, undertook the task of performing a systematic search for radioactivity among materials other than uranium compounds. Since radioactive radiations can discharge an electroscope, the latter instrument was an invaluable aid in their search. They soon found that the compounds of the element thorium emit penetrating radiations similar to those of uranium. Mme. Curie observed, in 1897, that samples of the uranium ore *pitchblende* caused discharge of an electroscope at a much greater rate than was expected on the basis of its known uranium content. She immediately postulated the presence, in the ore, of one or more new radioactive elements. By the end of 1898 she and her husband had proved the existence of the elements *polonium* and *radium*, the first to be detected on the basis of radioactive properties alone. To convince a doubtful scientific community, the Curies chemically processed a ton of pitchblende in an unheated shed in Paris, and succeeded in preparing about 0.1 gm of pure radium chloride after several years of hard labor. This quantity was sufficient to permit accurate determination of the atomic weight of the new element. Much of this work was first made public in Marie Curie's doctoral thesis, presented to the Faculte des Sciences de Paris in 1903, and the acclaim of the scientific world was made manifest by the award of the Nobel prize to both Curies later in the same year. Since 1903 many new radioactive elements have been discovered, and it is now known that all elements of atomic number greater than 83 can exist only in radioactive forms.

Although the radiation from radioactive substances, like x-rays, is capable of discharging an electroscope, it soon became apparent that the two are dissimilar. At least a part of radioactive radiation is influenced by a magnet in a manner reminiscent of electrons. The complexity of radiation was clarified by Ernest Rutherford (1871–1937), a man whose experimental genius and achievement rivaled that of Faraday. There are actually three different kinds of rays involved in radioactivity (Fig. 18–9): alpha particles, which Rutherford identified as positively charged helium atoms in rapid motion; beta particles, identical with cathode-ray electrons; and gamma rays, consisting of electromagnetic radiation similar to x-rays, but even shorter in wavelength. The occurrence of these radiations is spontaneous and independent of the state of chemical combination of any given radioactive element. The nature of radiation emitted does depend on the particular element involved, in a way which we shall consider in Chapter 29. In our present application we shall consider only the manner in which radioactivity, as a tool, led to one of the most important insights of 20th-century science. It was by letting alpha particles from radioactive substances strike metal foils, and observing the results, that Rutherford laid a foundation for the understanding of the internal structures of atoms.

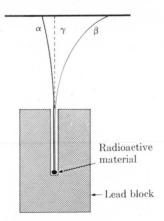

Fig. 18–9.   Schematic distinction between radioactive radiations by their behavior in a magnetic field. (α) Alpha rays are deflected slightly, and behave like a current of positive particles. (β) Beta rays are more strongly deflected, and behave like a current of negative particles. (γ) Gamma rays are not affected by the magnetic field.

We have noted that the "discovery" of the electron gave proof that atoms have structure, i.e., that they are not indivisible entities. But the mass of the electron is very small in comparison with that of an atom, even an atom of hydrogen. Moreover, all electrons are observed to be negatively charged, whereas atoms are ordinarily neutral. At first it was supposed by J. J. Thomson and others that the atomic mass must be due to the presence of many electrons, 1840 of them in the case of hydrogen, more for other atoms, embedded in some almost weightless plasma of positive charge that would make the whole electrically neutral. This concept of the atom was sharply refuted by Rutherford's discovery of the atomic nucleus in 1911.

Alpha particles produce little flashes of light, or scintillations, on a fluorescent screen. The apparatus used in the work which led to the discovery of the atomic nucleus is shown in the diagram of Fig. 18–10. A sample of an alpha-emitting radioactive substance is at R. The alpha particles are limited to a fine beam by a thick lead screen containing a small aperture. This beam of alpha particles falls on a thin foil of gold, and those that are deviated or scattered in various directions by the gold can be detected by counting the scintillations on a fluorescent screen placed at different angular positions. Rutherford found that most of the alpha particles went straight through the gold foil with little or no deviation, but that a few were scattered at large angles, some even nearly reversed. Wide-angle scattering was completely contrary to what had been expected; electrons, of which atoms were thought to consist, have so little mass that they could not possibly produce such deviations. Years later Rutherford remarked: "It was quite the most incredible event that has ever happened to me in my life. It was as though you had fired a 15-inch shell at a piece of tissue

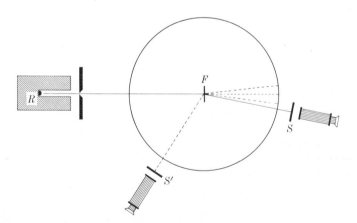

Fig. 18–10. Alpha particles emitted at R are scattered by the foil F and counted by their scintillations on the screen at S or S', viewed with lens.

paper and it came back and hit you." He found that he could account for the result, however, if he assumed that all the positive charge repelling the positive alpha particles, and practically all the mass of the atom as well, were confined to a very small volume at the center of the atom, which he termed the *nucleus*. Rutherford showed that the tremendous forces needed to produce the backward scattering would be exerted only at distances of the order of 10^{-12} cm, and by a positive charge which for the case of gold he first estimated to be about 100 times the charge on an electron. (The correct value later turned out to be 79, not 100.) Now even a rough determination of Avogadro's number, together with the reasonable assumption that in solids the atoms are practically contiguous, leads to the conclusion that atomic diameters are of the order of 10^{-8} cm. Rutherford's experiment indicated that while the negatively charged electrons may be distributed throughout a volume corresponding to this diameter, the positive charge and most of the atomic mass are much more concentrated.

It occurred to Rutherford and others that each atom might constitute a miniature solar system, with electrical attractions between the nucleus and the electrons playing the same role that gravitation fills in the actual solar system. There were, however, overwhelming objections to such a model. Electrons in circular motion about the nucleus would be accelerated, and according to the principles of electricity and magnetism any accelerated charge emits light and thus loses energy. Calculation showed that electrons would lose their kinetic energy and spiral into the attracting nucleus in a very short time, whereas the existence of matter (and thus presumably its component atoms) generally appears permanent. Atoms do emit light and other electromagnetic radiation in a discharge tube or in a flame, but not the kind of radiation that would be given off by a spiraling electron. Any satisfactory model of the atom must account for the radiation that is actually observed, and before we can proceed further in our attempt to understand atomic structure we must find out something about the light emitted by atoms.

18–7 Atomic spectra

Early in the 19th century it was discovered that if sunlight is transmitted through a narrow slit and separated into its colors by a prism (Newton's experiment) the spectrum is crossed by a series of dark lines—some wavelengths are apparently missing (see Frontispiece). These lines were discovered by Joesph Fraunhofer (1787–1826) and are called Fraunhofer lines, although he was not actually the first to observe them. The light emitted by white-hot metals does not exhibit dark lines. Fraunhofer did notice that in the spectrum of a candle flame there are two bright yellow lines (also shown in Frontispiece) that coincide with two dark lines of the solar spectrum, and much later Gustave Robert Kirchhoff (1824–1887) was able to produce these dark lines in the laboratory. First he had noted that the bright yellow lines of the candle flame were intensified by the addition of common salt to the flame, and by using other compounds he was able to trace the origin of the yellow color to sodium vapor. The next step was to allow intense white light to pass through sodium vapor. Passage of this light through a prism then reveals dark lines in the yellow part of the continuous spectrum. The emission and absorption of two particular wavelengths in the yellow is thus characteristic of sodium. Thus began the identification of substances by observation of their spectra, a method which permits chemical analysis of the stars.

Kirchhoff and Robert Bunsen began to study the flame spectra of a wide variety of substances. They found, for example, that the addition of lithium salt to a flame produces a bright light-red line and another weaker line more nearly orange colored. Just as in the sodium case, lithium vapor is capable of weakening light of the same color (wavelength) that it produces. Most spectra are more complex than those of sodium and lithium, although even these consist of numerous lines most of which are too faint to be seen in a Bunsen flame. It became clear that each element, when introduced into a flame, produces a *characteristic* set of lines by which it can be identified, and that it strongly absorbs light, under certain conditions, of the same frequencies it emits. Not all elements can be easily examined in flames, but the method of spectroscopic analysis was extended to light from the gaseous discharge tubes described in Section 18–2. The Fraunhofer lines in the solar spectrum were interpreted as absorption of light of characteristic wavelengths by materials in the sun's outer layers of gas. We know the composition of the solar atmosphere by identification of these dark absorption lines with those shown in laboratory experiments to be characteristic of certain substances. This analysis was begun almost within the lifetime of the French philosopher Auguste Comte, who had said that it is the nature of things that we should never be able to determine of what the stars are made! One series of strong solar lines (notably a dark green line) could not at first be identified with any element known on the earth; when an element giving the same spectrum was discovered terrestrially in 1905 it was appropriately termed *helium*, in honor of its prior discovery in the sun as early as 1878.

The very first elements to be discovered spectroscopically were cesium and rubidium; this was accomplished by the pioneers in the field, Kirchhoff and Bunsen. An American, David Alter, first described the spectrum of hydrogen in 1855. By means of the photographic plate and quartz prisms, it became possible to extend the examination of spectra to the ultraviolet region, and to observe more completely the wavelengths emitted by any one kind of atom. Certain regularities began to emerge, especially in the spectrum of hydrogen (Fig. 18–11). By means of a diffraction grating the wavelengths of hydrogen's spectral lines could be measured with great accuracy, and J. J. Balmer (1825–1898) succeeded in writing down a fairly simple empirical equation relating these wavelengths to one another. Balmer's formula is

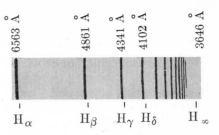

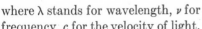

$$\frac{1}{\lambda} = \frac{\nu}{c} = R\left(\frac{1}{4} - \frac{1}{n^2}\right), \quad n \geq 3,$$

(18–8)

FIG. 18–11.   The series of hydrogen spectral lines described by Balmer's formula. (Reproduced by permission from *Atomic Spectra and Atomic Structure*, by Gerhard Herzberg, Prentice-Hall, Inc., 1937.) .

where λ stands for wavelength, ν for frequency, c for the velocity of light, R is a constant, and n takes the values 3, 4, 5, etc., for successive lines of the visible series shown in Fig. 18–11. Later a series of lines was discovered in the ultraviolet spectrum of hydrogen which could be described by the relation

$$\frac{1}{\lambda} = R\left(1 - \frac{1}{n^2}\right), \quad n \geq 2,$$

(18–9)

with R exactly the same constant as in the Balmer formula. (Here n may be equal to or greater than 2.)

The problem faced by Rutherford and others in designing a model for the atom was that it must account for observed atomic spectra. In particular, the hydrogen atom must radiate as described by the Balmer formula. The electromagnetic radiation theory of Maxwell and Hertz, confirmed for long wavelengths, could be used to predict the radiation emitted by electrons circulating about a nucleus; nothing like the radiation described by Balmer's formula could be obtained in this way. Rutherford's solar system model was thus wholly incompatible with experience and with the accepted radiation theory of 1911. Yet, coupled with another line of evidence, it led to a model which did yield the Balmer formula and unexpectedly brought a rational explanation for the periodic table of the chemical elements. Let us consider one other set of facts and ideas that was needed for the achievement of this great scientific advance.

18–8 The photoelectric effect and the quantum

As early as 1887, in connection with his experiments on electromagnetic waves, Hertz observed that a spark discharge was more easily produced when the metal electrodes were illuminated by light from another spark.

Later it was found that negatively charged plates of zinc, copper, and silver lose their charge when exposed to ultraviolet light (Fig. 18–12); the alkali metals, e.g., sodium, potassium, and cesium, behave in the same way when exposed to visible light. The phenomenon was called the *photoelectric effect*, and after discovery of the electron it became clear that these metals were emitting electrons as a result of illumination.

Upon investigation of the photoelectric effect, it was found that every metal has what is called a wavelength *threshold* for the emission of electrons. For wavelengths longer than a particular value, zinc, for example, gives off no electrons, while light of shorter wavelength (and thus higher frequency) does produce emission. For the more common metals this threshold is in the ultraviolet, while for the alkali metals it is in the infrared. When the velocity of the emitted electrons was determined a very astonishing discovery was made: the speed with which electrons leave a metal is entirely independent of the intensity of the light, and is thus apparently independent of the amount of light energy incident on the metal. More electrons per second could be obtained by using more light, but the energy of each individual electron was entirely unaffected. The velocity of the fastest electrons from any metal did depend on the *frequency* of the light used, however, and electrons of greater energy could be obtained by using light of frequency well above that of the threshold.

This feature of the photoelectric effect was quite inexplicable on the basis of ordinary electromagnetic theory, according to which radiant energy is simply proportional to intensity, without regard to wavelength or fre-

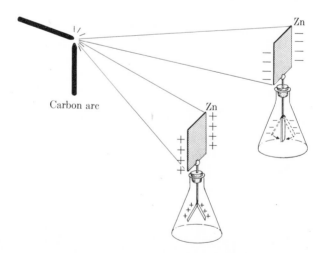

Fig. 18–12.   Light from a bare carbon arc discharges a negatively charged zinc plate but not a positive one, as shown by an electroscope.

quency. This was not the only contradiction between experimental facts and electromagnetic theory; there were also troubles in describing quantitatively, in terms of frequency, the radiation that is given off by a body as a result of its temperature. It was in connection with this latter problem that Max Planck (1857–1947), in 1900, postulated what is called the *quantum*. He had to assume that radiation energy is given off and absorbed in small discrete amounts, or *quanta*, each of magnitude proportional to the frequency of the radiation. The universal constant by which the frequency must be multiplied to give the energy per quantum is called Planck's constant, and is designated in the scientific literature by h. According to this very radical hypothesis, light consists of discrete "bundles," each of energy content $h\nu$. Quanta are now often called *photons*.

Albert Einstein (1884–1955) was the first to see that the behavior of photoelectrons could be very easily understood if Planck's quantum hypothesis is accepted. He pointed out that metals tend to hang onto their electrons, and that a certain amount of energy would be necessary simply to remove an electron from the metal. This energy would be equal to that of a quantum of light at the threshold frequency; the assumption here is that each photon must be swallowed whole, so to speak, by a single electron (Fig. 18–13). A photon of frequency lower than that of the threshold would not provide enough energy to detach an electron from the metal, while those of higher frequency would be capable of furnishing an excess that would appear as kinetic energy. If we call the energy required for escape W, we can write Einstein's photoelectric equation:

$$h\nu = W + \tfrac{1}{2}mv^2. \qquad (18\text{–}10)$$

Interpreting, one quantum of radiant energy, $h\nu$, is entirely absorbed in the interaction with one electron at the metal's surface; of this energy the amount W is consumed in the process of detaching the electron, and the remainder appears as the electron's kinetic energy, $\tfrac{1}{2}mv^2$. This equation was experimentally verified by the demonstration of a direct

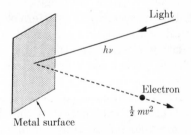

Fig. 18–13. A single quantum of light (photon), falling on a photosensitive surface, supplies energy for the escape of an electron.

proportionality between the frequency ν of incident light and the kinetic energy of emitted photoelectrons for any given metal. Its verification, in turn, added confirmation to the original hypothesis that light consists of quanta, and that Maxwell's electromagnetic description, despite its achievements, must be subject to certain limitations.

Note that the *particle* nature of light, as exhibited in the photoelectric effect and other phenomena, is in addition to, and not an alternative for, the *wave* nature of light. To a certain extent Huygens and Newton were *both* right: light and other electromagnetic radiations are wavelike, but they are also, in some respects, particle-like. From a strictly mechanical viewpoint, the concepts wave and particle are mutually exclusive, but this exclusiveness is imposed by the mechanical models themselves. It is impossible to visualize something which is at once a wave and a particle, yet both concepts are demanded by scientific experience.

18–9 Summary

A variety of lines of evidence pointed to the conclusion that atoms are not strictly indivisible, but are themselves composed of particles. The atomicity of electric charge was implied by Faraday's laws of electrolysis, and confirmed in 1897 by Thomson's discovery of the electron, i.e., by his measurement of the charge-to-mass ratio of cathode-ray particles. Electrons from all atoms have the same mass and the same charge. The discovery of x-rays led to that of natural radioactivity; alpha particles emitted by radioactive substances were identified by Rutherford as very high-speed helium ions. Rutherford also found that the scattering of alpha particles by metal foils could be understood only if all the positive atomic charge and nearly all the atomic mass is concentrated in a *nucleus*. An atom thus consists of a small but massive positive nucleus and a number of (negative) electrons. Atoms emit light of only a few distinct wavelengths (the so-called line spectra) in a pattern characteristic of the particular element, instead of the continuous spread of colors that would be expected from a rotating electron on the basis of electromagnetic theory. Meanwhile Planck introduced the quantum hypothesis, according to which light energy is emitted only in discrete amounts proportional to the frequency. Physical confirmation of the quantum hypothesis is most readily visualized in Einstein's explanation of the photoelectric effect. These are the chief factors that set the stage for the first fruitful model of an individual atom.

REFERENCES

HUMPHREYS, R. F., and R. BERINGER, *First Principles of Atomic Physics*, Chapters 17, 21, 22.

MAGIE, W. F., *A Source Book in Physics*, pp. 561–563 (Hittorf), 564–576 (Crookes), 583–597 (Thomson) 600–610 (Roentgen), 610–613 (Becquerel), 613–616 (P. and M. S. Curie), 354–365 (Kirchhoff), 360–365 (Balmer), and 518–519 (Hallwachs on photoelectric effect).

MILLIKAN, R. A., *Electrons, Protons, Photons, Neutrons, Mesotrons, and Cosmic Rays.* Begins with history of early ideas of electricity and goes on to evidence for atomicity of charge.

NEEDHAM, J., and W. PAGEL, (Editors), *The Background to Modern Science.* Includes the essay on "The Development of the Theory of Atomic Structure" by Lord Rutherford in which he recounts how the nucleus was discovered.

OLDENBURG, O., *Introduction to Atomic Physics.*

SEMAT, H., *Introduction to Atomic and Nuclear Physics.*

SEMAT, H., *Physics in the Modern World.* Parts of Chapters XI and XII.

TAYLOR, L. W., *Physics, the Pioneer Science,* Chapters 51, 52, and the first part of Chapter 53.

THOMSON, G. P., "J. J. Thomson and the Discovery of the Electron," *Physics Today,* 9, No. 8, August, 1956.

1. Compute Avogadro's number from the value of the faraday and the magnitude of the elementary charge.

2. A steady current of 1 amp flows through slightly acidified water for 16 min, 5 sec, liberating hydrogen and oxygen, as in Fig. 18–1. (a) How many coulombs of charge flow during this time? (b) How many grams of hydrogen are liberated? How many of oxygen? (c) How many molecules of hydrogen are liberated? Of oxygen? [Ans.: (a) 965; (b) 0.01 gm of H_2, 0.08 gm of O_2; (c) 3.01×10^{21} molecules of H_2, 1.51×10^{21} molecules of O_2]

3. How long must a current of 0.1 amp flow in the apparatus shown in Fig. 18–2 to deposit 1.08 gm of silver? [Ans.: 9650 sec, or 2 hr, 40 min, 50 sec]

4. In early attempts to determine the size of an elementary charge, water droplets were used instead of oil. Can you think of any reasons why the results should have been inaccurate?

5. X-rays are produced when high-speed cathode rays are stopped, but not while they are traversing the evacuated tube. Why is the stopping important?

6. The charge-to-mass ratio for alpha particles is found to be very nearly $\frac{1}{2}$ that for hydrogen ions, whereas the mass of an alpha particle is very nearly 4 times that of hydrogen. Assuming that the charge on the hydrogen ion is e, find the charge on an alpha particle.

7. Why should alpha particles be deflected less than beta particles by the same magnetic field? Consider the effects of both charge and mass.

8. What fundamental conservation law is responsible for Rutherford's surprise at the backward scattering of alpha particles from thin foils? Explain.

9. For an approximate calculation, assume that the density of gold is 20 gm/cm^3, and that its atomic weight is 200. This means that there would be about 6×10^{23} atoms in 10 cm^3 of gold (explain). Find how much volume is available to each atom of gold, and the length of the edge of a cube corresponding to this volume. [Ans.: $10^{-22}/6$ cm^3 per atom; edge of a cube is roughly 2.5×10^{-8} cm]

10. Wavelengths are not completely missing in dark line spectra but only very much weakened; the light absorbed by sodium vapor, in the example of Kirchhoff's experiment, is re-emitted in all directions, not just that of the original beam. Most stellar spectra, like that of the sun, are dark line spectra; what information does this fact alone convey about the stars? Can you infer anything at all about the interior structure of the stars from the nature of their spectra? What sort of spectrum would be observed in sunlight if the disk were obscured by an eclipse?

11. In Eq. (18–8) R is approximately 1.1×10^5 if λ is measured in cm. What is λ for the longest wavelength line described by the formula? [Ans.: 6.5×10^{-5} cm]

12. Ultraviolet light produces photo-electrons if it falls on a zinc plate. Would you expect x-rays to produce photoelectrons also?   Explain your answer.

13. In a particular experiment, radiation used to produce photoelectrons has a frequency such that $h\nu = \frac{3}{2}W$. Suppose that a frequency is substituted such that $h\nu = 2W$. By what factor is the kinetic energy of the electrons increased? [*Ans.*: By a factor of 2]

CHAPTER 19

ATOMIC STRUCTURE AND THE PERIODIC TABLE

We have seen why it became necessary to introduce what is called the quantum hypothesis, i.e., that electromagnetic radiation is emitted and absorbed by matter in discrete quantities of energy $h\nu$, where ν is the frequency of the radiation and h is a universal constant. This hypothesis was first applied to the problem of atomic structure by the great Danish physicist Niels Bohr in 1913, while he was working in Rutherford's laboratory at Manchester. Bohr's model of the atom has required extensive modification since 1913, yet its importance can hardly be over-estimated. Einstein has commented: "That this [quantum hypothesis] was sufficient to enable a man of Bohr's unique instinct and tact to discover the major laws of the spectral lines and of the electron shells of the atoms together with their significance for chemistry appeared to me like a miracle—and appears to me as a miracle even today [1947]. This is the highest form of musicality in the sphere of thought."

19–1 The Bohr model of the hydrogen atom

Bohr at first confined his attention to the element hydrogen, whose atoms are presumably the simplest of all. Assume that the hydrogen atom consists of a single negatively charged electron revolving rapidly about a particle containing equal positive charge but much greater mass. This particle, the hydrogen *nucleus*, is called a *proton.* As we have said, Rutherford had proposed such a "solar system" model of the atom, but accepted radiation theory predicted that the electron would radiate continuously and spiral in toward the nucleus, a prediction contrary to observation. Bohr departed from classical radiation theory by assuming that certain orbits are "allowed" in which an electron can move without losing energy by radiation. According to this proposal, an electron, within any allowed orbit, possesses a definite quantity of energy which is constant so long as it remains in that orbit. Loss of energy by radiation may then take place only if the electron makes a transition from one such orbit to another of lower energy.

Bohr's hypothesis is remarkable in the light of classical electromagnetic theory, but it followed logically from the quantum hypothesis. Electromagnetic radiation originates in matter and is absorbed by matter; its occurrence in photons, definite quantities of energy, must reflect a property by which atoms themselves can emit and absorb discrete amounts of energy. In other words, the most compelling reason for radiation to be "quantized" would be for matter itself to be constructed in a manner which requires it. This far one can reason qualitatively, but a fruitful theory must not only be logical, it must be capable of serving as a basis for quantitative predictions. Thus Bohr was faced with the immediate question: *which* of the infinite number of possible orbits are allowed, i.e., which are orbits in which the electron can move without radiating? Bohr's initial answer to this question was in part fortuitous; while it led to correct values of energies and to an expression in agreement with the Balmer formula, it was ultimately shown to be not entirely correct. We shall not go into the refinements of the theory, but in its application to circular orbits the argument is sufficiently simple that it can be followed with no more mathematics than a little elementary algebra. The results are so important that this elementary treatment is justified; later we shall note some of the corrections that were needed.

Just as in the case of planets moving about the sun, angular momentum is an important property of the atomic rotating system. As we have shown in Chapter 10, the magnitude of angular momentum is strictly conserved in the absence of external influences. By combining the quantum hypothesis with the mathematics of classical mechanics, Bohr was led to suppose that the allowed electron orbits he sought are just those for which the angular momentum, multiplied by 2π, is equal to a whole number times Planck's constant h. The angular momentum, mvr for a circular orbit of radius r, is dimensionally equal to energy times time, and thus dimensionally the same as h. Bohr's equation for an allowed orbit is

$$mvr = \frac{nh}{2\pi}, \qquad (19\text{–}1)$$

where n is any integer, 1, 2, 3, . . . Let us see what energies are associated with electrons whose angular momenta are fixed in this way. The difference between the energies of two allowed orbits should correspond to the energy of a quantum of radiation emitted in an electronic transition, if Bohr's hypothesis is correct.

In order to make this energy calculation, Bohr applied the laws of mechanics and electrostatics. The centripetal force that keeps the electron in its orbit is taken to be simply electrostatic attraction, expressible by Coulomb's law. Call the nuclear charge an integer Z times e, the electronic charge (Fig. 19–1). (Z is unity for hydrogen, but we shall retain Z for possible use of the model for atoms of higher nuclear charge.) Then, equating the expression for centripetal force and electrostatic force, we obtain

$$\frac{mv^2}{r} = K\frac{Ze^2}{r^2}, \qquad (19\text{-}2)$$

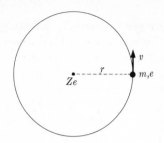

where K is a constant whose value depends upon units of measurement (see Eq. 14–1). If e is measured in coulombs and the other quantities in the centimeter-gram-second system, $K = 9 \times 10^{18}$, as we have seen in Section 14–2. The energy of a rotating electron is made up of two parts, kinetic and potential. It will be shown at the end of this section that

Fig. 19–1. For identifying symbols used in describing an electron orbit about a nucleus Ze.

the electrostatic potential energy of a charge $-e$ due to its location at a distance r from a charge $+Ze$ is $-KZe^2/r$. Granting the validity of this expression in advance, we have for the total energy of an electron moving in a circular orbit of radius r with speed v,

$$E = \text{Energy} = \tfrac{1}{2}mv^2 - \frac{KZe^2}{r}. \qquad (19\text{-}3)$$

Here K, e, and m are known experimental constants. Expressions for v and r can be obtained in terms of these known constants by combining Eqs. (19–1) and (19–2), and these may be substituted in Eq. (19–3).

The algebraic steps in this process are straightforward. If Eq. (19–2) is multiplied by r^2 and divided by Eq. (19–1),

$$\frac{mv^2r}{mvr} = v = \frac{2\pi KZe^2}{nh}. \qquad (19\text{-}4)$$

Equation (19–1) may be solved for r, and Eq. (19–4) used for v:

$$r = \frac{nh}{2\pi mv} = n^2\left(\frac{h}{2\pi}\right)^2\frac{1}{KmZe^2}. \qquad (19\text{-}5)$$

The final computation of the energy is facilitated by noting that Eq. (19–2) may be written as

$$mv^2 = \frac{KZe^2}{r},$$

showing that the kinetic energy, $\tfrac{1}{2}mv^2$, is equal in magnitude to one-half the potential energy $(-KZe^2/r)$, although the two are opposite in sign. Therefore, the total energy E is given by

$$E = \frac{1}{2}\frac{KZe^2}{r} - \frac{KZe^2}{r} = -\frac{KZe^2}{2r}.$$

Substituting the expression for r obtained in Eq. (19–5), we now find, for energy,

$$E = -\frac{2\pi^2 mK^2 Z^2 e^4}{n^2 h^2}. \tag{19-6}$$

The different allowed orbits are those for which n, any whole number, takes different values. The meaning of the minus sign is that an electron in an atom has less energy than it would if it were free and at rest—work would have to be done on it to *remove* it from the atom. This is analogous to the negative gravitational energy a boulder in the cellar would have if we measure potential energy from ground level.

By Bohr's hypothesis a quantum of radiation is emitted in the transition of an electron from one orbit to another. The frequencies characteristic of such radiation should be in accord with

$$h\nu = E_2 - E_1, \tag{19-7}$$

where E_1 is the energy of the final orbit and E_2 that of the initial orbit. If n_1 is the integer associated with E_1 and n_2 that associated with E_2, the frequency of the electromagnetic radiation that should be emitted or absorbed upon transition of the electron from an allowed orbit in which its energy is E_1 to another in which its energy is E_2 may be found by combining Eqs. (19–7) and (19–6):

$$\nu = \frac{E_2 - E_1}{h} = \frac{2\pi^2 mK^2 Z^2 e^4}{h^3}\left(\frac{1}{n_1^2} - \frac{1}{n_2^2}\right).$$

Since for electromagnetic radiation frequency and wavelength (λ) are related by the equation

$$\nu\lambda = c,$$

where c is the velocity of light, the above can be rewritten in the form

$$\frac{1}{\lambda} = \frac{\nu}{c} = \frac{2\pi^2 mK^2 Z^2 e^4}{ch^3}\left(\frac{1}{n_1^2} - \frac{1}{n_2^2}\right) = RZ^2\left(\frac{1}{n_1^2} - \frac{1}{n_2^2}\right). \tag{19-8}$$

Here the constant $R = 2\pi^2 mK^2 e^4/ch^3$ depends only on "universal" constants, e.g., the electronic charge and mass, Planck's constant, the velocity of light.

Let us now compare the derived Eq. (19–8) with the equation Balmer found empirically to represent the wavelengths of lines in the visible spectrum of hydrogen:

$$\frac{1}{\lambda} = R\left(\frac{1}{4} - \frac{1}{n^2}\right), \qquad n \geq 3. \tag{18-8}$$

Recalling that for the hydrogen atom $Z = 1$, it is clear that Eqs. (19-8) and (18-8) are identical if we put $n_1 = 2$. Furthermore, it is found that the "theoretical" value of the constant R, computed from the known values of m, e, c, h, etc., is in excellent agreement with the empirical constant derived from measurements of wavelengths of hydrogen spectral lines; R in Eq. (19-8) has the same value as in Eqs. (18-8) and (18-9). As interpreted on the Bohr model, the Balmer series consists of light emitted in transitions from various allowed orbits to that one for which $n = 2$. The ultraviolet series described by Eq. (18-9) corresponds to electronic transitions from various outer orbits to the orbit for which $n = 1$. Other series (in the infrared) have been observed for which the final orbits are $n = 3, 4$, etc.

Figure 19-2 represents Bohr's allowed orbits and the transitions corresponding to three series of lines in the hydrogen spectrum. This is a space

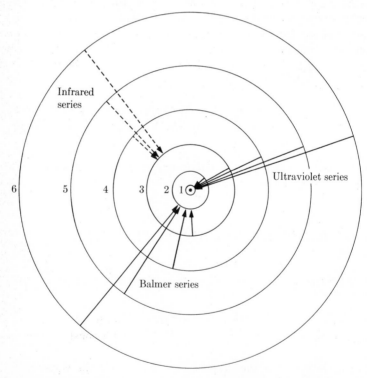

Fig. 19-2. Allowed Bohr orbits for $n = 1$ to 6. The arrows represent electron transitions corresponding to the Balmer series and those described by Eq. (19-8); with $n_1 = 1$, $n_1 = 3$.

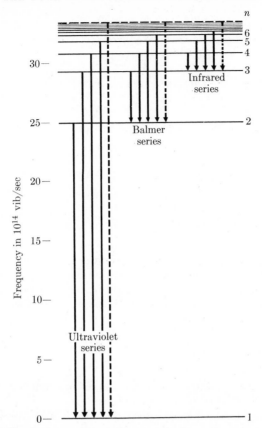

FIG. 19-3. Energy levels corresponding to orbits of Fig. 19-2. The difference between two levels on the vertical scale gives the frequency associated with a transition.

diagram of the orbits, whose radii are proportional to n^2, in accord with Eq. (19-5). As n increases, the electron gets farther and farther from the nucleus about which it revolves, and its energy approaches the energy of a free unattached electron at rest, i.e., no energy at all. Figure 19-3 is an energy diagram, showing the energy changes corresponding to the transitions of Fig. 19-2. Each energy level corresponds to a particular orbit of Fig. 19-2, and is designated by the appropriate value of n. The vertical scale is given in frequency units, however, so that the frequency of any line is the difference in scale between the final and intial levels.

Before proceeding to consider further successes of the Bohr model, let us justify the expression used above for potential energy of an electron of charge $-e$ at a distance r from a charge $+Ze$. This is an application of a general formula for the potential energy of a point charge q at distance r from another point charge Q. We begin by considering the difference in potential energy of a charge q in positions r_1 and r_2 from Q, as shown in Fig. 19–4, assuming that these two positions are very close together. This difference in potential energy should be equal to the work done in moving q from r_2 to r_1. If the force were constant, we could simply multiply it by the distance $r_2 - r_1$ to obtain this work; the difficulty arises from the fact that the force depends on the distance, being KQq/r_1^2 at r_1 and KQq/r_2^2 at

FIG. 19–4. The difference in potential energy of a charge q between r_2 and r_1 is the work done in moving it from r_2 to r_1.

r_2. The problem of using exactly the right force for each infinitesimal change in distance can be solved rigorously by use of Newton's calculus, but we can actually get the right answer by using an appropriate average of the forces at the beginning and end of our interval. What is called the geometrical average of r_1^2 and r_2^2 is the product r_1r_2; the average force over the interval is thus KQq/r_1r_2. With this average, the work done in moving q from r_2 to r_1 is

$$\text{Work} = (r_2 - r_1)\, K\, \frac{Qq}{r_1 r_2} = K\, \frac{Qq}{r_1} - K\, \frac{Qq}{r_2}. \tag{19–9}$$

If this expression is valid, the work done in bringing q from a very large distance r_2 (where we can say that its potential energy is zero) to r_1 is just KQq/r_1, since for very large r_2 the second term on the right of Eq. (19–9) vanishes. This should be true for any value of r, and we can generalize by saying that the potential energy of a charge q due to the presence of Q at a distance r is given by

$$\text{Potential energy} = K\, \frac{Qq}{r}. \tag{19–10}$$

By our definition, the potential energy is equal to the work done in bringing charge q from such a large distance that the electrostatic force is negligible. This potential energy is positive if the charges repel each other, so that work is done against the electrostatic force, negative if the charges attract. Equation (19–10) also follows from a rigorous mathematical derivation which does not depend on the use of a geometric average.

19–2 The general structure of atoms

Let us summarize Bohr's model of the hydrogen atom before we consider its extension and further consequences. Bohr assumed, in accord with Rutherford's discovery, that all the positive charge and almost all the mass of an atom are concentrated in a nucleus. An electron can revolve about the nucleus only in certain "allowed" orbits. The energy of the electron depends on which of these orbits is occupied; energy in the form of electromagnetic radiation is emitted or absorbed only on transition of the electron from one allowed orbit to another. Bohr postulated certain stable orbital possibilities by *quantizing* the angular momentum, i.e., by assuming that the electron's angular momentum is restricted to some integral multiple of Planck's constant h divided by 2π. On this basis he computed the orbital energies and arrived at an expression in agreement with the Balmer formula, the latter having been previously established as a purely empirical description of the observed frequencies of lines in the optical spectrum of hydrogen. Frequencies of hydrogen lines in the ultraviolet and infrared were also correctly predicted by Bohr.

The interpretation of the hydrogen spectrum was only the first triumph of Bohr's theory. When he began to work out his model, it was merely a guess that the positive charge on the nucleus is equal to the atomic number times the electronic charge, hence that the number of electrons in a neutral atom is the same as its atomic number. Within a year, however, this guess had been confirmed in a way that gave further evidence in favor of the theory.

This last accomplishment was due to the brilliant young physicist H. G. J. Moseley (1887–1915), who was killed in World War I. By 1913 the wavelengths of x-rays could be measured by means of spectrometers which employ crystals as gratings. It was found that the radiation produced when fast electrons strike various targets includes spectral lines characteristic of the target material. These lines form a pattern that is much simpler than the optical spectra of most elements, and one which is similar for all metals. The frequencies of these x-ray lines were found to increase with increasing atomic number of the target element, as indicated by Fig. 19–5. Moseley examined the x-ray spectra for all the solid elements ranging from

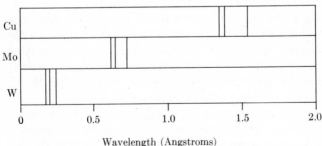

Wavelength (Angstroms)

FIG. 19–5. Diagram of three strong x-ray lines in copper ($Z = 29$), molybdenum ($Z = 42$), and tungsten ($Z = 74$), showing systematic variation of wavelength with atomic number.

aluminum to gold, and discovered that the square root of the frequency of the strongest line in the group of lines of shortest wavelength increases by the same amount from one element to the next in the periodic table. He was able to write an approximate formula for this frequency in terms of the atomic number, which we shall call Z:

$$\nu = b(Z - 1)^2. \tag{19–11}$$

Here b is a constant, the same for all elements. Moseley was quick to see that this formula is consistent with Eq. (19–8), Bohr's formula for emitted radiation frequencies, if atomic number is identified with nuclear charge: there ν is proportional to Z^2, and the difference between Z and $Z - 1$, even for electrons very near the nucleus, can be ascribed to the presence of other electrons. In detail, all the x-ray lines observed could be interpreted as transitions between allowed Bohr orbits very near the nuclei of atoms at least as heavy as those of aluminum. It was in this way that the nuclear charge and the number of electrons in a neutral atom were identified with atomic number, i.e., the position of an element in the periodic table.

The optical spectra of atoms other than hydrogen are, in general, more complicated than x-ray spectra. The helium spectrum was found to be quite different from that of hydrogen, but when helium is excited in a high-voltage discharge tube a series of lines appears which is accurately described by Eq. (19–8) with $Z = 2$. This spectrum is correctly ascribed to helium atoms which have been stripped of one electron so that they are like hydrogen atoms in then possessing only one electron. Painstaking analysis of atomic optical spectra reveals evidence of periodicity, as in chemical properties of the elements but unlike x-ray lines. The main features of the flame spectra of the alkali metals could be described by Bohr's theory, but only qualitatively. The constant RZ^2 in Eq. (19–8) was too large to describe the observations, as if the electron, in jumping from one orbit to another, was not subject to the full force of the nuclear charge; the number n appearing in the denominator did not give the correct energies if restricted to integral values. Another serious difficulty was that double, triple, and even more complex lines were often observed instead of the lines of a single frequency predicted by the Bohr theory. Elliptical orbits, like those of the solar system, were introduced to explain this "fine structure" of atomic spectra, but with only partial success.

A general systematic guide to atomic structure began to arise on the foundation of Bohr's theory, despite its limitations. In addition to identifying atomic number with nuclear charge, and thus with the total number of atomic electrons, Moseley's observations lent support to a new idea, that electrons in the heavier atoms are grouped into "rings," or "shells." If there are such shells, each capable of containing only a limited number of electrons, it would be reasonable to suppose that those nearest the nucleus are ordinarily "full" of electrons. If a bombarding electron in a cathode-ray tube were to arrive with sufficient energy, however, it might knock an electron out of one of these inner shells. Another electron may make a transition to fill this hole; the energy corresponding to such a transition would appear as a quantum of x-radiation. That the energy differences, and hence the frequencies of emitted radiation, are large for large Z and small n is clear from Eq. (19–8); that is, transitions between orbits near the nucleus for an atom of high atomic number produce high-frequency x-rays, not visible or even ultraviolet light. The visible spectrum, much more easily excited than x-rays and consisting of photons of lower frequency, must originate in transitions of outer electrons for which n is necessarily greater and the force of the positive nuclear charge Ze is weakened by the intervening negative electrons.

The cardinal feature of the Bohr theory, that there are distinct atomic energy levels and that radiation corresponds to transitions of electrons between these levels, was in indisputable agreement with experiment. It was the detailed application of the theory to observed data that provided difficulties. For several years the model was "tortured" to bring it into conformity with experimental facts, much as the Greek circles and spheres had been compounded to describe early astronomical observations. The analogy must not be pressed too far, but Bohr, in his initial theory, may be compared with Copernicus: the theory was fundamentally correct in principle but wrong in detail. In 1925, however, a simpler, more ordered description of the atom began to emerge. It was based on two main principles, which we may call (1) more complete and more accurate *quantization*, and (2) *exclusion*. Let us examine these principles one at a time.

19–3 Electronic quantum numbers

We will recall that Bohr began by quantizing electronic angular momentum, i.e., he assumed that the angular momentum of an electron in an allowed orbit must be some whole-number multiple of $(h/2\pi)$. Atomic angular momentum manifests itself rather directly in spectra by what is called the *Zeeman effect*. P. Zeeman (1865–1943) discovered in 1896 that spectral lines are split, that is, a single line is replaced by two or more, if the radiating atoms are located between the poles of a magnet. Qualitatively, this is easy to understand on the basis of electronic orbits: every circulating electron is equivalent to a little loop of current, and therefore to a tiny magnet. Different orientations of such a loop involve different amounts of energy, as you know if you have ever tried to hold a small magnet or even a nail the "wrong way" in a strong magnetic field. Therefore, transitions from orbits of different orientation in a magnetic field give rise to radiations of slightly different frequencies, corresponding to these differences in energy. Angular momentum is a measure of circulation in an orbit, and is thus proportional to the strength of the microscopic magnet. One should, then, get a quantitative measure of the angular momentum from a study of the Zeeman effect.

For a few spectral lines the Zeeman effect could be readily understood in terms of charge moving in a circular orbit, but most Zeeman patterns did not lend themselves to such simple explanation. For this reason, and in an attempt to account for the multiplicity of lines in the spectra of many-electron atoms, Arnold Sommerfeld (1868–1951) introduced elliptical orbits to the Bohr theory in 1915. An ellipse of the same average radius as that of a circular orbit yields very nearly the same total energy, but will have smaller angular momentum. This is clear from the correlation between angular momentum and area-per-unit-time swept over by the radius (Section 10–2). The introduction of elliptical orbits solved some of the problems of the Bohr theory, but by no means all. It did make clear, however, that more than one "quantum number" is needed to describe an orbit. The integer n, which gave a good value for the energy in Eq. (19–6), cannot specify the angular momentum of an electron in an elliptical orbit, even though it had been originally introduced to do just that for circular orbits!

In 1925 it became clear to George Uhlenbeck and Samuel Goudsmit that the Zeeman and related effects could not be systematically accounted for without assuming that an electron has *intrinsic* angular momentum. This is angular momentum quite independent of the orbit in which an electron may be, and is graphically called *spin*. Electron spin is analogous to the angular momentum of the earth due to rotation about its own axis, which it has in addition to that due to revolution about the sun.

With the discovery of spin the number of quantum numbers required for specification of the properties of an electron in an orbit came to *four*, when the various possibilities of orienting angular momentum in a magnetic field are included. Let us consider these numbers individually, to see what is specified by each.

The total or *principal* quantum number, n, gives the energies of the hydrogen atomic orbits, as in Bohr's elementary theory. For a particular n the energy of a Bohr hydrogenlike orbit is the same whether that orbit is circular or elliptical. For multi-electron atoms there may be considerable difference between the energies of circular and elliptical orbits with the same value of n. For circular orbits, inner electrons shield the nucleus and reduce the effective attractive force it may exert on outer electrons. Elliptical orbits penetrate near the nucleus, however, and the electron is strongly attracted over some part of its path. The principal quantum number may assume any positive integral value, i.e., $n = 1, 2, 3, \ldots$

Each value of n corresponds to a particular value of the average orbital distance from the nucleus, and determines what is called a "shell" of orbits about the nucleus. The concept of electron shells originated in the interpretation of x-ray spectra, and the x-ray vocabulary is still used to denote them: the shells designated K, L, M, . . . correspond to $n = 1, 2, 3, . . .$ Thus the K shell is that nearest the nucleus, L the next, and so on.

The *orbital* quantum number, l, specifies the number of units $(h/2\pi)$ of orbital angular momentum associated with an electron in a given orbit. For any orbit, l is only indirectly related to n: given a value of n, the number l may be zero or any positive integer equal to or less than $(n - 1)$. For example, an orbit for which $n = 2$ (L shell) may have associated with it total angular momentum of one unit or zero ($l = 0$, or $l = 1$). If $n = 1$, l is necessarily zero, and thus there is no orbital angular momentum. The possibility of zero angular momentum was at first hard to accept, for the only orbit in which the radius sweeps over no area at all is a straight line, with the electron going back and forth right through the nucleus. Thus the established existence of orbits with zero angular momentum is one piece of evidence that electronic orbits must not be taken quite so literally as those of the planets about the sun. If there is orbital angular momentum, the direction characterized by the rotation is that at right angles to the plane of the orbit, and l can be represented by a vector perpendicular to this plane, as in Fig. 19–6.

The third quantum number, designated m, is called the magnetic quantum number. In an external magnetic field an orbit with l units of angular momentum may be oriented only in certain "allowed" ways: the vector at right angles to the orbit, representing l, may be directed parallel to the field, against it (antiparallel), or in any other way such that the number of units of angular momentum in the direction of the field is a whole

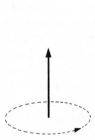

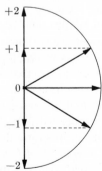

FIG. 19–6. Angular momentum may be represented by a vector at right angles to the orbit.

FIG. 19–7. Two units of angular momentum may be oriented with respect to the vertical axis so that $m = -2$, $-1, 0, +1, +2$.

number. One unit of angular momentum may be oriented so that $m = 1$, 0, or -1. When $l = 2$, m may be 2, 1, 0, -1, or -2, as in Fig. 19–7. When $l = 0$, m may have only the value 0. The restriction of m to whole numbers signifies that the amount of orbital angular momentum measured along any particular direction in space is restricted to integral multiples of $(h/2\pi)$.

Finally, s is the electronic spin quantum number. Electronic spin has but a single value, and is capable of orientation only in either of two ways, with or against an external magnetic field. For our purpose, we may call these two orientation possibilities simply plus and minus.

In terms of a planetary model, the quantum numbers seem highly artificial. The first three, however, arise naturally from a more advanced mathematical description of the atom which was developed about 1926. This newer theory, called the *wave mechanical* description of the atom, is virtually impossible to describe in physically visualizable terms. It indicates that each electron orbit is, on the average, "smeared out" into a sort of cloud, to which one of Bohr's mechanical orbits represents only a first crude approximation. Bohr's approximation remains a highly useful one for many purposes, and scientists continue to think and speak of electron orbits. Quantitative calculations of atomic properties are no longer made on the basis of the classical mechanical model, however, and we must remember that the Bohr orbits must not always be taken literally.

19–4 The exclusion principle

Almost concurrently with the recognition of an adequate set of integers for describing the orbits of electrons in atoms it became clear that successive shells of electrons could be understood if there were a property of "exclusion." The *exclusion principle* was originally formulated by Wolfgang Pauli in 1925, and is often called the *Pauli principle*. Scientists had worried about the stability of electron shells in atoms: granted the limitation of electrons to stable orbits, why don't all the electrons in an atom make transitions to the orbit of lowest energy? A natural tendency toward the condition of lowest energy is commonly observed in phenomena of all sorts, and for some time it was difficult to reconcile the new view of atomic structure with this known general tendency. Pauli's contribution to the problem was formulation of the rule that *no two electrons in an atom can have the same set of four quantum numbers*; electrons *do* tend to fill the orbits of lowest energy, subject to this new proviso.

Let us explore the consequences of Pauli's rule. If an atom has but one electron, this electron will normally be in the orbit of smallest n, that is, $n = 1$. Then l and hence m are both necessarily zero, although s may be either plus or minus. There are thus only two possible orbits, corresponding

TABLE 19–1

POSSIBLE QUANTUM NUMBERS WITH $n = 2$

n	2						
l	0		1				
m	0		-1		0		$+1$
s	$-$ | $+$		$-$ | $+$		$-$ | $+$		$-$ | $+$

to the two possible values of s, for an electron in the shell of lowest energy, for which $n = 1$. According to the exclusion principle, both of these orbits would be filled in an atom containing two electrons. A third electron would find no room in the K ($n = 1$) shell, since no unique set of four quantum numbers would be available there, and its lowest possible energy would be attained in an orbit for which $n = 2$. There are more possibilities consistent with $n = 2$, as shown in Table 19–1. As indicated, the L ($n = 2$) shell may consist of two electrons with $l = 0$ and six electrons with $l = 1$, that is, two *subshells* with a total population of eight.

The number of electrons actually present in a neutral atom is equal to its atomic number, and electrons tend to fill the available shells of lowest energy, or smallest n. A lithium atom, for example, with three electrons, would normally have a filled K ($n = 1$) shell and one electron in the L ($n = 2$) shell. Within any shell, the subshell having the smallest angular momentum (lowest value of l) is most stable, that is, the orbits of lowest energy are the most elliptical, in the language of Bohr theory. The third lithium atom electron would therefore normally have $n = 2$, $l = 0$. Carbon, with six electrons, would have four electrons in the L ($n = 2$) shell, while neon, with ten electrons, has both K and L shells completely filled. An eleventh electron, as in the neutral sodium atom, would find the orbit of lowest available energy in the M ($n = 3$) shell (Fig. 19–8).

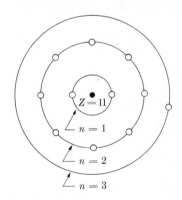

FIG. 19–8. Representation of electrons in a sodium atom. (Purely schematic and not to scale.)

TABLE 19-2

ELECTRON SHELLS IN ATOMS

n	l	H(1)	He(2)	Li(3)	Be(4)	B(5)	C(6)	N(7)	O(8)	F(9)	Ne(10)	Na(11)	Mg(12)	Al(13)	Si(14)	P(15)	S(16)	Cl(17)	A(18)
1	0	1	2	2	2	2	2	2	2	2	2	2	2	2	2	2	2	2	2
2	0			1	2	2	2	2	2	2	2	2	2	2	2	2	2	2	2
2	1					1	2	3	4	5	6	6	6	6	6	6	6	6	6
3	0											1	2	2	2	2	2	2	2
3	1													1	2	3	4	5	6

n	l	K(19)	Ca(20)	Sc(21)	Ti(22)	V(23)	Cr(24)	Mn(25)	Fe(26)	Co(27)	Ni(28)	Cu(29)	Zn(30)	Ga(31)	Ge(32)	As(33)	Se(34)	Br(35)	Kr(36)
1	0	2	2	2	2	2	2	2	2	2	2	2	2	2	2	2	2	2	2
2	0	2	2	2	2	2	2	2	2	2	2	2	2	2	2	2	2	2	2
2	1	6	6	6	6	6	6	6	6	6	6	6	6	6	6	6	6	6	6
3	0	2	2	2	2	2	2	2	2	2	2	2	2	2	2	2	2	2	2
3	1	6	6	6	6	6	6	6	6	6	6	6	6	6	6	6	6	6	6
3	2			1	2	3	5	5	6	7	8	10	10	10	10	10	10	10	10
4	0	1	2	2	2	2	1	2	2	2	2	1	2	2	2	2	2	2	2
4	1													1	2	3	4	5	6

For the M shell the possibilities for l are 0, 1, and 2; if a table similar to Table 19-1 is made for the subshell $l = 2$, it will be seen that ten electrons can be accommodated, making a total of eighteen distinguishable sets of the four quantum numbers for the $(n = 3)$ shell. For still higher n larger values of l are permitted, and the subshell for which $l = 3$ has room for fourteen electrons. The general formula for the number of electrons that can be accommodated in the subshell corresponding to a given value of l is $2(2l + 1)$. Note that the values of l repeat in successive shells, except that with each consecutively higher value of n an additional possible value for l is added.

19-5 Electron shells and the periodic table

In terms of possible electron arrangements or "configurations," the periodic table is more than an empirical arrangement based on chemical properties. Table 19-2 shows the electron shells for neutral atoms arranged in order of increasing atomic number. Let us begin by considering the lighter elements. We note that sodium, like lithium, has one electron outside a closed shell. Magnesium, like beryllium, has two electrons in an uncompleted shell, boron and aluminum three, carbon and silicon four, and so on. Group character of the elements thus appears to be related to the numbers of electrons *outside* closed shells. It should therefore be possible to relate chemical properties of the atoms to the configurations of electrons in incomplete outer shells. Apparently only the outermost electrons in atoms participate in chemical processes, at least to a very close approximation.

The concept of valence (see Chapter 9) is very simply related to the number of electrons outside closed shells in some groups of elements (see Table 19-3). All the alkali metal atoms (Li, Na, K, etc.) have single electrons in their outermost orbits, and we have seen that the chemical valence of these elements is 1. The alkaline earth atoms (Be, Mg, Ca, etc.) have two outer electrons, corresponding to their valence of 2. All the inert gas atoms except helium have in common an outer shell configuration of 8 electrons filling the subshells for which $l = 0$ and $l = 1$, regardless of the value of n. The inert gases never combine chemically with other atoms, a fact which suggests that the configuration of eight electrons of low angular momentum must bear remarkable stability. Atoms of other elements behave as though they seek to achieve this configuration: the halogens (F, Cl, Br, I) *lack* one electron of the eight needed to complete the first two subshells of their outer shells, and we have seen that their valence, or combining power, is unity. Moreover, they combine readily with the alkali metals in one-to-one atomic ratio; in such a combination the single outer-shell electron of the alkali metal atom could conceivably be taken up by the

TABLE 19-3

ELECTRON SHELLS IN ATOMS OF THREE MAIN GROUPS OF THE PERIODIC TABLE

GROUP 1a

n	Li	Na	K	Rb	Cs	Fr
1(K)	2	2	2	2	2	2
2(L)	1	8	8	8	8	8
3(M)		1	8	18	18	18
4(N)			1	8	18	32
5(O)				1	8	18
6(P)					1	8
7(Q)						1

GROUP 2a

Be	Mg	Ca	Sr	Ba	Ra
2	2	2	2	2	2
2	8	8	8	8	8
	2	8	18	18	18
		2	8	18	32
			2	8	18
				2	8
					2

GROUP 7a

F	Cl	Br	I	At
2	2	2	2	2
7	8	8	8	8
	7	18	18	18
		7	18	32
			7	18
				7

halogen atom, leaving both with electron configurations resembling that of an inert gas atom. Similarly, oxygen lacks two electrons of a complete group of eight; this must be related to its valence of two and the other properties of Group VI elements. We shall learn in Chapter 20 that the electron *octet* characteristic of a neutral inert gas atom plays a very important role in chemical combinations, and we shall also consider the relation between valence and electron configuration for other families of atoms. On the basis of the small number of examples cited here, we may indicate in advance that chemical combinations generally involve a give and take of outer electrons between combining atoms.

The electronic interpretation of the periodic table reflects in an interesting way the complications of the Bohr theory that are encountered for atoms of higher atomic number. We have noted that the configuration of eight electrons filling the subshells for which $l = 0$ and 1 seems to have special significance, regardless of the value of the total quantum number n. In general, the orbits of low angular momentum tend, for a particular total quantum number n, to be filled before those of high angular momentum in the previous shell $(n - 1)$. Since the orbits of lowest available energy should be preferred, this must mean that the total quantum number does not fully determine the energy of an orbit. It is the presence of closed inner shells and subshells of electrons, forming a "core" that remains virtually intact during chemical changes, which makes the orbits of heavier atoms different from those of the hydrogen atom. The atomic core, comprising closed electron shells, is effectively a sphere of negative charge, somewhat smaller in amount than the positive charge on the nucleus. This reduces the attractive force between the nucleus and an external electron to a considerable extent. For a circular orbit outside the core, the attracting charge is not Z times the electronic charge, but more nearly Z less the number of core electrons times the elementary charge. On the other hand, the external orbits of low angular momentum are highly elliptical, so that electrons in them penetrate the core and spend a part of their time near the nucleus, where they experience strong attractive force. Electrons in such orbits, for a given n, are more tightly bound to the atom than those in circular orbits of equal n.

On this basis, the electronic configurations of the transition elements become clear. In potassium and calcium the subshell for which $n = 4$ and $l = 0$ is filled before the $n = 3$, $l = 2$ subshell is started. This behavior is similarly repeated at the next alkali metal, rubidium, and again at cesium. In each case the orbit configuration of lowest possible energy is the normal state of the atom, and in each case the most recently completed subshells form a group of eight electrons corresponding to $l = 0$ and $l = 1$. As the atomic number increases further, the intervening subshells are gradually filled, during the long periods of the table. Among these long-period or transition elements themselves it is often difficult to predict the precise electronic configuration of a normal atom, for several orbits have almost the same energy. This situation is reflected in the chemical behavior of these elements; each of them may have several possible valences, which means that they may tend to interact with other atoms in ways involving various numbers of electrons. But in every case, as in the simpler examples, the external electrons (those outside closed shells that surround the nucleus) determine the chemical behavior of the element.

Bohr set out to account for atomic spectra (in particular the emission spectrum of hydrogen), not to explain the periodicity of the elements. X-ray lines, so readily interpretable in terms of Bohr's theory, were only in the process of being discovered in 1913. We have here a striking example of a theory whose success extended far beyond the limited problem it was originally designed to solve. It is true that modern quantum mechanical atomic theory has supplanted the rigid, mechanically conceived orbits of Bohr's original theory, but the fundamental idea of atomic energy levels and of radiation due to transitions between these levels remains intact. (We should note that Bohr's contributions to atomic theory did not cease with his historic 1913 paper: he has continued to participate in important ways to the development of modern theory.) The concept of orbits also remains useful as a qualitative approximation to more accurate mathematical treatments. On the basis of atomic theory, the chemical properties of the elements begin to fit together into an integrated whole, instead of appearing to be separate facts occasionally related to one another by regularities of an empirical nature. In the following chapter we shall see how the chemical combinations of atoms may be interpreted in terms of atomic structure.

19–6 Summary

To account for the lines of the hydrogen spectrum Bohr proposed a model in which a single electron may revolve about the nucleus in certain allowed orbits without radiating; energy is emitted or absorbed only if the electron makes a transition from one orbit to another. Neutral atoms possess a number of electrons equal to the atomic number; this identification of atomic number and nuclear charge was made by Moseley, in the analysis of characteristic x-ray spectra. The interpretation of x-ray spectra necessitated the concept of electron shells and subshells. This idea, together with the concepts needed to interpret complex atomic spectra, led to new assumptions of quantization, including the idea of electron spin, and to the exclusion principle. On the basis of these principles, the arrangement of elements in the periodic table becomes understandable: only those electrons outside closed shells participate in chemical reactions and may be called valence electrons. The periods of elements end with the filling of a shell (or subshell), and families or groups are those elements with the same numbers of electrons outside closed shells.

REFERENCES

GLOCKLER, G., and R. C. GLOCKLER, *Chemistry in Our Time.* Chapter X on atomic structure includes complete tables of electron shells.

HECHT, S., *Explaining the Atom.* Very readable, though occasionally over-simplified.

HUMPHREYS, R. F., and R. BERINGER, *First Principles of Atomic Physics.*

SEMAT, H., *Physics in the Modern World.* An excellent elementary presentation of atomic theory is to be found in Chapter XI.

TAYLOR, L. W., *Physics, the Pioneer Science*, Chapter 53.

WHITE, H. E., *Modern College Physics.*

1. Show that if $h\nu$ is measured in ergs, h is measured in erg·sec, or gm·cm^2/sec. Show that angular momentum can also be measured in gm·cm^2/sec.

2. What does the word *quantum* mean? It is said that charge itself is *quantized*—what is the meaning of this statement?

3. In your own words, show that the existence of discrete atomic energy levels follows logically from the quantum hypothesis for light and the fact that atoms radiate "line spectra."

4. In describing the Bohr model of the hydrogen atom we have tacitly assumed that the nucleus is stationary, while the electron moves around it. This is analogous to an assumption that the earth moves in a truly elliptical orbit about the sun, unaffected by the motion of the moon. Neither of these assumptions is completely justified. Why? How is it that we can obtain a very good approximation to the correct electron orbits while neglecting the nuclear motion? Suppose that the mass associated with the positive charge in a hydrogen atom were no larger than that of an electron. What sort of orbital motion could take place?

5. Which would you expect to have a smaller radius in its normal (lowest energy) state, a hydrogen atom or a helium atom? Why? The radius of the first ($n = 1$) Bohr orbit of hydrogen is 0.5×10^{-8} cm, just about half an angstrom unit. What is the radius of the first Bohr orbit of manganese, atomic number 25? [*Ans.*: 2×10^{-10} cm, or 0.02 angstrom unit]

6. How much more energy would be required to remove an electron from the first Bohr orbit of manganese than from the corresponding hydrogen orbit? From the first Bohr orbit of mercury? [*Ans.*: About 625 times as much for Mn; 6400 times as much for Hg]

7. It is found that ionized helium ($Z = 2$) emits a series of lines which almost exactly coincide with the lines of the Balmer series, although the helium spectrum has an additional line between every two successive Balmer lines. This helium series has been ascribed to transitions from outer orbits to the orbit for which $n_1 = 4$. Explain both the coincidence in frequency and the existence of the extra lines by means of Eq. (19–8).

8. Show that the number of electrons needed to complete a subshell for which $l = 3$ is fourteen. Can you prove that, in general, the maximum population for a subshell with quantum number l is given by $2(2l + 1)$?

9. How are characteristic (line spectra) x-rays produced, in terms of atomic structure? Is the collision between a high-energy cathode electron and an atom, which precedes the emission of an x-ray quantum, *elastic* or *inelastic*?

10. Make a table of electron shells, similar to those of Table 19–3, for inert gas atoms, Group 0 of the periodic table.

11. The line spectrum pattern of singly ionized beryllium (Be with *three* electrons, not four) would most resemble the spectrum of what neutral atom? Which spectrum would consist of the higher frequencies on comparison line by line?

CHAPTER 20

CHEMICAL BINDING AND THE ROLE OF ELECTRONS IN CHEMICAL CHANGE

In the preceding chapter we have finally achieved a solution to the problem we set for ourselves at the end of Chapter 9: we have succeeded in *explaining* the form of the periodic table of elements in terms of the structures of individual atoms. In so doing we have come a long way in knowledge and in sophistication concerning the fundamental nature of matter and energy. We must be aware, however, that we have merely reached the threshold of *possible* explanation of chemical processes; chemistry still lies before us. Insight into the arrangement of electrons in atoms is of the greatest importance in the science of chemistry because it enables us to give rational systematic interpretation to many phenomena which were previously known only empirically. This understanding, in turn, has led to many new discoveries. Still, a molecule is more than the simple sum of its atoms, and knowledge of atomic structure is only the starting point for understanding what happens when atoms combine. It had been apparent since Dalton's time that atoms must join together through the action of some kind of *chemical affinity*. The nature of that affinity, i.e., of the forces acting between atoms, began to become clear once there was some understanding of atomic structure.

20–1 Inert gases and the octet configuration

We have seen in Chapter 19 that atoms of all the elements in the family of inert gases, with the exception of helium, have eight electrons in their outermost shells. We have also seen that the chemical similarity of elements within a single group must be attributed to similarities in the electron configurations of their atoms. Hence, the conclusion is inescapable that the extraordinary property of inertness common to neon, argon, krypton, xenon, and radon is a property associated with the configuration of eight outermost electrons. We shall refer to this configuration as a *complete octet*. The inertness of helium, by the same token, must be associated with its completed K shell.

The nonreactivity of the Group 0 elements, it will be recalled, is virtually complete. Not only do their atoms fail to combine with those of other elements, they show no tendency to combine with one another to form diatomic molecules, as do the atoms of such gaseous elements as hydrogen, oxygen, nitrogen, and the halogens. If chemical change is interpreted in terms of rearrangements of external electrons, it is clear that electrons in inert gas atoms have no spontaneous tendency to rearrange themselves to form new configurations. To put it another way, we may say that these atoms are extraordinarily *stable*; in fact, the inert gas electron configuration is the most stable possible.

It has been pointed out several times previously that spontaneous processes in nature are generally those in which energy is given up. Thus a rock on top of a mountain is in a state of relatively high (potential) energy; if dislodged it will roll spontaneously (under gravitational influence) to the foot of the mountain, where its energy will be much lower and its *stability* (against further movement) correspondingly greater. Analogously, we may interpret the fact that inert gas atoms do not engage in spontaneous combination with other atoms to mean that they contain less energy by themselves than in any conceivable state of combination. We have not discussed all the factors which cause the octet configuration to be so very stable, but we must accept this stability as of basic importance to the interpretation of chemical change. Atoms of elements in the non-inert groups may combine, with loss of energy, in such a way that each atom involved achieves an octet structure. Often, this is the lowest possible energy state for the combination. Indeed, the tendency of atoms to assume inert gas structures accounts for the formation of more than 90 percent of the known chemical compounds. The importance of the octet configuration in chemical binding was first recognized by the American chemist G. N. Lewis (1875–1946) in 1916.

20–2 Metals and nonmetals. Electrovalence

Only the incomplete outermost shells or subshells of electrons contribute substantially to chemical binding. These electrons, responsible for the combining powers of atoms, are called *valence electrons*. From the periodic table and the table of electron configurations we have seen that the electronic feature common to all the alkali metals (Group 1a) is that of a single valence electron outside a completed octet. (Lithium is an exception, with a single valence electron outside the closed K shell.) We have also noted that the halogen elements (Group 7a) have atoms containing seven valence electrons, in each case one electron short of a completed octet. A Group 1a atom can thus achieve octet configuration by the outright loss of one electron, and a halogen atom can achieve it by attaching an extra electron. This process, which we have discussed briefly in the previous chapter, is exactly that which usually takes place when a metal combines with a non-

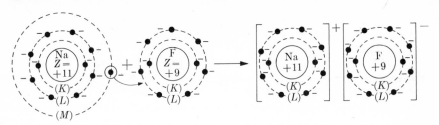

Fig. 20–1. Schematic representation of the reaction between an atom of sodium and an atom of fluorine, to form a positively charged sodium ion and a negatively charged fluoride ion ($Na + F \rightarrow Na^+ + F^-$). Electron shells are shown as static rings for convenience only; these drawings do not bear the least resemblance to actual atoms, either in physical appearance or in relative dimensions.

metal; the atoms of the metal *donate* electrons to those of the nonmetal. The reaction between an atom of sodium and one of fluorine is shown diagrammatically in Fig. 20–1. Upon losing an electron, the sodium atom is no longer complete, and cannot properly be called an atom; the new entity, bearing a single unit of positive charge, is called a sodium *ion* and is represented by the symbol Na^+. Similarly, the fluorine atom becomes a fluoride ion (F^-), with a single unit of negative charge. The electrostatic force of attraction between ions of unlike charge is the force that holds the constituents of the compound, sodium fluoride, together.

Most compounds formed between metallic and nonmetallic elements are called *electrovalent*, or *ionic*, compounds. The number of electrons lost by an atom of the metal, or gained by an atom of the nonmetal, in the formation of such a compound, is referred to as the *electrovalence* of the element in question. Thus the halogen elements all have electrovalence -1, the minus sign signifying the kind of charge on the ion formed; the alkali metals all have electrovalence $+1$. From Table 19–2 it is clear that the alkaline earth atoms (Group 2a) must lose two electrons to attain octet configuration, that the atoms in Group 3a must lose three, and that the atoms of nonmetals in the oxygen group must gain two. Figure 20–2 schematically represents reactions involving some of these elements. Examination of the formulas for common ionic compounds, for example, CaF_2, CaO, $BaCl_2$, BaS, AlF_3, Al_2O_3, shows that the electrovalence of each element corresponds exactly to the number of electrons its atoms must gain or lose to achieve octet structures. Calcium atoms, for example, have two electrons to donate; in combination with fluorine atoms, which can accept only one apiece, there must be two fluorine atoms available to accept the electrons from a single calcium atom. Upon combination of calcium with oxygen, on the other hand, both electrons from a single calcium atom can be accepted by a single oxygen atom.

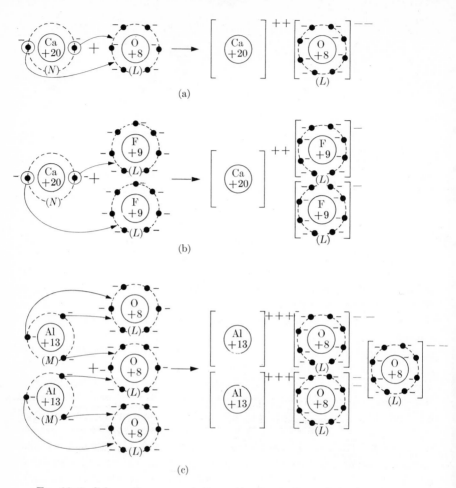

(a)

(b)

(c)

FIG. 20–2. Schematic representations of ionic reactions. Only valence electrons are shown.

Not all ionic compounds involve the attainment of octet configurations. The ions Li^+ and Be^{++} have only the completed K shell of two electrons, hence the stability of the helium configuration. The major exceptions are atoms of the transitional elements, constituting the long periods in which subshells of high angular momentum are being gradually filled. Most of these atoms would have to gain or lose large numbers of electrons to achieve octet configurations; the high ionic charges that would be formed are not energetically feasible, as we shall see below. Iron atoms, for example, would have to lose eight electrons to achieve the electron structure of argon, or gain ten to achieve that of krypton. Iron is a metallic element, and tends to donate electrons. Instead of losing eight, however, its atoms may in some circumstances lose two to form ferrous ions (Fe^{++}), in other circumstances three to form ferric ions (Fe^{+++}). Exhibition of more than one electrovalence is common among the transitional metals, but rare among the elements of the main groups.

20-3 Ionization potential and electron affinity

Atoms of a metal cannot lose energy simply by giving up electrons. An isolated individual atom is in its lowest energy state with its full complement of electrons, and to remove any one of them requires work from the external world. The valence electrons in a metallic atom are so loosely held by the electrostatic attraction of the nucleus that *relatively* little energy is needed to detach them; in chemical changes they become detached upon interaction with the atoms of a nonmetal. Energy may actually be given up during *attachment* of an electron to a nonmetal atom to form a negative ion. Such energy is available to bring about the detachment of electrons from the metal atoms. The process of forming positive and negative ions from neutral atoms generally occurs with over-all loss of energy, and brings the atoms of metal and nonmetal, taken together, into a state of lowered energy.

Of the combinations of a number of metals with a given nonmetallic element, the most vigorous reaction would be expected with the metal whose electrons are most readily detached. Here, then, we find an explanation for the observation that the reactivity of metallic elements within a group increases with increasing atomic weight. In the metals of Group 1a, for example, activity is known to increase in the order lithium, sodium, potassium, rubidium, cesium (see Chapter 9). The single valence electron of the lithium atom is relatively close to the lithium nucleus, since only the two electrons of the K shell intervene. The nuclear charge of the sodium atom is greater, but the sodium valence electron, on the average, is at a greater distance from the nucleus, and there are eight L shell electrons intervening; the net effect is that this valence electron is held less firmly than that of lithium. Similarly, the force acting on outermost electrons decreases further with increasing atomic weight, due to shielding and increased distance, and despite the increase in nuclear charge.

A useful index to metallic activity of the elements is the energy required to detach a single electron from one of their atoms. It is possible to measure this quantity of energy, called *ionization potential*, by examination of the emission spectrum of a given element, for the energy lost on electron capture by an ion may be emitted as light. The ionization potentials of the elements are shown in Fig. 20-3, plotted against atomic number. (The energy unit in which the values are expressed is the electron-volt, ev, which

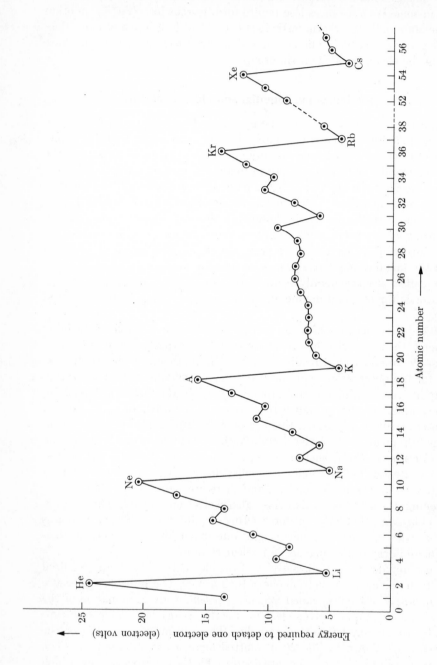

Fig. 20-3. Ionization potentials of the elements.

is simply the energy acquired by a single electron upon free passage across a potential difference of one volt.) It is seen that periodicity in this property is beautifully illustrated by the graph. The curve rises more or less steadily for the elements within a given period of the periodic system, then falls sharply to a minimum upon the beginning of a new period. The highest ionization potential exhibited within any period is that of an inert gas, the lowest that of an alkali metal. As we go from period to period, ionization potentials become smaller within any given group; thus the highest value is that for helium (24.5 ev), and those for neon, argon, krypton, etc., are successively lower. The reason for this, as we have seen, is the increasing distance of outer electrons from their corresponding nuclei and the shielding furnished by the inner electron shells.

An element will behave as a metal only if its ionization potential is low, that is, if a valence electron can be relatively easily detached. The distribution of metallic elements in the periodic table can thus be understood on the basis of the ionization potential curve. A rough separation of metals and nonmetals may be accomplished by means of a zigzag line tending generally down and toward the right in the periodic table (Fig. 9–3). In Group 4a, for example, the four valence electrons of carbon and silicon are held so tightly by their nuclei that the ionization potentials are high; carbon and silicon have no tendency to lose electrons in chemical processes. The third element of the group, germanium, has an ionization potential that is sufficiently low for the element to exhibit some of the characteristics of a metal. Atoms of the last two elements, tin and lead, have valence electrons far from their nuclei; both are characteristically metallic elements. Similar considerations applied to other groups show the emergence of metallic character as we go to higher atomic number, and make understandable the fact that metals constitute the overwhelming majority of the elements.

Ionization potentials give us no direct information concerning non-metallic activity, since ionization potential is work which must be done on a normal atom to take away an electron, while a nonmetal atom generally undergoes net $loss$ of energy when it accepts an electron. The proper index of nonmetal activity is the energy given up by an atom upon acquisition of an extra electron, a quantity known as $electron\ affinity$. Some general features of nonmetal behavior may be discussed without detailed consideration of the quantitative measurement of electron affinity. The fluorine atom has a stronger tendency to acquire an extra electron than the atom of any other element. The octet completed by the added electron in this case is as close to the nucleus as is possible, and the electron is therefore held with maximum force. Continuing down the halogen group, we can understand why the elements chlorine, bromine, and iodine become less active nonmetals in order of increasing atomic weight. When two extra electrons are acquired by oxygen, forming oxide ion (O^{--}), they are tightly held because they are in the L shell, although there is much less force on each than there would be if a single added electron were involved. It is clear why the strongest nonmetal should be found in the upper right-hand corner of the periodic chart, whereas the most active metal is found in the lower left-hand corner.

The unique element hydrogen occasionally acts as a nonmetal. On direct combination with some of the most active metals, hydrogen atoms can acquire a single electron, thus completing the K shell and forming the hydride ion H^-. The resulting electrovalent compounds, e.g., lithium hydride, LiH, and calcium hydride, CaH_2, are relatively unstable, however, and react vigorously with water to form hydrogen gas and the corresponding metal hydroxide.

20–4 Electron-pair bonds. Covalence

So far we have spoken chiefly of elements near the sides of the periodic table, those that can form ions with completed octet structures by outright loss or gain of electrons. What about an element in a middle group? The carbon atom, for example, has four valence electrons in a shell near its nucleus. Detachment of all four, to achieve the helium configuration, would require a very large amount of energy, and we should not expect carbon to be a metal. Acquisition of four electrons to make up the neon configuration is not probable either, due to the mutual repulsion to be expected of the crowded electrons in such a highly charged ion. (More succinctly we might say that carbon has both high ionization potential and low electron affinity.) Yet carbon participates in the formation of more compounds than any other element. Even among the strong nonmetals we find diatomic molecules formed by pairs of like atoms, for example, F_2, Cl_2, O_2, and N_2; the existence of these molecules cannot depend on electron loss by one atom of the pair and electron gain by the other. Moreover, many compounds are formed between elements near each other in the periodic table, e.g., nitrogen and oxygen, oxygen and sulfur, which could hardly be expected to be ionic.

Explanation of the nature of the bonds between atoms in the many non-electrovalent compounds goes somewhat beyond the Bohr theory of atomic structure. The existence of a chemical bond consisting of a pair of electrons which is *shared* between two atoms was first postulated by G. N. Lewis in 1916. A detailed theory of such a bond was developed by W. Heitler and F. London in 1927 on the basis of the then new quantum mechanics, already mentioned in Chapter 19. Simplified, the idea is briefly this: as two atoms approach each other, each containing a valence electron in a stable orbit, a new single orbit may form about both nuclei. This new two-atom orbit may be occupied by two electrons if their spins are directed opposite to each other, as permitted by the exclusion principle. Neither electron, ideally, may be said to belong more to one atom than to the other; they are truly *shared*. Heitler and London showed that the energy of an electron in a two-atom orbit may be substantially lower than in its original Bohr orbit. When this is so, electrons tend to stay in two-atom orbits, and in so doing hold the atoms together in molecules. Such bonds are known as *electron-pair bonds* or, more commonly, as *covalent bonds*; molecules which are held together by this kind of bond are known as *covalent molecules.*

For a first example of covalent binding let us choose the simple hydrogen molecule. Here each individual atom contributes a single electron to the union, and the two electrons are shared by two nuclei in the molecule. If we count both electrons of the pair toward the total electron complement of each atom we obtain a helium-like configuration for each, although this configuration is shared between the two nuclei, and can no longer be spherically symmetric. The time-average distribution of the electrons in hydrogen atoms and in a hydrogen molecule is indicated in Fig. 20–4. Representing electrons by single dots, the formation of a hydrogen molecule from two hydrogen atoms may be written

$$\mathrm{H} \cdot + \cdot \mathrm{H} \rightarrow \mathrm{H} : \mathrm{H}$$

The situation in the diatomic chlorine molecule is somewhat different. Here each atom possesses seven valence electrons, or one short of the eight needed for octet structure. The two odd electrons may be shared between the two atoms, so that if both electrons of the pair are again counted as part of the retinue of each atom, each will have achieved octet structure:

$$: \overset{\cdot\cdot}{\underset{\cdot\cdot}{\mathrm{Cl}}} \cdot + \cdot \overset{\cdot\cdot}{\underset{\cdot\cdot}{\mathrm{Cl}}} : \rightarrow : \overset{\cdot\cdot}{\underset{\cdot\cdot}{\mathrm{Cl}}} : \overset{\cdot\cdot}{\underset{\cdot\cdot}{\mathrm{Cl}}} :$$

We shall discuss this diagrammatic representation, or "dot picture" in the

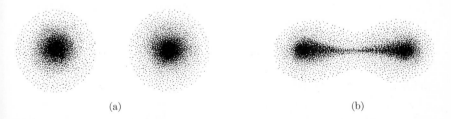

(a)   (b)

Fig. 20–4, A representation of the time-average electron distribution around two hydrogen atoms individually (a), and a hydrogen molecule (b).

next section; here we need note only that each dot represents a valence electron.

Let us now consider the combination of carbon and chlorine atoms. Carbon atoms have four valence electrons, chlorine atoms seven. Each atom of carbon is then capable of forming a total of four covalent bonds, whereas the chlorine atom, only one electron short of its octet, can form only one. Thus one carbon atom combines with four chlorine atoms to form a covalent molecule of carbon tetrachloride:

$$
\begin{array}{c}
\cdot\cdot \\
:\text{Cl}: \\
\cdot\cdot \quad \cdot\cdot \quad \cdot\cdot \\
:\text{Cl}:\ \text{C}\ :\text{Cl}: \\
\cdot\cdot \quad \cdot\cdot \quad \cdot\cdot \\
:\text{Cl}: \\
\cdot\cdot
\end{array}
$$

To generalize: if formation of an octet configuration is at all feasible, the number of covalent bonds which an element can form is the number of electrons which its atoms lack for an inert gas configuration. The case of transitional elements, those in the longer periods of the table, is of course more complicated. Although the majority of covalent compounds are formed among nonmetallic elements, many metals, particularly the transitional metals, are capable of participating in covalent bonds. The more active metals, however, do not form covalent bonds at all.

20-5 "Dot pictures" and bond notation

In the preceding section the molecules of hydrogen, chlorine, and carbon tetrachloride have been symbolized, with dots representing valence electrons. In these diagrams, or "dot pictures," only valence-shell electrons are given consideration. Each elemental symbol is thus intended to represent the nucleus of an atom of a given kind plus all the electrons present in inner shells, a combination sometimes referred to as the "kernel" of an atom. All valence-shell electrons are shown in pairs, since quantum mechanical calculations have indicated that even those which are not involved in binding tend to pair off. The use of "dot pictures" to represent molecules is convenient, and we shall encounter them frequently. The convenience must not overshadow the fact that in using them we do not attempt *real* picturization of molecules. They constitute simply a formal shorthand for the quick description of electron arrangements in covalent molecules.

An even shorter shorthand which we shall frequently employ is *bond* notation, in which a single line is drawn between the symbols for two atoms to indicate a pair of shared electrons. No dots are used to represent single electrons, hence electrons which may be present but are unshared are simply ignored. H_2, Cl_2, and CCl_4 would be represented as follows in this notation:

$$\text{H—H}; \quad \text{Cl—Cl}; \quad \text{Cl—}\underset{\underset{\displaystyle \text{Cl}}{|}}{\overset{\overset{\displaystyle \text{Cl}}{|}}{\text{C}}}\text{—Cl}$$

While bond notation is very quick, "dot pictures" convey more information. We shall find both helpful.

20–6 Variations of covalent bonding

There are many examples of compounds in which more than one pair of electrons is shared between a single pair of atoms. A *double bond* is formed when two pairs are so shared; if three pairs are shared the bond is called a *triple bond*. If all electrons so shared are counted as part of the valence shells of *both* atoms, it will often be observed that a closer approach to octet structure is achieved than would be possible with single covalent bonds. Thus carbon, in carbon dioxide, forms double bonds with oxygen atoms:

$$: \overset{..}{O} :: C :: \overset{..}{O} : , \quad \text{or} \quad O{=}C{=}O.$$

In this way all three atoms have completed octets, while if single covalent bonds were formed only the oxygen atoms would have octets. Similarly, the diatomic nitrogen molecule has a triple bond between the nitrogen atoms:

$$: N ::: N : , \quad \text{or} \quad N{\equiv}N,$$

giving each an octet structure.

The electrons in a covalent bond are not always shared truly equally between the atoms involved. Consider a molecule of hydrogen chloride. We know that chlorine has a greater tendency to hold added electrons than hydrogen, since, in terms of its chemical behavior, chlorine is a more strongly nonmetallic element than hydrogen. The resulting two-atom orbit occupied by the valence electrons is unsymmetric, and may be thought of as one in which the electrons spend somewhat more of their time in the vicinity of the chlorine atom than in that of the hydrogen nucleus. The resultant molecule may be called *partially ionic*: it will possess a slight excess of negative charge in the vicinity of the chlorine atom, relative to the hydrogen atom. The molecule as a whole thus has oppositely charged *poles*, and is said to be a *polar* covalent molecule. One consequence of the polar character of hydrogen chloride and substances like it is a tendency for its molecules to become oriented in an externally applied electric field, as shown in Fig. 20–5.

All bonds between unlike atoms are unsymmetric to some degree, but not all molecules comprising unlike atoms are polar. Consider a molecule of carbon dioxide, $O=C=O$. The oxygen atoms are *both* slightly negative as compared with the carbon atom, yet are symmetrically placed on either side of it, and there is therefore no preferred direction for the molecule to orient in an electric field. One might expect water molecules to behave like those of carbon dioxide, but water is actually strongly polar. This polarity can be attributed to lack of symmetry in the water molecule itself, as well as in its hydrogen-to-oxygen bonds. The two hydrogen atoms are not in line with the oxygen, but are arranged as shown in Fig. 20–6, with an average angle of 104 degrees between the two H—O bonds. The result is that they do tend to line up in an electric field, and we shall see that many interesting properties of water can be traced to the polarity of its molecules. In general, the arrangement of atoms within a molecule can affect its polarity profoundly. We shall learn in Chapter 23, for example, that the four single covalent bonds of the carbon atom are directed toward the corners of a regular *tetrahedron* (see Fig. 23–1). The tetrahedral arrangement is highly symmetric; any plane through the carbon atom in carbon tetrachloride (CCl_4) or methane (CH_4) has as many bonds on one side as on the other. These substances are therefore nonpolar, although each individual bond has slight partial ionic character. The disturbance of this symmetry found in methyl chloride (CH_3Cl), however, results in a slightly polar molecule.

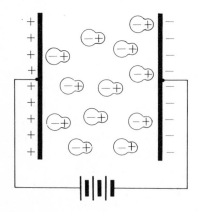

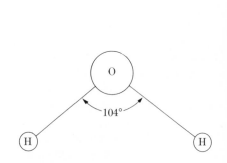

FIG. 20–5. Polar molecules, such as hydrogen chloride, tend to line up in an electric field.

FIG. 20–6. The "bent" polar water molecule.

It must be emphasized that polar covalence is quite different from electrovalence, even though examples of compounds ranging over all degrees of properties from completely covalent to completely ionic could be cited. *An electrovalent compound does not consist of molecules,* but of individual, discrete ions of opposite charge. A covalent bond holds two particular atoms together, hence *covalent compounds, whether polar or nonpolar, consist of discrete molecules.* In a covalent bond there may be charge separation to a degree depending on the particular pair of elements involved, but the regions of charge thus established always occur within single molecular units. It was this property of the electron-pair bond which led its discoverer, G. N. Lewis, to call it *the* chemical bond.

A special case of the covalent bond is that in which both electrons in an electron pair are furnished by the same atom. Such a bond is called a *coordinate covalent* bond. A two-atom orbit occupied by an electron pair in coordinate covalence is indistinguishable from an orbit in which each atom contributes an electron. Many of the radicals, or atom groups, of which we learned in Chapter 8 contain coordinate covalent bonds, although their occurrence is by no means limited to radicals. The sulfate radical, an ion with charge minus two (SO_4^{--}), is an example. The group contains two extra electrons that must initially have been gained upon interaction with atoms of a metal. Considering the sulfur atom first, and recalling that it contains six valence electrons, we see that the two extra electrons would complete its octet if added to that atom alone. The sulfide ion (S^{--}) thus formed would then have four electron pairs which it could share with other atoms. Since an oxygen atom contains only six electrons, four such atoms can be grouped around a central sulfide ion with formation of four coordinate covalent bonds:

$$
\begin{bmatrix}
: \overset{..}{O} : \\[2pt]
: \overset{..}{\underset{..}{O}} : \overset{..}{\underset{..}{S}} : \overset{..}{\underset{..}{O}} : \\[2pt]
: \underset{..}{O} :
\end{bmatrix}^{--}
$$

The actual formation of sulfate ion would not necessarily involve an intermediate sulfide ion stage, but the assumption that it does is convenient for purposes of discussion. In any case, neither of the electrons in the pair forming each sulfur-to-oxygen bond was originally possessed by the oxygen atom.

20–7 The relation between bond type and properties of solids

The foregoing discussion of the chemical bond has been all about electrons, atoms, molecules, and ions. Yet when we examine a piece of solid matter, such as a rock, we do not see any of these submicroscopic

(a)

(b)

FIG. 20–7. Natural crystals exhibiting faces: (a) halite, or rock salt, (b) diamond. (Courtesy of Ward's Natural Science Establishment.)

units; all of our information about the electronic structure of chemical bonds has been inferred from various lines of more or less indirect evidence. The study of the structures of solids, however, does start with observations we can readily make with our eyes, and has contributed to and benefited from the theory of electronic binding.

The kinds of solids which will be considered here are *crystalline* solids. A crystal is a solid body which is characterized by plane surface boundaries (faces) in a symmetrical arrangement. The regular arrangement of faces in rock salt crystals, for example, is easy to observe in coarse salt, and a microscope reveals similar faces on the particles of pulverized table salt. The existence of these symmetrical crystal faces (Fig. 20–7) must reflect an internal orderly arrangement of whatever structural units go to make up the crystal.

Practically all solids are crystalline or mixtures of crystals. Those which do not exhibit such regularities are called *amorphous*. Examples are glass, asphalt, and sulfur which has been suddenly cooled from the molten state. In these materials the unit particles are arranged more or less at random, as in a liquid. They may be considered as supercooled liquids rather than as true solids.

The structural units composing a crystal may be ions, atoms, or molecules; the latter may be nonpolar, or polar in varying degrees. The forces holding these units together vary widely, from very weak to extremely strong, and the gross physical properties of a crystal are in large part determined by the nature and strength of its internal cohesive forces.

An *ionic crystal* is held together by electrostatic forces acting between discrete charged particles. Since large numbers of both positively and negatively charged ions are present, both attractive and repulsive forces act in such a crystal. The ions seek an arrangement which brings oppositely charged particles close together, while at the same time achieving as much separation of like ions as possible. There are many ways in which ions may be arranged in an ionic crystal, one of the simplest of which is that exhibited by sodium chloride (Fig. 20–8). In this crystal each sodium ion (Na^+) is surrounded by six negative chloride ions (Cl^-), each chloride ion by six sodium ions. The result is a regular *lattice* array of ions, pervading the entire crystal. It is this internal symmetry, made discoverable by the technique of x-ray

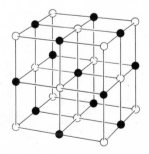

Fig. 20–8. Schematic representation of sodium and chloride ions in a cubic lattice array in the rock salt crystal.

diffraction (Section 18–5), which is responsible for the regular arrangement of crystal faces shown in Fig. 20–7.

The electrostatic cohesive forces in ionic crystals are very strong; in consequence, ionic substances generally exhibit high melting points. The melting point of a solid, it will be recalled, is that temperature at which its unit particles have sufficient kinetic energy to overcome the forces which act between them. Sodium chloride melts at 801°C, for example, barium chloride at 962°C, cupric sulfate at 200°C, and calcium carbonate (calcite) at 1339°C. The majority of ionic solids are hard, although their extreme rigidity generally makes them brittle. They tend to break smoothly along clearly defined *cleavage planes* which are related to the internal arrangement of their constituent ions.

A unique property of ionic substances is their ability to conduct an electric current when in the molten state. If a container of potassium nitrate is incorporated into a circuit in series with a light bulb, as in Fig. 20–9, the bulb will begin to glow as soon as some of the salt has been heated to the melting point with a Bunsen flame. Ability to conduct a current can be associated only with the presence of charged particles which are free to move, and this property of ionic substances constitutes one of the important pieces of evidence that they consist of ions.

There are a few known crystalline substances whose fundamental structural units appear to be atoms. The internal forces holding such

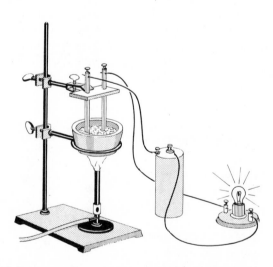

Fig. 20–9. Molten potassium nitrate conducts electric current. Electrodes are embedded in solid salt, but circuit is not complete and bulb does not light up until the salt has been melted with a Bunsen flame.

atomic crystals together are covalent bonds; since these are generally stronger than electrovalent bonds, the resulting crystals are extraordinarily hard, and resist melting up to very high temperatures. Diamond, the outstanding example of an atomic crystal, is the hardest known substance; its melting point, in excess of 3500°C, is higher than that of any other material. Other examples of atomic crystals are silicon carbide (SiC), which melts at 2600°C, and tungsten carbide (WC), which melts at 2900°C. In addition to hardness and high melting point, atomic crystals exhibit no tendency to dissolve in water and other solvents. The diamond crystal lattice consists entirely of carbon atoms, each covalently joined to four others at the corners of a regular tetrahedron. A diamond crystal could be considered to bè a single, gigantic molecule.

Crystals whose structural units consist of molecules are unlike either atomic or ionic crystals. The covalent bonds present in a *molecular crystal* act entirely within the molecular structural units, and not between such units in the crystal. The forces which hold molecular crystals together are of the type called van der Waals forces, which we discussed in Chapter 13 in connection with the departures of gases from ideal behavior. These are weak electrostatic attractions, generally between the nuclei and electrons of molecules which are brought very close together. While van der Waals forces are all weak, there is great variation in their strength, depending upon the particular molecules involved. The forces between molecules of hydrogen, which melts at −259°C, are obviously much weaker than those between molecules of naphthalene ($C_{10}H_8$), which melts at +80°C. The molecules of molecular crystals are arranged in regular lattice arrays, as are the ions and atoms of the other crystal types. Because intermolecular forces are weak, these crystals are generally very soft and brittle, melt at low temperatures, and volatilize readily. The property of volatility is well illustrated by the fact that solid CO_2 ("dry ice") passes directly from the solid to the vapor state at −79°C under ordinary atmospheric pressure.

When the molecules of a molecular crystal are polar there is an electrostatic force present in addition to that described by the term van der Waals force. The molecules generally tend to orient in such a way that oppositely charged ends are adjacent to one another, as shown in Fig. 20–10. The presence of additional electrostatic force in this way lends some strength to the crystal.

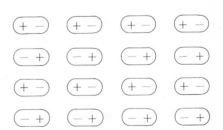

Fig. 20–10. Schematic representation of molecular orientation to be expected in a crystal whose units are polar molecules.

Although comparisons are very difficult to make, the properties of polar molecular crystals are generally intermediate between those of nonpolar molecular and ionic crystals. Examples are ice, which melts at 0°C, and acetic acid ($C_3H_6O_2$), which melts at 17°C. The most important difference between these and nonpolar substances lies in the realm of solubility in various liquid solvents, a topic that will be discussed in the next chapter.

The graphite crystal constitutes an interesting combination of the features of both atomic and molecular crystals. Like diamond, graphite consists entirely of carbon atoms. (The two distinct crystal forms, diamond and graphite, are called *allotropic modifications* of the element carbon.) The carbon atoms in graphite are arranged in hexagons, and are held together by strong covalent bonds. Each hexagon is an integral part of six others, by virtue of covalent bonds acting between the carbon atoms within it and those of its neighbors. The basic structure of the crystal thus consists of planes of carbon atoms in a characteristic hexagonal array (see Fig. 20–11). While each such plane constitutes a miniature atomic crystal by itself, there are no covalent bonds extending *between* sheets. Only relatively weak van der Waals forces are present to hold the planes of carbon atoms together, and the distance between layers is known to be much greater than that between carbon atoms within a single layer. Since the weak bonds between planes are easily broken, very little force is required to cause layers of carbon atoms to slide past one another. It is this aspect of the graphite structure which accounts for its usefulness as a solid lubricant.

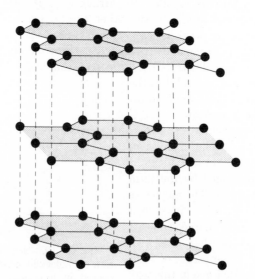

FIG. 20–11.   Schematic representation of the crystal structure of graphite.

Since a metal, e.g., iron, consists exclusively of a single kind of atom, we might conclude that metals are atomic crystals; the properties of a metallic crystal, however, are entirely unlike those of diamond. The ready ability to conduct electric current, exhibited by all metals, is not shared by any of the other classes of crystals. Since the nature of the binding forces in the metallic state is complex, we shall mention here only that the structural units in these crystals appear to be positive metal ions and free valence electrons. The valence electrons belong to the crystal as a whole, rather than to particular metal atoms. Their consequent freedom to move throughout the crystal provides the metal with its ability to conduct current, under the influence of an applied potential difference.

20-8 Valence and valence number. Oxidation and reduction

The valence concept was introduced in Chapter 9 as a purely empirical aid to the writing of formulas for chemical compounds. Through our enhanced understanding of the nature of chemical combination, however, this concept has acquired deeper meaning. The combining power of an atom, or its valence, is determined by the number of electrons it gains, loses, or shares in combining with other atoms. The valence of any ion is just equal to the charge that it bears, while the valence of an element in covalent combination is equal to the number of electron pairs which its atoms share with other, unlike atoms. Thus the valence of barium ion (Ba^{++}) in the compound barium chloride ($BaCl_2$) is 2, and the valence of chlorine is 1, corresponding to the charge on chloride ion (Cl^-). In carbon tetrachloride (CCl_4) each carbon atom shares four electron pairs, each chlorine atom one; the valence of carbon in this case is 4, the valence of chlorine 1.

In an earlier section, we spoke of electrovalences bearing positive and negative signs, e.g., $+2$ for barium and -1 for chlorine in barium chloride, where the signs simply refer to the kinds of charge on the individual ions involved. The concept of valence, in a strict sense, deals with the absolute combining powers of atoms, and the idea of a negative valence is not meaningful. While it might seem to arise naturally for electrovalent compounds, where ions of opposite charge are involved, there is no corresponding manner in which positive and negative signs could be assigned to the valences of atoms in covalent combinations. It is often convenient to employ such signs in interpreting compound formation, however, and for this reason the concept of *valence number* (also called *oxidation number*) has been devised. The valence number of an ion is expressed by stating the number of units *and the sign* of its charge. Where covalent bonds are present, positive and negative assignments are made in accordance with a set of generally accepted conventions. The basis of these conventions is an attempt to assign negative valence number to the more strongly nonmetallic element present in any combination. In carbon tetrachloride, for example, in which chlorine is the more strongly nonmetallic element, the valence number of carbon is recorded as $+4$, that of chlorine as -1.

For our present purposes a few simple rules about valence number will suffice. First, the concepts of valence and valence number apply only to atoms in combination with others which differ from them, hence the valences of oxygen (O_2), sulfur (S_8), iodine (I_2), and all other elemental substances are zero. Second, to assign valence numbers by the inspection of formulas it is convenient to remember that the valence number of oxygen is almost always -2, that of hydrogen is $+1$ in all compounds except metal hydrides (e.g., LiH), in which it is -1, that the valence numbers of the alkali metals are $+1$ in all their compounds, of the alkaline earth elements $+2$, and that the halogen elements exhibit valence number -1 in most of their binary (two-element) compounds. Finally, by convention, *the algebraic sum of the valence numbers of all atoms present in the formula unit of a compound is zero.* Thus in nitric acid, HNO_3, for example, since the valence number of hydrogen is $+1$ and that of oxygen -2, the sum of the valence numbers of these two elements in the formula unit is $+1 +$ $(3 \times -2) = -5$. The valence number of nitrogen in this compound must then be $+5$, in keeping with the convention we have just stated.

When the metal calcium combines with the nonmetal oxygen to form the ionic crystal calcium oxide:

$$2Ca + O_2 \rightarrow 2CaO,$$

two valence electrons from each calcium atom are transferred to an oxygen atom. Similarly, when barium metal reacts with chlorine to form barium chloride:

$$Ba + Cl_2 \rightarrow BaCl_2,$$

electrons are transferred from barium to chlorine atoms. Indeed, metal atoms *lose* electrons in direct combination with a nonmetallic element, whose atoms simultaneously *gain* electrons. For processes involving electron transfer, electron loss is designated by the term *oxidation*. The converse process of electron gain is called *reduction*. In the simple combination reactions cited above, the metals calcium and barium are oxidized and the nonmetals oxygen and chlorine are reduced.

It is obvious from its name that the concept of oxidation has evolved from a more restricted usage, combination with the element oxygen. From this fact it must also be clear that the view of oxidation as electron loss is too narrow, since there are many examples of combination with oxygen that do not involve outright electron transfer. The combustion of charcoal to form carbon dioxide,

$$C + O_2 \rightarrow CO_2,$$

for example, would certainly be called an oxidation, although no electrons are exchanged between carbon and oxygen atoms during formation of the covalent CO_2 molecule. We may note, however, that carbon in this instance, like calcium and barium in the reactions considered in the previous paragraph, undergoes an *increase in valence number*. Since oxygen in the compound CO_2 has its usual valence number of -2, the valence number of carbon is $+4$, and increases to this value from zero in the course of this oxidation reaction. Conversely, the valence number of oxygen has decreased from zero to -2. The valence number of calcium increases from 0 to $+2$ when this element combines with oxygen, and the valence number of barium increases by the same amount during combination with chlorine. In its most general sense, the concept of *oxidation* may be taken to mean *increase in valence number*, while *reduction* corresponds to *decrease in valence number*.

Reactions involving oxidation and reduction are the most numerous of chemical changes, and many of them have great practical significance. The combustion of fuels to obtain heat or mechanical work, the production of electrical energy in batteries, the extraction of metals from their ores, are all examples of oxidation-reduction processes. In the production of metallic zinc from an ore containing zinc oxide, for example, the ore is intimately mixed with coal and roasted at high temperature. The carbon in the coal oxidizes, in a limited supply of air, to carbon monoxide:

$$2C + O_2 \rightarrow 2CO,$$

and the latter compound reduces the zinc oxide:

$$ZnO + CO \rightarrow Zn + CO_2;$$

oxidation of carbon from a valence number of $+2$ (in CO) to $+4$ (in CO_2) accompanies the reduction of zinc from $+2$ (in ZnO) to zero (in Zn). The essential reaction occurring in the common lead storage battery, when it is discharging, is

$$PbO_2 + Pb + 2H_2SO_4 \rightarrow 2PbSO_4 + 2H_2O.$$

In this process, metallic lead is oxidized to a valence number of $+2$ in $PbSO_4$, while the lead in PbO_2 is reduced from its initial valence number of $+4$ to $+2$ in the sulfate.

The process of electrolysis (see Section 18–1) is an outstanding example of electron transfer, hence of oxidation-reduction. When electric current is passed through a solution or melt containing ions, positive ions may gain electrons at the negative electrode, negative ions may lose them at the positive electrode. Current through cupric chloride solution ($CuCl_2$), for example, produces metallic copper and chlorine gas; since Cu^{++} gains two electrons, it is reduced, and Cl⁻, which loses an electron, is oxidized. Passage of current through a water solution of sodium chloride results in the production of hydrogen gas, rather than sodium metal, at the negative electrode, and chlorine gas at the positive electrode. The sodium ion reduces less readily than the hydrogen in water, and to produce sodium metal by electrolysis it is necessary to exclude water. Sodium and the other alkali metals are therefore prepared by electrolysis of their salts in molten condition. Electrolytic reduction is important industrially for the production of very active metals like sodium; even the much less active metal aluminum is prepared commercially in this way.

20–9 Summary

The inert gas atoms undergo no chemical reactions, hence have exceptionally stable electron configurations. Helium atoms contain only the two electrons needed to complete the innermost electron shell. The other inert gas atoms have outermost shells containing eight electrons in a characteristic, stable configuration called *octet* structure. In most chemical compounds the interaction of valence electrons is such that each participating atom achieves inert gas structure. Metals tend to donate and nonmetals to accept electrons in such numbers that each resultant *ion* in the combination has an electron configuration resembling that of an inert gas atom. (The number of electrons donated or accepted by each atom is called its *electrovalence.*) Atoms may also achieve the inert gas configuration by sharing electrons, forming *covalent* bonds. Bonds between like atoms can only be covalent, and atoms of elements in the middle groups of the periodic table are particularly prone to covalent bond formation. The structural units of crystals may be atoms, ions, or molecules, and solids owe their rigidity to forces between these units. These forces may be strong covalent bonds between atoms (e.g., diamond), strong electrostatic attractions between ions (e.g., sodium chloride), and weak van der Waals attractions between molecules (e.g., "dry ice"). Oxygen tends to accept electrons, and metals which combine with oxygen are said to be oxidized. The term *oxidation* has been broadened to include all processes that involve electron loss or, even more generally, any increase in valence number. The inverse process (most simply, electron gain) is called *reduction.*

REFERENCES

BRAGG, W., *The Universe of Light.* Includes discussion of the use of x-rays in crystal structure determination.

PAULING, L., *General Chemistry*, Chapters 8 and 9.

SISLER, H. H., and others, *General Chemistry, a Systematic Approach.* Chapters 9 and 10 discuss electronic concepts of chemical binding, and the relation of physical properties of substances to bond type.

1. Of the following compounds, which would you expect to be ionic, which covalent? What are your reasons?

(a) N_2O (b) MgS   (c) CsI

(d) SO_2 (e) B_2H_6 (f) SrI_2

(g) $AgNO_3$ (h) BrCl   (i) HBr

(j) P_2O_5

2. Write formulas for the oxides of nitrogen listed in Table 7–1. What is the valence of nitrogen in each? Explain how it is possible for nitrogen to exhibit such a wide variety of valences.

3. In nitrous oxide, the two nitrogen atoms are known to be bound to each other, so that only one of them is bound directly to oxygen. See whether you can construct a plausible "dot picture" of this molecule, showing all the valence electrons of the three atoms involved.

4. We have said that the tendency of atoms to form octet configurations accounts for the formation of more than 90 percent of the known chemical compounds. Explain just what is meant by this tendency, for the cases of both electrovalent and covalent substances. Use examples.

5. Draw a "dot picture" representation of the boron trifluoride molecule, BF_3. Does the boron atom have an octet configuration? The fluorine atom? What would the boron atom have to do to attain octet configuration in an ionic compound? Why is this unlikely?

6. Draw "dot pictures" of both boron trifluoride and ammonia molecules. When these two substances are brought together, a compound having the formula BF_3NH_3 tends to form. Can you deduce from the "dot pictures" why formation of this compound is possible? What kind of chemical binding is involved? Explain.

7. Ferrous salts, in ammonia solution, tend to form a complex ion with the formula $[Fe(NH_3)_6]^{++}$. By examining iron's position in the periodic table, determine how many electrons a ferrous ion would have to pick up to give it an inert gas configuration. How many electrons can be contributed by ammonia molecules? What kind of bonds must be involved? Draw a diagram.

8. Construct diagrams, showing all valence electrons in all atoms involved, to represent the following reactions:

(a) $2Li + O_2 \rightarrow 2Li_2O$

(b) $Mg + I_2 \rightarrow MgI_2$

(c) $2H_2 + O_2 \rightarrow 2H_2O$

(d) $2As + 3H_2 \rightarrow 2AsH_3$

(e) $2Ba + Se_2 \rightarrow 2BaSe$

(f) $Si + 2F_2 \rightarrow SiF_4$

9. Of the following substances, which would you expect to have crystals consisting of ions, which of molecules? Of the latter, which molecules would you expect to be strongly polar, which weakly polar or nonpolar? Explain.

(a) H_2O (b) $CuSO_4$ (c) PCl_3

(d) I_2 (e) HI   (f) CBr_4

(g) CH_3Br (h) Cr_2O_3 (i) PCl_5

(j) BCl_3

10. For the following reactions, determine which element is oxidized, which reduced:

(a) $P_4 + 5O_2 \rightarrow 2P_2O_5$

(b) $H_2 + S \rightarrow H_2S$

(c) $3H_2S + 2HNO_3 \rightarrow 3S + 2NO + 4H_2O$

11. From the following list of reactions, choose those which involve oxidation-reduction and determine the change in valence number undergone by each element either oxidized or reduced:

(a) $Cu_2O + CO_2 \rightarrow 2CuO + CO$

(b) $CaCO_3 \rightarrow CaO + CO_2$

(c) $H_2 + CuO \rightarrow Cu + H_2O$

(d) $2KClO_3 \rightarrow 2KCl + 3O_2$

(e) $NH_3 + HCl \rightarrow NH_4Cl$

(f) $AgNO_3 + KCl \rightarrow AgCl + KNO_3$

(g) $HgCl_2 + FeCl_2 \rightarrow HgCl + FeCl_3$

CHAPTER 21

THE BEHAVIOR OF MATTER IN SOLUTION

A great deal of our empirical knowledge of chemistry has come from the observation of reactions between dissolved reagents. The chemist's time-honored implement, for this purpose, is his humble test tube. It is said that the German chemist Adolph von Baeyer once invited his colleague and fellow Nobel laureate Emil Fischer into his laboratory to view an important new development in chemical apparatus. The innovation turned out to be a test tube, held by a clamp over a Bunsen burner!

Because of their extensive use in the everyday practice of chemistry, solutions play a role of obvious importance in that science. Many geological processes involve the transport of matter in the dissolved state, and most of the essential fluids found in living organisms are solutions. In this chapter, however, we shall be primarily concerned with the fundamental knowledge of the properties of matter that has been gained from the study of solutions.

21-1 General properties of solutions

A solution, by definition, is a mixture that is homogeneous. The composition of a solution, unlike that of a true chemical compound, may be altered continuously between limits. A solution of salt in water, for example, may be made more dilute by addition of water, or more concentrated by addition of salt. Homogeneity, an important attribute of solutions, is not always easy to establish by direct visual observation, because there are many heterogeneous suspensions that the unaided eye cannot distinguish from solutions. Such suspensions, called *colloids*, consist of particles of microscopic size which are uniformly dispersed in a fluid medium. Milk and fog are examples of colloids. Unlike those of a colloid, the dispersed particles of a solution, which are of atomic or molecular size, cannot be seen under microscopic magnification. An interesting phenomenon called *Tyndall effect*, illustrated in Fig. 21-1, is useful in distinguishing true solutions from colloidal dispersions. Light passing through a quantity of colloid is seen as a full, solid beam by an observer at right angles to its direction of passage, but little or no light is seen from this direction when the beam is passed through a solution. The relatively large dispersed particles of the colloid are strong light scatterers, while the small molecules of the solution scatter very little light.

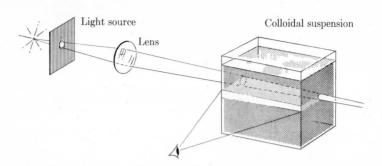

Fig. 21-1. Tyndall effect. Path of focused light beam through a colloidal suspension is visible to an observer at right angles to its direction. Practically no light would be seen from this angle if beam were traversing a true solution.

While we shall confine our attention largely to solutions of solids in liquids, solutions involving all combinations of the states of matter are possible. Air is a homogeneous mixture of gases, hence, by definition, a gaseous solution. Carbonated water is an example of a solution of a gas (CO_2) in a liquid, and wine contains one liquid, ethyl alcohol, dissolved in another, water. Most of the preparations of gold used in jewelry and in dentistry are solid solutions, usually silver and copper dissolved in gold. These are examples of *alloys*—solid, metallic mixtures—although not all alloys are solutions; some, e.g. steels, are not homogeneous.

Useful terms which are commonly encountered in discussions of solutions are *solute*, meaning that which is dissolved, and *solvent*, that which dissolves. The distinction is one of quantity, rather than of fundamental difference. In the most common kind of solution, solids dissolved in liquids, the liquid is usually present in much greater quantity than the solid and is called the solvent. Many pairs of liquids, on the other hand, are miscible (soluble) in all proportions. Homogeneous mixtures of ethyl alcohol and water of any conceivable concentration may be prepared, for example. In such cases it may not be meaningful to call one a solvent and the other a solute.

The description of a solution is not complete when the names of the substances it contains have been reported. In addition, it is necessary to specify the *concentrations* of its constituents. If a particular salt solution is said to contain 15% of sodium chloride by weight, for example, it has been quantitatively described. We know that each 100 gm of the solution contains 15 gm of NaCl and 85 gm of water, assuming the analysis of the solution to have been reliable. For chemical purposes it is generally most convenient to express the concentration of a solution in terms which specify the number of molecules of solute present in a given quantity of solution.

The *molarity* of a solution is defined as the number of moles (gram-molecular weight units) of solute present in one liter of the solution. A 1.5 *molar* solution of hydrogen chloride in water, for example, would contain 1.5 × 36.5 gm, that is, 54.75 gm, of HCl in each liter of solution. One liter of this solution would contain 1.5 times Avogadro's number, or 9.03 × 10²³ dissolved hydrogen chloride molecules.

The mutual solubilities of gases are complete, by virtue of the nature of this state of matter. Many pairs of liquids and some pairs of solids are also miscible in all proportions. For most solutions, however, there is a definite upper limit to the concentration that can be achieved at any given temperature. If sodium chloride crystals are added slowly, with stirring, to an arbitrary volume of water, say 100 ml, some excess of solid will eventually be observed which does not dissolve. At the particular temperature of this observation, the fixed quantity of water has reached the limit of its ability to dissolve sodium chloride, and the solution is said to be *saturated*. The concentration of solute in a saturated solution is called the *solubility* of the dissolved substance for whatever temperature saturation was achieved. The solubility of sodium chloride, for example, is 35.7 gm per 100 ml of water at 0°C, and 39.8 gm per 100 ml at 100°C. Solubilities, characteristic properties of substances, vary widely: 100 ml of water at 100°C will dissolve 487 gm of cane sugar, but only 0.00037 gm of silver bromide.

The solubility of any substance in a given solvent is dependent upon temperature. The water-solubilities of most solids, though not all, increase

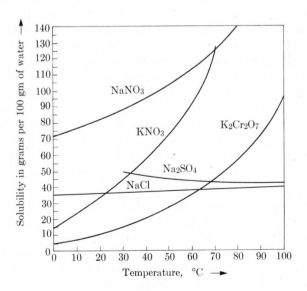

Fig. 21–2. Variations of water solubilities of several salts with temperature.

with increasing temperature, as is shown in the solubility curves of Fig. 21–2. The solubilities of gases in liquids, in all cases, decrease with increasing temperature. It is possible to remove dissolved air from water entirely by boiling, for example.

Frequently, it is possible to prepare solutions that are *supersaturated*, that is, which contain solute at a concentration greater than its normal solubility. This is most readily done by preparing a saturated solution at elevated temperature, then cooling the solution slowly and carefully. The compounds sodium thiosulfate ($Na_2S_2O_3$) and sodium acetate ($NaC_2H_3O_2$) are examples of solutes which form supersaturated solutions readily. A supersaturated solution may stand for some time without showing crystallization of the excess of solute it contains. Addition of a tiny crystal of solute produces almost immediate crystallization, however, the added crystal acting as a "nucleus" for the growth of crystals throughout the solution. Some pure substances behave the same way when *supercooled*. Liquid water, for example, may be brought to a temperature many degrees below its normal freezing point by careful, slow cooling, but will quickly crystallize as soon as a tiny ice crystal is introduced.

21–2 Solubility relations and the process of solution

It is frequently said that *like dissolves like*. A few examples will help us to interpret this slogan. The nonpolar liquid carbon tetrachloride and the polar liquid water do not mix (see Section 20–6). CCl_4 will dissolve in the nonpolar liquid benzene, however, and water is miscible with the somewhat polar liquid alcohol. The gas hydrogen chloride, whose molecules are strongly polar, is highly soluble in water, but only slightly soluble in CCl_4 or benzene. The nonpolar molecular crystal naphthalene dissolves in CCl_4 but not in water. The ionic solid sodium chloride is very soluble in water, insoluble in CCl_4, only slightly soluble in alcohol. The atomic crystal diamond has virtually no tendency to dissolve in other substances at ordinary temperatures. The generalization that "like dissolves like" implies that the solubility relations of substances are determined by similarities, or dissimilarities, of bond type, yet explains very little. For example, water consists of polar molecules, sodium chloride of ions; in what way are these substances, which dissolve each other readily, "like"? More complete understanding of the subject of solubility relations can be gained by considering the details of the process of solution itself.

The formation of any solution depends upon complete, uniform dispersion of the structural units (molecules, ions, or atoms) of solute and solvent. In the gaseous state, molecules are not bound to one another in any way, hence there is no bar to the molecular mixing of two or more dissimilar gases. In the liquid state, while no individual molecule is rigidly bound to any other, intermolecular forces are generally much stronger than in gases. The forces between polar water molecules are much stronger than those between nonpolar carbon tetrachloride molecules. Water molecules therefore tend to hold one another back, and to prevent the migration of their fellows into a region which contains CCl_4 molecules, which exert very much weaker forces on them and on each other. When water is brought in contact with ethyl alcohol, on the other hand, the molecules of the latter, having some polar character, exert attractive force on water molecules. This force is sufficient to promote migration, and water and ethyl alcohol molecules mix freely. CCl_4 and benzene, both consisting of nonpolar molecules, are mutually miscible because intermolecular forces in both liquids are relatively small. Since CCl_4 molecules attract benzene molecules about as strongly as either attracts its own kind, there is no restriction on molecular mixing.

When a substance is crystalline, mixing of its structural units with those of a liquid must be preceded by some process which effectively weakens cohesive crystal forces. Solution of a solid in a liquid, in some ways, is equivalent to the physical process of melting. When the forces within a crystal are covalent bonds, as in the atomic crystal diamond, no solvent can weaken them. When they are weak intermolecular forces, such as those between nonpolar naphthalene molecules in the crystalline form of that substance, any liquid whose molecules can gain entry to positions *between* molecules at the surface will weaken them and gradually dissolve the crystal. The molecules of a polar liquid, e.g. water, cannot dissolve a non-polar solid like naphthalene because their entrance into the crystal is prevented by their own, stronger, mutual interactions. The molecules of benzene, with intermolecular forces similar in strength to those between naphthalene molecules, are free to enter positions between solute molecules. The forces which hold the crystal together are weakened and, gradually, naphthalene molecules enter the liquid state, in intimate mixture with benzene molecules.

The process of solution of an ionic solid in a polar liquid is perhaps the most instructive case of all. The cohesion of a sodium chloride crystal, for example, results from electrostatic attractions between the sodium ions (Na^+) and chloride ions (Cl^-) which it contains. Polar water molecules are single units, yet bear net negative charge in the vicinity of their oxygen atoms and net positive charge in the vicinity of their hydrogen atoms. When water is brought in contact with a sodium chloride crystal, electrostatic interaction must be expected between water molecules and the ions on the surface layer of the crystal. The nature of this interaction is represented schematically in Fig. 21–3; in this diagram, each water molecule is represented as a unit *dipole*, with oppositely charged ends. Each sodium ion at the crystal surface develops an "envelope" of water dipoles, with

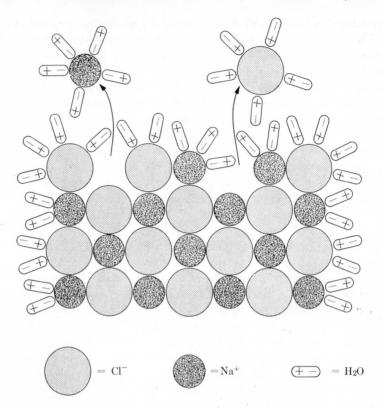

= Cl⁻ = Na⁺ = H₂O

Fig. 21–3. Solution of sodium chloride in water. (Water molecules are represented as shown to emphasize their dipolar character.)

negatively charged ends oriented toward the positively charged ion. Each chloride ion develops a similar "envelope" of opposite orientation. The net effect of these "envelopes" is partial insulation of neighboring ions from one another: the attractive force of a large number of solvent molecules weakens the force with which an ion attracts its neighbor ions. In this way the cohesive forces of the crystal are weakened near its surface, and ions are set free to move apart and to migrate into the main body of liquid. Each Na⁺ and Cl⁻ ion carries its complement of water molecules along. A nonpolar liquid cannot dissolve an ionic crystal because its molecules have no tendency to interact with ions. Only the most strongly polar liquids will do the job, in fact; ethyl alcohol, although its molecules will mix with those of water, is too weakly polar to dissolve sodium chloride.

Water molecules can attack only the surface layers of a crystal of sodium chloride. As ions move out into solution new surface layers become exposed; gradually, if sufficient water is present, the entire crystal dissolves.

If the crystal is large and the solution is not stirred, the process will be extremely slow. Small crystals present more surface to the solvent than larger ones, and stirring serves to remove dissolved ions from the scene, permitting more rapid orientation of water molecules about undissolved ions. The process of solution is accelerated by an increase in temperature, since the average motion of solvent molecules is then more rapid.

Frequently, the solution of one substance in another is accompanied by interaction of a more specific nature than the general orientation of water molecules described for the case of sodium chloride. Sugar crystals, which consist of polar covalent molecules and are extraordinarily soluble in water, are dissolved by a process called *hydration*. Water molecules become loosely attached to sugar molecules in a rather specific chemical manner. The great solubility of hydrogen chloride in water, we shall learn in the next section, results from a chemical reaction in which the polar bonds between hydrogen and chlorine atoms are broken, and an ionic solution is formed.

21–3 Electrolytes and the Arrhenius theory

Water solutions of certain substances possess the property of conducting electric current. Faraday, whose work on electrolysis has been discussed in Section 18–1, introduced the term *electrolyte* for such substances. Sodium chloride, potassium hydroxide, hydrogen chloride, and ammonia are examples of electrolytes; sugar, alcohol, and nitrous oxide are examples of *nonelectrolytes*.

Faraday was the first scientist to interpret electric conduction in solution in terms of the movement of charged atoms, or ions. It was his belief, however, that ions were formed from molecules by the action of applied electric current, and were present in solution only so long as current passed. Today we know that there is no such thing as a molecule of sodium chloride, that ions are present in the crystal of this substance and have independent existences in water solutions. An electric current passes through sodium chloride solution *because* ions are present and are free to migrate: sodium ions carry positive charge toward a negative electrode, while chloride ions carry negative charge toward a positive electrode. All electrolytic solutions contain ions, hence are able to conduct currents. In many cases, however, ions are not contained in the substances themselves, but are formed during the process of dissolving. The picture is further complicated by the fact that some electrolytes, such as sodium chloride and hydrogen chloride, conduct currents very strongly, while others, such as ammonia and acetic acid, conduct weakly. Our present understanding of the nature of electrolytic solutions developed over a long period, and it will be instructive for us to note some of the highlights of its history.

Prior to 1879 it had not been possible to compare the conducting abilities (*conductances*) of different electrolytic solutions, in a quantitative sense. The trouble was caused by the use of direct currents, which produced changes in concentration near the electrodes, by electrolysis. The German physicist Friedrich Kohlrausch (1840–1910) devised a means of measuring the electrical conductances of quantities of solutions, using alternating currents. By this method, in which the directions of motion of the ions are continually reversed, electrolysis of the solution is very nearly eliminated. The method of Kohlrausch, with refinements, is still in use today. Once quantitative comparisons were possible, Kohlrausch and others found that electrolytes may be divided into two distinct classes, *strong* and *weak*. When compared at equivalent concentrations, certain electrolytic solutions conduct current much more strongly than others. A solution containing one mole per liter of hydrogen chloride, for example, has a conductance about twice that of potassium sulfate, but nearly 230 times that of acetic acid and 330 times that of ammonia, all at the same concentration. The first two substances, HCl and K_2SO_4, are typical *strong* electrolytes, while the other two are classed as *weak*.

Another feature of electrolytic solutions that was learned from Kohlrausch's experiments is that the conductance of any electrolytic solution varies with concentration. Conductance itself decreases with increasing diluteness of a solution, but conductance *per mole* of solute present is found to increase as the concentration is diminished. The rate of change of conductance per mole with dilution is relatively small and regular for strong electrolytes, but much more marked and irregular for weak electrolytes, as shown in Fig. 21–4. In other words, strong electrolytes conduct well at all concentrations, while the conducting powers of weak electrolytes improve radically at very high dilution.

Ability to conduct electric currents is not the only property common to all electrolytic solutions. Francois-Marie Raoult (1830–1901), in 1882, discovered an important regularity in the behavior of nonelectrolytic solutes. It had long been known that the freezing point of a solution is lower than that of its corresponding pure solvent. Raoult demonstrated that nonelectrolytes depress the freezing points of solvents in a perfectly predictable way, and to the same extent at equivalent concentrations. One gram-molecular–weight of sugar dissolved in 1000 gm of water, for example, produces a solution which freezes at $-1.86°C$, and the same freezing point is observed for water solutions of any other nonelectrolyte at the same concentration. If the concentration is halved, the freezing point becomes $-0.93°C$, and if doubled it becomes $-3.72°C$. But Raoult observed that *electrolytic* solutes are "abnormal" in that they produce *greater* depression of the freezing point of water than nonelectrolytes. Furthermore, the extent of their "abnormality" varies with concentration. The freezing-point

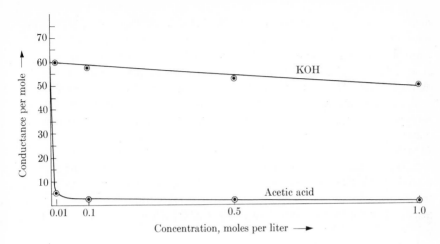

FIG. 21–4. Variation of conductance per mole of a strong electrolyte, KOH, and a weak electrolyte, acetic acid, with concentration. Note behavior of acetic acid at very low concentration.

depression produced by potassium chloride in water is greater than that expected of a "normal" nonelectrolytic solute at all concentrations, but the discrepancy becomes larger with increasing dilution. In very dilute solution the depression is very nearly twice the expected "normal" value. The freezing point of sulfuric acid solution at great dilution is nearly three times the "normal" value.

The freezing-point depression behavior of weak electrolytes is distinctly different from that of strong electrolytes. Acetic acid solutions, for example, show only slightly "abnormal" freezing points at most concentrations, but deviate very markedly from "normal" behavior when very dilute.

In addition to their unusual conductance and freezing-point properties, the vapor pressures and boiling points of electrolytic solutions were found to exhibit unique behavior.* The nature of this behavior is similar in detail to that observed in the freezing-point depression property. The vapor pressure of a solvent is reduced, and its boiling point elevated, in a perfectly regular and predictable manner when nonelectrolytic solutes are present, but to a greater (and less predictable) extent when the solute is an electrolyte. In 1887 the Swedish chemist Svante Arrhenius (1859–1927) succeeded in fitting these many known facts together into the first compre-

---

Osmotic pressure is another important solution property in which electrolytes exhibit "abnormal" behavior. The studies of osmosis carried out by J. H. van't Hoff occupied a position of great importance in the development of our understanding of electrolytes, but the subject has been deliberately omitted in this very brief account.

hensive theory of electrolytic solution behavior. Since Faraday's time, electrolytic conduction had been interpreted in terms of the assumed presence of ions in solution. Arrhenius now realized that ions must be responsible for the "abnormal" solute behavior of electrolytes, as well as conductance. The principal features of Arrhenius' theory are as follows:

1. An electrolytic solute is caused to dissociate into electrically charged ions by the action of the solvent, water. (Arrhenius thus assumed, in contradiction to Faraday, that ions are present whether an electric current is present or not.)

2. Only a fraction of the total number of solute molecules present is dissociated at one time, so that any electrolytic solution contains both neutral molecules and ions. (A potassium chloride solution, for example, was assumed to contain a mixture of neutral KCl molecules, positive K^+ ions, and negative Cl^- ions.)

3. The extent of dissociation of any electrolytic solute is increased by dilution of the solution, so that the number of neutral molecules present becomes smaller. At *very* great dilution for strong electrolytes, dissociation into ions is essentially complete.

4. Weak electrolytes are only slightly dissociated in solution, in comparison with strong electrolytes.

5. The ions present in electrolytic solution are as effective as neutral molecules in depressing the freezing point and vapor pressure, and in elevating the boiling point, of water.

The conducting ability of an electrolyte, as we have seen, increases with dilution; if a solute were completely dissociated in solution, Arrhenius believed, its conductivity should not change with concentration. He therefore assumed that there is *partial* dissociation of the solute and that ion formation (dissociation) increases upon dilution. Arrhenius was right in this assumption, but *only for weak electrolytes*. A solute such as acetic acid, in water solution, does consist of neutral molecules and charged ions in a state of equilibrium (see Chapter 22), and the degree of dissociation of neutral molecules does increase with dilution. The difference between strong and weak electrolytes has been proved to be one of type, rather than of degree, however. Strong electrolytes are *completely* dissociated in water solution, and the fact that their conductances vary with concentration has required explanation in another way (the Debye-Hückel theory, to be discussed below).

Nearly concurrently with Arrhenius' development of his dissociation theory, Jacobus Henricus van't Hoff (1852–1911) was extending the ideas of the kinetic theory of gases to the behavior of substances in dilute solution. In his view, individual solute molecules move about in solution independently, and van't Hoff was able to explain the lowering of vapor pressure and freezing point in terms of the sum of the independent effects of individual solute molecules on the escaping tendencies of solvent molecules. Since nonelectrolytic solutes depress freezing point to an extent which depends only upon molar concentration, it seemed clear that it is the *number* rather than kind of molecules present in solution which is important. Arrhenius extended this idea to electrolytic solutions by assuming that ions are just as effective as molecules in depressing vapor pressure and freezing point, that "abnormality" in these properties simply reflects the presence of a greater number of particles (molecules *plus* ions), and that increase in the extent of "abnormality" with dilution is caused by increasing dissociation. KCl, HCl, and KOH, each of which would be expected to form two ions on dissociation, do depress the freezing point of water very nearly twice as much as a nonelectrolyte, in very dilute solution. K_2SO_4, which should dissociate into three ions, is nearly three times as effective as a "normal" solute, again at high dilution. But again the original Arrhenius theory, in its explanation of "abnormal" solute behavior, was wholly right only for weak electrolytes.

21–4 Debye-Hückel theory

During the early years of the twentieth century, evidence that salts (e.g., KCl) consist of ions in the crystalline state began to accumulate. It was difficult to reconcile the fact that molten salts conduct current with Arrhenius' assumption that ions are formed by the action of water. Furthermore, while the detailed predictions of the Arrhenius theory for weak electrolytes were able to withstand the test of prolonged experimental scrutiny, those for strong electrolytes were not. The notion that strong electrolytes are completely dissociated in solution gained increasing acceptance, despite the observed dependence of conductance and freezing point "abnormality" on concentration. A new explanation of these effects was required, and was in fact supplied, in 1923, by the chemists Peter Debye and Erich Hückel. The assumption underlying the theory of Debye and Hückel is that strong electrolytes *are* completely dissociated into ions in solution, but that the ions are prevented from acting in an entirely independent manner by virtue of the fact that they are charged. Pairs of ions of opposite charge do not join to form neutral units, but the independence of any given ion is restricted by the large number of other ions present. Let us consider a single K^+ ion in a potassium chloride solution, for example (Fig. 21–5): as it moves through the solution it will be accelerated *away* from other K^+ ions as it approaches them, and *toward* any Cl^- ion that may come near. As a consequence, the K^+ ion may be considered to be surrounded, *on the average*, by a slight excess of negative charge; similarly, any given Cl^- ion will be surrounded by an average, small surplus of positive charge. If a current is passed through the solution, a potassium ion migrating toward the

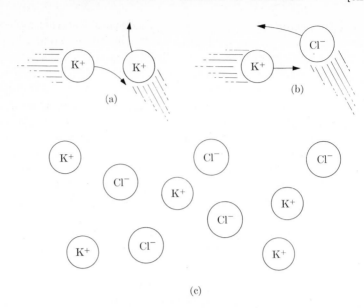

FIG. 21–5. Interionic attractions. A potassium ion in motion in solution will be repelled when approaching another potassium ion (a), attracted by a chloride ion (b). Net result, on the average, is a slight excess of negative charge in the vicinity of any potassium ion, and a slight excess of positive charge in the vicinity of any chloride ion (c).

negative electrode is held back in its passage by the presence of this slight negative charge, and the migration of chloride ions toward the positive electrode is similarly hampered. If the solution is made more dilute, however, the average distance between ions becomes larger, the interaction smaller, and the migration of ions toward electrodes correspondingly freer. Because of the presence of interionic attractions ions are unable to act with complete independence in lowering vapor pressure and freezing point, but do have increasing independence of action with dilution, until at high dilution the freezing point of KCl solution becomes nearly twice that expected of an undissociated solute at corresponding concentration. Debye and Hückel were able to make detailed predictions, based on their theory, which have been fully confirmed by experiment, and their theory of strong electrolytes is entirely accepted today.

21–5 Ionic and covalent substances as electrolytes

The success of the Debye-Hückel theory left no doubt that strong electrolytes are completely dissociated into ions, and thus reenforced the other lines of evidence which indicated that crystalline salts consist of ions. These substances ($NaCl$, KOH, K_2SO_4, etc.) are the ionic crystals we have discussed in Chapter 20, and all are conductors of electric current in the molten state. Not all strong electrolytes are salts, however. Pure, liquid sulfuric acid does not conduct current, for example, yet the properties of its solutions are unquestionably those of a strong electrolyte. Hydrogen chloride (HCl) forms a nonconducting solution in benzene, yet in water solution it appears to be completely dissociated into ions. These substances, then, consist of molecules which are readily broken up into ions by the action of water. In all cases these molecules are strongly *polar*, and it is undoubtedly an interaction between them and the similarly polar water molecules which leads to ionic dissociation. The water molecule contains strongly negative oxygen atoms with unshared electron pairs, and it is believed that these atoms attach hydrogen ions from the polar solute molecules:

$$
\overset{..}{\underset{..}{H : Cl}} : + H : \overset{..}{\underset{..}{O}} : \rightarrow \left[\overset{H}{\underset{H}{H : \overset{..}{O} :}} \right]^{+} + \left[: \overset{..}{\underset{..}{Cl}} : \right]^{-}
$$

The new species of ion formed in this process, H_3O^+, is called *hydronium* ion. Its existence is indicated by several distinct lines of evidence, and this interpretation of the observed dissociation of covalent molecules into ions seems almost certainly correct. HCl and H_2SO_4 molecules are very readily broken up by interaction with H_2O molecules because they are so strongly polar themselves. In the case of HCl, for example, this means that an H_2O molecule has more attraction for the hydrogen ion than does the negative (chlorine atom) half of the HCl molecule. Weak electrolytes consist of less strongly polar covalent molecules, which interact with water less vigorously than those of strong electrolytes.

In summary, then, there are two types of electrolytes, strong and weak. Strong electrolytes are completely dissociated into ions in solution, some because they consist of ions when undissolved, others because they react completely with water to form ions. The former are all ionic substances, the latter strongly polar covalent substances. Weak electrolytes are solutes which react incompletely with water to form ions. Their molecules are weakly polar, and a solution of a weak electrolyte contains both neutral molecules and ions. Ammonia, for example, reacts with water to form ammonium ion and hydroxide ion:

$$NH_3 + H_2O \rightarrow NH_4^+ + OH^-;$$

acetic acid reacts to form hydronium ion and acetate ion:

$$HC_2H_3O_2 + H_2O \rightarrow H_3O^+ + C_2H_3O_2{}^-.$$

In both cases, however, the fraction of dissolved molecules which reacts is very small at ordinary concentrations, although it increases as the solution is made increasingly dilute (see Fig. 21–6).

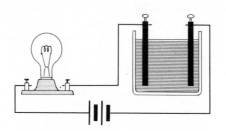

FIG. 21–6. Checking the conductivity of acetic acid. When pure acetic acid is present between the electrodes there is no current in the circuit and the light filament does not glow. When the acid is diluted with water the filament begins to glow, and glows more brightly with increasing dilution.

21–6 Ionic reactions and equations

Many important chemical changes take place in solutions of electrolytes, and it will now be well for us to consider such reactions in an ionic context. It is well known, for example, that when a solution of silver nitrate ($AgNO_3$) is added to a solution of sodium chloride (NaCl) a white solid precipitates out. The composition of this solid is known to correspond to the formula AgCl. Traditionally, the equation for this reaction would be written

$$AgNO_3 + NaCl \rightarrow AgCl \downarrow + NaNO_3,$$

the downward arrow indicating precipitation. A solution of the ionic substance silver nitrate actually contains Ag^+ and $NO_3{}^-$ ions, however, rather than $AgNO_3$ units; similarly, the solution of sodium chloride contains Na^+ and Cl^- ions. We could therefore represent the reaction by the equation

$$Ag^+ + NO_3{}^- + Na^+ + Cl^- \rightarrow AgCl \downarrow + Na^+ + NO_3{}^-.$$

Na^+ and $NO_3{}^-$ ions are shown on both sides of the equation; they are unaffected by the reaction, and remain in solution. If the AgCl precipitate were removed and the remaining solution evaporated to dryness, sodium nitrate crystals would appear; it cannot be said that sodium nitrate, as a substance, is formed during the reaction, however. Ions which are present during a chemical change but do not participate in the change are often called *spectator* ions, and are conventionally left out of the ionic equation representing the reaction. The simplest possible equation representing the silver chloride precipitation would then be

$$Ag^+ + Cl^- \rightarrow AgCl \downarrow .$$

We have written the formula for silver chloride as AgCl in the above ionic equation, although we know that its crystals consist of silver and chloride *ions*. This is simply a matter of convention—a pure, undissolved ionic substance is represented by its simplest unit formula. It is not possible, of course, to carry out the reaction between silver and chloride ions in the *absence* of spectator ions. The ionic equation simply reduces the reaction to its essentials, and expresses the fact that it is of no consequence what particular kinds of other ions are present. The same equation would serve to describe the reaction between the soluble salts silver perchlorate ($AgClO_4$) and magnesium chloride ($MgCl_2$).

Another example of a simple ionic reaction is the production of the bright yellow precipitate lead iodide by addition of potassium iodide solution to lead nitrate. In non-ionic form the equation for this reaction would be

$$2KI + Pb(NO_3)_2 \rightarrow 2KNO_3 + PbI_2 \downarrow .$$

In ionic form, however, this reduces simply to the equation

$$Pb^{++} + 2I^- \rightarrow PbI_2 \downarrow .$$

Another instructive example is the reaction between solutions of hydrochloric acid and sodium hydroxide. In non-ionic terms, we would have to say that this *neutralization* reaction leads to the products salt and water, according to the equation

$$HCl + NaOH \rightarrow NaCl + H_2O.$$

Water molecules are produced, but sodium and chloride ions are simply spectators. Remembering that hydrochloric acid solution contains hydronium ions, the simplest ionic equation for this reaction becomes

$$H_3O^+ + OH^- \rightarrow 2H_2O.$$

21-7 Acids and bases: proton transfer

Acids and *bases* are substances whose opposite properties have been known for centuries. Acids are sour in taste, turn blue litmus to red, liberate hydrogen upon reaction with active metals, liberate carbon dioxide when added to a carbonate and, most important, neutralize bases. Bases have their own distinct set of properties, the most important of which is that they neutralize acids. Arrhenius proposed, as definitions, that an acid is a substance whose water solution contains hydrogen ions (H^+), a base a substance whose water solution contains hydroxide ions (OH^-). As knowledge of electrolytic solutions advanced it became apparent that these definitions were not sufficiently general, however, and the Danish chemist J. N. Bronsted proposed new ones in 1923: *an acid is any substance which can donate protons (hydrogen ions), and a base any substance which can accept protons in chemical change.** Because of their powerful generality, these definitions have won almost universal acceptance. *Proton-transfer* reactions constitute an important class of chemical change.

Let us begin with acids as *proton donors*, and recall that solution of hydrogen chloride in water is accompanied by the reaction

$$HCl + H_2O \rightarrow H_3O^+ + Cl^-.$$

In this reaction a proton (H^+) is transferred from the polar HCl molecule to a water molecule. HCl thus donates a proton, water accepts it; HCl is therefore an acid, H_2O a base. Similarly, when pure nitric acid is dissolved in water, proton transfer occurs:

$$HNO_3 + H_2O \rightarrow H_3O^+ + NO_3^-.$$

In this case HNO_3 is the donor and H_2O is again the acceptor. When a *solution* of either hydrochloric acid or nitric acid reacts with a base, however, the proton donor present is hydronium ion:

$$H_3O^+ + OH^- \rightarrow 2H_2O.$$

In this case hydronium ion is the acid, hydroxide ion the base. The reactions between HCl or HNO_3 and water proceed to completion (these are strong electrolytes) and the acid property of the solutions which form is

---

*The nuclei of atoms are known to contain protons, but these are not involved in any of the proton transfer processes discussed here. These are *chemical* processes in which hydrogen ions (protons) are transferred from one molecular environment to another.

solely that of hydronium ion. Such substances, of which sulfuric (H_2SO_4) and perchloric ($HClO_4$) acids are also examples, are called *strong* acids.

When acetic acid is dissolved in water most of its molecules are unaffected, while a small fraction of them donate protons to water molecules:

$$HC_2H_3O_2 + H_2O \rightarrow H_3O^+ + C_2H_3O_2^-.$$

The tendency of acetic acid molecules to donate protons is slight, and this substance is called a *weak* acid. Carbonic acid is another example in this category. It forms when CO_2 is dissolved in water:

$$CO_2 + H_2O \rightarrow H_2CO_3,$$

and a fraction of the H_2CO_3 molecules which form donate protons to the solvent:

$$H_2CO_3 + H_2O \rightarrow H_3O^+ + HCO_3^-.$$

Reversibility of chemical change is an important subject which we shall discuss in Chapter 22; for present purposes we must simply state that for a weak acid the *reverse* of the proton donation reaction has a marked tendency to proceed, e.g.,

$$C_2H_3O_2^- + H_3O^+ \rightarrow HC_2H_3O_2 + H_2O,$$

and

$$HCO_3^- + H_3O^+ \rightarrow H_2CO_3 + H_2O.$$

In these two examples both acetate and bicarbonate ions accept protons, and may therefore be called bases. In a solution of sodium hydroxide it is hydroxide ion which accepts protons; this tendency is strong, and OH^- is called a strong base. The proton-accepting tendencies of acetate and bicarbonate ion are small, and these are weak bases. Ammonia, which accepts protons from water molecules when it is dissolved, is another example of a weak base:

$$NH_3 + H_2O \rightarrow NH_4^+ + OH^-.$$

In this example, water behaves like an acid, while in our earlier examples its behavior was that of a base. There are several substances, called *amphiprotic*, which can either donate or accept protons, depending upon the circumstances. Bicarbonate ion is another example of an amphiprotic substance; we have seen that it can accept protons from hydronium ion, and it can also donate them to hydroxide ion:

$$HCO_3^- + OH^- \rightarrow H_2O + CO_3^{--}.$$

Whenever an acid combines with a base, a new acid and a new base are formed. Thus whenever an acetic acid molecule donates a proton, acetate ion, a base, is formed. If the proton is donated to a water molecule, hydronium ion, an acid, is formed. Whenever acetate ion acts as a base, on the other hand, acetic acid forms, and whenever hydronium ion donates a proton, water is formed. It is convenient, then, to introduce the concept of the *conjugate acid-base pair*, one member of which always appears when the other acts as an acid or base. Acetic acid-acetate ion is one such pair, hydronium ion-water is another. In the case of neutralization,

$$H_3O^+ + OH^- \rightarrow H_2O + H_2O,$$

one of the H_2O molecules formed must be regarded as the acid-conjugate of OH^-, the other as the base-conjugate of H_3O^+. In the case of the reaction between HCl and water, chloride ion is the product which always will form when HCl donates a proton; logically applying our conjugate pair concept, Cl^- must be called the conjugate base of HCl. Chloride ion has virtually no tendency to accept protons from hydronium ion or any other acid, however; as a base, it is weak in the extreme. The bases which are conjugate to all strong acids are similarly very weak.

TABLE 21-1

CONJUGATE ACID-BASE PAIRS

Acid	Base
$HClO_4$	ClO_4^-
HNO_3	NO_3^-
HCl	Cl^-
H_3O^+	H_2O
H_3PO_4	$H_2PO_4^-$
$HC_2H_3O_2$	$C_2H_3O_2^-$
H_2CO_3	HCO_3^-
NH_4^+	NH_3
H_2O	OH^-

(Acid column: Increasing strength ↑)   (Base column: Increasing strength ↓)

As our discussion in the last paragraph has brought out, the stronger an acid, the weaker is its conjugate base. This relation is double edged, since strong bases have weak conjugate acids. The virtue of the conjugate pair concept resides in this relation, in a way that is shown in Table 21-1. In this partial listing, the acids are shown in order of decreasing strength, and their conjugate bases are then automatically arranged in order of increasing strength. It will be noted that the number of strong acids in this list greatly exceeds the number of strong bases; the basic strength of NH_3 is roughly equivalent to the acid strength of acetic acid, although the former is only second from the bottom in the list of bases. The relative strengths of acids depend upon the degrees of polar character with which their acid hydrogen atoms are attached, and the relative ease with which the attachment may be broken. For bases, it depends upon the availability of an unshared electron pair on an electronegative atom (e.g., the oxygen atom in hydroxide ion) and the force with which this electron pair can hold an added proton.

The listing of conjugate acid-base pairs shown in Table 21-1 may be used to illustrate an interesting generalization, that acid-base reactions tend toward production of the weakest possible acid and the weakest possible base. The reaction between a very strong acid, e.g. HCl, and water proceeds essentially to completion, and produces an acid (H_3O^+) which is weaker than HCl and a base (Cl^-) which is weaker than water. The reverse reaction has almost no tendency to proceed. When acetic acid donates protons to water, however, an acid (H_3O^+) which is stronger than acetic acid and a base (acetate ion) which is stronger than water are formed. In this case the tendency of the forward reaction to proceed is slight, but that of the reverse process, which results in formation of an acid and a base each of which is weaker than its original counterpart, is relatively strong. What we have said here is that the concentration of acetate ion present in an acetic acid solution tends to be limited by its own basicity. The whole question is one which is much more readily understood in terms of the principles of chemical equilibrium, however, which forms most of the subject matter of the next chapter. We shall have occasion to consider acid-base systems again in the light of these principles.

21-8 Summary

The study of solutions, homogeneous mixtures of two or more substances, has contributed materially to our fundamental understanding of matter. As a guide to solution formation it is said that "like dissolves like," but, to be useful, this rule requires interpretation in terms of the physical details of the process of solution. Solutions of electrolytes, which conduct electric current, have played a particularly important role in the histories of chemical and electrical science. While Faraday thought that ions are formed by the application of potential difference to an electrolytic solution, Arrhenius proposed that they are formed by dissociation of molecules on solution in water. The theory of Arrhenius was devised to account for the unique freezing-point properties of electrolytic solutions, as well as their electrical conductivities. This theory proved completely successful in accounting for the properties of weak electrolytes, substances whose molecules react incompletely with water to form ions. For strong electrolytes a newer view introduced by Debye and Hückel, that dissociation into discrete ions in solution is complete but that attractions between ions must be taken into account, has been adopted. There are two kinds of strong electrolytes, solutes whose crystals consist of ions and others which consist of strongly polar molecules which react completely with water to form ions. The latter category includes all the strong acids. Many chemical changes take place as reactions between ions, and proton transfer reactions between acids and bases are important examples.

REFERENCES

LEICESTER, H. M., and H. S. KLICKSTEIN, *Source Book in Chemistry*, 471–475 (Raoult), 453–458 (van't Hoff on "The Role of Osmotic Pressure in the Analogy between Solutions and Gases"), 483–490 (Arrhenius).

PAULING, L., *General Chemistry*, Chapter 16.

SISLER, H. H., and others, *General Chemistry, a Systematic Approach*, Chapters 16 and 17.

1. What does it mean to say that two substances are "miscible in all proportions"? Give examples of such pairs of substances, and explain their mutual miscibilities.

2. The molecules of hydrogen sulfide gas are slightly polar. Arrange the following three substances in what you believe to be decreasing order of ability to dissolve hydrogen sulfide, and justify your answer: alcohol, benzene, water.

3. After examining Fig. 21–2, describe possible ways of forming supersaturated solutions of sodium sulfate and potassium dichromate.

4. Nickel fluoride (NiF_2) has a solubility in water of 2.6 gm/100 ml at 20°C. What is the concentration of a saturated solution of this substance in moles per liter? [*Ans.*: 0.27 molar]

5. As fully as you can, describe the molecular or ionic processes which accompany formation of the following solutions: (a) potassium permanganate in water, (b) iodine in carbon tetrachloride. (c) hydrogen chloride gas in water, (d) hydrogen chloride gas in benzene.

6. Why would the concentration of a hydrochloric acid solution change during the course of a measurement of its conductance in which direct current is passed through it? What processes would occur at the electrodes?

7. 9.6 gm of methyl alcohol (CH_3OH) is dissolved in 100 gm of water. What is the freezing point of the solution?

8. To protect an automobile radiator to a temperature of $-20°C$ using ethylene glycol ($C_2H_4(OH)_2$) as antifreeze, what percentage of ethylene glycol should be present? [*Ans.*: about 41%]

9. The freezing point of a solution containing 17.4 gm of K_2SO_4 in 1000 gm of water is $-0.432°C$; the freezing point of a solution containing 1.74 gm of K_2SO_4 in 1000 gm of water is $-0.0501°C$. Can you demonstrate that the more dilute solution is more "abnormal" than the more concentrated one? Do so and explain.

10. Hydrocyanic acid (HCN) forms a water solution which conducts current weakly. (a) How would you classify HCN as an electrolyte? (b) Write an equation for the interaction between HCN and water. (c) What base is conjugate to HCN? (d) What reaction would you expect to occur if hydrochloric acid solution were added to a solution containing cyanide ion? Write an equation.

11. Sodium chloride solution is "neutral to litmus," i.e., it gives neither an acidic nor a basic test. Ammonium chloride solution turns blue litmus paper to red, while sodium acetate solution turns red litmus paper blue. Explain with equations.

12. When hydrochloric acid solution is added to sodium bicarbonate, carbon dioxide is evolved. Write equations for this process.

13. The *amide* ion, NH_2^-, is a

stronger base than hydroxide ion; it accepts protons from water in a vigorous reaction. What must the products of this reaction be? What substance is the conjugate acid of amide ion? What word must be applied to this substance?

14. The bisulfate ion HSO_4^- is an example of an amphiprotic substance. Write equations illustrating its action (a) as an acid, and (b) as a base.

15. Proton-transfer reactions in water solution are often divided into the two classes *neutralization* and *hydrolysis*. Neutralization reactions are those proton-transfer reactions in which water is a product, hydrolysis reactions those in which water is a reactant. Write equations illustrating at least two examples of each kind of reaction.

CHAPTER 22

CHEMICAL REACTION RATE AND CHEMICAL EQUILIBRIUM

In the last several chapters we have been preoccupied with questions concerning the structure of matter. We have found that these questions cannot be divorced from the transformations which matter undergoes, and that transformations of matter are always accompanied by transformations of energy. We have considered the detailed structures of atoms and molecules in terms of the energies of their constituent particles, and in Chapter 21 we returned to consideration of certain aspects of the behavior of matter in bulk. In our discussion of acid-base systems, we have encountered the interesting question of the *reversibility* of chemical change. The degree of completeness of any given reaction, long a question of great importance to the chemist, will obviously be affected by any reacting tendency on the part of its opposite, or reverse, process. Closely related to this problem is that of the *rate* at which a reaction takes place under given conditions, and because of the nature of this relationship we shall discuss reaction rate questions first. Neither rate of reaction nor reversibility can be interpreted without also considering transformations of chemical energy.

22–1 Rates of chemical reactions

There is an exceedingly wide range of rates at which reactions may take place. The explosive decomposition of a sample of nitroglycerine, for example, may be completed in the span of a few millionths of a second, while the rusting of iron at ordinary temperatures is almost imperceptibly slow. The combination of silver and chloride ions to form silver chloride appears to occur instantaneously, while the reaction between magnesium and hydronium ion to liberate hydrogen occurs at a conveniently measurable rate. For quantitative purposes, it will be necessary for us to have a precise idea of the meaning of reaction rate, and we shall define it as *the quantity of a reactant consumed, or of a product formed, per unit of time*. To measure the rate of the magnesium-hydronium ion reaction

$$Mg + 2H_3O^+ \rightarrow H_2 \uparrow + Mg^{++} + 2H_2O,$$

for example, an investigator could measure the concentration of the reactant acid at regular, measured intervals of time or, more conveniently,

collect the escaping hydrogen gas
and make periodic measurements of
its total accumulated volume (Fig.
22–1).

The rate of any given chemical reaction clearly depends upon the
nature of the particular reactants
involved. It is not often possible,
however, to apply chemical structural principles directly to the prediction of reaction rates. We know
that carbon has a great tendency to
combine spontaneously with oxygen,
for example, yet charcoal can be
stored in air indefinitely without
oxidizing to carbon dioxide. Only
when the temperature of a portion of
the charcoal is raised sufficiently
does the reaction get under way, and
the combustion is then sustained, at
the necessary high temperature, by
the large quantity of heat that is
given up in the reaction itself. Elemental nitrogen and hydrogen can
be stored together for years at ordinary temperatures and pressures
without forming detectable amounts
of ammonia, even though substantial energy is given off when they do

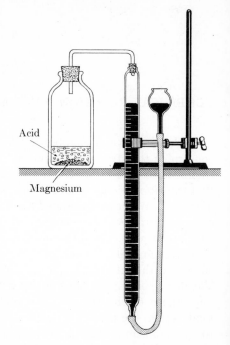

FIG. 22–1. Measuring the rate of
evolution of hydrogen in the reaction
between magnesium and an acid. The
vessel on the right must be lowered as
hydrogen evolves, so that all measurements will be made at the same
pressure.

combine and we should expect the reaction to occur spontaneously.
Conditions can be found, as we shall learn, under which this reaction
can be made rapid. We shall, then, have to bear in mind that the chemical
nature of reactants is of underlying importance to all reaction rates, but
we shall turn our attention to the profound alterations in rate that can be
brought about by certain changes in conditions.

As we have indicated, the *temperature* of reacting materials has a strong
determining effect on chemical reaction rate. Laboratory burners (e.g., the
Bunsen burner) have long been an indispensable part of the chemist's
equipment, so that he may accelerate reactions which may be very slow at
ordinary temperatures. The first recorded quantitative measurements of
the effect of temperature on reaction rate were made in 1850, by Ludwig
Wilhelmy (1812–1864). It was already known that increasing temperature
always increases reaction rate. Wilhelmy and later investigators showed

that the exact extent to which temperature affects reaction rate depends upon the particular reactants involved, but that a very approximate generalization can be made: the rate of chemical reaction is roughly doubled by a temperature increase of 10°C. This approximate empirical rule is illustrated in Fig. 22–2; the rule does not describe any particular reaction precisely, but represents a convenient expression of average, general behavior.

When Priestley plunged a lighted candle into a container of pure oxygen and observed that it burned very brightly, he was observing the effect of increased reactant concentration on reaction rate. In air, roughly 20% oxygen, the candle burned relatively slowly, but its burning rate was greatly enhanced by the presence of pure oxygen. All reaction rates are strongly dependent upon the concentrations of reacting materials, and the quantitative nature of this dependence will be discussed in a separate section. As a corollary to the concentration dependence of reaction rate, we may mention that when one of the reactants involved in a reaction is a solid, the rate is very sensitive to the state of subdivision of that material. Large lumps of coal burn relatively slowly, pieces of pea-size much more rapidly, and the combustion of finely divided coal dust may proceed with explosive rapidity. When acid of a given concentration is poured over two samples of zinc, one powdered and the other granulated, hydrogen is liberated much more rapidly by the former. It is the available reacting surface of the solid (which increases with finer sub-division) that determines reaction rate in these cases.

When potassium chlorate is heated in a Bunsen flame, it decomposes to liberate oxygen slowly. When a small quantity of manganese dioxide is added to the potassium chlorate, the same reaction takes place very rapidly. The manganese dioxide can be recovered after decomposition is complete, and is found unaltered. There are numerous known instances of reaction rates which are profoundly altered by the presence of materials which are not themselves transformed. Such materials are called *catalysts*, a name proposed by Berzelius, who was the first to recognize the existence of

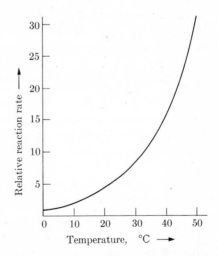

FIG. 22–2. Approximate effect of temperature on reaction rate. If the value 1 is arbitrarily assigned to the rate of any reaction at 0°C, rate increases roughly as shown in the graph.

the general phenomenon called *catalysis*. There are many reactions which are catalyzed by the presence of noble metals such as platinum. Sir Humphry Davy found in 1817, for example, that a spiral of platinum wire becomes heated to incandescence when suspended in a mixture of ethyl alcohol vapor and air. The oxidation of the ethyl alcohol is catalyzed by the platinum, and since heat is evolved in the reaction, the wire is strongly heated. Many chemical reactions of industrial importance have been made possible only through discovery of materials capable of catalyzing them. Many important reactions in biological systems are catalyzed by substances called *enzymes*; *amylase*, for example, is an enzyme which promotes the decomposition of starches to form the sugar *glucose*.

There is no single underlying principle which can be employed to explain all known cases of catalytic effect. There are many different mechanisms by which catalysts can act, and while numerous catalyzed reactions are well understood, many others are not. Catalysis at metallic surfaces generally seems to involve the dissociation of molecules. It is known that hydrogen molecules dissociate to form hydrogen atoms on the surface of platinum, for example, and that hydrogen atoms are much more reactive than hydrogen molecules. Reactions involving elemental hydrogen are generally catalyzed by the presence of platinum. Other kinds of catalysis appear to involve formation of an intermediate compound between reactant and catalyst molecules; when the reaction has gone to completion the intermediate compound has broken down and restored the catalyst molecule to its original state, so that no *over-all* change in catalyst concentration occurs.

22–2 Collisions and activation energy

If we stop now to ask *why* concentration and temperature changes affect reaction rates strongly, we must think in terms of molecular motions. Rates are controlled, in an underlying sense, by collisions between particles of the reacting materials. When hydrogen and iodine molecules react, for example:

$$H_2 + I_2 \rightarrow 2HI,$$

the formation of bonds between hydrogen and iodine atoms could not take place unless unlike molecules were to collide. If collision were to occur with sufficient impact to break bonds between like atoms, a rearrangement of electrons might take place in which *un*like atoms which find themselves near one another join to form HI molecules. The motion of molecules, we know, is random, so that collisions between them is entirely a matter of chance. If the number of molecules of either kind per unit volume (i.e., the concentration of either reactant) is increased, the probability of collision must also be increased. Rate of reaction should therefore depend upon concentration, as is observed.

While chemical reactions undoubtedly depend upon collisions between particles, their mechanisms are rarely as simple as might be inferred from our discussion of the hydrogen-iodine reaction. A similar interpretation of the reaction between hydrogen and nitrogen,

$$N_2 + 3H_2 \rightarrow 2NH_3,$$

for example, would require the assumption of collisions involving four molecules, which must certainly be rare events. In most cases other than the very simplest of reactions, two or more distinct steps are involved, so that improbable multiple collisions are not required. In the case of the nitrogen-hydrogen reaction, dissociation of molecules into atoms must certainly be one of the steps which prepare the way for formation of the final product molecules of ammonia.

Under the same conditions of temperature and pressure some reactions are very fast, others very slow. Observation of so wide a range of rates indicates that in most cases molecular collisions which lead to reaction constitute only a small fraction of the total that occur per unit of time. The increase in reaction rate observed to accompany an increase in temperature is expected from the relation between temperature and average molecular kinetic energy: the average velocity of the molecules is increased, and the frequency with which they collide is enhanced. The increase in collision rate corresponding to a 10° temperature rise can be calculated, however, and it became apparent long ago that the approximate doubling of reaction rate which a 10° rise brings about cannot possibly be accounted for in terms of increased collision rate alone. It was Arrhenius who first proposed a way out of this dilemma, and his explanation has proved indispensable to our present understanding of reaction rate phenomena.

In brief, Arrhenius' explanation centers upon the small fraction of collisions which *do* lead to reaction, and interprets this fraction in energetic terms. If a molecule of hydrogen collides with one of iodine, reaction will not occur unless the sum of their kinetic energies exceeds a certain minimum quantity. In general, reaction is brought about by collision between molecules whose kinetic energies are *greater* than the average. Such collisions are called *activated* collisions, and the minimum energy requirement for a given reaction to occur is called its *activation energy*. Arrhenius was able to demonstrate that relatively small temperature rises result in very substantial increase in the numbers of molecules present whose kinetic energy greatly exceeds the average. This being the case, the frequency of *activated* collisions, and hence the fraction of the total number of occurring collisions which lead to reaction, is increased. Arrhenius' proposal has turned out to be quantitatively useful in interpreting the effect of temperature on individual reaction rates.

Hydrogen and oxygen, with great release of energy, combine to form water. The reaction will take place with explosive violence if initiated by a spark or by introduction of finely divided platinum catalyst, but hydrogen and oxygen, in 2:1 volume ratio, can be mixed and stored in the same container for years without appreciable reaction taking place. This is an example, then, of a reaction which has very high activation energy. Only collisions which occur between molecules of very high kinetic energy are effective in breaking the bonds between atoms in the reactant molecules and leading to the formation of water. At ordinary temperatures, activated collisions require energies so greatly in excess of the average that they are exceedingly rare. The reaction between hydrogen and nitrogen, which also involves substantial energy release, is another example of a reaction with high activation energy. An analogy appropriate to these cases, perhaps, would be a giant boulder reposing in a deep glacial lake near the peak of a high mountain. A very great spontaneous lowering in potential energy is available to the boulder: let it just roll down the mountain. Before this energy loss can occur, however, a smaller but substantial quantity of energy must be *supplied* to the boulder to lift it to the rim of the lake basin (Fig. 22–3).

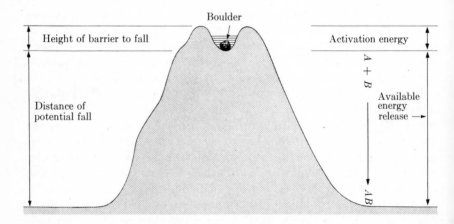

FIG. 22–3. Activation energy.

22–3 Reversibility and chemical equilibrium

Reaction rates, as we have said, are dependent upon the concentrations of reacting substances. The nature of this dependence was the subject of several investigations during the eighteenth and nineteenth centuries. Berthollet had recognized the effect of reactant mass on reaction rate, and Wilhelmy, in 1850, discovered that the rate of a certain reaction between cane sugar and water, in the presence of acid, is directly proportional to the concentration of the sugar. Marcellin Berthelot (1827–1907) and Péan de St. Gilles (1832–1863), in 1862, established that the rate of the reaction between ethyl alcohol and acetic acid to form ethyl acetate and water,

$$C_2H_5OH + HC_2H_3O_2 \rightarrow C_2H_3O_2(C_2H_5) + H_2O,$$

$\quad$ (ethyl alcohol) $\qquad$ (acetic acid) $\qquad$ (ethyl acetate)

is directly proportional to the concentrations of *both* reactants. Numerous examples of direct proportionality between concentration and reaction rate have been found subsequently. For a reaction which we may represent simply as

$$A + B \rightarrow \text{products},$$

it is thus quite generally found that the reaction rate R, at any fixed temperature, may be expressed algebraically as

$$R = kc_Ac_B , \qquad (22\text{–}1)$$

where c_A and c_B represent the concentrations of reactants A and B, and k is a constant of proportionality. This relation is illustrated in Fig. 22–4.

It is not surprising that rate is proportional to reactant concentrations for a simple combination reaction, if we think of the process in terms of molecular collisions. If the number of molecules of either kind per unit volume is doubled, the frequency with which molecules of that kind

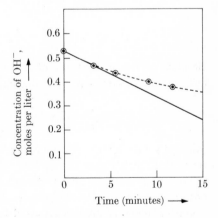

FIG. 22–4. Rate of the reaction between ethyl acetate and hydroxide ion to form ethyl alcohol and acetate ion. Straight line represents direct proportionality between rate and concentration. (Actual result in this case deviates from a straight line, as shown, because the reaction is reversible; as concentrations of products increase, rate of reverse reaction increases.)

collide with molecules of the other kind, and hence reaction rate itself, should also be doubled. For many other reactions in which two molecules of a single reactant are involved, rate is found to be proportional to the *square* of the concentration of that reactant. For the formation of nitrogen tetroxide from nitrogen dioxide,

$$2NO_2 \rightarrow N_2O_4,$$

for example, the reaction rate at a fixed temperature is found to conform to the equation

$$R = k(c_{NO_2})^2. \tag{22-2}$$

In this case, since reaction to form N_2O_4 must involve collision between two molecules of NO_2, doubling the concentration of reactant *quadruples* the frequency of collision between like molecules. In the earlier days of reaction rate study, it was believed that rate is proportional to the concentration of each reactant raised to a power corresponding to the coefficient of that reactant in the balanced equation for the reaction, i.e., that for the general reaction

$$aA + bB \rightarrow products,$$

$$R = k(c_A)^a(c_B)^b. \tag{22-3}$$

Because of the complexity of many reactions, this relation frequently does not hold, however. The decomposition of nitrogen pentoxide,

$$2N_2O_5 \rightarrow 4NO_2 + O_2,$$

exhibits a rate which is proportional only to the *first* power of N_2O_5 concentration, rather than the square. The reason for this, presumably, is that the reaction occurs in two or more steps, the slowest of which, at least, does not depend upon collisions between two N_2O_5 molecules.

Out of the early investigations of reaction rates there gradually emerged a realization that reactions may reverse themselves, and that measured rates may be strongly affected by such reversals. Berthollet had observed a striking instance of reaction reversal with alteration of the quantities of reactants, but because of his celebrated mistake in challenging Proust's law of definite proportions (Chapter 7) nearly all his work was neglected by the generations of chemists that followed him. Berthelot and St. Gilles, in their work on the rate of reaction of ethyl alcohol with acetic acid to form ethyl acetate, observed that the reaction does not go to completion. They also observed that acetic acid and ethyl alcohol form when water is added to ethyl acetate, which clearly demonstrated the reversibility of this reaction. Numerous other examples gradually became known, and in 1867 the Norwegian chemists C. M. Guldberg (1836–1902) and Peter Waage (1833–1900), building on the work of Berthelot and St. Gilles and on observations of their own, formulated an important, quantitative, general principle concerning reversible reactions.

If a reaction does not go to completion, Guldberg and Waage argued, occurrence of its opposite, or reverse reaction, must be the factor which prevents it from doing so. Furthermore, as the concentrations of reactants diminish, the forward reaction will gradually slow down, but at the same time the concentrations of products increase and the reverse reaction gradually becomes faster. Ultimately, then, a condition should be reached at which forward and reverse reactions occur at *equal rates*; when this *equilibrium* condition is reached, the concentrations of all reactants and products should remain constant with time. This is the basis of our contemporary view of *dynamic* chemical equilibrium, a view which was first proposed by A. W. Williamson (1824–1904) in 1850, but first placed on a quantitative basis by Guldberg and Waage.

To illustrate the meaning of the chemical equilibrium principle, let us use the example of the ethyl alcohol-acetic acid reaction, which was discussed by Guldberg and Waage in their original paper. We shall study the molecular nature of the substances involved in this reaction in Chapter 23, but for present purposes, let us represent the reaction in the following manner:

$$\text{EtOH} \ + \ \text{HAc} \ \rightleftarrows \ \text{EtAc} \ + \ \text{H}_2\text{O}.$$
$$\text{(ethyl alcohol)} \quad \text{(acetic acid)} \quad \text{(ethyl acetate)} \quad \text{(water)}$$

Two arrows are shown, to indicate that both forward and reverse reactions may proceed. When EtOH is added to HAc, their molecules collide to form EtAc and H_2O, at a rate which diminishes as these reactants become used up, but which can be expressed, for the concentrations present at any instant, by the expression

$$R_f = k_f c_{\text{EtOH}} \, c_{\text{HAc}}. \tag{22-4}$$

In this equation R_f designates rate of *forward* reaction, and k_f is the appropriate proportionality constant. After some product molecules, EtAc and H_2O, have formed, they begin to collide with one another, with a frequency which increases as their numbers are increased by the forward reaction. Some of these collisions lead to reaction to *re*-form EtOH and HAc molecules, and the rate of the reverse reaction can be expressed in the equation

$$R_r = k_r c_{\text{EtAc}} \, c_{\text{H2O}}. \tag{22-5}$$

Eventually, a state is reached in which forward and reverse reaction rates are equal, hence EtOH and HAc are re-formed by the reverse reaction as rapidly as they are used up in the forward reaction, and the concentrations of all four substances remain constant. The condition for this state of equilibrium, since

$$R_f = R_r,$$

is that

$$k_f c_{\text{EtOH}}\, c_{\text{HAc}} = k_r c_{\text{EtAc}}\, c_{\text{H2O}} . \tag{22–6}$$

Rearranging,

$$\frac{c_{\text{EtAc}}\, c_{\text{H2O}}}{c_{\text{EtOH}}\, c_{\text{HAc}}} = \frac{k_f}{k_r} = K, \tag{22–7}$$

where K, the ratio of forward and reverse rate proportionality constants, is called the *equilibrium constant* for this chemical system at equilibrium.

The equation just developed constitutes a quantitative prediction: if the rate expressions and the equilibrium principle are both correct, the product of the concentrations of products divided by the product of reactant concentrations should be constant at any given temperature. (It may vary with temperature, since forward and reverse rates may be altered to different extents by temperature changes.) This prediction was made by Guldberg and Waage, who verified it for the ethyl alcohol-acetic acid reaction. If one mole (gram-molecular weight) of acetic acid and one mole of ethyl alcohol are mixed and allowed to stand at 25°C until equilibrium is attained, analysis of the resulting mixture shows the presence of $\frac{2}{3}$ mole of ethyl acetate, $\frac{2}{3}$ mole of water, and $\frac{1}{3}$ mole each of ethyl alcohol and acetic acid. If these values are substituted in the equilibrium constant expression,*

$$K = \frac{(2/3) \times (2/3)}{(1/3) \times (1/3)} = 4.$$

This same value of K, 4, is found to result at equilibrium from *any* initial combination of reactants or products. If *two* moles of acetic acid are added to one mole of ethyl alcohol, for example, analysis of the final mixture at equilibrium at 25°C shows the presence of 0.84 mole each of ethyl acetate and water, 1.16 mole of acetic acid, and 0.16 mole of ethyl alcohol. If these numbers are substituted in the equilibrium constant expression, the constant will be found to have the same value as for the case of equal numbers of moles of initial reactants.

---

*This is permissible, since these numbers of moles all refer to the same total volume, hence are proportional to concentrations.

Chemical equilibrium, then, is *a state of unchanging concentration of reactants and products brought about by equal forward and reverse reaction rates.* An equilibrium state can be established only at constant pressure and temperature, and the particular set of concentrations present in a chemical system at equilibrium under a given set of conditions is often referred to as a *point of equilibrium.* Two different points of equilibrium for the ethyl alcohol-acetic acid system have been mentioned in the last paragraph, for example. When equal molar quantities of reactants are mixed initially, $\frac{2}{3}$ mole of ethyl acetate is present at equilibrium; when two moles of one reactant are mixed with one mole of the other, a larger quantity of ethyl acetate, 0.84 mole, is present when equilibrium is established. Although equilibrium points may be shifted by changes in temperature and pressure, in a manner which we shall discuss in the next section, catalysts cannot affect them. Catalysts, it will be recalled, alter the *rates* of chemical reactions. Remarkably, they accelerate forward and reverse rates to the same extent, and hence hasten the attainment of equilibrium, but they do not alter the final equilibrium point of a reversible system.

It may seem that the equilibrium principles we have discussed are applicable to only a small number of special cases of reactions which do not go to completion in the forward direction. Degree of completeness of a chemical reaction is an entirely relative matter, however; in general, it is found that *nearly all* chemical processes are reversible, even though the tendency to reverse is frequently very small. In some cases one or more of the products of a reaction are removed by gas evolution or precipitation, and the effect of such removal is to drive the forward reaction to completion. When calcium carbonate is heated, it decomposes to form calcium oxide and carbon dioxide, for example:

$$CaCO_3 \leftrightarrows CaO + CO_2 \uparrow ;$$

if the decomposition is carried out in a closed container so that no CO_2 escapes, a definite equilibrium point is established for any given temperature, but if the CO_2 is allowed to escape the forward reaction will go to completion. In many instances in which product molecules do not leave the reaction container the tendency of the reverse process to proceed is so small that the forward process appears to go to completion. The reaction between HCl and water to form hydronium and chloride ions is an example of a reaction which becomes complete for all *practical* purposes, and the reaction between hydrogen and oxygen to form water is another. The completeness of both reactions is still only *relative*, not actual, and can be altered by changes in conditions. The reversibility of the system

$$2H_2 + O_2 \rightleftarrows 2H_2O,$$

for example, becomes obvious at very high temperatures, since under such conditions hydrogen and oxygen molecules in equilibrium with water molecules are readily detected.

Every chemical equilibrium system exhibits its own characteristic equilibrium *constant* at specified temperature. The general equilibrium constant expression, for any reaction represented as

$$aA + bB \rightleftarrows cC + dD,$$

is

$$K = \frac{(c_C)^c (c_D)^d}{(c_A)^a (c_B)^b}.$$

This expression holds accurately for all equilibrium systems, even though the corresponding rate expressions,

$$R_f = k_f (c_A)^a (c_B)^b$$

and

$$R_r = k_r (c_C)^c (c_D)^d ,$$

may not always hold, as we have said. The numerical values of equilibrium constants reflect the relative tendencies for forward and reverse processes to proceed, since K is the ratio of the two rate proportionality constants k_f and k_r. The value $K = 4$ for the ethyl alcohol-acetic acid system, for example, indicates that the forward tendency is stronger than its reverse. In the case of the equilibrium

$$N_2 + O_2 \rightleftarrows 2NO,$$

for which

$$K = \frac{(c_{NO})^2}{(c_{N_2})(c_{O_2})} ,$$

the equilibrium constant is found to have a very small value at 25°C, indicating a relatively small tendency of the forward reaction to proceed. If equal numbers of nitrogen and oxygen molecules are mixed at 25°C, the final equilibrium mixture will contain no more than a minute fraction of NO molecules.

22–4 The principle of LeChatelier

The industrial chemist is frequently able to accelerate an economically important reaction by the use of catalysts. For a reaction that is *reversible*, however, mere increase in rate may not be sufficient. The reaction between nitrogen and oxygen to produce nitric oxide, for example, has so small a tendency to proceed in the forward direction under ordinary conditions that it could not be used for practical production of NO unless means could be found to achieve a favorable shift in the point of equilibrium of the system. It is of great importance to the practicing chemist, therefore, to know what factors can affect the point of equilibrium of a reversible re-action. The most significant of these factors are *concentrations* of reactants and products, *temperature*, and *pressure*. It is equally important to have some basis for prediction of the manner in which changes in these factors will affect equilibrium points, and the necessary basis is found in a general principle first proposed by the French chemist Henri Louis LeChatelier (1850–1936) in 1888.

LeChatelier's principle may be stated in the following way: *if a stress is applied to any system at equilibrium, the point of equilibrium will shift in a manner which tends to relieve the stress.* To interpret this statement, read for *stress*: "Alteration of any condition—temperature, pressure, or con-centration—which determines the final state of equilibrium." Relieving the stress, then, means *offsetting* the altered condition. *Shift* in the equilib-rium point means that one reaction, forward or reverse, proceeds until a new state of equilibrium, with new concentrations of reactants and prod-ucts, is attained. If it is the forward reaction that proceeds temporarily, so that in the new equilibrium state the concentrations of products are higher than before, we shall say that the equilibrium point *shifts to the right*. If the new state is one in which concentrations of reactants are greater than before, we shall say that the equilibrium point *shifts to the left*.

Consider the equilibrium system consisting of nitric oxide, oxygen, and nitrogen dioxide at some fixed temperature and pressure:

$$2NO + O_2 \rightleftarrows 2NO_2.$$

At the steady state of equilibrium forward and reverse reaction rates are equal and the concentrations of all three component substances remain constant. If some additional oxygen is now introduced into the container, however, a *stress* is applied and the existing equilibrium is upset. Applying LeChatelier's principle, we may say that the equilibrium point will shift in a manner that will *relieve* this stress, i.e., remove oxygen. This means that the forward reaction will now become temporarily faster than the reverse and all three concentrations will change. Finally, reverse and forward rates will again become equal and a new state of equilibrium is established in which the concentration of NO_2 is now greater than before (Fig. 22–5). This sequence of events may be summarized by saying that the equilibrium point has *shifted to the right*. If some additional NO_2 were now added to the reaction vessel, the reverse reaction rate would become temporarily greater and the equilibrium point would *shift to the left*.

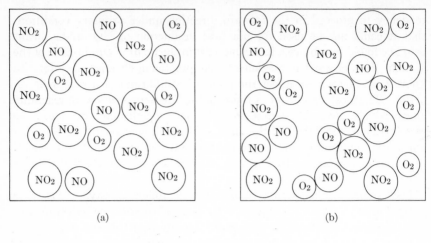

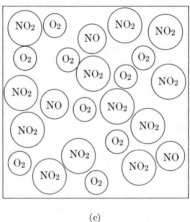

Fig. 22–5. (a) NO, O_2, and NO_2 molecules at equilibrium. (b) Equilibrium is temporarily upset by addition of new oxygen molecules. (c) New equilibrium state is achieved, with smaller numbers of NO and O_2 molecules than in (b), more NO_2 molecules.

Next let us inquire what would happen if our nitrogen oxide-oxygen system were subjected to an increase in temperature. The LeChatelier principle predicts that, in this case, the equilibrium point will shift in whichever direction will have the effect of lowering temperature, i.e., of *absorbing* heat. To apply the principle specifically, we must know one more fact about this system: the reaction between NO and O_2 is known to *evolve* heat. Quantitatively, it is known that 26,000 calories of heat are evolved for every 2 moles of NO_2 formed, and we may express this information in a *thermochemical equation:*

$$2NO + O_2 \rightleftarrows 2NO_2 + 26,000 \text{ calories.}$$

Reactions which evolve heat are called *exothermic*, those which absorb heat *endothermic*. It is an elementary application of the energy conservation principle to say that in this case the reverse reaction must be endothermic, and must absorb exactly as much heat per mole of NO_2 consumed as is evolved in the forward reaction. An increase in the temperature of our equilibrium system, therefore, will favor the reverse, heat-absorbing reaction, according to the LeChatelier principle. A new equilibrium will be established at the higher temperature in which the NO_2 concentration is smaller than before. We may say that increased temperature, in this case, causes the point of equilibrium to shift to the left.

Suppose now that our equilibrium system is suddenly subjected to an increase of pressure. Since all three constituents are gases, they will be compressed and occupy a smaller total volume than before. If the total number of molecules present were fixed, as in a pure gas, there could be no possible response in the gas itself that could reduce the applied pressure. In this system, however, 3 molecules of NO and O_2 combine to form only 2 of NO_2, in the forward direction. If the forward reaction proceeds, then, a smaller total number of molecules will be present, fewer impacts between molecules and container walls will occur per unit of time, and the stress of increased pressure will be relieved (Fig. 22–6). The LeChatelier principle thus predicts that increased pressure on this system will cause a shift of the equilibrium point to the right.

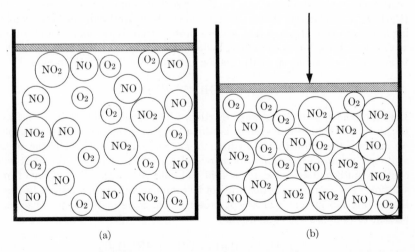

(a)   (b)

Fig. 22–6. Effect of increased pressure on NO—O_2—NO_2 equilibrium: by shifting of the equilibrium point to the right, the total number of molecules is reduced.

Next consider the equilibrium system

$$N_2 + O_2 + 43,000 \text{ calories} \rightleftarrows 2NO.$$

The thermochemical equation indicates that in this case the forward reaction is endothermic, hence an increase in temperature would shift this equilibrium to the right. Removal of NO from the system, or addition of oxygen, would also shift the equilibrium to the right. Application of pressure to this system would have no effect; since 2 molecules react to form the same number, in both forward and reverse reactions, neither shift to the right nor to the left would have the effect of reducing the number of molecules present.

Acid-base systems generally are examples of chemical equilibria, and the significance of conjugate acid-base pairs is related to the equilibria established between their members. When a very strong acid like HCl reacts with the weak base water,

$$HCl + H_2O \rightleftarrows H_3O^+ + Cl^-,$$

the forward reaction proceeds almost to completion before equilibrium is established. Weakness of the conjugate base, in this case Cl^-, reflects the small tendency of the reverse reaction to proceed. However, for a weak acid like acetic acid,

$$HC_2H_3O_2 + H_2O \rightleftarrows H_3O^+ + C_2H_3O_2^-,$$

an equilibrium point is reached in which a high concentration of undissociated acetic acid molecules remains. In this case the conjugate base, acetate ion $(C_2H_3O_2^-)$, is relatively strong. Acetic acid can be neutralized, however, by adding a base which is stronger (i.e., accepts protons from H_3O^+ more readily) than acetate ion. If a solution containing hydroxide ion (e.g., NaOH solution) is added to an acetic acid solution, neutralization between H_3O^+ and OH^- occurs:

$$H_3O^+ + OH^- \rightleftarrows 2H_2O.$$

Here the tendency of the forward reaction, which removes hydronium ion from the acetic acid equilibrium system, is strong. Applying the LeChatelier principle, we may say that reduction of hydronium ion concentration will shift the acetic acid equilibrium to the right. As more and more OH^- is added, this shift will continue until undissociated acetic acid molecules are essentially removed from solution. The resulting solution will not be completely neutral, however, because the acetate ion present will accept protons from some of the water molecules present to establish the equilibrium

$$C_2H_3O_2^- + H_2O \rightleftarrows OH^- + HC_2H_3O_2.$$

There are thus several equilibria which compete with one another, and it is not possible to remove *all* undissociated acetic acid molecules from a water solution.

As an illustration of practical application of the LeChatelier principle, no more impressive example can be given than the development by Fritz Haber (1868–1934) of a process for the production of synthetic ammonia. The importance of this development is closely related to the so-called "nitrogen cycle" (Fig. 22–7). Complex nitrogen compounds called *proteins* (Chapter 24) constitute the basic structural materials of the animal world. Animals obtain them either by eating each other, or by eating plants which contain protein materials that animals are able to utilize. Although nitrogen compounds are thus essential to both animal and plant life, neither plants nor animals are able to utilize elemental, atmospheric nitrogen directly. Continual return of utilizable nitrogen to the soil is therefore essential to the maintenance of life on this planet. Certain "nitrogen-fixing" bacteria play a small part in return of nitrogen to the soil, decay of organic matter plays another part, and a certain amount of atmospheric nitrogen is "fixed" by formation of soluble nitrogen oxides in the presence of lightning discharges. All of these processes combined, however, are not sufficient to return nitrogen to the soil at a rate equivalent to that at which man removes it, and it is necessary to add nitrogenous fertilizers. Extensive deposits of sodium nitrate in Chile have long been an important source of combined nitrogen for fertilizer production, and synthetic ammonia is now an even more important source. Haber's ammonia synthesis process was first extensively used in Germany during World War I to meet that country's need for combined nitrogen for production of high explosives. Most military high explosives—trinitrotoluene (TNT) and nitroglycerine are examples—are compounds that are high in nitrogen content, and require nitrogen in combined form for convenient synthesis.

Production of ammonia from elemental hydrogen and nitrogen involves the equilibrium system

$$N_2 + 3H_2 \rightleftarrows 2NH_3 + 22{,}900 \text{ calories.}$$

If equilibrium were established for this system at ordinary temperatures, the concentration of ammonia would be much greater than that of either hydrogen or nitrogen. As we have said earlier, however, the forward reaction is so exceedingly slow that it is not practical to wait for ammonia to form. No catalyst has been found which will accelerate this reaction appreciably at ordinary temperatures, so that it is necessary to raise the temperature to get any ammonia at all. However, the forward reaction is exothermic to the extent of 22,900 calories; applying the LeChatelier principle, this means that the equilibrium point will shift to the left with increasing temperature. At temperatures which are high enough to give satisfactory reaction rate, the concentration of ammonia at equilibrium becomes very small. There is a way of increasing it, however. Since 4

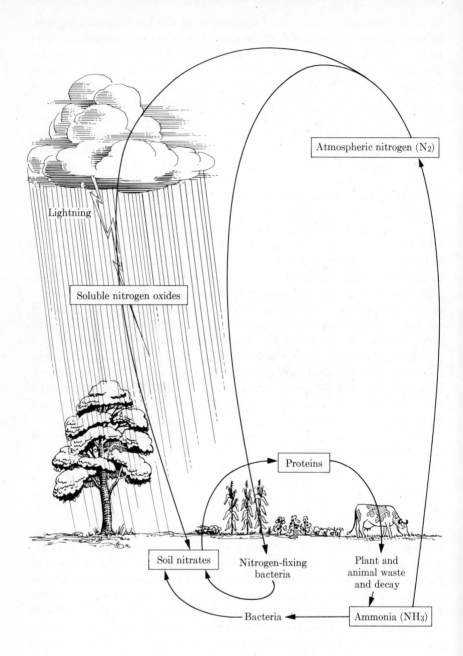

FIG. 22–7. The nitrogen cycle.

molecules of reactants combine to yield only 2 molecules of products, increased pressure will improve the yield of ammonia substantially. Haber sorted out these factors in a detailed study of the ammonia equilibrium system, then found the best combinations of conditions for obtaining optimum yield of ammonia at practical rates. He found catalysts which would accelerate the attainment of equilibrium at temperatures between 400 and 600°C. In this temperature range, the equilibrium ammonia concentration at low pressures is small, but application of high pressures partially offsets this effect so that high yields of ammonia may be obtained. The Haber process is capable of very rapid production of ammonia in a continuous process, and production is especially rapid in modern plants in which pressures between 500 and 1000 times atmospheric pressure are applied. Ammonia produced in this way, as a starting material for the production of fertilizers and high explosives, is a major item in the world's economy today.

22-5 Chemical energy

In our discussion of the effects of temperature changes on systems at equilibrium we have found it necessary to speak of the energy which is either evolved or absorbed in *exo*thermic and *endo*thermic reactions. As we have stated earlier, it is seldom possible to describe transformations of matter without also considering transformations of energy. Although it bears directly on the question of equilibrium, the science of chemical energy, its measurement and its interpretation, had independent origins. Measurements of the quantities of heat evolved in several chemical reactions were carried out by Lavoisier. Important contributions to the subject were made by several nineteenth-century investigators, particularly by Marcellin Berthelot. Berthelot devised a special calorimeter for measurement of the energies evolved in combustion of compounds, and he performed a very large number of measurements. Today the quantities of energy evolved or absorbed in thousands of chemical reactions are readily available in the chemical literature. Several quantitative values have been cited in the preceding section; these and several others are shown in Table 22-1.

Berthelot, working in the nineteenth century, knew nothing of the electron and its role in chemical binding. The question of chemical *affinity* was one of the principal unsolved chemical problems of his time, and in carrying out his many measurements of chemical energies he was motivated by the search for a measure of this property. He concluded, in 1878, that "Every chemical change accomplished without the intervention of an external energy tends toward the production of the body or system of bodies that sets free the most heat." In other words, Berthelot believed that the quantity of heat evolved in a chemical reaction is a direct measure of the

TABLE 22–1

MEASURED HEATS OF REACTION

Reaction	Quantity of heat*		
C $+ O_2 \rightarrow CO_2$	94,400 calories (exothermic)		
2C $+ O_2 \rightarrow 2CO$	52,800	"	"
2CO $+ O_2 \rightarrow 2CO_2$	136,000	"	"
2H$_2$ $+ O_2 \rightarrow 2H_2O$	115,600	"	"
H$_3$O$^+$ $+ OH^- \rightarrow 2H_2O$	13,700	"	"
N$_2$ $+ 3H_2 \rightarrow 2NH_3$	22,900	"	"
2Li $+ Cl_2 \rightarrow 2LiCl$	195,400	"	"
2Na $+ Cl_2 \rightarrow 2NaCl$	196,800	"	"
2K $+ Cl_2 \rightarrow 2KCl$	208,800	"	"
2Rb $+ Cl_2 \rightarrow 2RbCl$	210,200	"	"
2Cs $+ Cl_2 \rightarrow 2CsCl$	212,600	"	"
2N$_2$ $+ O_2 \rightarrow 2N_2O$	−39,400	"	(endothermic)
N$_2$ $+ O_2 \rightarrow 2NO$	−43,200	"	"
N$_2$ $+ 2O_2 \rightarrow 2NO_2$	−15,900	"	"
N$_2$ $+ 2O_2 \rightarrow N_2O_4$	−2,200	"	"
2NO $+ O_2 \rightarrow 2NO_2$	26,140	"	(exothermic)

*Each quantity refers to the corresponding reaction *as written*. 94,400 calories is the heat evolved on formation of *one* mole of CO_2, 52,800 calories the quantity evolved on formation of *two* moles of CO, etc.

spontaneous tendency of that reaction to proceed. For the examples of reactions listed in Table 22–1, the most strongly exothermic should have greatest tendency to "go." At equilibrium, if all are compared at the same temperature, those forward reactions involving greatest heat release should have the greatest equilibrium constant values. Endothermic reactions, on this interpretation, have little tendency to proceed unless energy is supplied externally, as is consistent with the general observation that equilibria are shifted in favor of endothermic processes by increases of temperature.

Berthelot's conclusion, although consistent with the observation we have made before that systems in nature generally tend toward states of lowered energy, has been proved incorrect. It rules out the possibility of spontaneous occurrence of endothermic reactions, whereas some examples of highly spontaneous reactions in this class are known. But, most important, it has been found that the heat evolved in a chemical reaction cannot be *quantita-*.

tively related to the position of the equilibrium point for that reaction under given conditions. A thermal measure of chemical affinity *has* been found, and can be used to make exact, verifiable prediction of equilibrium states; this quantity involves not only the heat evolved or absorbed in a chemical reaction but also the change in "unavailable energy" (Section 13–10) which the reaction brings about. Speaking *qualitatively* of the majority of chemical reactions, however, we may still generally regard those in which electrons in participating atoms achieve new states of *lowered* energy to be spontaneous.

The energy available in chemical change need not always manifest itself as heat. The production of radiant energy in many reactions, such as the oxidation of metallic magnesium, is well known. As we have learned in Chapter 14, chemical energy may be converted to electrical energy in special devices called batteries. A particularly simple (though not very practical) form of battery is the Daniell cell, shown diagrammatically in Fig. 22–8. A strip of zinc metal dips into zinc sulfate solution, a strip of copper dips into copper sulfate solution, and the two portions of the cell are separated by a porous ceramic partition. If a wire is attached across the two strips, a current is set up in such a direction that electrons will travel from zinc to copper. The circuit is closed inside the cell, because ions can migrate through the pores of the partition. If zinc metal were dipped *directly* into copper sulfate solution, the following oxidation-reduction reaction would occur spontaneously:

$$Zn + Cu^{++} \rightarrow Cu + Zn^{++}.$$

This reaction is exothermic. In the Daniell cell, the same reaction takes place, but the available chemical energy is released in the form of motion of electrons in the external wire, rather than as heat. In any battery, a similar principle applies: the chemical energy available in a spontaneous oxidation-reduction re-

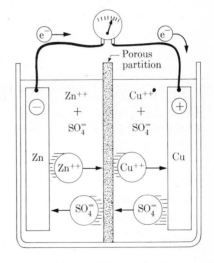

Fig. 22–8. The Daniell cell.

action is released as electrical rather than as thermal energy. In the ordinary "dry cell" zinc is oxidized to zinc ion at one electrode and manganese dioxide (MnO_2) is reduced to manganic hydroxide ($Mn(OH)_3$) at the other; the cell is not actually "dry," but contains ammonium chloride solution, absorbed in porous paper, between the electrodes. In a lead storage battery, metallic lead is oxidized at one electrode, and lead dioxide (PbO_2) is reduced at the other. The special feature of this or any other *storage* battery is that the electrode reactions may be exactly reversed by application of electric current from an external source.

The storage of energy in chemical form plays a role of overwhelming importance in our everyday lives. Much of the energy that we use in heating our homes, in transportation, and in industry is released by the combustion of coal, petroleum, or their products. These materials, in turn, consist of complex mixtures of compounds of the element carbon, transformed remnants of the vast forests of past geologic ages. It is a remarkable fact that plant life, through the agency of the catalyst chlorophyll in the process of photosynthesis, is able to promote certain very strongly endothermic reactions on an enormous scale. Thus the production of a single formula unit, $C_6H_{10}O_5$, of the complex carbohydrate *starch* from carbon dioxide and water,

$$6CO_2 + 5H_2O \rightarrow C_6H_{10}O_5 + 6O_2,$$

requires absorption of 671,000 calories of energy per mole. This is representative of the many complex processes which occur through photosynthesis, all of which require absorption of very large quantities of energy. The external energy supply utilized for this purpose, of course, is radiant energy from the sun. The prodigious capacity of plant life to store energy in chemical form is but one facet of the complex chemistry at work in the fundamental processes of living organisms. This wonderfully intricate chemistry would not be possible, in turn, without the extraordinary chemical versatility which is displayed by the element carbon. In the next two chapters we shall illustrate the properties of this important element.

22–6 Summary

Rates of chemical reactions are strongly influenced by temperature and by concentrations of reactants, and may be affected by the specific actions of substances called catalysts. The effects of temperature and concentration may be understood by viewing the basic mechanism of reaction as one requiring collisions between reactant particles. Reaction rates are increased by rising temperature to a much greater extent than can be accounted for in terms of collision frequency alone, however, and this is the basis for the concept of *activation energy*. Many reaction rates are found to be directly proportional to the concentrations of reacting substances, and Guldberg and Waage utilized this fact in devising the first quantitative description of *reversibility* in chemical reactions. All chemical changes are reversible to some extent, and the degree of completeness of any reaction depends on two competing processes. The condition under which the forward and reverse reactions proceed at the same rate is known as *equilibrium*. Equilibrium states attained by any given system depend upon the particular reactants and products involved, their initial concentrations, and temperature. When a reversible system is subjected to changes in concentration, temperature, and pressure its equilibrium may be temporarily upset, causing a shift which results in a new equilibrium state. The effects of these factors can be predicted qualitatively on the basis of LeChatelier's principle. In the case of temperature change, the prediction cannot be made unless it is known whether the forward reaction is *exothermic* or *endothermic*. Energy relations in chemical change bear a close relation to the subject of chemical equilibrium.

REFERENCES

LEICESTER, H. M., and H. S. KLICKSTEIN, *Source Book in Chemistry*, 468–471 (Guldberg and Waage), 480–483 (LeChatelier), 431 (Berthelot on thermochemistry).

PARTINGTON, J. R., *A Short History of Chemistry*, Chapter XIV.

PAULING, L., *General Chemistry*, Chapters 19 and 20.

SISLER, H. H., and others, *General Chemistry, A Systematic Approach*. Chapter 15.

1. A piece of magnesium metal, in contact with dilute acid, is causing the evolution of hydrogen at the rate of 5 cm³ per minute at 10°C. Approximately what rate of hydrogen evolution would you expect to observe if the same piece of magnesium were held in acid at the same concentration at 40°C?

2. For the reaction

$$I_2 + I^- \rightarrow I_3^-,$$

predict how the rate of production of I_3^- (triiodide ion) will be affected by (a) doubling the concentration of iodine, (b) doubling the concentration of iodide ion, (c) trebling the concentration of iodine and reducing the concentration of iodide ion to one-third its original value, and (d) raising the temperature 20°C.

3. When iron and sulfur are mixed at room temperature, no reaction takes place. If the mixture is strongly heated, however, iron sulfide begins to form; the heat source can then be removed, and the mixture glows brightly until the reaction is essentially complete. Explain.

4. What features of *chemical* equilibrium are similar to the *physical* equilibrium which a liquid establishes with its vapor (Section 13–9)? In what fundamental way are these two kinds of equilibrium different from the *equilibrium of forces* which holds a book at rest on a table? Explain.

5. Although silver chloride is an example of an "insoluble" compound, when crystals of this substance are placed in water, silver and chloride ions, at very minute concentration, can be detected in solution in the water. No ionic solid is *completely* insoluble in water, but solubilities of these materials vary widely. The most satisfactory definition of a saturated solution that can be given is that it is *a solution in which dissolved and undissolved solute are in equilibrium.* Interpret and explain this statement for ionic solutes, and write an appropriate equation for the case of silver chloride.

6. Berthelot and St. Gilles noted that ethyl alchohol (EtOH) and acetic acid (HAc) can be formed by adding water to ethyl acetate (EtAc). If one mole of each of these substances were mixed, would you expect their final concentrations at equilibrium to be different from those attained when equal molar quantities of ethyl alcohol and acetic acid are mixed? You can check your answer by using the equilibrium constant expression:

$$K = 4 = \frac{c_{EtAc}\, c_{H_2O}}{c_{HAc}\, c_{EtOH}}.$$

Let x equal the number of moles of HAc at equilibrium, which will also be the number of moles of EtOH formed. Since for each molecule of EtAc and water used up a molecule of HAc and one of EtOH must form, the concentrations of EtAc and H_2O at equilibrium must be $(1 - x)$. Substitute and solve.

7. At 25°C, the equilibrium constants for the following reversible reactions are approximately as shown:

$CO_2 + H_2 \rightleftarrows CO + H_2O,$
$$K = 1.2 \times 10^{-5};$$

$CO + Cl_2 \rightleftarrows COCl_2,$
(phosgene) $K = 6.3 \times 10^{11};$

$2NO_2 \rightleftarrows N_2O_4, \quad K = 6.3.$

For reactants at comparable initial concentrations, contrast the relative concentrations you would expect products of these reactions to have when equilibrium is established at 25°C.

8. For the reaction

$$CO + 2H_2 \rightleftarrows CH_3OH,$$
(methyl alcohol)

the equilibrium constant at 25°C is approximately 100 times larger than at 400°C. Can you deduce from this whether the forward reaction evolves or absorbs heat? [*Ans.*: Forward reaction is exothermic]

9. Although the yield of methyl alcohol obtained in the reaction shown in Exercise 8 decreases with increasing temperature, this substance can be made in this way, with catalysts, and rather high temperatures are required. In what way may high yields of methyl alcohol be obtained despite the requirement of elevated temperature?

10. For the exothermic reaction

$$2SO_2 + O_2 \rightleftarrows 2SO_3,$$

predict how the point of equilibrium will be affected by (a) removal of oxygen from the reaction container, (b) removal of sulfur trioxide from the reaction container, (c) reduction of the temperature of the equilibrium mixture, (d) application of increased pressure.

11. The principle of LeChatelier is valid for all *dynamic* equilibrium systems. As an example of its application to physical equilibria, interpret the fact that ice, held at constant temperature, tends to melt when pressure is applied to it. Remember that the density of ice is less than that of liquid water, i.e., a given mass of ice occupies more volume than the same mass of water.

12. The vapor pressure of water increases with increasing temperature. Interpret in terms of LeChatelier's principle.

13. For the reactions

$C_2H_6 + Br_2 \rightleftarrows C_2H_5Br + HBr$
(ethane)   (ethyl bromide)
(exothermic),

$2N_2 + O_2 \rightleftarrows 2N_2O$
(endothermic),

and

$4NH_3 + 3O_2 \rightleftarrows 2N_2 + 6H_2O$
(exothermic),

predict how equilibrium points will be shifted by (a) increased temperature, (b) increased pressure. Assume that temperatures are sufficiently high so that all reactants and products are gases.

14. In photographic development it is necessary to remove silver bromide crystals from film. (Reduction of silver ion to metallic silver is initiated by the action of light, and to preserve a photographic image all unreduced AgBr must be removed.) Although "insoluble" in water, AgBr can be brought completely into solution by the action of sodium *thiosulfate* ("hypo"). Silver and bromide ions, at very small concentration in the solution over the solid AgBr, are in equilibrium with the solid:

$$Ag^+ + Br^- \rightleftarrows AgBr.$$

When thiosulfate ion ($S_2O_3^{--}$) is introduced, a complex ion, $[Ag(S_2O_3)_2]^{---}$, has a strong tendency to form:

$$Ag^+ + 2(S_2O_3)^{--} \rightleftarrows [Ag(S_2O_3)_2]^{---}.$$

Interpret the fact that silver bromide dissolves in the presence of thiosulfate ion, in terms of LeChatelier's principle.

15. Remember that when CO_2 dissolves in water it does so by forming carbonic acid in the equilibrium system

$$CO_2 + H_2O \rightleftarrows H_2CO_3.$$

Explain why CO_2 is very much less soluble in strongly acid solutions than in pure water.

16. *Buffer solutions* are solutions to which appreciable quantities of either acid or base can be added without making the solution itself any more acidic or basic. A simple example is a solution containing a weak acid, e.g., acetic acid, and one of its salts, e.g., sodium acetate. Remember that acetic acid and acetate ion are acid-base conjugates in the equilibrium

$$HC_2H_3O_2 + H_2O \rightleftarrows H_3O^+ + C_2H_3O_2^-.$$

Explain how it would be possible for the hydronium ion concentration to remain nearly unchanged in a solution which contains both acetic acid and acetate ion at high concentration, when either excess hydronium ion or hydroxide ion is added.

17. Consider the thermochemical data shown in Table 22–1 for the reactions between chlorine and each of the alkali metal elements. Interpret the general trend which the quantities of heat evolved show, in terms of elec-

tronic structures of the participating atoms.

18. If a reaction proceeds in two or more steps, the reaction rate of the whole process is as a rule approximately equal to the reaction rate of the slowest step. Explain why this should be so.

19. The atmosphere contains elemental nitrogen and oxygen, but the equilibrium

$$N_2 + O_2 \rightleftarrows 2NO$$

is such that the concentration of the toxic gas nitric oxide in the air we breathe is vanishingly small. Nitric oxide formed under the influence of lightning discharge is a major item in the nitrogen cycle (Fig. 22–7), however. Explain the probable role of lightning discharge in production of nitric oxide in the atmosphere. (See Table 22–1.)

20. In Chapter 21 we learned that the conducting abilities of weak electrolytes are invariably improved by dilution. For the equilibrium

$$NH_3 + H_2O \rightleftarrows NH_4^+ + OH^-$$

the fraction of nitrogen atoms found in the form of ammonium ion increases as water is added. Considering water as a diluent, not as a reactant, the equilibrium constant expression for the process would be

$$K = \frac{(c_{NH_4^+})(c_{OH^-})}{c_{NH_3}}.$$

Can you interpret the increased conductivity of ammonia solutions that is observed on dilution? (*Hint:* Consider the expressions for the rates of forward and reverse reactions corresponding to the equilibrium constant expression shown, and the manner in which the two rates would be altered by dilution.)

CHAPTER 23

CARBON, THE KEY ELEMENT IN ORGANIC PROCESSES

It should not seem surprising that the science we call chemistry achieved its initial impetus, as a modern science, about a century later than the science of physics, and that chemistry is today in a markedly less advanced state of theoretical development than physics. Traditionally, chemistry has dealt with more complex problems than physics, and the formulation of its great generalizations has required long, intense periods of fact-gathering as well as brilliant interpretive achievement. Perhaps the most complicated set of problems which has ever confronted the science of chemistry is that dealing with the compounds of carbon, a subject called *organic* chemistry. One can sympathize wholly with the sentiments expressed by Friedrich Wöhler (1800–1882), in a letter addressed to his friend and teacher, Berzelius, in 1835:

"Organic chemistry just now is enough to drive one mad. It gives me the impression of a primeval tropical forest, full of the most remarkable things, a monstrous and boundless thicket, with no way of escape, into which one may well dread to enter."

Wöhler labored long and hard in the "jungle" of organic chemistry, and contributed materially toward the location of an escape route. His intensive investigations and those of many other equally devoted organic chemists, over a long period of time, led very gradually to the development of a set of structural principles which made carbon chemistry comprehensible. With these principles the molecular arrangements of more and more complicated substances could be unraveled and, in the laboratory, synthesis of materials which had previously been found only in nature became possible. The process of refinement of these principles continues today, greatly enriched by our deeper present-day knowledge of the nature of atoms and of the bonds between them. Our ever-increasing understanding of the structures and properties of the complicated substances which participate in the vital processes of organisms is now making it possible for science to probe the chemistry fundamental to life itself. Many industrial technologies, such as those basic to synthetic dye, drug, and plastics production, owe both their existence and their present advanced state of development to the science of organic chemistry.

23–1 The origins of organic chemistry

The name "organic" comes from the phrase "organized matter." All substances associated with living organisms, plant or animal, were once called organic, while all those associated with the "dead" mineral kingdom were called *in*organic. Although this distinction is no longer useful in its original sense, the terminology is retained. In present usage, the compounds of carbon are called organic, the compounds of all other elements, inorganic.

The organic compound alcohol, as a pure substance, was known in the 12th century, and ether in the 16th. During the 18th century many organic substances were discovered, among them glycerine and acetic acid. During the 1780's Lavoisier demonstrated that organic compounds consist predominantly of the elements carbon, hydrogen, and oxygen. By the beginning of the 19th century, then, many organic compounds were known and there was some knowledge of their elemental compositions. These substances were thought to be different from inorganic compounds in a sense more fundamental than composition, however. Experience had taught that many inorganic materials could be synthesized in the laboratory, but it was believed that organic compounds could be produced only by nature. To a certain extent this belief can be ascribed to the fact that no one had succeeded in synthesizing an organic compound, but it is undoubtedly true that the strength of the belief itself dissuaded chemists from even attempting to achieve such a synthesis. It was supposed that some *vital force* must act in production of the compounds of life. Berzelius, in 1814, reported that he had analyzed several organic compounds and found their compositions consonant with the law of definite proportions, yet at the same time expressed a continuing belief that only "natural" organic processes could manufacture them.

The first laboratory "synthesis" of an organic compound was performed in 1828 by Wöhler. He found that the "inorganic" substance *ammonium cyanate* (NH_4NCO), when heated, becomes transformed into the "organic" substance *urea*, $(NH_2)_2CO$. Actually this process is too simple to be called a synthesis ("rearrangement" would be a better word) but by whatever name, Wöhler's observation had a substantial effect upon organic chemistry. A compound that was known as part of the "mineral" world, ammonium cyanate, had been shown to undergo transformation into urea, a compound which had previously been known only as a constituent of animal urine. With this discovery a major psychological stumbling block to the development of organic chemistry had been weakened, although the effect was by no means immediate. In the years that followed, laboratory syntheses of other known animal and vegetable products were achieved, and belief in a special vital force gradually declined, then disappeared.

The first half of the 19th century was a period of intense empirical investigation, in which Wöhler and many others played important parts. Michel Eugène Chevreul (1786–1889) was the first to investigate the compositions of oils and fats, and to elucidate the chemical nature of soaps. Gay-Lussac discovered the gas *cyanogen* (C_2N_2) and a related series of compounds, Dumas established empirical formulas for anthracene, camphor, and other natural products, and Robert Bunsen made many contributions to organic chemistry, as well as to spectroscopy. One of the liveliest centers of instruction in organic chemistry during this period was the laboratory of Justus von Liebig (1803–1873) at Giessen University. Liebig, whose tireless investigations covered an unbelievably wide range of subjects in natural product chemistry, founded and edited the chemical journal *Annalen der Chemie*, whose prestige has survived to the present time. One of Liebig's most important scientific contributions was the development of an improved method for elemental analysis of organic compounds, which made possible the assignment of empirical formulas to these substances with greater reliability.

One reason for the chaotic quality of early organic chemistry, quite apart from the complexity inherent in the subject itself, was the confusion that reigned over questions of atomic weight, molecular weight, and formula. Different "schools" of chemistry used different atomic weight scales, did not even agree upon the selection of relative weights within a given scale, and were highly individualistic in their modes of writing chemical formulas. For this reason fluent communication between laboratories, so necessary to the growth of any science, was greatly inhibited. The general confusion concerning atomic weights also served to perpetuate the belief that organic and inorganic chemistry were fundamentally distinct, since two sets of atomic weights were traditionally used for compounds of the two types. Cannizzaro's success in bringing order to the chaos of atomic weights in 1860 (Chapter 7) thus also had the salutary effect of bringing organic and inorganic chemistry together into a single science.

23–2 Characteristics of carbon

Carbon is a nearly insignificant element, viewed in terms of relative numbers of atoms; it constitutes no more than 0.08% of the total weight of the earth's crust. Direct elemental analysis of any organism reveals the presence of a large percentage of carbon, however, and it is indeed *the* key element in the world of life. There is a continuous exchange of carbon, in the form of carbon dioxide, between the earth's surface and its atmosphere. Animal respiration, organic decomposition, and combustion charge the atmosphere with CO_2, plants remove it by photosynthesis. A substantial fraction of the carbon in the earth's crust is found in the form of *carbonates*.

Calcium carbonate is the principal constituent of the shells of many forms of marine life, and the mountain-building materials limestone and marble, also composed of this substance, can usually be traced in origin to marine sediments (see Chapter 26). There is no doubt of the organic origin of our common "fossil fuels," coal and petroleum, and natural deposits of the two crystalline forms of pure carbon, diamond and graphite, are also thought to be the remnants of ancient living things, transformed by deep burial.

The most impressive single fact about carbon is that while more than 500,000 of its compounds have been described in the chemical literature, the total number of known compounds of *all* other elements is only about 50,000. Carbon exhibits great versatility in its ability to form compounds, and it is this very property which lends the element its importance in the many complex and highly articulated chemical reactions of life. We may find clues to the source of carbon's versatility by considering its position in the periodic table. It is the first member of the Group 4a family of elements, and its electrons are therefore held more tightly than those of any other member of the group. The carbon atom has four valence electrons, hence an expected valence of 4; because of its position at the top of a center group we should expect it to form covalent rather than ionic compounds. Bonds to carbon atoms are exclusively covalent, indeed, and carbon compounds tend generally to be nonpolar, although polar character may be found in carbon compounds containing oxygen, and other electronegative atoms.

Carbon's unique qualities are related, then, to the presence in its atom of four tightly bound valence electrons and its exclusive tendency to form covalent bonds. One further property must be cited, if we are to account for its great versatility: carbon atoms readily form strong covalent bonds *with each other*, and do so both in open chain and closed ring structures. Because of this ability, organic compounds are almost infinitely variable. Only an element in Group 4a can form covalent compounds in which its atom achieves octet configuration by normal sharing of all its valence electrons. Since carbon is the first element of this group, its atoms hold their valence electrons, and those that they share, tightly. Bonds between carbon atoms are remarkably strong and unreactive, and carbon is the only element capable of forming stable chain and ring structures. Silicon (Chapter 25), its nearest competitor, can form chains of limited length, but because of its strong tendency to form silicon-oxygen structures these compounds are unstable in air.

The tetravalence of carbon and the ability of atoms of this element to link with each other to form chains and rings are crucial points in the interpretation of organic chemistry. The tetravalence of carbon was first deduced independently by Hermann Kolbe (1818–1884) and Friedrich Kekulé (1829–1896), in 1857 and 1858. It was Edward Frankland's valence theory, extended into the realm of organic chemistry, that made this important understanding possible. Kekulé, one of the most brilliant of all 19th-century organic chemists, is generally regarded as the true initiator of modern molecular structural theory. It was he, in 1858, who conceived the idea that carbon atoms may be linked together to form long open chains. According to his own account, this notion came to him while he was riding on top of a London omnibus. Later, in 1865, he proposed the first satisfactory explanation of the structure of benzene, in which six carbon atoms are linked together to form a closed ring. This time, Kekulé wrote, the idea came in a dream: snake-like carbon chains writhed and twisted until one suddenly gripped its own tail and began whirling about in a ring. These stories, of the bus ride and the dream, do not mean that Kekulé was an idle speculator; they simply serve to emphasize the fact that achievement of scientific insight is an intensely creative process and may occur in unexpected ways. It is rare that great scientists have written of the circumstances of their creative moments in comparable detail.

Kekulé was not the "father" of modern structural chemistry in any single-handed sense. A Scotsman, A. S. Couper, deduced the tetravalence of carbon and proposed the existence of chain structures independently, and nearly simultaneously. The Russian chemist A. M. Butlerov (1828–1886) made the first attempts to construct structural formulas depicting the manner of linkage between individual atoms in molecules, and in 1861 expressed a conviction that clues to their nature can be found in the properties and modes of synthesis of organic compounds. The further important point that molecular structures must be considered in three dimensions was conclusively demonstrated by J. H. van't Hoff and J. A. LeBel (1847–1930), independently, in 1874. This demonstration was made possible, in

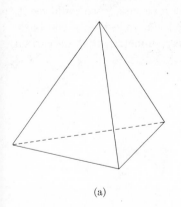

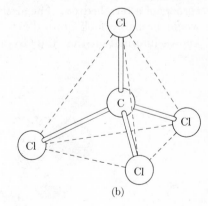

(a)   (b)

Fig. 23–1. (a) Regular tetrahedron, (b) tetrahedral orientation of bonds in the carbon tetrachloride molecule.

turn, by some early work of the great Louis Pasteur (1822–1895) on the phenomenon of *optical isomerism*, which we shall discuss in Section 23–5.

The conclusion reached by van't Hoff and LeBel was that in compounds in which carbon is bound by four single covalent bonds, these bonds are directed in space toward the corners of a regular *tetrahedron*. This geometric figure, a regular, four-sided solid, is shown in Fig. 23–1. The drawing also shows a molecule of carbon tetrachloride, drawn to conform to the confines of a regular tetrahedron; the lone carbon atom is located at the exact center of the solid, the four chlorine atoms at its apexes. There is no mystery about the tetrahedral arrangement of bonds about the carbon atom. A tetrahedron simply represents the *most symmetric possible manner in which four like objects may be arranged about a single center in space*. While carbon tetrachloride is a completely symmetric structure, the actual arrangement of bonds about a carbon atom may often be only approximately tetrahedral. In the molecule of chloroform, $CHCl_3$, for example, the presence of one bond (C—H) which is different from the other three (C—Cl) introduces small electrostatic forces which very slightly distort the molecule from true tetrahedral form.

Actual models of molecules are often a great aid, both to the practicing chemist and to the student, in visualizing the arrangements of atoms in molecules. In Fig. 23–2, two typical kinds of models in common use are shown. The first of these is deliberately crude, showing covalent bonds as though they were slender sticks, but at least possessing the virtue of causing the wooden spheres ("atoms") to stand away from one another for ready visibility. The second undoubtedly comes closer to representation of a "real" molecule than the first; here the atom spheres are in mutual contact, and the difference in size between carbon and hydrogen atoms is given due recognition. In both model systems the four bonds are oriented toward the corners of a tetrahedron. The actual methane molecule, if we could see it, would probably look quite different; a model can reflect only the basic known information that the CH_4 molecule is symmetric, that its carbon

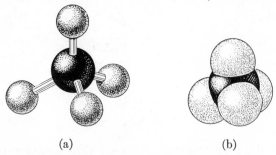

(a)   (b)

Fig. 23–2. Models of the methane molecule (CH_4). (a) Sphere-and-stick model, (b) scale model.

atom is centrally located, and that the angles between neighboring C—H bonds conform very closely to those of a regular tetrahedron. Although molecular models are enormously helpful, we must be scrupulously careful to remember that they are mechanical aids, not molecules.

23–3 Hydrocarbon chain structures

The simplest of organic compounds, called *hydrocarbons*, consist solely of the elements hydrogen and carbon. Natural gas and petroleum are complex mixtures of hydrocarbon compounds, although petroleum contains organic compounds of sulfur, oxygen, and nitrogen as well. The principal constituent of natural gas is the simplest of the hydrocarbons, *methane*, CH_4. Also found in natural gas are *ethane*, C_2H_6, *propane*, C_3H_8, and *butane*, C_4H_{10}. If the formulas of these compounds are arranged in the order in which they have been mentioned, it will be noted that each contains one more carbon atom and two more hydrogen atoms, per molecule, than its immediate predecessor. These four compounds are the first members of an indefinite series of compounds, called a *homologous series*. The first ten members of this series, with their formulas and boiling points, are listed in Table 23–1. The table shows that there is a regular increase in boiling point with increasing numbers of carbon atoms; regular gradations in

TABLE 23–1

TEN MEMBERS OF THE METHANE HYDROCARBON SERIES,
$C_nH_{(2n + 2)}$

Name of compound	Formula	Boiling point	Name of derivative group (hydrocarbon minus one hydrogen atom)	Formula of derivative group
1. Methane	CH_4	−161°C	Methyl	CH_3—
2. Ethane	C_2H_6	−89°C	Ethyl	C_2H_5—
3. Propane	C_3H_8	−42°C	Propyl	C_3H_7—
4. Butane	C_4H_{10}	+1°C	Butyl	C_4H_9—
5. Pentane	C_5H_{12}	36°C	Amyl	C_5H_{11}—
6. Hexane	C_6H_{14}	69°C	Hexyl	C_6H_{13}—
7. Heptane	C_7H_{16}	98°C	Heptyl	C_7H_{15}—
8. Octane	C_8H_{18}	126°C	Octyl	C_8H_{17}—
9. Nonane	C_9H_{20}	151°C	Nonyl	C_9H_{19}—
10. Decane	$C_{10}H_{22}$	174°C	Decyl	$C_{10}H_{21}$—

boiling point and other physical properties are characteristic of homologous series of compounds. It is also characteristic of such families of compounds that a single *type formula* can be written which expresses the relations of atoms present for all compounds in the series. In the case of this family, called the *methane series*, the characteristic type formula is $C_nH_{(2n+2)}$. A third characteristic of homologous series is that chemical properties of the compounds within a single series are generally similar. In this case, the methane hydrocarbons are all rather unreactive toward most reagents, though all are combustible and burn exothermally to produce CO_2 and water. There is no theoretical upper limit to the number of carbon atoms which may be present in the molecules of these compounds and, as we shall learn in Chapter 24, hydrocarbons containing many thousands of carbon atoms per molecule are known. The hydrocarbons in petroleum range up to about 50 carbon atoms per molecule.

Two-dimensional *structural* formulas for the simple methane hydrocarbons are readily constructed, since these compounds are known to consist of open chains of carbon atoms, as originally conceived by Kekulé. For methane, we may write

$$
\begin{array}{c}
\text{H} \\
| \\
\text{H--C--H} \\
| \\
\text{H}
\end{array}
$$

for ethane:

$$
\begin{array}{c}
\text{H}\ \ \text{H} \\
|\ \ \ | \\
\text{H--C--C--H} \\
|\ \ \ | \\
\text{H}\ \ \text{H}
\end{array}
$$

and for pentane:

$$
\begin{array}{c}
\text{H}\ \ \text{H}\ \ \text{H}\ \ \text{H}\ \ \text{H} \\
|\ \ \ |\ \ \ |\ \ \ |\ \ \ | \\
\text{H--C--C--C--C--C--H} \\
|\ \ \ |\ \ \ |\ \ \ |\ \ \ | \\
\text{H}\ \ \text{H}\ \ \text{H}\ \ \text{H}\ \ \text{H}
\end{array}
$$

In such structural formulas each dash represents a covalent bond, and in constructing them we must bear in mind that each carbon atom forms a total of four bonds with other atoms. Not all methane hydrocarbons consist solely of extended chains of this sort; *branch* chains may also be present, as we shall learn in Section 23-4. Any *three*-dimensional representation of

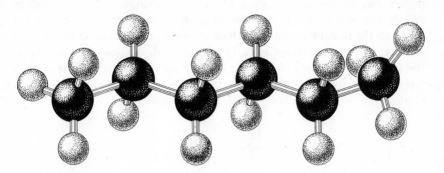

FIG. 23-3. Sphere-and-stick model of the molecule of hexane, C_6H_{14}.

these structures must take into account the tetrahedral orientation of the carbon valence bonds; when this point is considered it becomes obvious that the chains cannot actually be straight, but that successive carbon-carbon bonds must form a zigzag. This statement is illustrated in the molecular model shown in Fig. 23-3. It is most readily appreciated when one constructs sphere-and-stick models of specific molecules oneself.

In a second homologous hydrocarbon series, the *ethylene* family, the general type formula C_nH_{2n} applies. The simplest member of the series, the compound ethylene, has the molecular formula C_2H_4. Other members are *propylene* (C_3H_6), *butylene* (C_4H_8), *pentene* (C_5H_{10}), *hexene* (C_6H_{12}), etc. These compounds show regular gradations in physical properties, like the methane hydrocarbons, and are generally much more reactive chemically than the latter. All react readily with bromine, for example:

$$C_2H_4 + Br_2 \rightarrow C_2H_4Br_2.$$

Because of their reactivity ethylene hydrocarbons are not generally found as such among natural products, although they are readily synthesized. They are formed in the petroleum-refining process called *cracking*, for example. In this process, employed to break up long-chain methane hydrocarbons into the smaller molecules of value for motor fuels, hydrocarbons are exposed to high temperatures in the absence of oxygen. Tetradecane ($C_{14}H_{30}$), for example, could break up to form hex*ane* and oct*ene* under these conditions:

$$C_{14}H_{30} \rightarrow \underset{\text{(hexane)}}{C_6H_{14}} + \underset{\text{(octene)}}{C_8H_{16}}.$$

Methane hydrocarbon molecules contain the maximum number of hydrogen atoms which can be bound to the carbon atoms present; for this reason they are frequently called *saturated* compounds. Every molecule of an ethylene hydrocarbon, on the other hand, contains two hydrogen atoms less than the maximum number; these are examples of *un*saturated hydrocarbons. The tetravalency of carbon is satisfied, in these compounds, by the presence of a *double bond* between one pair of carbon atoms in each molecule, i.e., by the sharing of two pairs of electrons between two carbon atoms. We may then write as structural formulas, for ethylene:

$$\begin{array}{ccc} H & & H \\ \diagdown & & \diagup \\ & C = C & \\ \diagup & & \diagdown \\ H & & H \end{array}$$

for propylene:

$$\begin{array}{ccc} H & H & H \\ \diagdown & | & | \\ & C = C - C - H \\ \diagup & & | \\ H & & H \end{array}$$

and for hexene:

$$\begin{array}{ccccccc} H & & H & H & H & H & H \\ \diagdown & & | & | & | & | & | \\ & C = C - C - C - C - C - H \\ \diagup & & | & | & | & | \\ H & & H & H & H & H \end{array}$$

In the sphere-and-stick model system it is customary to use flexible springs which can be bent around to occupy two "valence" holes in each of two adjacent spheres, to represent double bonds (Fig. 23–4). The tetrahedral orientation of bonds in an open chain molecule is not altered by the presence of a double bond. Geometrically, a double bond between

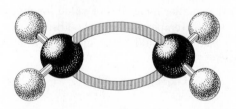

FIG. 23–4. Sphere-and-stick model of ethylene, C_2H_4, using flexible springs to represent the double bond.

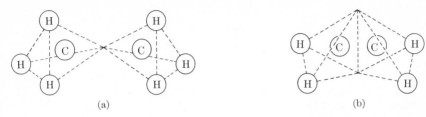

(a)   (b)

Fig. 23–5. Geometric representation of single and double bonds. The carbon-carbon bond in ethane (a) may be regarded as two tetrahedra sharing an apex. The double bond in ethylene (b) may be regarded as two tetrahedra sharing an edge.

carbon atoms may be represented by two tetrahedra sharing an edge in common, a single bond by the sharing of a corner, as shown in Fig. 23–5.

The reactivity of the ethylene hydrocarbons is directly related to the double bonds they contain. When a bromine molecule adds to an ethylene molecule, for example, its two atoms take up positions on the two doubly-bound carbon atoms, removing the double bond or, we might say, *saturating* the ethylene molecule. This reaction is more fully represented using structural formulas:

$$\begin{matrix} H & & H \\ \diagdown & & \diagup \\ & C = C & \\ \diagup & & \diagdown \\ H & & H \end{matrix} \quad + \; Br_2 \; \rightarrow \; \begin{matrix} H & H \\ | & | \\ Br-C-C-Br \\ | & | \\ H & H \end{matrix}$$

Reaction with bromine is used as a convenient test for the presence of double bonds, or unsaturation, in hydrocarbons, since the tendency of bromine to add in this way is strong. Bromine will not usually react with saturated compounds except at elevated temperatures; when it does so the gas hydrogen bromide is evolved:

$$\begin{matrix} H & H \\ | & | \\ H-C-C-H \\ | & | \\ H & H \end{matrix} + Br_2 \; \rightarrow \; \begin{matrix} H & H \\ | & | \\ H-C-C-Br \\ | & | \\ H & H \end{matrix} + HBr$$

A second series of unsaturated hydrocarbons, exhibiting the type formula $C_nH_{(2n-2)}$, is called the *acetylene* series. The first member of this family is acetylene itself, C_2H_2. This compound contains a *triple* bond (i.e., three shared electron pairs) between its two carbon atoms:

$$H-C\equiv C-H.$$

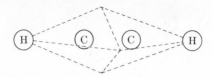

FIG. 23–6. Geometric representation of the triple bond in acetylene as two tetrahedra sharing a face.

Acetylene is more reactive than ethylene, since a triple bond between carbon atoms shows even greater tendency to become saturated than a double bond. A triple bond between carbon atoms may be considered, geometrically, as two tetrahedra sharing a face, as shown in Fig. 23–6. Acetylene forms readily when water comes in contact with calcium carbide, CaC_2:

$$CaC_2 + H_2O \rightarrow Ca(OH)_2 + H—C \equiv C—H \uparrow$$

Acetylene is a colorless gas which burns brilliantly in air. One of its principal uses is in high-temperature welding, since temperatures up to 2800°C may be obtained by combustion of acetylene-oxygen mixtures.

23–4 Hydrocarbon ring structures

The hydrocarbons discussed in Section 23–3 are members of a general class called *aliphatic* hydrocarbons. There is a second broad class, called *aromatic* compounds, of which the interesting compound *benzene* is the simplest example. This substance, discovered by Michael Faraday in 1825, is found as a constituent of petroleum and other oils, and is particularly abundant in the distillate of coal. It is a colorless liquid at ordinary temperatures, boils at 80°C, and melts at 5.5°C. It has considerable commercial importance as a solvent for nonpolar substances and as a starting material in the manufacture of dyes, drugs, and other products.

Benzene has been found to have the molecular formula C_6H_6. Since it contains eight fewer hydrogen atoms than the maximum number possible for six carbon atoms, one might conclude that its properties should be those of a highly unsaturated molecule. Its behavior, however, is not at all similar to that of ethylene or acetylene; it will react with bromine only at high temperatures in the presence of specific catalysts, and does so, under these conditions, with evolution of hydrogen bromide. In other words, it exhibits the stability characteristic of a *saturated* aliphatic hydrocarbon. As we have said, Kekulé was the first person to perceive what the structure of benzene must be: a regular hexagonal array of carbon atoms in a single plane, a hydrogen atom attached to each. There must be three double bonds present to satisfy the tetravalence of carbon:

Since there *are* double bonds present, by analogy to the ethylene hydrocarbons we should, perhaps, expect benzene to be highly reactive; the observed fact, as we have said, is that it is not. This can be explained only by saying that there is special stability inherent in the symmetric, planar hexagonal configuration of the benzene molecule. It is interesting to note that this special stability is achieved despite considerable widening of the usual tetrahedral carbon-carbon bond angle; the internal angles of a regular hexagon are 120°, those of a regular tetrahedron 109°28′. Construction of a model of the benzene molecule helps to illustrate the point that the six carbon atoms must lie in a single plane (Fig. 23–7).

FIG. 23–7. Scale model of the benzene molecule.

The aromatic hydrocarbons are so called, historically, because of the pleasant aromas associated with some of their natural sources: cinnamon, cloves, wintergreen, and vanilla. *Naphthalene, anthracene,* and *phenanthrene* are examples of aromatic hydrocarbons found, along with benzene, in coal distillate. Naphthalene, $C_{10}H_8$, a solid at ordinary temperatures which exerts substantial vapor pressure through sublimation, was once widely used as a moth repellent. Its structure is that of two benzene rings fused together:

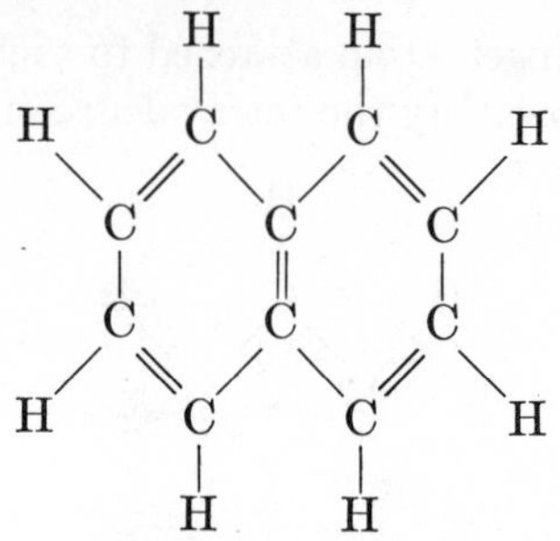

Anthracene, closely related to compounds of importance in the dye industry, has the molecular formula $C_{14}H_{10}$ and consists of three fused benzene rings:

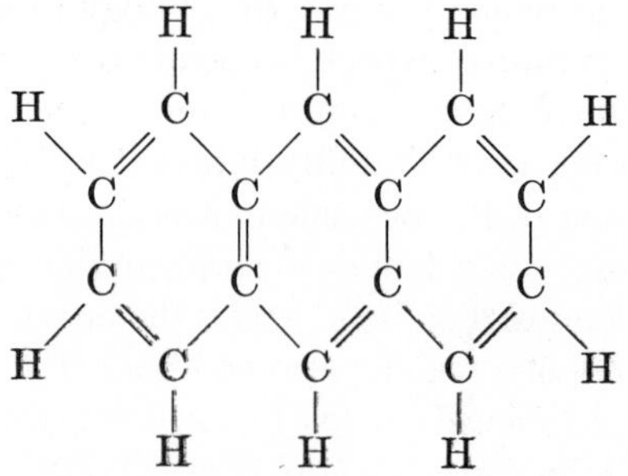

Phenanthrene also has empirical formula $C_{14}H_{10}$, but consists of three benzene rings fused in a somewhat different manner:

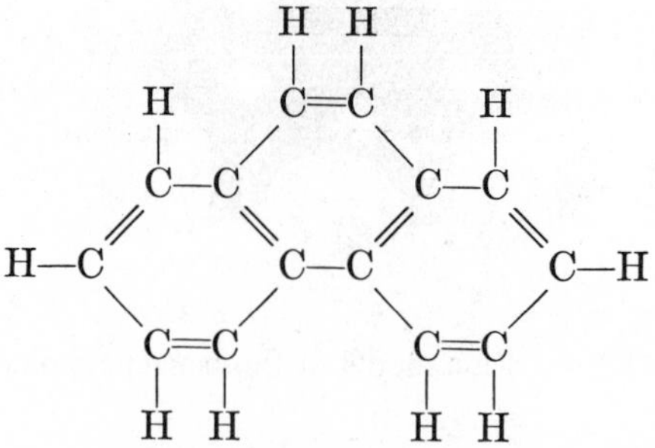

Aliphatic hydrocarbon molecules can often be made to react with other molecules, in nature or in the laboratory, in such a way that new atoms or groups of atoms replace hydrogen atoms in their structures. For this reason it is convenient to think in terms of *aliphatic groups* in relation to aliphatic hydrocarbons. When methane reacts with bromine at high temperature, for example, the compound CH_3Br is formed; this compound is named *methyl bromide*, and the group of atoms $(-CH_3)$ is called the *methyl* group (see Table 23–1). CH_3CH_2Br is called *ethyl* bromide, and the group of atoms ($-CH_2CH_3$) —an ethane molecule which is lacking one hydrogen atom—the *ethyl* group. Aliphatic groups may take the place of one or more hydrogen atoms on aromatic ring structures, forming distinct homologous series of compounds. The compounds *toluene* (methyl benzene):

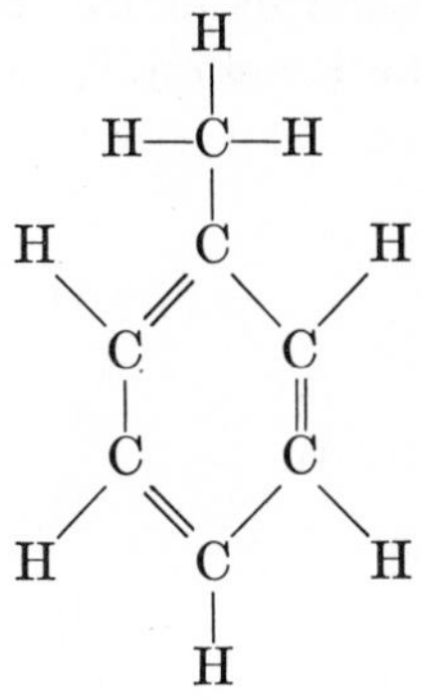

and ethyl benzene:

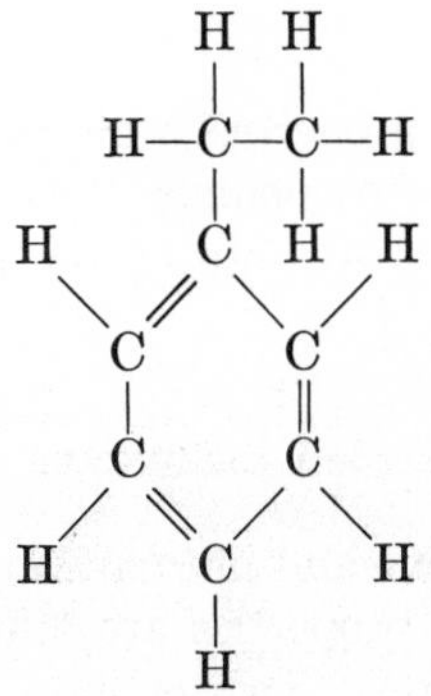

for example, are members of a common family with type formula C_nH_{2n-6}. *Xylene* is an example of a compound in which aliphatic groups have taken the places of *two* hydrogen atoms on the benzene ring:

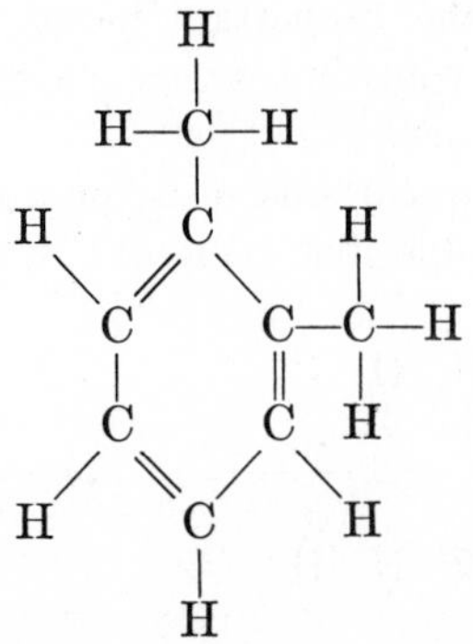

Although all aromatic hydrocarbons contain ring structures, not all hydrocarbons with ring structures are aromatic. At high temperatures, usually in the presence of appropriate catalysts, many aliphatic hydrocarbon molecules can be caused to form *cyclic* structures. This involves loss of two hydrogen atoms and formation of a new carbon-carbon bond, as shown in the case of formation of *cyclohexane* from hexane:

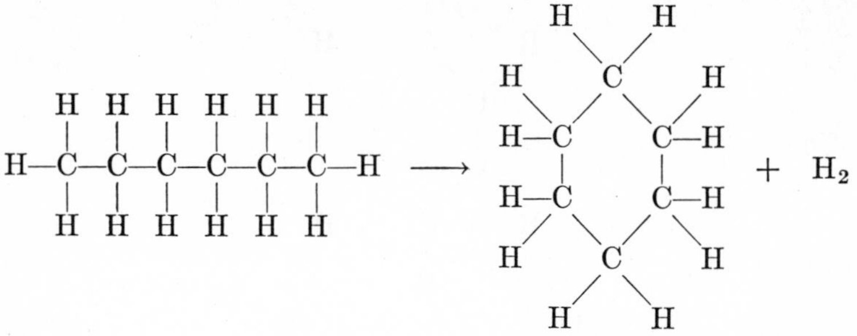

Cyclohexane

Cyclic hydrocarbons have properties which generally resemble those of their parent, straight-chain compounds. The six carbon atoms of cyclohexane, unlike those of benzene, need not lie in a single plane, as is illustrated in Fig. 23–8.

23–5 Isomerism

The compounds anthracene and phenanthrene both have the molecular formula $C_{14}H_{10}$, yet their properties are different because they possess different molecular structures. Two or more compounds are said to be *isomers* (Greek *iso*, "same," plus *mer*, "part") if their molecules contain the same numbers and kinds of atoms yet differ in structure and properties. Because carbon atoms are able to combine with one another in so many different ways, isomerism is very common among organic compounds. This phenomenon is another important factor in the rather astounding versatility of carbon, and contributes very materially to the large number of known organic compounds.

Among the methane hydrocarbons, no isomers of the compounds methane through propane are possible, but there are two forms of butane:

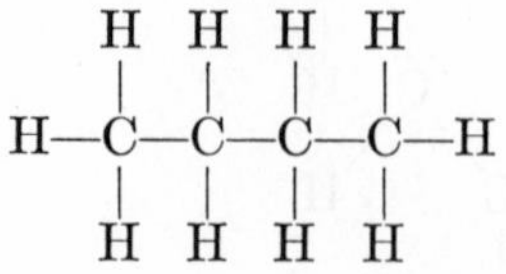

normal butane

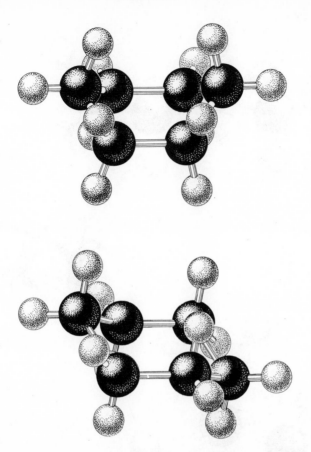

FIG. 23–8. Two possible nonplanar arrangements of the atoms in cyclohexane.

and

$$
\begin{array}{c}
\text{H}\quad\text{H}\quad\text{H}\quad\text{H}\quad\text{H} \\
\backslash\;|\quad|\quad|\;/ \\
\text{C}-\text{C}-\text{C} \\
/\quad|\quad\backslash \\
\text{H}\quad\;\text{C}\;\quad\text{H} \\
/\;|\;\backslash \\
\text{H}\quad\text{H}\quad\text{H}
\end{array}
\qquad \textit{iso}\text{butane}
$$

Models of these molecules are shown in Fig. 23–9. The crux of the structural difference between these compounds is that the carbon atoms in normal butane are bound either to one or two others, but in isobutane there is one carbon atom which is bound to *three* others. Isobutane is not a

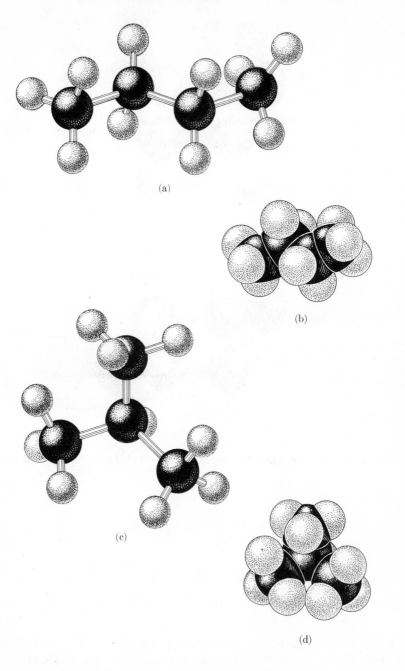

FIG. 23–9. Sphere-and-stick and scale models of normal butane, (a) and (b), and isobutane, (c) and (d).

straight-chain hydrocarbon, but contains a *branch*. The physical properties of these compounds are distinctly, though not greatly, different; while butane boils at 1°C, isobutane boils at −10°C, for example. The number of isomers possible for a given molecular formula increases rapidly with increasing numbers of carbon atoms. There are three known isomeric forms of pentane, those in addition to the normal, straight-chain variety being *iso*pentane:

$$
\begin{array}{c}
\text{H} \quad \text{H} \quad \text{H} \quad \text{H} \\
| \quad\; | \quad\; | \quad\; | \\
\text{H--C--C--C--C--H} \\
| \quad\; | \quad\; | \quad\; | \\
\text{H} \quad \text{H} \quad \text{C} \quad \text{H} \\
\diagup\; | \;\diagdown \\
\text{H} \quad \text{H} \quad \text{H}
\end{array}
$$

and *neo*pentane:

$$
\begin{array}{c}
\text{H} \quad \text{H} \quad \text{H} \\
\diagdown \; | \diagup \\
\text{H} \qquad \text{C} \qquad \text{H} \\
\diagdown \quad | \quad \diagup \\
\text{H--C--C--C--H} \\
\diagup \quad | \quad \diagdown \\
\text{H} \qquad \text{C} \qquad \text{H} \\
\diagup \; | \diagdown \\
\text{H} \quad \text{H} \quad \text{H}
\end{array}
$$

There are 35 possible isomers of nonane (C_9H_{20}), and it has been calculated (but not demonstrated in the laboratory!) that 6.95×10^{13} distinct isomeric forms of tetracontane ($C_{40}H_{82}$) are possible.

In the unsaturated aliphatic hydrocarbons isomerism may exist because of the possibility of branching, but also by virtue of different, nonequivalent locations of double bonds. There are two possible forms of normal pent*ene*, for example:

$$
\begin{array}{c}
\text{H} \quad \text{H} \quad \text{H} \quad \text{H} \quad \text{H} \\
| \quad\; | \quad\; | \quad\; | \quad\; | \\
\text{H--C=C--C--C--C--H} \\
| \quad\; | \quad\; | \\
\text{H} \quad \text{H} \quad \text{H}
\end{array}
$$

and

$$
\begin{array}{c}
\text{H} \quad \text{H} \quad \text{H} \quad \text{H} \quad \text{H} \\
| \quad\; | \quad\; | \quad\; | \quad\; | \\
\text{H--C--C=C--C--C--H} \\
| \qquad\qquad | \quad\; | \\
\text{H} \qquad\qquad \text{H} \quad \text{H}
\end{array}
$$

For *iso*pentene there are four possible isomers, i.e., four possible non-equivalent positions for the double bond.

Benzene has no isomers, but when two or more of its hydrogen atoms are replaced by other atoms or groups of atoms the possibility of isomerism arises. Xylene, for example, is but one of three known derivatives of benzene with molecular formula C_8H_{10}. The compound which contains two methyl groups attached to adjacent carbon atoms is called *ortho*-xylene:

$$
\begin{array}{c}
CH_3 \\
| \\
H \quad C \quad CH_3 \\
\diagdown \quad \diagup\diagdown \\
C \quad\quad C \\
\| \quad\quad \| \\
C \quad\quad C \\
\diagup \quad \diagdown \\
H \quad C \quad H \\
| \\
H
\end{array}
$$

When the methyl groups are separated by one carbon atom the compound is called *meta*-xylene:

$$
\begin{array}{c}
CH_3 \\
| \\
H \quad C \quad H \\
\diagdown \quad \diagup \quad \diagup \\
C \quad\quad C \\
\| \quad\quad \| \\
C \quad\quad C \\
\diagup \quad \diagdown \\
H \quad C \quad CH_3 \\
| \\
H
\end{array}
$$

and when two carbon atoms intervene, *para*-xylene:

$$
\begin{array}{c}
CH_3 \\
| \\
H \quad C \quad H \\
\diagdown \quad \diagup \quad \diagup \\
C \quad\quad C \\
\| \quad\quad \| \\
C \quad\quad C \\
\diagup \quad \diagdown \\
H \quad C \quad H \\
| \\
CH_3
\end{array}
$$

From the form of our structural formulas it may seem that a further possibility of isomerism exists for ortho-xylene, depending on the relation of the two methyl groups to a double bond in the benzene ring:

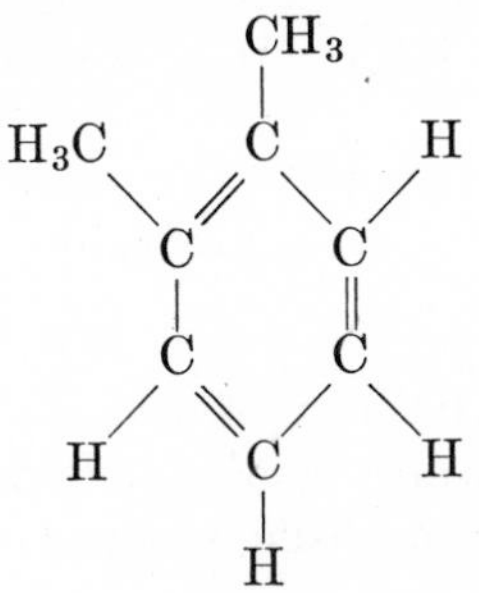

and

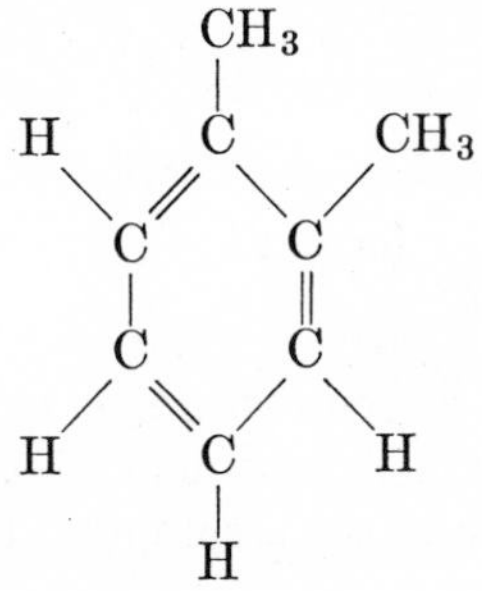

This possibility was very eagerly pursued in the past, but no evidence of such isomerism has ever turned up. Organic chemists have had to conclude that all six positions on the benzene ring are equivalent. This has been interpreted by Linus Pauling and others, in terms of what is called "resonance" theory, to mean that there are no rigidly *fixed* double bond positions in benzene, but that all carbon-carbon bonds in the ring are equivalent to one another, and intermediate between single and double bonds in character.

The cases of isomerism we have discussed so far, all dependent upon different arrangements of chemical bonds, fall within a general class called *structural* isomers. A second class, called *stereo*isomers (Greek *steros*, "solid"), consists of compounds which contain similar basic arrangements of bonds but different arrangements of atoms in space. As a simple example, the structural isomer of butene which would be represented by the following formula:

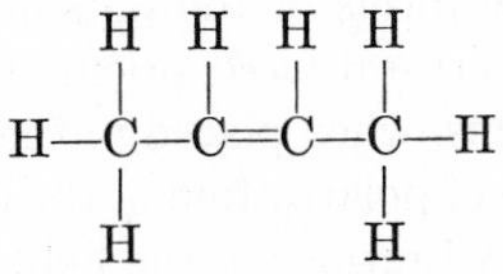

is found to exist in *two* forms, which differ in boiling point by about 3°C. These forms can be interpreted only by assuming that the central double bond is rigid, i.e., that the carbon atoms it joins cannot rotate with respect to one another, and that all four carbon atoms plus the hydrogens attached to the two central carbons lie in a single plane. Accepting these assumptions, it becomes possible to represent two *geometrically* different forms of this molecule as follows:

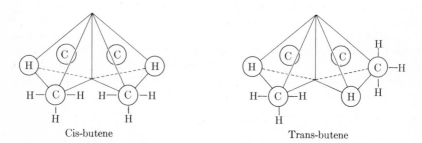

An alternative representation of these forms is shown in Fig. 23–10. Here the two doubly-bound carbon atoms are regarded as tetrahedra sharing an edge, and the assumption that the molecule is planar follows automatically.

Fig. 23–10. Tetrahedral representation of the geometric isomers of butene.

A special kind of stereoisomerism, called *optical* isomerism, can be interpreted only in three dimensions, in terms of the tetrahedral orientation of bonds on the carbon atom. Pasteur, in 1848, discovered that there are two distinct crystalline forms of the organic compound *tartaric acid*, with certain characteristic crystal *facets* oriented in opposite directions. A solution of one of these forms, when placed in the path of a beam of polarized light, rotates the plane of polarization of the light to the *left* (i.e., alters the direction of transverse vibrations in the light beam; see Section 17–6), the other is found to rotate it to the *right*. Several crystals are known to exist in left- and right-handed forms which have this remarkable effect on polarized light but lose this property in solution (e.g., Iceland spar). Since tartaric acid is capable of rotating polarized light while in solution, its right- and left-handedness must be intrinsic to its molecules, not just to its crystals. Since Pasteur's discovery many other organic molecules have been found which exhibit this property, i.e., can exist in two forms, called optical isomers. In the cases of all these compounds, a carbon atom is present in the molecule which is bound to four unlike atoms or groups. The following hydrocarbon is a possible example:

$$\begin{array}{ccccccc}
\text{H} & \text{H} & \text{H} & \text{H} & & \text{H} & \text{H} \\
| & | & | & | & & | & | \\
\text{H—C—C—C—C*—C—C—H} \\
| & | & | & | & & | & | \\
\text{H} & \text{H} & \text{H} & \text{C} & & \text{H} & \text{H} \\
& & & \diagup | \diagdown \\
& & & \text{H H H}
\end{array}$$

The carbon atom which is labeled with an asterisk contains covalent bonds to a *propyl* group ($CH_3CH_2CH_2$—), a hydrogen atom, a *methyl* group (CH_3—), and an *ethyl* group (CH_3CH_2—).

It was in the interpretation of optical isomerism that LeBel **and** van't Hoff were led to the conclusion that the bonds on carbon atoms are directed toward the corners of a regular tetrahedron. If the four unlike

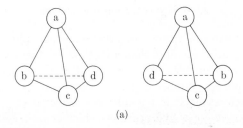

(a)

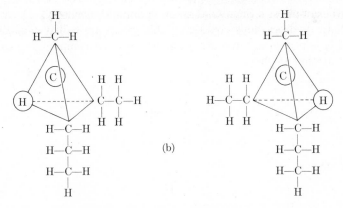

(b)

FIG. 23–11. Optical isomerism, (a) for the general case of a carbon atom asymmetrically substituted, i.e., containing four unlike groups (*Cabcd*), and (b) for the case of a specific hydrocarbon compound. The isomers are mirror images which cannot be exactly superimposed on one another.

groups attached to the carbon atom shown in the above hydrocarbon molecule are oriented tetrahedrally, then two distinct forms *can* exist, each a *mirror image* of the other. This is illustrated in Fig. 23–11; it will be seen, with a little study, that there is no way in which one of these structures may be exactly superimposed on the other, and that these forms are therefore different in a real geometric sense. Their real physical difference is made manifest in their opposite effects on a beam of polarized light. The subtlety of distinction between right- and left-handed forms of the same molecule is an important factor in the highly articulated character of the organic chemistry of life. Lactic acid, glucose, and adrenaline, examples of important products of vital processes, exhibit optical isomerism. Pasteur's famous work in bacteriology had its origins in his early studies of the optical isomers of tartaric acid and its salts; he observed that the mold *penicillium glaucum* can destroy only one of the two optical forms of ammonium tartrate.

23–6 Hydrocarbon derivatives

With our discussion of the hydrocarbons and the phenomenon of isomerism we have gained no more than a foothold in description of the complexity of organic chemistry. When atoms other than carbon and hydrogen are introduced, the number of possible compounds becomes multiplied many fold. Fortunately, it is possible to consider a very broad class of compounds as *derivatives* of hydrocarbons which contain certain characteristic *functional groups*. For each of these characteristic groups a distinct homologous series of compounds is known. The hydroxyl group, $-OH$, is a typical example of a functional group in organic chemistry. Derivatives of aliphatic hydrocarbons containing this group are called *alcohols*, and when it is joined to an aromatic ring the resulting compound is called a *phenol*. Methyl alcohol,

$$\begin{array}{c} H \\ | \\ H-C-OH \\ | \\ H \end{array}$$

ethyl alcohol,

$$\begin{array}{cc} H & H \\ | & | \\ H-C-C-OH \\ | & | \\ H & H \end{array}$$

and propyl alcohol,

$$\begin{array}{c}
\quad\ \text{H}\quad\ \text{H}\quad\ \text{H} \\
\quad\ | \quad\ \ | \quad\ \ | \\
\text{H}\!-\!\text{C}\!-\!\text{C}\!-\!\text{C}\!-\!\text{OH} \\
\quad\ | \quad\ \ | \quad\ \ | \\
\quad\ \text{H}\quad\ \text{H}\quad\ \text{H}
\end{array}$$

are the first three members of a homologous series of alcohols. A partial listing of important functional groups and their names is shown in Table 23–2.

Since oxygen has a much more negative atom than carbon, alcohols have considerable polar character and are generally soluble in water. There are several hydrogen atoms present in each molecule of any alcohol, hence it is an important part of our structural understanding to know that one of these is bound in a fashion different from the others. The molecular formula C_2H_6O for ethyl alcohol, for example, indicates no difference among the six hydrogens present. When ethyl alcohol reacts with sodium metal, however, it is found that only *one* hydrogen per molecule is replaced. Sodium does not react with hydrocarbons; it seems clear that one hydrogen in an alcohol must be bound to oxygen, and that it is that hydrogen which is attacked by sodium. Although this hydrogen atom is relatively reactive, alcohols do not tend to donate protons, i.e., to act as acids. In certain reactions they behave like exceedingly weak bases, but for all practical purposes they may be regarded as neither acidic nor basic. When the hydroxyl group is attached to an aromatic ring structure, however, as in *phenol*:

$$\begin{array}{c}
\text{OH} \\
| \\
\text{H}\quad\ \ \text{C}\quad\ \ \text{H} \\
\diagdown\ \diagup\!\!\!\diagdown\ \diagup \\
\text{C}\qquad\text{C} \\
|\qquad\ \| \\
\text{C}\qquad\text{C} \\
\diagup\ \diagdown\!\!\!\diagup\ \diagdown \\
\text{H}\quad\ \ \text{C}\quad\ \ \text{H} \\
| \\
\text{H}
\end{array}$$

the resulting compound has the properties of a weak acid.

Most alcohols are strongly toxic substances, and ethyl alcohol, in fact, is the only one which can be tolerated by the human system in appreciable quantities. Methyl alcohol, as is well known, can cause blindness. Both are important materials in industry and are produced in large volume.

TABLE 23–2

ORGANIC FUNCTIONAL GROUPS

Name of group	Structural formula*	Typical example of compound containing the group
Hydroxyl	—OH	$H-\overset{\displaystyle H}{\underset{\displaystyle H}{C}}-OH$ (methyl alcohol)
		(phenol)
Ether	—O—	$H-\overset{\displaystyle H}{\underset{\displaystyle H}{C}}-O-\overset{\displaystyle H}{\underset{\displaystyle H}{C}}-H$ (methyl ether)
Aldehyde	$\overset{\displaystyle O}{\overset{\|}{-C}}-H$	$H-\overset{\displaystyle O}{\overset{\|}{C}}-H$ (formaldehyde)
Ketone	$\overset{\displaystyle O}{\overset{\|}{-C-}}$	$H-\overset{\displaystyle H}{\underset{\displaystyle H}{C}}-\overset{\displaystyle O}{\overset{\|}{C}}-\overset{\displaystyle H}{\underset{\displaystyle H}{C}}-H$ (acetone)
Carboxyl	$-C\overset{\displaystyle O}{\underset{\displaystyle OH}{}}$	$H-C\overset{\displaystyle O}{\underset{\displaystyle OH}{}}$ (formic acid)

(cont.)

Name of group	Structural formula*	Typical example of compound containing the group
Ester		(methyl acetate)
Primary amine		(methylamine)
Nitro		(nitrobenzene)
Mercapto	—S—H	(methyl mercaptan)
Sulfonic acid		(methyl sulfonic acid)
Halide	—F, —Cl, —Br or —I	(ethylene chloride)

*The dashes represent open valency positions; in the cases of the aldehyde and carboxyl groups these may be joined either to a hydrogen atom or to a carbon atom. In all other cases they may be joined to a carbon atom only.

Although ethyl alcohol can now be made synthetically, using hydrocarbons as starting materials, much of it is still produced by the process of fermentation, the degradative action of certain microorganisms on sugars. In addition to the alcohols we have mentioned, there are others which contain two or more hydroxyl groups per molecule. *Ethylene glycol*, widely used as an antifreeze, has the structure

$$
\begin{array}{ccc}
 & H & H \\
 & | & | \\
H- & C- & C-H \\
 & | & | \\
 & HO & OH \\
\end{array}
$$

Glycerine, a viscous liquid of considerable industrial importance, contains three hydroxyl groups in its molecule:

$$
\begin{array}{ccc}
H & OH & H \\
\diagdown & | & \diagup \\
HO-C- & C- & C-OH \\
\diagup & | & \diagdown \\
H & H & H \\
\end{array}
$$

Butyl alcohol has the molecular formula $C_4H_{10}O$. If ethyl alcohol is mixed with concentrated sulfuric acid and the mixture is allowed to stand at elevated temperature, a compound is formed which also has molecular formula $C_4H_{10}O$ but is entirely unlike butyl alcohol (or any other alcohol) in properties. It is nonpolar, hence will not mix with water, and does not react with sodium to yield hydrogen, as an alcohol will. This isomer of butyl alcohol, called *ethyl ether*, is the ether commonly used for anaesthesia, and its molecules contain an oxygen atom bound *between* two carbon atoms:

$$
\begin{array}{cccccc}
H & H & & H & H \\
| & | & & | & | \\
H-C- & C- & O- & C- & C-H \\
| & | & & | & | \\
H & H & & H & H \\
\end{array}
$$

The ether functional group is simply the oxygen atom $(-O-)$, and the linkage of two carbon atoms to an oxygen atom is characteristic of the entire family of *ethers*.

The action of a mild oxidizing agent upon alcohols can produce, under varying conditions, three new distinct classes of hydrocarbon derivatives, *aldehydes*, *ketones*, and *carboxylic acids*. The functional groups characteristic of these families are shown in Table 23–2; in each case, an oxygen atom is attached to a carbon atom by a double bond. The preservative properties of the aldehyde *formaldehyde* are well known, and the ketone *acetone* is a very common solvent. The carboxylic acids which are derivatives of

aliphatic hydrocarbons are sometimes called the *fatty acids*. The reason
for this is that many of the compounds of this class were first prepared from
animal and vegetable fats. Indeed, the word *aliphatic* itself (Greek,
aliphatos, "fat") was originally proposed because of this association. The
strongest acid among the fatty acids is the simplest one, *formic acid*; this
substance is found in red ants (Latin, *formica*, "ant"), and is also found in
bees and stinging nettles. Acid strength in the fatty acids decreases with
increasing numbers of carbon atoms, and it will be recalled that we have
used the second member of the series, acetic acid:

$$
\begin{array}{ccc}
\text{H} & & \text{O} \\
| & & \parallel \\
\text{H---C---C} & & \\
| & & \diagdown \\
\text{H} & & \text{OH}
\end{array}
$$

as a prominent example of a weak acid. When these substances act as acids
it is the oxygen-bound hydrogen that is donated; the acetic acid-water
equilibrium may be shown as follows, using structural formulas:

$$
\begin{array}{c}
\text{H} \quad\quad \text{O} \\
| \quad\quad\quad \parallel \\
\text{H---C---C} \quad + \text{H}_2\text{O} \rightleftarrows \text{H}_3\text{O}^+ + \left(\text{H---C---C}\right)^- \\
| \quad\quad \diagdown \\
\text{H} \quad\quad \text{OH}
\end{array}
$$

(acetate ion)

The disagreeable odor of rancid butter is caused by the presence of *butyric*
acid, whose molecules consist of a carboxyl group attached to a propyl
group. Most soaps are mixtures of the sodium salts of several long-chain
fatty acids, most prominently *palmitic* acid (16 carbon atoms) and *stearic*
acid (18 carbon atoms). There are acids which contain two or more
carboxyl groups per molecule, such as *oxalic* acid:

$$
\begin{array}{ccc}
\text{O} & & \text{OH} \\
\diagdown\!\!\!\diagdown & & \diagup \\
& \text{C} & \\
& | & \\
& \text{C} & \\
\diagup\!\!\!\diagup & & \diagdown \\
\text{O} & & \text{OH}
\end{array}
$$

adipic acid:

$$
\begin{array}{ccccccc}
\text{O} & \text{H} & \text{H} & \text{H} & \text{H} & & \text{O} \\
\diagdown\!\!\!\diagdown & | & | & | & | & & \diagup\!\!\!\diagup \\
\text{C---C---C---C---C---C} \\
\diagup & | & | & | & | & & \diagdown \\
\text{HO} & \text{H} & \text{H} & \text{H} & \text{H} & & \text{OH}
\end{array}
$$

and *citric* acid, the sour constituent of lemon juice:

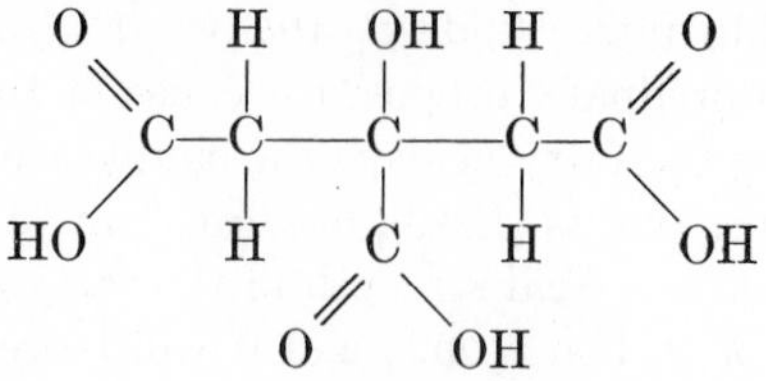

$$\begin{array}{ccccc}
O & H & OH & H & O \\
\diagdown\!\!\diagup & | & | & | & \diagup\!\!\diagdown \\
C-C-C-C-C \\
\diagup & | & | & | & \diagdown \\
HO & H & C & H & OH
\end{array}$$

$$\begin{array}{cc}
\diagup\diagdown \\
O & OH
\end{array}$$

When a carboxylic acid and an alcohol are brought together a molecule of water may form in reaction between them while a molecule of an *ester* is produced. The reaction is usually catalyzed by the presence of hydronium ion. *Ethyl acetate* is an ester formed in the reaction between ethyl alcohol and acetic acid, which we have discussed in Chapter 22. Using structural formulas, we may represent this reaction as follows:

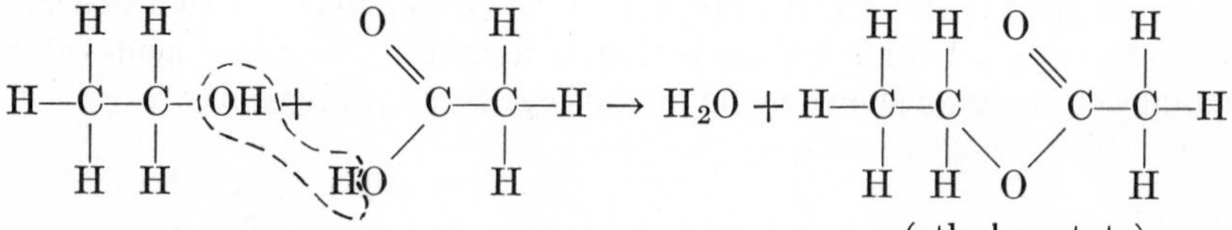

$$\begin{array}{ccccccc}
H & H & & O & H & & H & H & O & & H \\
| & | & & \diagdown & | & & | & | & & & | \\
H-C-C-(OH + & & C-C-H & \rightarrow & H_2O + H-C-C & & C-C-H \\
| & | & \diagup & | & & | & | & \diagdown & \diagup & | \\
H & H & HO & H & & H & H & O & & H
\end{array}$$

(ethyl acetate)

Esters are often extremely fragrant, and are widely used in the preparation of perfumes and flavorants. The characteristic odor of banana oil, for example, is that of the ester *isoamyl acetate:*

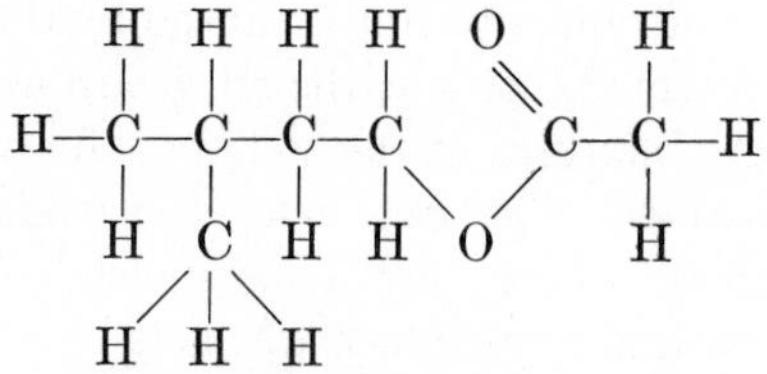

$$\begin{array}{cccccccc}
H & H & H & H & O & & H \\
| & | & | & | & \diagdown & & | \\
H-C-C-C-C & & & & C-C-H \\
| & | & | & | & \diagup & & | \\
H & C & H & H & O & & H
\end{array}$$

$$\begin{array}{ccc}
\diagup & | & \diagdown \\
H & H & H
\end{array}$$

Oil of wintergreen is methyl salicylate, formed in the reaction between methyl alcohol and the aromatic acid *salicyclic* acid:

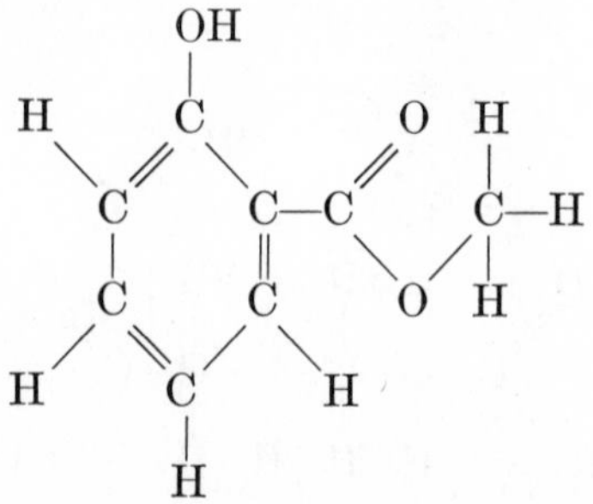

$$\begin{array}{c}
OH \\
| \\
H \quad C \quad\quad O \quad H \\
\diagdown \diagup\diagdown \quad \diagdown \quad | \\
C \quad C-C \quad C-H \\
\diagup\diagdown \quad \diagup \quad | \\
C \quad C \quad O \quad H \\
\diagup \diagdown \\
H \quad C \quad H \\
| \\
H
\end{array}$$

Fats and oils, an important class of esters, may be regarded as products of reaction between the alcohol glycerine and long-chain fatty acids. A characteristic fat, for example, is *glyceryl palmitate*, which is found in the oil of palm trees. Glycerine molecules contain three hydroxyl groups, and each molecule of this fat contains three molecules of palmitic acid, which is a straight chain fatty acid with 16 carbon atoms. A structural formula for glyceryl palmitate may be shown as follows:

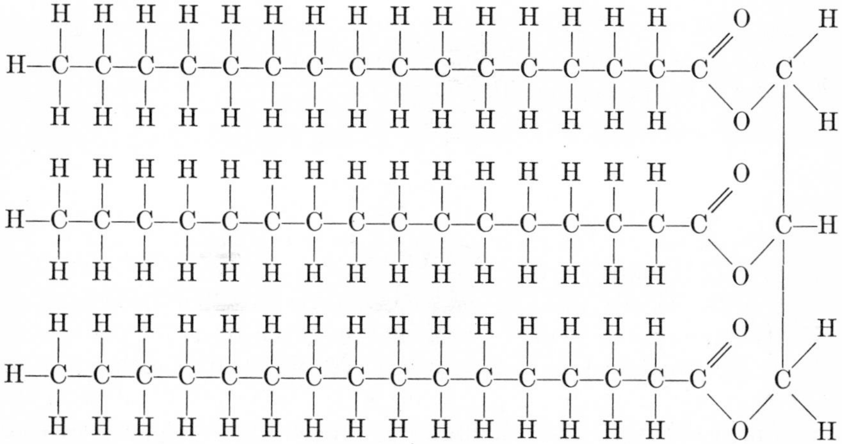

Although most of our discussion of hydrocarbon derivatives has dealt with oxygen compounds, oxygen is certainly not the only third element of importance in organic chemistry. Nitrogen, phosphorus, iodine, sulfur, and several metallic elements are a few of those essential to the chemistry of life. Of these elements, nitrogen is found to the greatest extent in natural products, principally in plant and animal proteins. Proteins, as we shall learn in Chapter 24, are built of *amino acid* molecules, each of which contains both a *primary amine* functional group and a carboxyl group. *Aminoacetic acid* is a simple example of an amino acid:

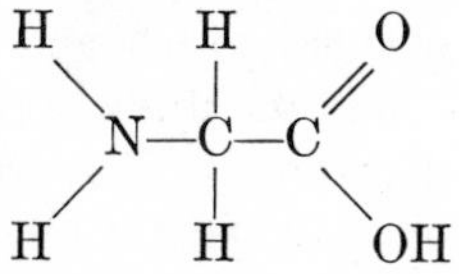

This is but one example of a *mixed* hydrocarbon derivative; in addition to the possible compounds containing just one of the functional groups listed in Table 23–2, many possible combinations, like this one, are known.

So far, then, we have seen that there is a virtually endless number of possible hydrocarbon compounds and that there are many functional groups with which they may combine to form derivatives in staggering variety. The number of organic compounds which have been described in the chemical literature, in excess of one-half million, represents no more than a small fraction of the number that are capable of existence. In the next chapter, we shall discuss some selected topics dealing with organic synthesis. Many of the molecules we shall encounter there will be recognized as built of the basic organic structural units we have discussed, such as those listed in Tables 23–1 and 23–2. We shall learn that there are even greater possibilities of complication in organic molecular structure than have been divulged in the present chapter, however.

23–7 Summary

Although the compounds of organized, or living matter were once believed to be the products of a special "vital" force, it was found in the 19th century that some of them, at least, may be synthesized in the laboratory. The field of organic chemistry, originally the chemistry of the products of life, is now defined simply as the study of the compounds of carbon. These are more than ten times as numerous as the compounds of all the other elements combined. The extraordinary versatility of carbon is related to the ability of its atoms to form strong bonds with one another in chain and ring structures. The simplest compounds of carbon, the hydrocarbons, occur in numerous homologous series as saturated compounds based on chains, unsaturated chain compounds (containing double bonds), and compounds whose molecules contain rings of carbon atoms. Many more organic compounds are conveniently regarded as derivatives of hydrocarbons, their molecules containing one or more characteristic functional groups attached to hydrocarbon groups. The complexity of organic chemistry is enhanced by numerous possibilities of compounds having identical molecular formulas but different molecular structures, called *isomers*. In the most subtle kind of isomerism, called optical, the molecules of two substances are mirror images of one another and have opposite effects on a beam of polarized light. Through the study of this kind of isomerism it was deduced that the four covalent bonds of a carbon atom are normally directed toward the corners of a regular tetrahedron, a deduction of great importance to the general structural interpretation of organic chemistry.

REFERENCES

BERNAL, J. D., *Science and Industry in the* 19*th Century*. Contains a fascinating account of Pasteur's discovery of optical isomerism.

FINDLAY, A., *A Hundred Years of Chemistry*, Chapters II, IV, and VII.

GLOCKLER, G., and R. C. GLOCKLER, *Chemistry in Our Time*, Chapter XV.

LEICESTER, H. M., and H. S. KLICKSTEIN, *Source Book in Chemistry;* pp 287–291 (Chevreul), 299–305 (Gay–Lussac), 309–312 (Wöhler), 317–320 (Liebig), 320–327 (Dumas), 374–379 (Pasteur), 417–425 (Kekulé), 445–453 (van't Hoff), 459–462 (LeBel).

PARTINGTON, J. R., *A Short History of Chemistry*, Chapters X, XI, XII, and XIII.

READ, J., *A Direct Entry to Organic Chemistry*. Simply written, this is a stimulating brief introduction to the intricacies of carbon chemistry.

SISLER, H. H., and others, *General Chemistry, a Systematic Approach*, Chapters 30 and 31.

1. A certain hydrocarbon is found to contain 82.8% by weight of the element carbon, the rest hydrogen. What is its simplest empirical formula? Can the tetravalence of all carbon atoms present be satisfied in a hydrocarbon of this formula? Of the various possible multiples of this formula, which corresponds to a possible compound? What is the name of the compound? its structural formula? [*Ans.*: The compound is butane]

2. What is the general type formula for the saturated fatty acids (formic, acetic, propionic, butyric, etc.)? What trends would you expect to observe in the boiling and melting points of these compounds?

3. Two compounds are found, on analysis, to contain 60% carbon, 26.67% oxygen, 13.33% hydrogen. By gas-volume measurement they are found to have the same molecular weight, 60. What molecular formula fits both compounds? One of them is miscible with water and releases hydrogen when metallic sodium is added to it; the other is immiscible with water and does not react with sodium. What kinds of hydrocarbon derivatives are they, in all probability? What are their probable structural formulas? [*Ans.*: One compound is propyl alcohol, the other *methylethyl* ether]

4. A certain hydrocarbon of molecular formula C_4H_8 is found to have the properties of an *aliphatic* compound which is *saturated* (Section 23–3). What do these terms mean? What test could be applied to determine that the com-

pound is a saturated one? What *un*saturated compound is an isomer of this one? What is the probable structural formula of the saturated compound? (*Hint*: The structure is *cyclic*; see Section 23–4.)

5. Cyclohexane (C_6H_{12}) is almost as nonreactive as its straight-chain counterpart, hexane. *Cyclopropane* (C_3H_6), on the other hand, is found to be highly reactive. Write a structural formula for cyclopropane, and deduce what is likely to be the geometric relation of its three carbon atoms. What will the bond angles between carbon atoms be in this structure? Remembering that the normal angles between carbon atoms in organic structures are tetrahedral (109° 28′), can you find a possible reason for the reactivity of cyclopropane?

6. Write structural formulas for the three isomers ortho-, meta-, and para-dichlorobenzene (Section 23–5). A common practice, which will facilitate formula writing for aromatic structures, is to represent the benzene ring as a hexagon, showing double bonds, but tacitly understanding each apex to represent a carbon atom:

For an aromatic derivative, like chlorobenzene, the attached group is shown, but the presence of hydrogen atoms at other positions is tacitly understood:

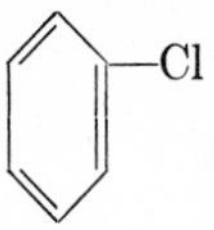

7. In the methane hydrocarbon series, the first compound to exhibit structural isomers is butane. *On paper*, however, we might write two structures of propane, as follows:

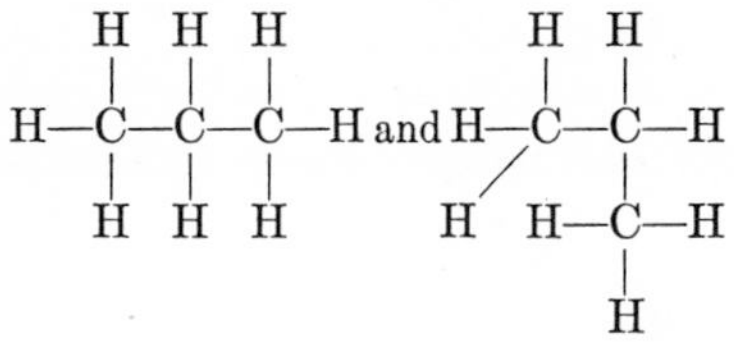

The second structure is exactly equivalent to the first, and we must be careful to remember that structural formulas of this sort are *two*-dimensional representations of *three*-dimensional molecules. In terms of the carbon-carbon bonds shown in these structures, and in terms of the spatial orientations of these bonds, explain why the two are equivalent.

8. Although there is only one form of propane, *derivatives* of this compound are generally found to exist in two structurally different forms. There are thus two kinds of propyl group, *propyl* and *isopropyl*. Write structural formulas for *propyl alcohol* and *isopropyl alcohol*. (*Hint*: The difference lies in the placement of the hydroxyl group.)

9. There are five known isomers of hexane. Can you write structural formulas for them? An exercise of this sort is facilitated by the use of *skeleton* formulas, showing only carbon atoms. The skeleton formula for the straight-chain form of hexane, for example, would be

C—C—C—C—C—C

You will find that you may write more than five structures for hexane unless you are careful to rule out those that look different on paper but would actually be equivalent in space. The following two *heptane* structures, for example, are identical:

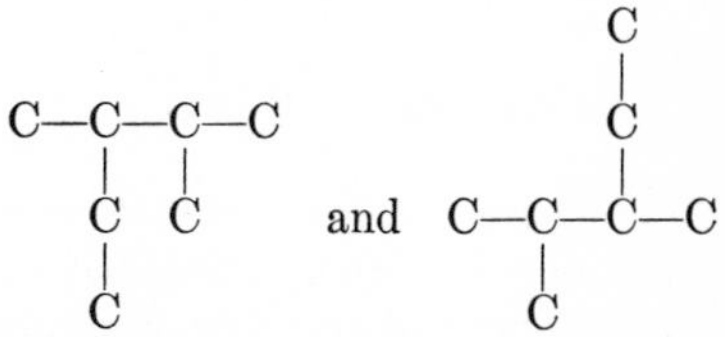

With a little mental manipulation, one may be visualized as exactly superimposed on the other.

10. How many forms of butylamine are possible? Illustrate with structural formulas. [*Ans.*: Four]

11. Of the following compounds, which may be expected to exist in two forms, capable of rotating the plane of polarization of polarized light in opposite directions? (See *optical isomerism*, Section 23–5.)

(a)

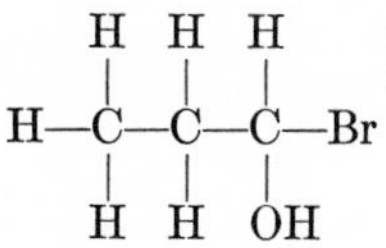

(b)

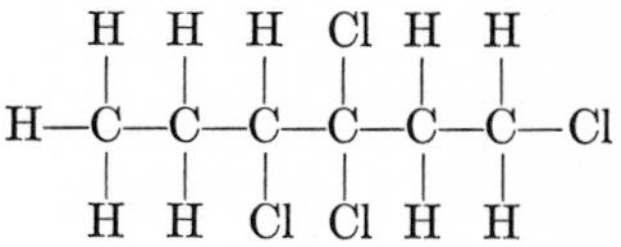

(c)

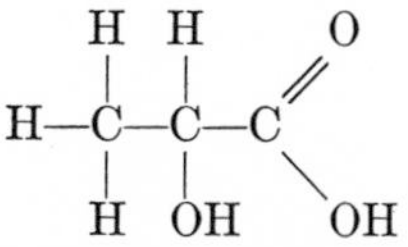

(cont.)

14. How many isomers of *trinitrotoluene* are possible? In the particular form of trinitrotoluene (TNT) used as an explosive, two of the three nitro groups are in positions *ortho* to the toluene methyl group, the third in *para* position. Show the structural formula for this compound. [*Ans.*: Number of isomers is six]

15. Most synthetic *detergents* are sodium salts of sulfonic acids. (Sul-

(d)

$$
\begin{array}{c}
H \\
| \\
H-C-H \quad H \\
\diagdown \; \diagup \\
C \\
\| \\
C \\
\diagup \; \diagdown \\
H-C-H \quad C \\
| \qquad \diagup \; \diagdown \\
H \quad OH \quad O
\end{array}
$$

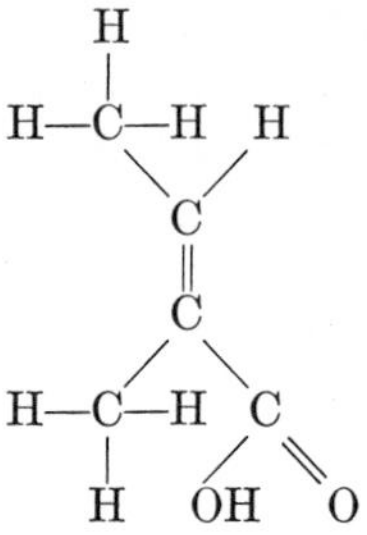

12. Using structural formulas, write an equation for the reaction between propyl alcohol and butyric acid to form the ester *propyl butyrate* (Section 23–6).

13. Write structural formulas for the following organic compounds:

(a) nonyl alcohol,
(b) propionaldehyde,
(c) *iso*propylethyl ether (see Exercise 8),
(d) acetaldehyde (two carbon atoms),
(e) amyl acetate,
(f) nitromethane,
(g) butyl mercaptan,
(h) octanoic acid,
(i) methylethyl ketone,
(j) aminobenzene (common name *analine*)
(k) chloronaphthalene,
(l) ethyl sulfonic acid.

fonic acid groups,

$$
\begin{array}{c}
O \\
\| \\
-S-OH, \text{ tend to} \\
\| \\
O
\end{array}
$$

donate protons, and sulfonic acids are generally stronger than carboxylic acids.) An example is the sodium salt of *para-lauryl-benzenesulfonic* acid. To decipher this name: a sulfonic acid group is attached to a benzene ring, and in the position in the ring *para* to this group a *lauryl* group is attached. The lauryl group is a straight-chain, saturated aliphatic group, containing 12 carbon atoms. Write a structural formula for this acid, and indicate which hydrogen atom is replaced when its sodium salt is formed.

CHAPTER 24

ORGANIC PRODUCTS, NATURAL AND SYNTHETIC

The products of nature can be understood, in a fundamental sense, only in terms of the arrangements of atoms in their molecules, and the organic chemist can rarely be certain that he understands the structure of a natural product until he has succeeded in duplicating the material in his laboratory. Organic structures can be exceedingly subtle and complex, as we have begun to see in Chapter 23, and laboratory syntheses of most natural products have required years of concentrated effort. When Robert B. Woodward and William von E. Doering succeeded in synthesizing the antimalarial drug quinine, in 1944, their achievement crowned the efforts of many, over more than a century. There are numerous natural products which cannot yet be called fully understood, structurally, because no one has succeeded in duplicating their molecules in the laboratory. The entire past history of organic chemistry comes into play in the synthesis of any complex organic compound, since without understanding of the simpler organic structures and the reactions in which they are broken up, rearranged, or combined, synthesis of the more complicated structures would not be possible.

Synthetic organic chemistry has had economic consequences. In numerous instances it has been feasible to produce organic products more cheaply by synthetic means than to extract them from plant or animal materials. We must not conclude that organic synthesis is inherently more economical than natural production, however. Although quinine can now be synthesized, the entire world production of this substance is still based upon cultivation of the cinchona tree. Nor should we conclude that the sole function of organic synthesis in industry lies in sheer duplication of the products of nature. Through structural understanding of such handsome natural dyes as indigo and alizarin, organic chemists have been able to produce thousands of new dyestuffs, differing from the natural products in molecular configuration and possessing variation, in color and in other properties, that plant extracts had not provided. The many resources of chemotherapy (e.g., the *sulfa* drugs) and the plastics and synthetic fibers which find such extensive application today are other examples of the material accomplishments of organic synthesis. The production of substances different from those found in nature does not mean that man's prowess in molecular synthesis has exceeded that of nature in any sense, however.

Man's comprehension of the more complicated products and processes of life has barely begun.

Organic synthesis has become a spectacular and fascinating subject not only to the professional chemist but also to the nonchemist who takes pleasure in subtle and complicated design patterns. We offer here a selection of examples, chosen to illustrate the general principles and various types of molecular patterns. They may seem difficult at first sight, but their development needs only to be followed from one step to the next; the reader will probably have no reason to memorize any of the details.

24–1 Determination of organic structure

The first task to be performed, in the attempt to determine the structure of any compound, is elemental *analysis* for the kinds and numbers of atoms present in each of its molecules. Organic compounds of very different structures may contain nearly identical percentages of constituent elements, and small errors in analysis can lead to serious difficulties. A synthesis for the dye *alizarin* was sought for many years during the 19th century, for example. During the 1850's alizarin was assigned the formula $C_{10}H_6O_3$, and on the basis of this formula it was thought to be a derivative of the aromatic hydrocarbon *naphthalene;* all efforts toward its synthesis were based on this assumption. In 1868, however, it was found that alizarin is a derivative of *anthracene,* and that its correct formula is $C_{14}H_8O_4$. The percentages of the elements which correspond to this formula, by weight, are 70.0% carbon, 3.3% hydrogen, 26.7% oxygen. For the formula $C_{10}H_6O_3$ they would be 68.9% carbon, 3.5% hydrogen, 27.6% oxygen. The errors in analysis which led to the incorrect assignment, then, were not large.

Once a satisfactory molecular formula for an organic compound has been established, guesses may be made as to its structure. Since there may be several possible isomers corresponding to the same formula, however, guessing cannot produce reliable answers. If the problem is one of identification of a *known* substance, careful measurement of its physical properties, such as boiling and melting points, will often provide a sufficient clue. In addition, there are many specific chemical tests for the presence of the various functional groups. Reaction with sodium metal, we have seen in Chapter 23, can be used to distinguish between an alcohol and an ether. Aldehyde groups (see Table 23–2) may be detected by the use of "Tollen's reagent," silver oxide dissolved in ammonia solution. The reagent oxidizes aldehyde groups to carboxylic acid groups, while the silver it contains is reduced to the metallic state. Production of a black precipitate of metallic silver with this reagent may thus be a positive test for the presence of aldehyde groups.

Although a chemist may know with certainty what functional groups the molecules of a given compound contain and what hydrocarbon it is derived from, he may still be uncertain of its structural formula because it is one of two or more possible isomers. There are three *dichlorobenzenes*, for example, all with molecular formula $C_6H_4Cl_2$. They have distinctly different properties, but there is no clue in these properties to indicate which of the three is the *ortho* compound, which *meta*, and which *para*. For identification of the isomers of aromatic derivatives of this sort, an ingenious method was developed by W. G. Koerner (1839–1925), a student of Kekulé. As indicated in Fig. 24–1, addition of a third atom or group to a benzene ring which contains two in ortho positions should lead to formation of *two* new compounds. If the two original groups are in meta positions, there should be *three* isomers of the new compound, and if para, only *one*. If a dichlorobenzene whose structure is unknown is treated so that each molecule acquires one nitro group, then, the number of distinct new compounds that form indicates how the two chlorine atoms are arranged in the molecule of the parent compound. These new compounds, isomers of *dichloronitrobenzene*, can be separated from one another because of their differences in physical properties.

Koerner's method is but one of many devices which organic chemists may use in the elucidation of organic structure, and it is impossible to set down a single set of procedural rules for this task; for the more complicated structures, it is an art. Examination of the products of partial degradation, of oxidation and reduction, provide some of the necessary clues, but the final test of the chemist's understanding of a new structure often resides in his ability to synthesize it from simple, known starting materials. Well-understood reactions, which result in the placement of particular kinds of atoms in specific molecular positions, are the indispensable tools of the organic molecular architect, for if he understands all the individual chemical reactions involved in building up a molecule from its constituent elements he will know how its atoms are arranged. By comparison of their physical and chemical properties, he can determine whether his synthetic product is identical with the natural product of interest to him.

As a single example of a problem in proof of organic structure, let us consider the synthesis of alizarin. This red dye, known since antiquity to occur in the root of the madder plant, was first isolated as a pure compound in 1826. There was widespread effort to effect a synthesis of this valuable product and, as we have noted earlier, slight errors in elemental analysis led chemists in the 1850's to believe it a derivative of naphthalene. In 1866 Adolf Baeyer (1835–1917) developed a method for the reduction of hydrocarbon derivatives to their parent hydrocarbon compounds. Carl Graebe (1841–1927) and Carl Liebermann (1842–1914) applied Baeyer's method (distillation over finely divided zinc) to natural alizarin, and found

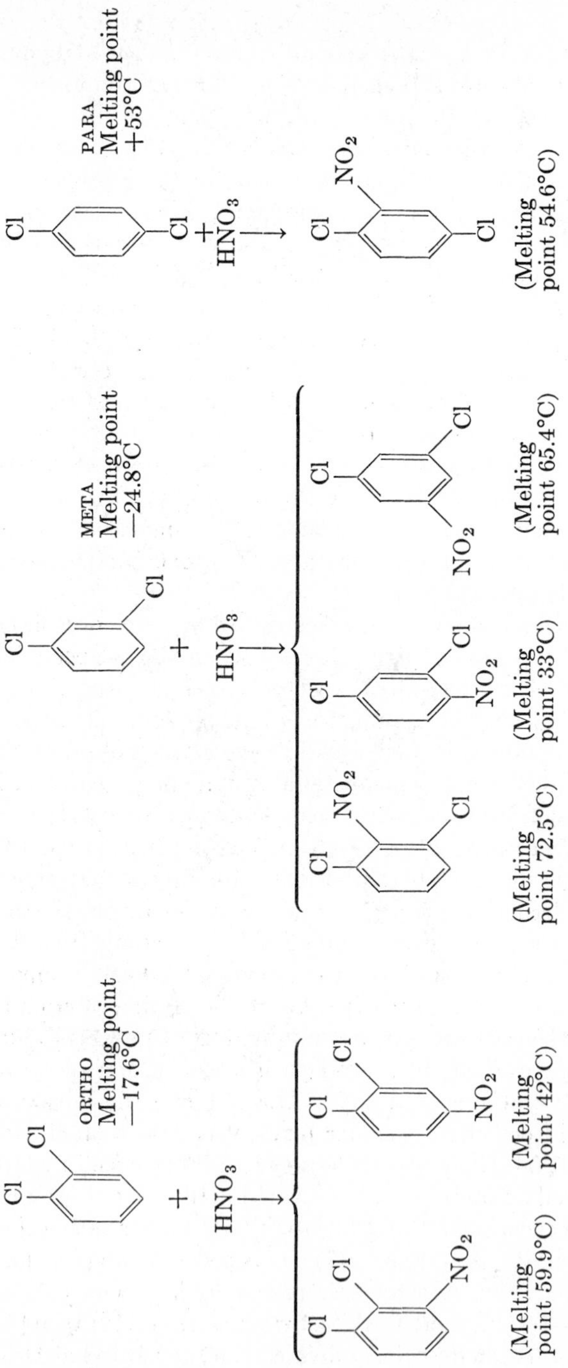

FIG. 24–1. Koerner's method applied to the isomers of dichlorobenzene.

that the hydrocarbon they obtained was not at all like naphthalene, but identical with *anthracene*:

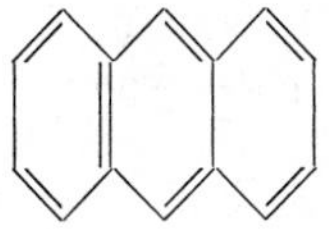

(In this chapter we shall represent all aromatic structures in this way; each apex of each hexagon is the position of a carbon atom, and hydrogen atoms are implicitly understood to be attached to those apexes not joined to other hexagons. See Exercise 23–6.)

It was known that alizarin molecules contain oxygen atoms, and Graebe and Liebermann quickly concluded that it must be related to an oxidation product of anthracene, which was then well known, called *anthraquinone*:

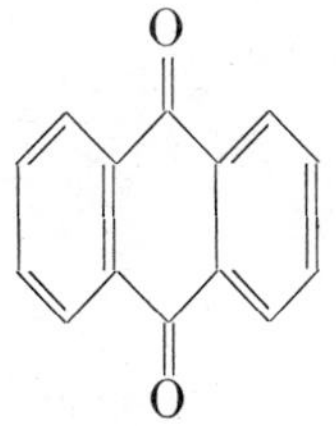

Alizarin was not identical with anthraquinone, however, and if their deduction was correct its molecule must contain substituent groups in the place of one or more hydrogen atoms on the ring structure. By careful scrutiny of the analytical evidence, they saw that it was entirely possible that the empirical formula for the compound could be $C_{14}H_8O_4$. If so, each molecule would have two oxygen atoms in excess of those in anthraquinone itself, which could be the case if there were two hydroxyl groups present in ring positions. To test this hypothesis, Graebe and Liebermann prepared anthraquinone by mild oxidation of anthracene, then caused the anthraquinone to react with just enough bromine to form a *dibromo* derivative:

$$C_{14}H_8O_2 + 2Br_2 \rightarrow C_{14}H_6O_2Br_2 + 2HBr.$$

Finally, they fused this dibromo compound with potassium hydroxide, a procedure which was known to cause replacement of bromine atoms by hydroxyl groups:

$$C_{14}H_6O_2Br_2 + 2OH^- \rightarrow C_{14}H_6O_2(OH)_2 + 2Br^-.$$

The product, *dihydroxyanthraquinone*, was found to be identical in all respects with the natural plant product, alizarin, and Graebe and Liebermann had thus carried out the first successful synthesis of a natural dye. Within a year (1870) an economically feasible synthesis, involving the sulfonic acid derivative of anthraquinone rather than its dibromide, had been developed and patented, and the inexpensive synthetic product quickly replaced natural alizarin in the market.

Graebe and Liebermann's technological triumph left the scientific problem of the structure of alizarin incompletely resolved. Their product could be only one of *nine* structural isomers, since there are that many different ways in which two hydroxyl groups may be oriented on an anthraquinone molecule. Baeyer pursued the problem further, using simpler compounds whose structures had already been firmly established. He found that when *catechol* (ortho-dihydroxybenzene),

and *phthalic acid*

are heated together in the presence of sulfuric acid, alizarin is obtained. In this reaction, water is split out between carboxyl groups on phthalic acid and ring hydrogen on catechol, and the hydroxyl groups are left undisturbed:

Since alizarin is formed in this reaction, its two hydroxyl groups must be in *adjacent* ring positions, as they are in catechol. This reduces the number of isomeric possibilities but does not completely solve the problem, since there are still two forms which meet this prescription: that shown above, and

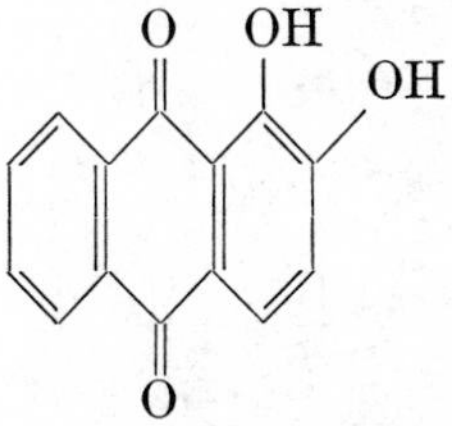

To distinguish between these, Baeyer heated phthalic acid with *phenol*, and obtained the two isomers of *mono*hydroxyanthraquinone:

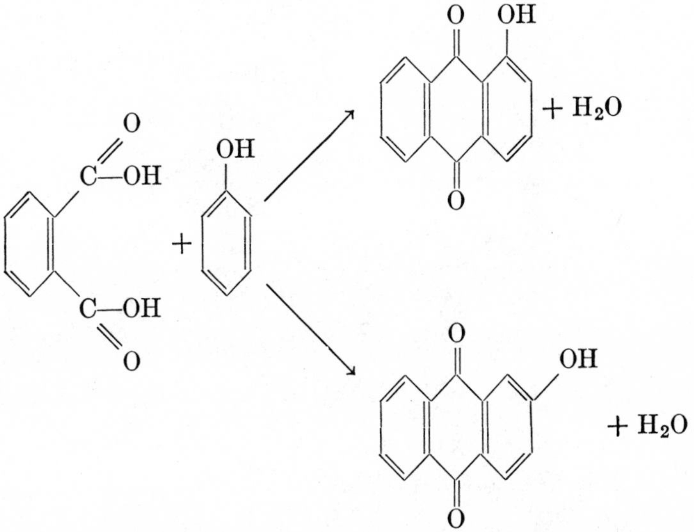

Finally, in each of these compounds he replaced a ring hydrogen atom with a hydroxyl group, and in *both* cases obtained alizarin as a product. Since the alizarin hydroxyls must be adjacent, this last result could then be consistent only with the structure

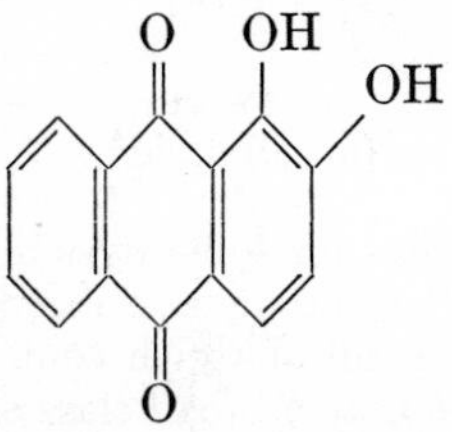

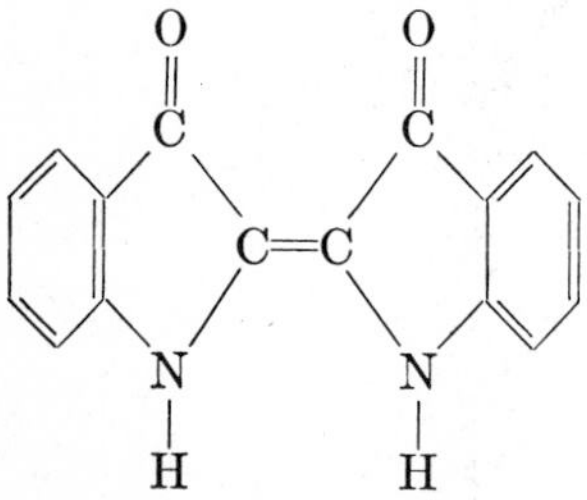

INDIGO
(a dye)

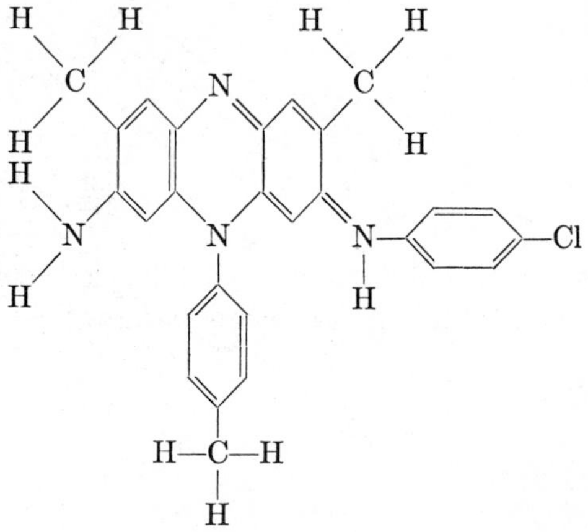

MAUVE
(a dye)

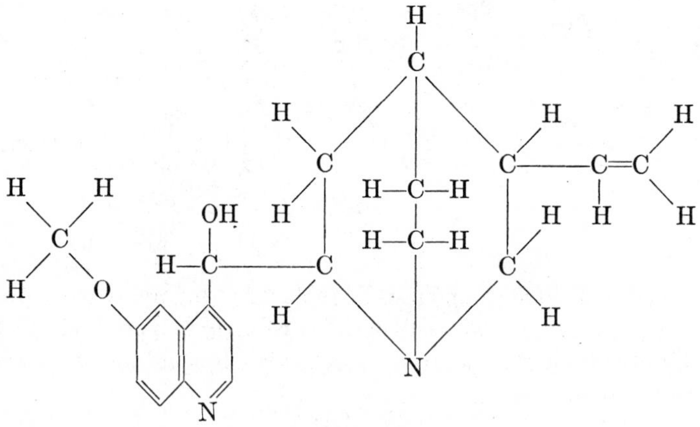

QUININE
(an alkaloid)

FIG. 24–2. Structural formulas for some dyes and medicinals. Note that of those shown, only aspirin and sulfanilamide can be considered simple hydrocarbon derivatives. The others, all of which contain ring systems with one or more atoms unlike carbon, belong to a broad class called *heterocyclic* compounds.

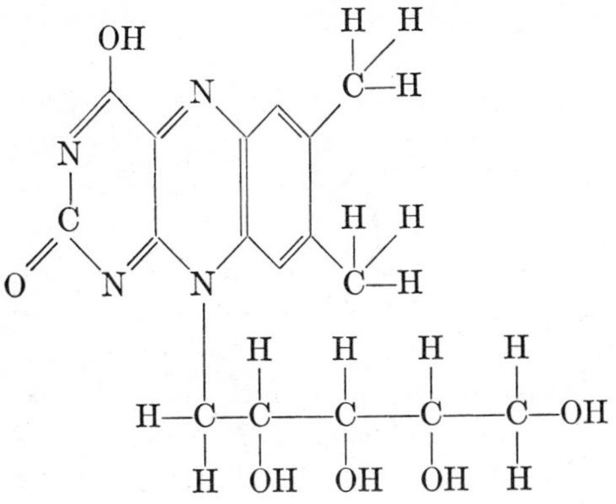

RIBOFLAVIN
(Vitamin B$_2$)

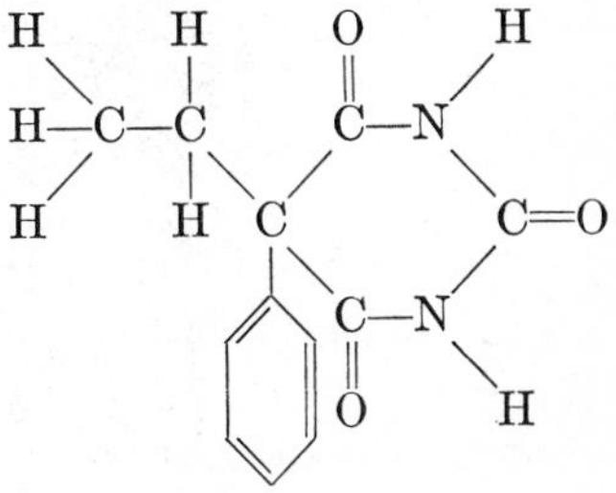

PHENOBARBITAL
(a barbiturate sedative)

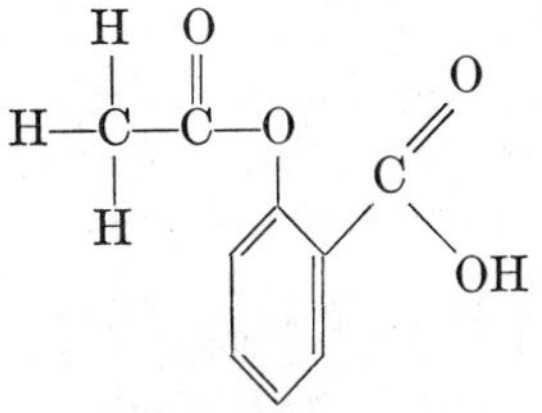

ASPIRIN
(a mild analgesic)

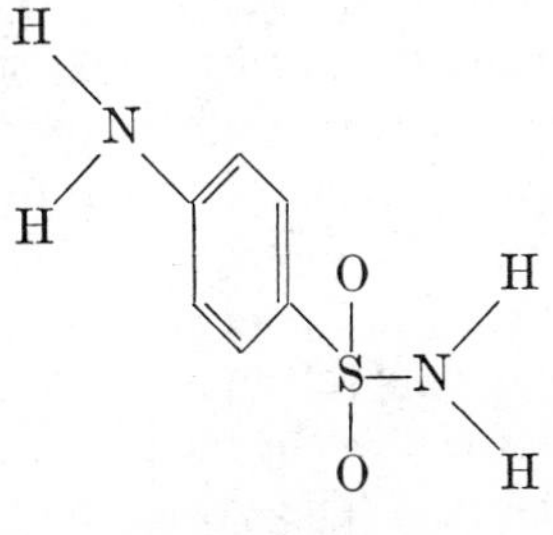

SULFANILAMIDE
(a typical "sulfa" drug)

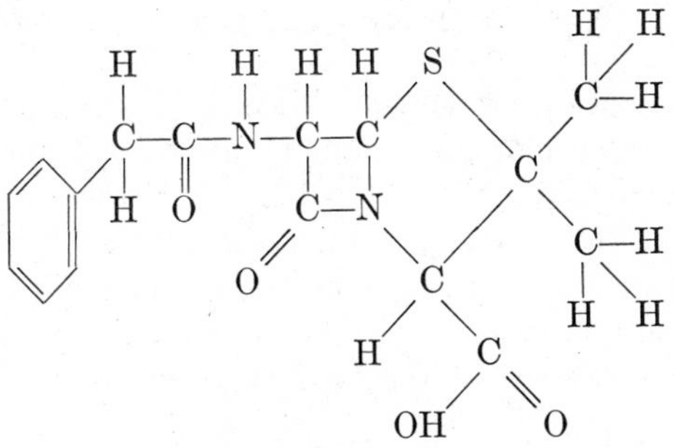

PENICILLIN G
(an antibiotic)

FIG. 24–2 (cont.)

The story of the alizarin synthesis, which we have recounted in incomplete historical detail, is but one of countless possible examples of the intensive search for syntheses and structural understanding that has characterized the past 100 years of organic chemistry. The dye and drug industries have been particularly lively centers in this search. The commercial synthesis of dyestuffs from the cheap starting materials available in coal tar did not have its beginning with alizarin, but with *mauve*. In 1856 William Henry Perkin (1837–1907), an 18-year-old student in London, attempted to synthesize quinine. Quinine was known to have the empirical formula $C_{20}H_{24}N_2O_2$, and Perkin thought that it might be an oxidation product of the known compound *allyltoluidine*, empirical formula $C_{10}H_{13}N$. When he treated this compound with the oxidizing agent potassium dichromate he did not obtain quinine, but did find a water-soluble purple compound with all the attributes of a good dye. He immediately began the manufacture of this compound, mauve, which soon became one of the most popular dyestuffs of the era. The synthesis of quinine, as we have said, was not accomplished until 1944. Alizarin was the first *natural* dye to be synthesized, and *indigo*, synthesized by Baeyer in 1880, was the second. The chemotherapeutic *sulfa* drugs were discovered, in 1936, after it had been observed that a certain industrial synthetic dye (prontosil) was effective against streptococcus infections. These compounds played a role in medicine which declined in importance only when the even more potent *antibiotics* (e.g., penicillin) became commercially available after their discovery in 1939. While the structure of penicillin has been established, it is still prepared exclusively by growth of the mold, *penicillium notatum*, that produces it. The structures of penicillin, sulfanilamide, indigo, mauve, quinine, and several other interesting dyes and medicinals are shown in Fig. 24–2.

24–2 Polymerization and giant molecules

The complexity of organic chemistry is greatly compounded by the fact that many small molecular units, under suitable conditions, may join together to form giant molecules, or polymers (Greek: *poly*, "many," *mer*, "part"). Although the hypothesis of giant molecules can be traced back to the 19th century, it did not gain general acceptance until relatively recent years. Today there is no doubt of its correctness, and the scientific and technological development of the field of polymer chemistry since 1930 has been impressively rapid.

In the process of *polymerization*, a great number of small molecules, called *monomers*, join together to form a single polymer molecule. A simple example is the polymerization of ethylene to form the plastic substance *polyethylene*, which takes place readily in the presence of suitable catalysts.

First, two molecules join, by the shift of a hydrogen atom in one to saturate the double bond in the other and formation of a new single carbon-carbon bond:

$$H_2C{=}CH_2 + H_2C{=}CH_2 \rightarrow H{-}CH_2{-}CH_2{-}CH{=}CH_2$$

The new molecule, a structural isomer of butylene, can add a third ethylene molecule at its double bond, and by repetition of the process to an indefinitely great extent a giant, straight-chain molecule with a double bond at one end is formed. The empirical formula for the polyethylene molecule is simply $(C_2H_4)_N$, where N is a large number which may vary from molecule to molecule in a given sample of the plastic.

An example of a *natural* polymer which is built of small units in a fashion very similar to that of synthetic polyethylene is natural rubber. The monomer, in this case, is a doubly unsaturated hydrocarbon called *isoprene*:

$$
\begin{array}{c}
CH_3\\
H_2C{=}C{-}CH{=}CH_2
\end{array}
$$

The polymer molecule is itself unsaturated (Fig. 24–3), since buildup of its chain saturates only one double bond for each new carbon-carbon bond formed. Untreated natural rubber is a viscous fluid, and it is found that its tensile strength and other properties are improved by addition of sulfur in the process called *vulcanization*. Sulfur atoms form *cross links* between polyisoprene chains in several ways, one of which, involving attachment at unsaturated positions, is shown in Fig. 24–3. Another natural elastic polymer, *gutta percha*, is an isomer of natural rubber. Its monomer units are also isoprene molecules, but they are oriented with respect to one another in a manner different from that found in natural rubber molecules. The existence of such subtlety in the structure of polyisoprene helps to explain the fact that although the structure of natural rubber has long been well known, its synthesis in the laboratory was not achieved until 1955.

Polyethylene, natural rubber, and gutta percha are examples of *addition* polymers: in formation of their molecules, monomer units simply add on to one another, and no atoms are split out in the course of the reaction. In the formation of a second broad class of polymeric materials, called

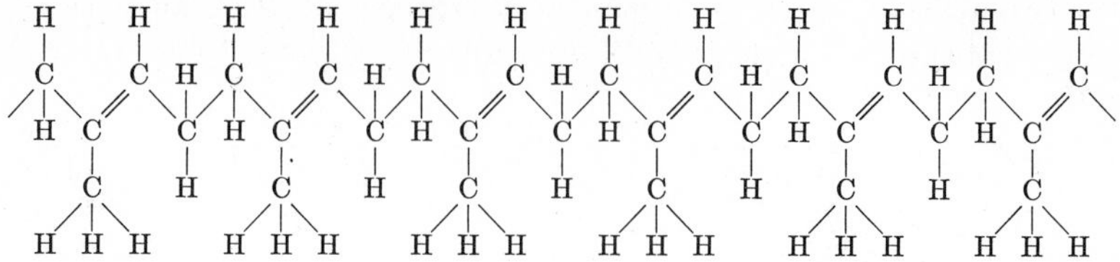

(a)

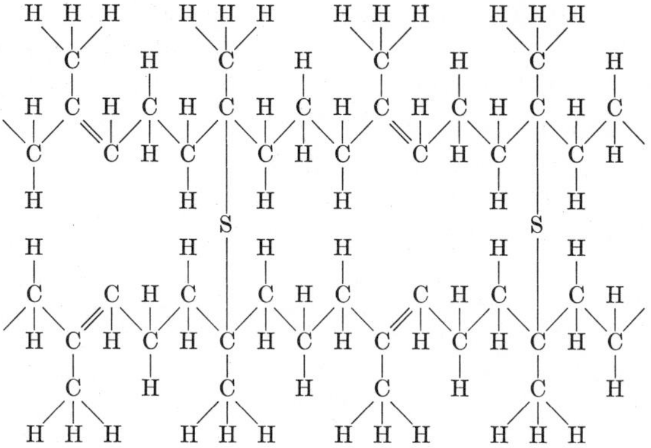

(b)

FIG. 24–3. (a) Structural formula for a portion of the polyisoprene chain molecule of natural rubber. (b) Portions of two polyisoprene chains, cross-linked by sulfur atoms at two positions, in vulcanized natural rubber.

condensation polymers, one or more atoms are removed from each monomer molecule. The formula for any condensation polymer is a large multiple of a unit which contains fewer atoms than the actual monomer molecule. Most commonly, two hydrogen atoms and one oxygen atom split off two monomer molecules to form a water molecule. In the reaction between two molecules of *aminohexanoic acid*, for example, hydrogen atoms from the amino groups combine with hydroxyls from carboxyl groups to form water molecules:

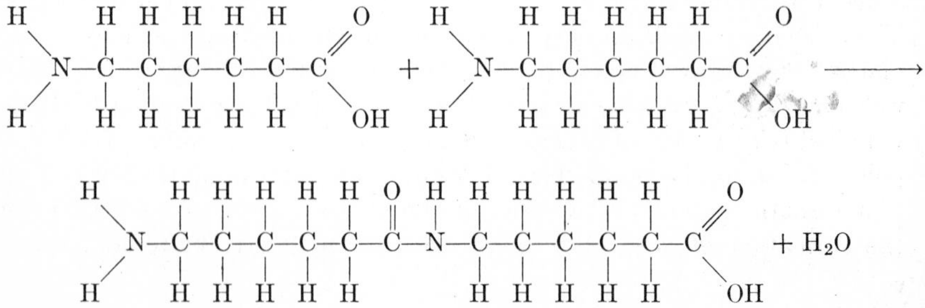

Similar additions of monomer units, each accompanied by loss of a water molecule, lead to formation of a long-chain polymer molecule in which every sixth carbon atom is bound to a nitrogen atom, and which contains an unaltered amino group at one end, a carboxyl group at the other.

Most condensation polymers, and many addition polymers as well, contain more than one kind of monomer unit in their large molecules. In such cases, the process is called *copolymerization*. An example is formation of the synthetic fiber *nylon* from its monomers *hexamethylene diamine*

and adipic acid

Water molecules split out as hydrogen atoms from amino groups combine with —OH groups from adipic acid, and a long-chain molecule forms in which the basic repeating unit has the structure

Not all polymer molecules consist of long chains. A simple addition polymer like polyethylene can consist only of chains, since there is only one possible mode of attachment of succeeding monomer units, but a monomer molecule like *butadiene*,

presents a choice of two positions of addition. Saturation of either double bond is possible, and polymers (and copolymers) of butadiene may have

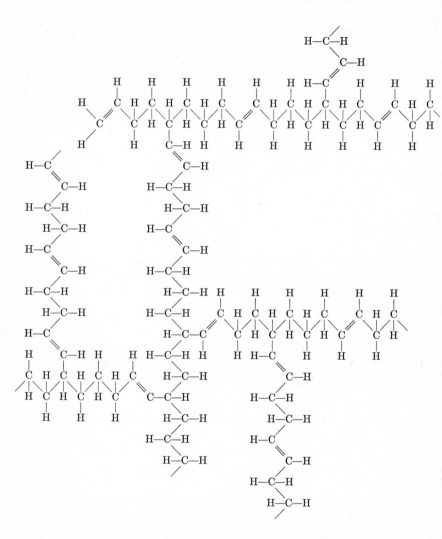

Fig. 24–4. Structural formula for a possible *branched* configuration in a portion of a molecule of the polymer of butadiene.

highly branched molecular structures, as illustrated in Fig. 24–4. In some polymeric substances, the formation of branches proceeds to the same extent as linear growth, links form *between* branched chains, and *network* structures, reminiscent of the arrangement of layers of hexagons in graphite (Section 20–7), are formed. When attachment is possible at three or more positions on each monomer molecule, *space networks*, reminiscent of the diamond structure, may form.

It is not possible to determine an absolute molecular weight for any polymeric substance, since there are molecules of many different sizes present. Methods have been developed to measure the *average* molecular weights of polymers, however. Synthetic addition polymers are generally found to have average molecular weights in the approximate range 100,000 to 1,000,000. Since the molecular weight of ethylene is 28, polyethylene molecules of molecular weight 100,000 would contain nearly 3600 monomer units. Synthetic condensation polymers generally have average molecular weights in the range 10,000 to 25,000, seldom higher. The average molecular weights of natural polymers are variable, but often range up to exceedingly high values. The protein of tobacco mosaic virus, a polymer, has been found to have an average molecular weight of the order of 50 million.

Polymeric *fibers* are usually highly crystalline materials. In order for polymer molecules of any kind to assume a regular crystal configuration, substantial forces must act between them. In fibers of nylon, for example, neighboring molecule chains are bound together by electrostatic attractions between polar groups. Since these groups occur at regularly repeated intervals, they lend themselves readily to the production of a neat crystalline array (Fig. 24–5). Since its component molecules are long chains, the nylon crystal has considerable strength along its long direction, and it is for this reason that nylon fibers are tough. Elastic polymers, or rubbers, are generally almost devoid of crystalline character. Natural rubber, for example, consists of long chains, with very little branching and cross-linking, and its molecules have no polar groups to encourage crystal formation. Since there are no forces present which cause rubber molecules to stay straight, as in nylon, rubber molecules tend to coil up in a random manner. When a bulk sample of rubber is stretched, then, some of its molecules are straightened, and when the stretching force is removed they revert to their original coiled configurations. *Plastic* polymers, like polyethylene, are usually *semi*-crystalline in bulk structure. They contain some regions in which the large molecules are held together and oriented with respect to one another, others in which they are randomly coiled. The property of plasticity is related to this mixed character, since randomly coiled molecules will permit stretching or other deformation, while oriented molecules in crystalline regions tend to prevent restoration after the stretching force is removed.

24–3 Proteins

There are four broad classes of compounds common to all living organisms: *fats, carbohydrates, nucleic acids,* and *proteins.* Of these, the simplest are the fats, esters of glycerol and aliphatic acids, as we have

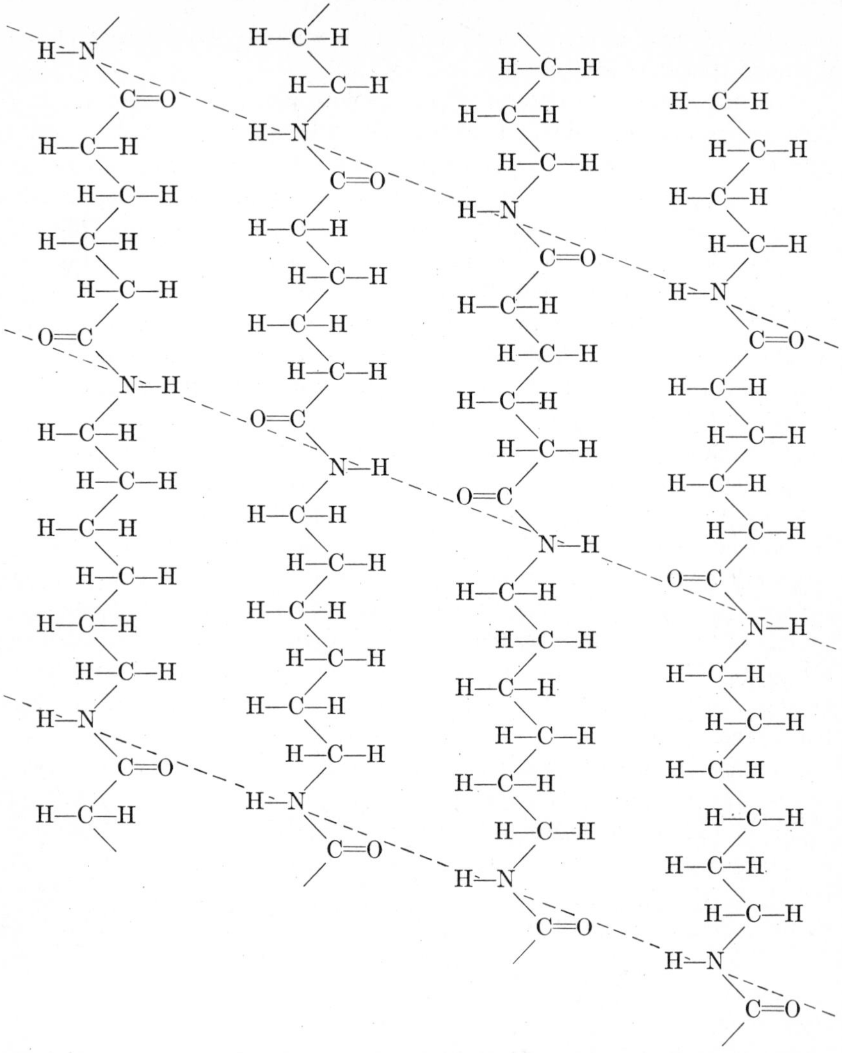

FIG. 24–5. Arrangement of chains in the crystalline polymer, nylon. Because of forces between polar —N—H, and —C=O groups, molecules are held straight and in a definite orientation with respect to one another.

learned in Chapter 23. The carbohydrates, compounds of the elements carbon, hydrogen, and oxygen, range in complexity from the simple *sugars* to the polymeric *starches* and *cellulose*. The nucleic acids, particularly important because of recent mounting evidence that they are the principal constituents of the heredity-bearing genes, are complex polymers based upon long chains of alternating phosphate radicals and sugar molecules.

Each sugar molecule in a nucleic acid structure contains a nitrogenous side chain; the number of kinds of such side chains is small, and the sequence of their arrangement along the main nucleic acid chain is undoubtedly one of the keys to the understanding of life. The most complex of all the products of nature, however, are the proteins, polymeric substances of high nitrogen content. We might also say that they are the most important products of nature, since without them there would be no creatures to ponder the nature of substances of lesser importance.

Every living cell contains protein, and these structures, along with nucleic acids, appear to play the central role in performance of the very process, self-reproduction, which distinguishes living from inanimate matter. The hundreds of enzymes, each a catalyst of great specificity to the syntheses of life, are all proteins, as is hemoglobin, the component of red blood cells which enables animals to assimilate atmospheric oxygen. Most of the hormones, regulators of such vital processes as growth, are proteins, although some consist of simpler molecules. The principal structural materials of the animal kingdom, horn, hair, skin, and nails, are all proteins. The importance of these materials was recognized, early in the nineteenth century, by Berzelius. It was he who proposed the name, protein, based on the Greek word *proteios*, "first rank."

The number of distinct proteins in the world of life is larger than one could possibly assess; the human body, for example, probably contains tens of thousands of different varieties, and different species of organisms tend to contain sets of proteins unique to themselves. The molecular weights of these polymers range from about 10,000 to many millions. Despite their diversity, however, there are striking features common to proteins of all kinds. They are polymers of the condensation type, and to break them down, or *depolymerize* their molecules, water molecules must be added. When this is done, the monomeric units of all proteins are found to be *amino acids*, molecules containing both amino and carboxyl groups. The simplest amino acid, aminoacetic acid, or *glycine*,

is abundant among the degradation products of most proteins. The total number of amino acids found associated with proteins at the present time is 24, although it is not improbable that more will be discovered in the future. No single kind of protein contains as many as 24 kinds of amino acid in its structure, although some contain as many as 18 or 19.

Of the amino acids in proteins, all but glycine are *capable* of existence in either of two optically isomeric forms. It is a remarkable fact that amino acids obtained from proteins consist exclusively of the left-handed form, i.e., the form which rotates the plane of polarization of light to the left. Thus there is great uniformity in the midst of overwhelming complexity. Syntheses of the same amino acids in the laboratory invariably give rise to mixtures of left- and right-handed isomers, understandably, since the reactions on which they depend must result from the random collisions of molecules. In the syntheses of life, however, only those chance collisions which give rise to one kind of product, and not its mirror image, are selected.

The structures of many of the protein amino acid molecules, as will be seen in the examples shown in Fig. 24–6, are complex in themselves. All of them, simple or complex, possess one important structural feature: the amino group is always attached to the carbon atom *adjacent* to the carboxyl group. This is necessarily true of glycine, which contains only two carbon atoms, and equally true of valine, tryptophan, and the rest of the 24 protein amino acids. The main feature of the polymer chain of proteins, common to all, is related to this feature of its monomer constituents. If we imagine the condensation process in which a protein chain is synthesized, we must think of water molecules splitting out between the amino group of one amino acid molecule and the carboxyl group of another. Considering only the amino-carboxyl ends of two monomer molecules, we may represent this process as follows:

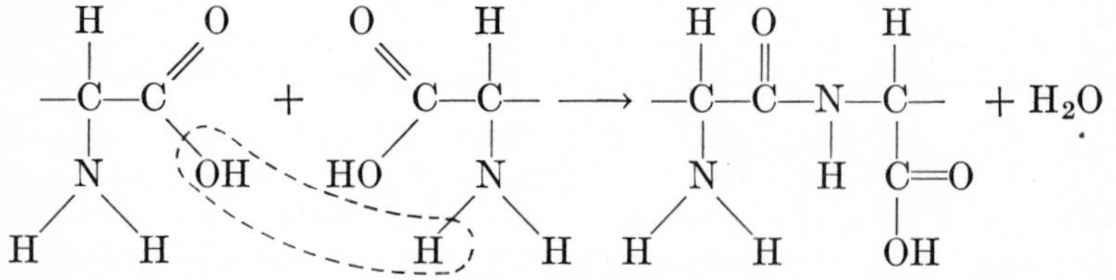

What may be termed the *backbone* of the protein polymer chain, formed by indefinite continuation of this process, is then the following structural array:

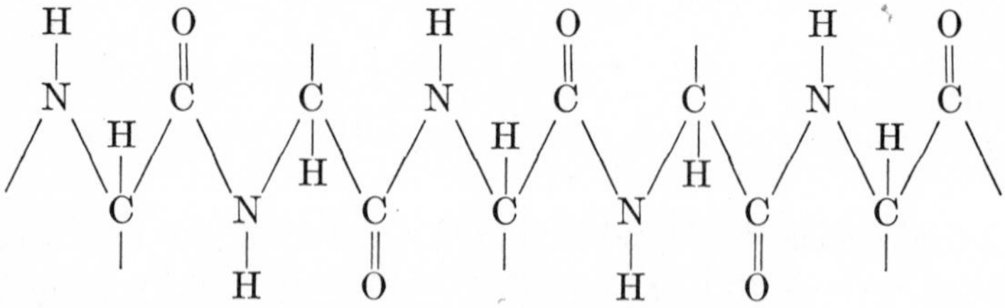

The structure shown above is well established as the basic molecular configuration of the polymer chains of *all* proteins. This is the source of their

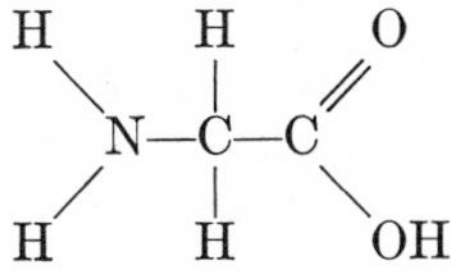

GLYCINE 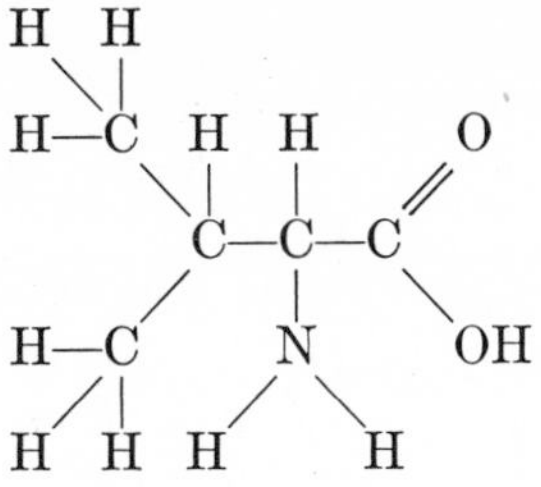   VALINE

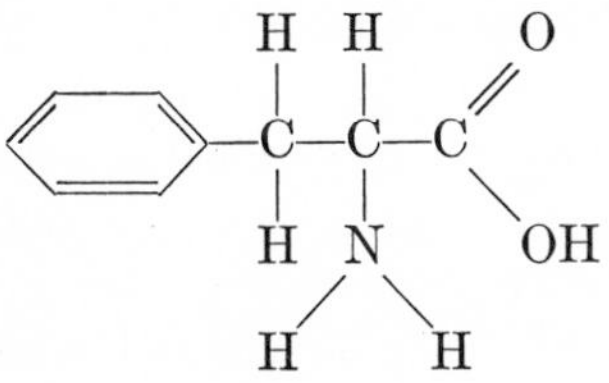

PHENYLALANINE 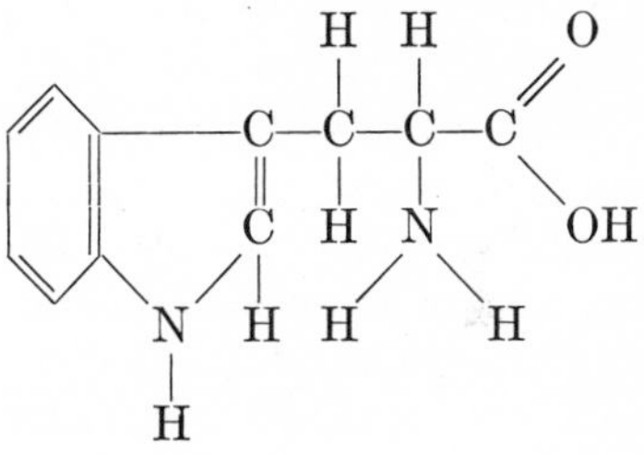   TRYPTOPHAN

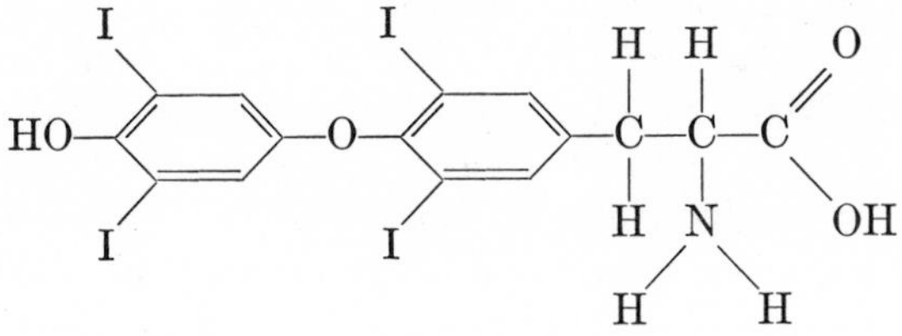

THYROXINE

Fig. 24–6. Structural formulas for 5 of the 24 amino acids found associated with proteins.

uniformity as a class of substances, and their variability lies in the great variety of ways in which amino acid molecules may be attached to the chain. Each dash shown in this structure represents a position of attachment for the main portion of an amino acid molecule. There are at least 24 kinds of molecules to choose from, any one kind of protein may contain as many as 18 or 19 of these kinds, and the properties of the protein will be influenced by the particular *sequence* in which the amino acids of different kinds are arranged along the chain. No stretch of the imagination is required, therefore, to realize that the number of possible molecular configurations in proteins is staggeringly large. A further contribution to this variability is brought about by the existence of several possible cross-linkages between amino acid molecules in different polymer chains. One such linkage (Fig. 24–7), involves the amino acid *cystine*, whose molecules contain sulfur atoms in positions such that they may form bonds with carbon atoms attached to simpler amino acids, like glycine. Other cross linkages between chains are made possible by the fact that three of the 24 amino acids contain more than one amino group per molecule, and two of them contain two carboxyl groups. Condensation may thus occur between unused amino groups in one chain and unused carboxyl groups in another, forming new nitrogen-carbon bonds between chains.

Although we are able to outline the basic elements of chemical structure of protein molecules, the complete, detailed knowledge, and synthesis, of a single kind of protein is quite a different matter. The detailed sequence of arrangement of amino acid molecules in a protein chain is undoubtedly of first importance in establishing the relation between its structure and its function, and must be known before we can hope to understand such important processes as the interaction between protein and nucleic acid molecules which takes place in living cell division. At this date (1956) the structure of only one relatively simple protein molecule is completely known. The English chemist Frederick Sanger and his colleagues, after ten years of work, announced proof of the complete, detailed structure of the hormone protein *insulin* in 1954. The insulin molecule has a molecular weight of about 5700, and is thus relatively small. It contains 17 different kinds of amino acids, and a total of 51 amino acid molecules per insulin molecule. Each insulin molecule consists of two protein chains, cross-linked at two positions. Sanger and his group were able to determine the sequence of arrangement of amino acids along these chains. Although insulin *is* simple as proteins go, its structure is the most complicated that has ever been unraveled by organic chemists! With the methods that Sanger has devised, the future for understanding of nature's most intricate products and their functions is now very bright indeed.

In addition to the chemical problems of protein structure, there is a difficult and important question concerning the arrangement of molecular units within bulk protein material. The molecular units themselves may range from simple coiled chains through units made straighter by moderate cross-linking, to highly cross-linked, relatively rigid structures. Many of the proteins are *globular* in bulk character (e.g., hemoglobin), others are fibrous (e.g., hair and muscle). Very little is known about the structures of globular proteins, but Linus Pauling, employing the techniques of x-ray diffraction, has recently made significant contributions to our knowledge

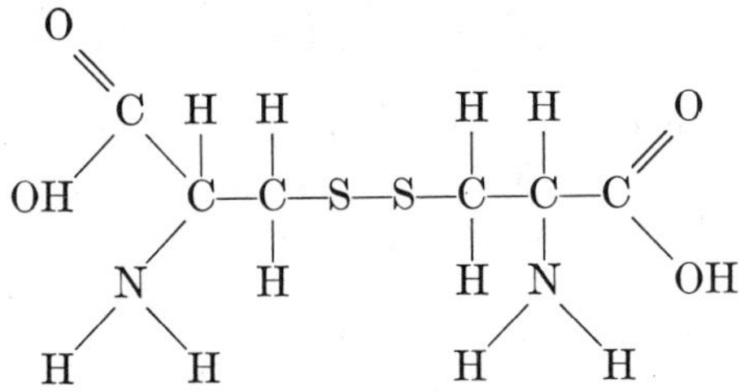

CYSTINE

(a)

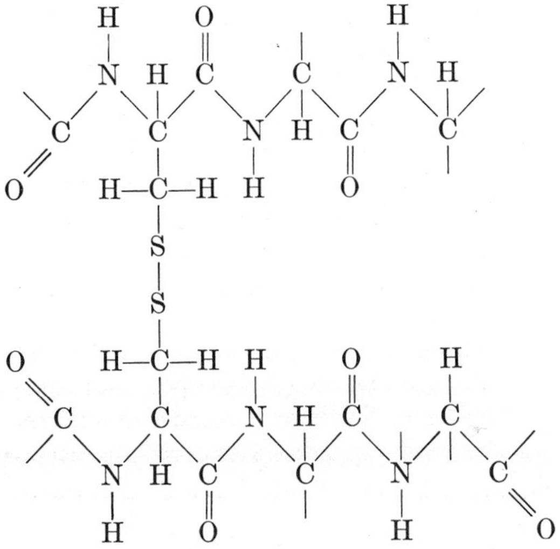

(b)

Fig. 24–7. The amino acid cystine (a) has amino and carboxyl groups on both ends, hence can form cross linkages between protein chains, as shown in (b).

of fibrous protein structures. Very briefly, these substances appear to consist of long-chain protein molecules which are wound around one another in the form of a *helix*. Neighboring molecules are loosely bound to one another through interaction between —NH and —C=O groups in their chains. In at least some cases the turns in the helix are such that 18 amino acid molecules are accommodated within the span of 5 turns. Futher evidence indicates that the helices within some fibrous proteins (e.g., hair) are arranged in cables, each of which contains seven molecular strands.

24–4 Carbohydrates and photosynthesis

The entire phenomenon of life runs counter to the general energetic trend of the universe: living organisms exist at higher levels of energy than their surroundings and, during their lifetimes, defy the mechanisms which are available for the lowering of those levels. The breakage of bonds within a protein chain is a much more probable process, energetically, than synthesis of the chain, since the latter requires fixation of relatively large quantities of energy. (A higher animal organism, of course, must be able to both synthesize those proteins essential to its function, and digest those which form part of its diet; enzymes, themselves proteins, are present to catalyze both of these processes.) The contraction of muscle fiber requires expenditure of energy, and to maintain a temperature higher than that of its surroundings a warm-blooded animal must generate heat constantly. The energy necessary for these and many other vital processes is made available by oxidation of the molecules of *carbohydrate* compounds. The syntheses of these high-energy molecules are themselves strongly endothermic. While animal organisms are able to rearrange carbohydrate molecules to forms which suit their particular requirements, they are incapable of manufacturing them from the compounds CO_2 and water, hence are completely dependent upon the organisms that can do so, the plants. In the process of photosynthesis, in which plants manufacture carbohydrates, oxygen is restored to the atmosphere. Without it, the earth's oxygen supply would rapidly become depleted, so that the indebtedness of animals to plants is a double one.

The name *carbohydrate* implies that these compounds are *hydrates* of carbon; it was originally adopted because the empirical formulas of many compounds in this class, e.g., $C_6H_{12}O_6$, contain hydrogen and oxygen atoms in the same $2:1$ ratio observed in water. There are many carbohydrates in which this ratio is not observed, however, and the name is not a good one. The simplest carbohydrates are the *sugars* and, of these, *glucose,* found in mammalian blood and in fruit juices, is probably the most important. Its formula is $C_6H_{12}O_6$, and as a hydrocarbon derivative it may be considered both an aldehyde and a complex alcohol:

$$\begin{array}{ccccccccccc}
\text{O} & & \text{OH} & & \text{OH} & & \text{OH} & & \text{OH} & & \text{OH} \\
\diagdown & & | & & | & & | & & | & & | \\
& \text{C}-\text{C} & - & \text{C} & - & \text{C} & - & \text{C} & - & \text{C}-\text{H} \\
\diagup & & | & & | & & | & & | & & | \\
\text{H} & & \text{H} & & \text{H} & & \text{H} & & \text{H} & & \text{H}
\end{array}$$

Another common sugar, *fructose*, found in fruit juices and in honey, is a structural isomer of glucose containing a ketone functional group:

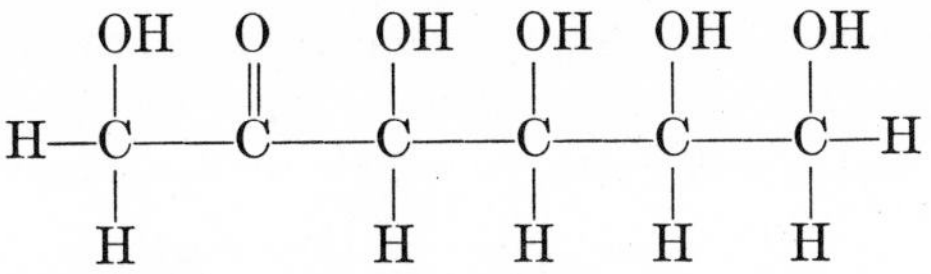

$$
\begin{array}{ccccccc}
\text{OH} & \text{O} & \text{OH} & \text{OH} & \text{OH} & \text{OH} \\
| & \| & | & | & | & | \\
\text{H—C} & \text{—C} & \text{—C} & \text{—C} & \text{—C} & \text{—C—H} \\
| & & | & | & | & | \\
\text{H} & & \text{H} & \text{H} & \text{H} & \text{H}
\end{array}
$$

The molecules of glucose and fructose may exist in the form of optical isomers, but nature produces only one of the two forms in each case. The common sugar *sucrose*, which is produced by plants of all kinds, consists of *di*mer molecules containing one unit each of glucose and fructose, with oxygen atoms participating in the formation of a ring structure:

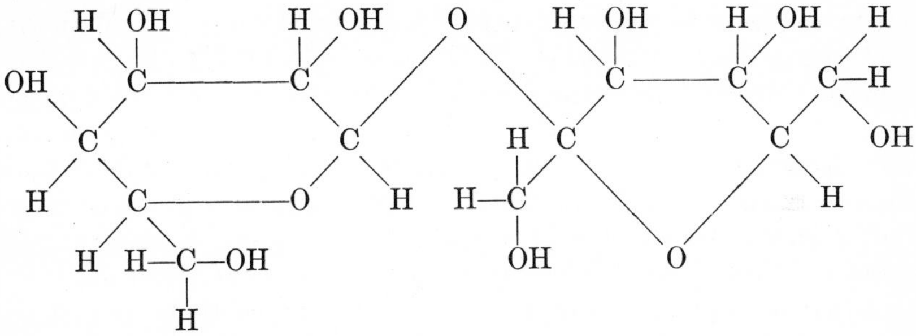

We have called glucose the most important of the carbohydrates because it is the monomer unit found in the more complicated carbohydrate polymers *glycogen*, the *starches*, and *cellulose*. These are condensation polymers, and one molecule of water is split out between each pair of glucose molecules incorporated into their structures. Since there is such wide variation in the configurations of these substances we shall not attempt to represent them structurally. In most of them, ring structures, as in the sucrose molecule, are present. Starches are readily *de*polymerized in the presence of the proper enzymes, combining with water molecules to reconstitute simple glucose molecules. Cellulose, the structural material of the plant kingdom, cannot be digested (depolymerized) by the human system, although the ruminant mammals possess enzymes capable of breaking it down to glucose. The carbon dioxide given up in animal respiration results from the oxidation of sugars by atmospheric oxygen, and from some of the glucose units taken into the body as such or produced by digestion of glucose polymers, animals synthesize the polymer glycogen. This synthesis represents the animal's principal mode of storing energy. Glycogen is found in the liver and around muscle fibers, and it is the particular form of carbohydrate which is oxidized in the course of muscle contraction. Its oxidation (and energy release) in the absence of atmospheric oxygen is made possible by the presence of certain complex organic phosphate compounds.

In its most fundamental sense, the marvel of energy assimilation in the processes of life goes back to the radiant energy of the sun, since it is energy from this source that plants utilize in their production of carbohydrates. In broadest outline, we may represent the photosynthesis of glucose by the equation

$$6CO_2 + 6H_2O + Energy \rightarrow C_6H_{12}O_6 + 6O_2.$$

This strongly endothermic reaction takes place, in plants, only in the presence of the green pigment *chlorophyll*. Although we know the molecular structure of chlorophyll (Fig. 24–8), the manner of its catalytic action is far from understood. Much penetrating information has been gained in recent years by the use of isotopically "tagged" atoms (see Chapter 29). With the use of "heavy" oxygen atoms (O^{18}), for example, it has been learned that the oxygen given off in photosynthesis comes *exclusively* from water molecules. This result indicates that the first step in the process consists of the oxidation of combined oxygen atoms, which is known to require considerable energy. Simultaneously, the hydrogen atoms in water must reduce carbon dioxide molecules to begin the synthesis of a carbohydrate molecule. Using radioactively "tagged" carbon atoms (C^{14}), it has been found that the uptake of CO_2 by green leaves can continue for a short time in the dark, although oxygen production proceeds only during the time that sunlight is available. This probably means that the hydrogen atoms which reduce CO_2 are held by the leaf in some intermediate form. Using "tagged" CO_2 molecules during short periods of photosynthesis, "tagged" carbon atoms have been found in a large number of different compounds. The compounds probably represent intermediate stages in the synthesis of carbohydrates, and a complex, cyclic mechanism has been proposed which agrees well with the facts which are presently known. When photosynthesis is truly understood, it may become possible to duplicate it in the laboratory, in the absence of organisms other than chemists. Such understanding still seems to be well beyond the scientific horizon.

———————

The problems of protein structure and function, of carbohydrate synthesis by plants, and the many other chemical reactions of life, constitute today's "primeval tropical forest" of organic chemistry. The great strides in understanding of these complicated processes which have been made in recent years have been made possible only by the successful scientific penetration of the organic chemistry forests of the past. As science has found ways to imitate nature and to synthesize products in the laboratory that are identical with the products of organisms, the complexity of the questions for which we can even remotely hope to find answers has steadily increased.

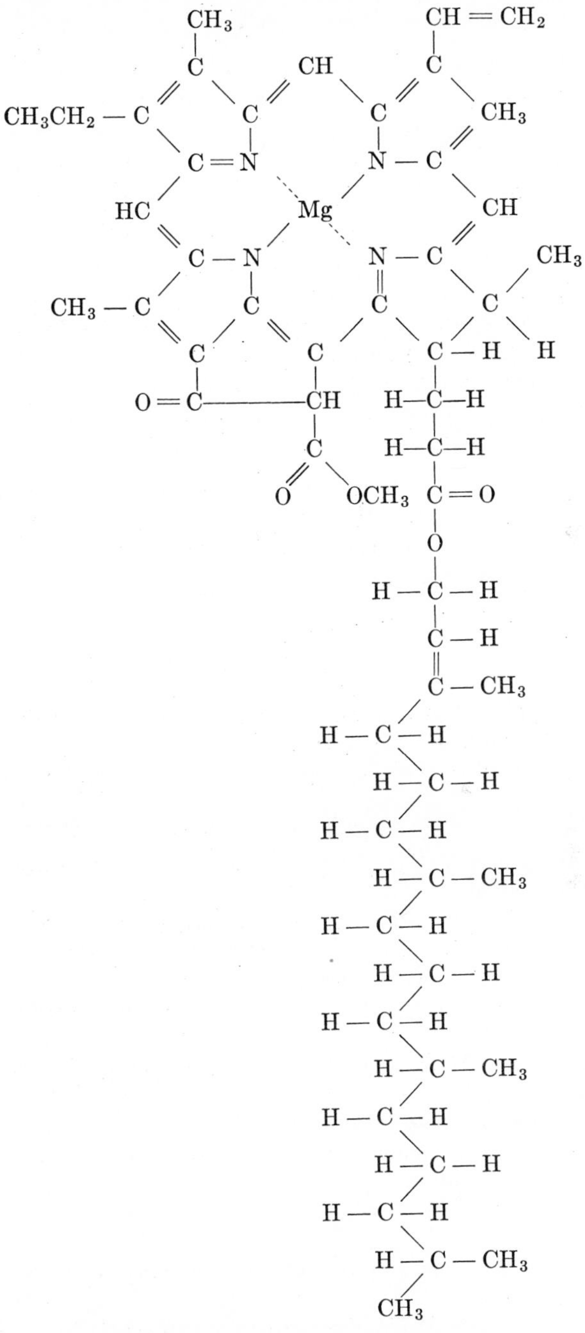

Fig. 24–8. Structural formula of chlorophyll.

24–5 Summary

Organic chemistry has made possible the synthesis of many of the products of life and the preparation of many desirable products unknown in nature. As understanding of molecular structure has increased, natural compounds of increasing complexity have been duplicated in the laboratory, and it has become ever more possible to interpret the fundamental chemistry of the processes of life. The relatively recent realization that some substances may contain giant or *polymer* molecules has contributed greatly to our understanding of natural products and has brought about development of the entirely new synthetic fiber and plastics industry. The most complicated and important of organic compounds, the proteins, are polymers based upon chains of amino acids. Since one kind of protein may contain as many as 19 different kinds of amino acid the problem of determination of protein structure is extraordinarily difficult, and only one protein structure, that of insulin, has been completely unraveled so far. Protein structure and its relation to physiological function, the role of nucleic acids in cell division, the mechanism of photosynthesis—these are among the most challenging problems along today's frontier of organic chemistry.

REFERENCES

CRICK, F. H. C., "The Structure of the Hereditary Material," *Scientific American*, 191, No. 4, 54 (October, 1954).

FIESER, L. F., "History of the Alizarin Synthesis," *Journal of Chemical Education*, 7, 2609 (1930).

FINDLAY, *A Hundred Years of Chemistry*, Chapters VIII and IX.

LINDERSTROM-LANG, K. U., "How is a Protein Made?" *Scientific American*, 189, No. 3, 100 (September, 1953).

NASH, L. K., *Plants and the Atmosphere* (Number 5 of Harvard Case Histories in Experimental Science). A full and fascinating account of the earlier history of man's understanding of photosynthesis.

PAULING, L., *et al.*, "The Structure of Protein Molecules," *Scientific American*, 191, No. 1 (July, 1954).

RABINOWITCH, E., "Progress in Photosynthesis," *Scientific American*, 189, No. 11 (November, 1953).

READ, J., *A Direct Entry to Organic Chemistry*.

SCHORLEMMER, C., *The Rise and Development of Organic Chemistry*, Chapter XI, on the synthesis of aromatic compounds.

SISLER, H. H., and others, *General Chemistry, a Systematic Approach*, Chapter 32.

THOMPSON, E. O. P., "The Insulin Molecule," *Scientific American*, 192, No. 5, 36 (May, 1955).

WALD, G., "The Origin of Life," *Scientific American*, 191, No. 2, 44 (August, 1954).

1. Study Fig. 24–1, and by writing out the structures convince yourself that the six structural isomers of dichloronitrobenzene that are shown are all that are possible. Show that attachment of a nitro group to any of the four available ring positions in paradichlorobenzene leads to the same compound, for example.

2. How many isomers of trichlorobenzene are possible? Could Koerner's method be applied to tell them apart? To answer this question, write structures for all the possible isomers of a derivative of trichlorobenzene, e.g., the nitro derivative. [*Ans.*: There are three parent isomers, the derivatives of which will give rise to one, two, and three isomers, respectively.)

3. What kind of compound is aspirin (Fig. 24–2)? Can you write structural formulas for two compounds that should react to form aspirin? An equation for the reaction?

4. The plastic material *lucite*, or "plexiglass," is *polymethylmethacrylate*, an addition polymer. The unsaturated ester *methyl methacrylate*, its monomer, has the following structural formula:

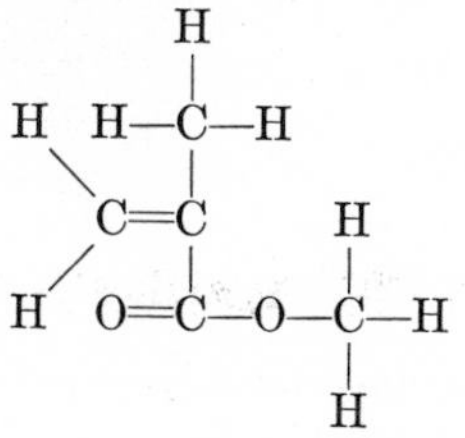

Using structural formulas, write an equation for the reaction in which two molecules of methylmethacrylate add to each other. Write a structural formula for a portion of the polymer molecule.

5. *Bakelite*, a hard-setting resin, is a condensation *co*polymer, based upon *phenol* and *formaldehyde* as monomers. In its formation, the oxygen atom from the formaldehyde molecule combines with hydrogen atoms from ring positions on each of two phenol molecules. Water is split out, and carbon-carbon bonds form between the formaldehyde molecule and the two phenol molecules. Look up the structures of these molecules in Table 23–2, if necessary, and write an equation representing this condensation. Reconstruct the structural formula for a portion of the polymer molecule of bakelite.

6. Examine the structures of glucose, fructose, and tryptophan, and try to identify a carbon atom in each case which meets the requirements for existence of these compounds in the form of optical isomers.

CHAPTER 25

SILICON, SILICATES, AND THE WORLD OF MINERALS

Carbon is the only element in the periodic table capable of forming stable chain and ring structures in which large numbers of its own atoms are joined together. There are several combinations of elements, however, which can and do form complex structures, both chains and rings. The particular combination which exhibits greatest versatility is *silicon* and *oxygen*, in the vast variety of natural materials called *silicate minerals*. Nearly nine-tenths of that part of the earth accessible to direct examination consists of silicates, and the element silicon occupies a position in our inorganic surroundings analogous to that of carbon in living matter.

The word "mineral" originally meant simply "that which is mined," but has come to mean any naturally occurring element or compound which is *in*organic in nature, i.e., unrelated to recent biological processes. In practical use the term applies primarily to substances of which the earth's crust is composed. The earth minerals, as we encounter them, are mainly solids whose properties depend on the *arrangements* of constituent atoms as well as on the kinds and numbers of atoms present. They are, in a word, crystals, some large, others microscopically small. Silicon, accompanied by oxygen, is peculiarly qualified to combine in stable crystalline compounds with other elements, as we shall see, and it is this unique qualification that makes it the key element in the mineral world. We must be careful not to carry our analogy between carbon and silicon, in terms of their respective roles in organic and inorganic structures, too far. In our discussion of organic chemistry we dealt constantly with the arrangements of atoms in individual *molecules*. Mineral crystals do not consist of discrete molecules. The properties of these structures are determined in large part by the arrangements of atoms or ions in crystalline arrays of indefinite extent.

25–1 Characteristics of silicon

Since the element silicon lies directly below carbon in Group 4a of the periodic table, we should expect it to resemble carbon more closely than any other element. Like carbon, it forms binary compounds with many other elements—$SiCl_4$ and $CaSi_2$ are examples. Of particular interest are the binary compounds it forms with hydrogen, analogues of the hydrocarbons, called the *silanes*. Straight-chain compounds with formulas SiH_4 to Si_6H_{14}, based upon linkages of silicon atoms to one another, have been prepared. Unlike the hydrocarbons, these compounds ignite spontaneously in air to form silicon dioxide, SiO_2. While carbon tetrachloride is a very stable substance, silicon tetrachloride reacts readily with water to form silicon dioxide, or compounds related to it, and hydrochloric acid. Silicon atoms have a strong tendency to form bonds with oxygen atoms. It is for this reason that all the silicon in the earth's crust is found in the form of oxygen compounds.

Pure elemental silicon may be prepared by reduction of silicon compounds, and is found to have the slight luster and electrical conductivity characteristic of an element on the borderline between metallic and nonmetallic properties (Chapter 9). Its crystal structure, however, is similar to that of elemental carbon in the form of diamond (Section 20–7). The silicon crystal is much less hard, less dense, and has a very much lower melting point than diamond. The silicon-silicon bonds which hold it together are much weaker than the carbon-carbon bonds which impart extraordinary hardness to the diamond crystal. The silicon atom has one more completed electron shell than does carbon; it is therefore larger and its four valence electrons are held much less tightly by its nucleus, with the result that bonds between silicon atoms have only about half the strength of bonds between carbon atoms. It is for this reason that silicon does not resemble carbon in molecular versatility, a property possible only in a Group 4a element, with four valence electrons. While the carbon-carbon bond has greater energy, hence greater stability, than the carbon-oxygen bond, the energy of the silicon-oxygen linkage is more than twice as great as that of a bond between silicon atoms. Although a few silicon chain molecules can be made, as we have said, they are unstable in air because of this high energy difference.

Like carbon, silicon atoms tend to form four covalent bonds, but, unlike carbon, do not tend to form unsaturated compounds containing double or triple bonds. While carbon's covalent bonds with other elements are generally almost nonpolar, bonds to silicon are in many cases very strongly polar. Oxygen atoms hold shared electrons more tightly than silicon atoms, and the bond between silicon and oxygen is a polar covalent bond, with net negative charge at its oxygen end and positive charge at the silicon atom (Section 20–6). This result of the slightly metallic nature of silicon does not mean that silicon atoms may lose electrons outright, to form Si^{+4} ions, but does mean that electrostatic forces between polar bonds may play a substantial binding role in the crystal structures of some of its compounds.

We see, then, that silicon, the element most closely resembling carbon, hardly resembles it at all! One important point of resemblance, however, is basic to the mineral structures of which silicon is a constituent. The four bonds which join other atoms to silicon atoms in compounds are arranged at the apexes of a regular tetrahedron. The tetrahedral orientation of silicon bonds has been demonstrated most clearly by techniques in which mineral crystals act as diffraction gratings toward x-rays (Section 18–5). It is the tetrahedron that constitutes the structural unit for silicate structures, as it does for so many organic molecules. In this case, however, silicon atoms are not bonded to one another directly, but through the intermediary of oxygen atoms.

Silicon atoms form moderately strong bonds with carbon atoms, and many compounds containing both elements are known. Silicon carbide, SiC, is an example of a very hard, high melting atomic crystal (Section 20–7). A series of complex polymers called the *silicones* have properties which give them value as lubricants for special applications, for the formation of water repellent surfaces and for other purposes. The monomer of a typical, simple silicone, is *dimethyldichlorosilane:*

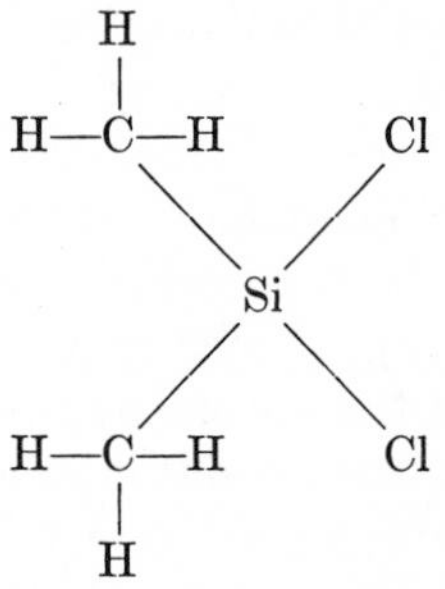

This substance polymerizes in the presence of water, by condensation. First, the chlorine atoms are replaced by hydroxyl groups, then water molecules split out between the hydroxyl groups of adjacent molecules, forming -O-Si-O- linkages. A portion of the molecule of the resultant silicone polymer has the structural formula

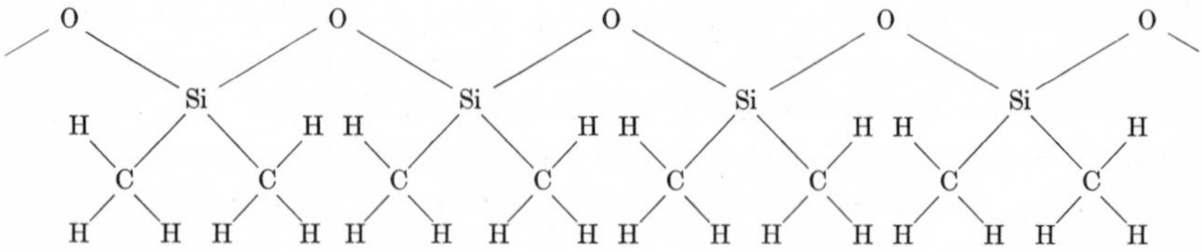

25–2 Silicon dioxide

Carbon dioxide, CO_2, consists of stable, discrete molecules, and is a gas under ordinary conditions. Silicon dioxide may be represented by the formula SiO_2, but there the resemblance ends. Carbon dioxide molecules contain double bonds between carbon and oxygen atoms, but silicon does not tend to form such bonds. With only single bonds between silicon and oxygen atoms, neither element achieves octet structure, and individual SiO_2 molecules are not found. The valence of silicon may be satisfied by formation of single bonds to *four* (rather than two) oxygen atoms, and each oxygen atom may achieve octet structure by joining to two silicon atoms. *Silica*, as this oxide is often called, thus tends to exist as an intricate structure in which these bonding relations are observed. There are three crystalline forms of silica, and all are very high melting, hard materials. The formula SiO_2 reflects little more than an atomic ratio, since a crystal of silica could be considered to be a single giant polymer molecule, in which the monomer unit is SiO_2.

The basic structural unit of all three crystalline forms of silica is the tetrahedron, four oxygen atoms symmetrically grouped about a central silicon atom. We shall refer to this unit as the SiO_4 tetrahedron. Each apex of each SiO_4 tetrahedron is shared with another tetrahedron, which is equivalent to saying that each oxygen atom present is bound to two silicon atoms. Basically, this is the way in which silicon dioxide crystals

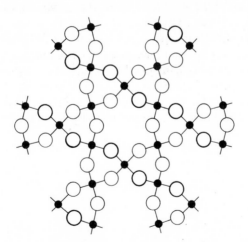

FIG. 25–1. Schematic plan diagram of the structure of quartz. Small black circles represent silicon atoms, open circles oxygen atoms. Since basic unit is the SiO_4 tetrahedron, oxygen atoms are at different heights; those with heavier circles rise farther above the plane of the paper than others. (Redrawn from A. F. Wells, *Structural Inorganic Chemistry*, 2nd ed., Clarendon Press, Oxford.)

are built up. SiO_4 tetrahedra, joined together at their corners, extend indefinitely in the three dimensions of the crystal. These structural features are illustrated schematically in Fig. 25–1.

The existence of different crystal forms of silica is evidence that there are subtleties in the orientations of SiO_4 tetrahedra with respect to one another. Subtleties of structure in naturally occurring crystals of all kinds were studied long before the existence of atoms was confirmed, however. Correlation between atomic arrangement and crystal structure is a relatively modern concept. Single crystals are often bounded by smooth planes, or *faces*, and the arrangements of such surfaces have long been used for the identification of particular substances. During the 19th century these and other characteristics were correctly interpreted as evidence of an orderly arrangement of atoms making up the crystal, in which geometric structural patterns are indefinitely repeated. We have noted (Section 18–5) that this interpretation was beautifully confirmed by the interference patterns obtained when x-rays strike crystals, and that x-rays are now used to determine the internal structures of crystals. The structures we shall discuss in this chapter have all been determined by the methods of x-ray diffraction.

The most common form of silica, called *quartz*, is found as sand, or as a constituent of many kinds of rock, where its crystals are interspersed between those of other minerals. Complete single crystals of quartz are characteristic hexagonal prisms with pyramidal ends, as shown in Figs. 25–2 and 25–3(a). Whatever the size of the crystal, corresponding faces meet at the same angle. The SiO_4 tetrahedra in quartz are arranged in such a way that they form spirals, each of which is bonded to its neighbors. Because of this internal arrangement there are two kinds of quartz, one in which the spiral is right-handed, like an ordinary screw, the other in which it is left-handed. The two forms are easily differentiated in either of two ways. The "screw sense" of a quartz crystal is betrayed by the arrangement of faces at the base of the pyramid at its end, as indi-

Fig. 25–2. Right- and left-handed quartz crystals, as indicated by the position of face x with respect to face m. Not all quartz crystals show the face marked x, however.

(a)

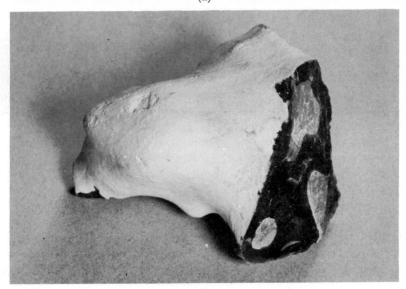

(b)

FIG. 25–3. Samples of natural quartz. (a) "Rock crystal," (b) flint. (Courtesy of Ward's Natural Science Establishment.)

cated in Fig. 25–2. Quartz crystals are capable of rotating the plane of polarization of polarized light, and the direction of rotation depends upon whether the crystal is of the right- or left-handed form. This is an important optical property of quartz, directly related to its internal structure, as are all optical properties of crystals with the exception of color. The color of a given mineral may be profoundly affected by traces of impurity which do not affect its internal arrangement. Pure quartz, for example, is transparent, but a wide variety of colors· of this mineral— black, rose, smoky, and others— is found in nature.

As we have said, there are two other crystalline forms of silica; the spiral arrangement is not the only possible stable orientation of SiO_4 tetrahedra with respect to one another. Neither of the two other forms, *cristobalite* and *tridymite*, is a common or important mineral, however. Quartz, as a matter of fact, is the most stable of the three forms at ordinary temperatures, and the atoms of the other forms have a definite, though exceedingly slow, tendency to rearrange into the quartz structure. In cristobalite, the basic structural units, SiO_4 tetrahedra, are arranged in a regular cubic array, and tridymite has a somewhat similar, though more closely packed, structure.

If any of the three forms of crystalline silicon dioxide is melted, the regular pattern of repetition of SiO_4 units is destroyed. If the melt is cooled fairly rapidly it will solidify, but without regaining its initial structural regularity. The material thus formed, with SiO_4 tetrahedra randomly distributed, is an example of the kind of supercooled liquid called a *glass*. Silica glass, or *fused quartz*, is transparent to ultraviolet light, and is therefore used in optical apparatus in which windows for light of very short wavelength are required. Ordinary glass is made by liquefying and then cooling complex mixtures of silica and *silicates*. While glasses are supercooled liquids and should be expected to crystallize in time, their constituent atoms have so little mobility in the solid bulk structure that rearrangement to form regular crystal arrays is imperceptibly slow.

25–3 Silicate minerals

Thousands of minerals have been identified and classified, and by far the most abundant and numerous are those silicon-oxygen compounds which are called *silicate* minerals. Here we are concerned primarily with the structures of mineral crystals, and for so bewildering a variety of materials as the silicates, we cannot pretend to do justice to the complexity of the subject. Silicates may contain many other elements, in varying proportions, in addition to silicon and oxygen. In most cases their simple empirical formulas are complicated and do not reveal very much, since again it is crystalline structure that is important in determining characteristic properties. A single general principle will carry us far in this discussion, however: no matter what other atoms are present, the SiO_4 tetrahedron is the most important structural unit in all the silicates.

In the simplest of the silicates, SiO_4 tetrahedra are present in negative ions containing relatively small numbers of silicon and oxygen atoms. In zinc silicate (*willemite*), for example, (SiO_4^{-4}) ions are present, one for each pair of Zn^{++} ions. The crystal of the common mineral *olivine* contains magnesium and ferrous ions interspersed with ionic (SiO_4^{-4}) groups. (Olivine is the simplest of the large group called *ferromagnesian minerals*, all of which are silicates of iron and magnesium and characteristically dark in color.) Negative ions that are larger than the SiO_4^{-4} ion, but definite in extent, may be built of two or more SiO_4 tetrahedra. Several examples, shown structurally in Fig. 25–4, are the ions $(Si_2O_7^{-6})$, $(Si_3O_9^{-6})$, and $(Si_6O_{18}^{-12})$. The mineral *beryl*, for example, has the empirical formula $Be_3Al_2Si_6O_{18}$, and consists of discrete ions. The positive charges on three beryllium and two aluminum ions add up to twelve, just the number of negative charges on the $(Si_6O_{18}^{-12})$ ion.

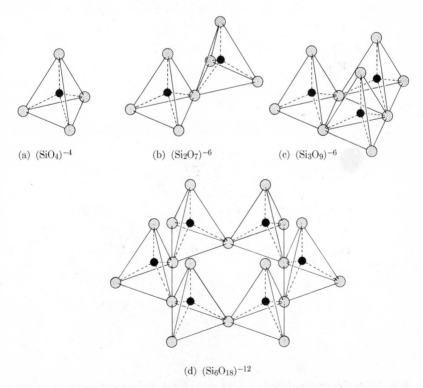

(a) $(SiO_4)^{-4}$ (b) $(Si_2O_7)^{-6}$ (c) $(Si_3O_9)^{-6}$

(d) $(Si_6O_{18})^{-12}$

FIG. 25–4. Schematic diagrams of four kinds of discrete silicate negative ions.

The tendency for SiO_4 tetrahedra to share edges, forming extended structures, is strong, and the number of silicate minerals containing discrete negative ions of definite, relatively small size is limited. Structures such as those shown in Fig. 25–4 may become indefinitely extended by adding SiO_4 tetrahedra, to form very large negative ions. Several important classes of silicate minerals, notably the *pyroxenes* and the *amphiboles*, have structures which are based upon such extended negative ions. In the pyroxenes, these ions consist of long, single chains, as shown in Fig. 25–5(a). To balance charge, positive ions must be interspersed between chains. *Spodumene,* empirical formula $LiAl(SiO_3)_2$, is an example of this kind of mineral; lithium and aluminum ions are present in the ratio shown, and the crystal is held together by electrostatic forces between

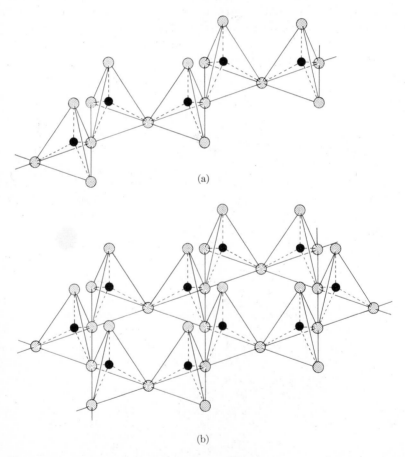

(a)

(b)

Fɪɢ. 25–5. Portions of two kinds of ions of indefinite extent, based on chains of SiO_4 tetrahedra: (a) a single chain, (b) a double-chain structure.

Fig. 25–6. A crystal of asbestos which has been pulled apart. Note the fibers, which are a consequence of the extended chain structure of this silicate mineral. (Courtesy of Ward's Natural Science Establishment.)

these ions and the negative charges on the silicate chain. In the amphibole minerals, the chains are double, as shown in Fig. 25–5(b). An interesting group of substances, called the *asbestos* minerals, have chain structures of this sort. These and most other minerals with silicate chains are fibrous; while the covalent bonds which hold the negative ions together are strong, the electrostatic forces between chains are relatively weak, so that the mineral crystals are easily broken into long, tough fibers (see Fig. 25–6).

Negative silicate ions are not restricted to chains, as will be understood by noting the many unshared tetrahedral corners in the diagrams of Fig. 25–5. If all those oxygen atoms which lie in a single plane in the double-chain structure were to become shared with other SiO_4 tetrahedra, a negative ion extending indefinitely in two dimensions would form. This may be regarded as the equivalent of cross-linking of polymer chains. Many minerals consist of such *layered* structures, based on negative ion sheets such as that shown schematically in Fig. 25–7. Again, positive ions must be present between sheets to preserve electrical neutrality, and crystals of these minerals are held together by the attractions between positive ions and negative sheets. The familiar *micas* and the *clay minerals* have this kind of layered structure. In the very soft clay minerals, e.g., *kaolinite*, empirical formula $Al_2Si_2O_5(OH)_4$, and *talc*, $Mg_3(OH)_2Si_4O_{10}$, the crystal layers are composites of silicate sheets with positive ions (magnesium or aluminum) and hydroxyl ions, and are electrically neutral.

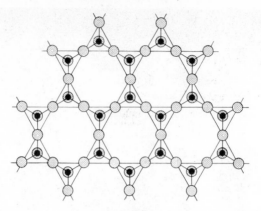

Fig. 25–7. Layered structure of tetrahedra. Each tetrahedron is surrounded by three others, to form an array that extends indefinitely in two dimensions. Dark circles represent silicon atoms at the centers of tetrahedra.

The forces between such layers are extremely feeble, and these minerals crumble easily. In the micas, however, the layers are negatively charged, and positive ions between layers neutralize this charge and hold them together. Micas are therefore harder than clay minerals, but may be separated into thin sheets rather easily since the forces between layers are weaker than those within them.

The layers of white mica (transparent *muscovite*) have been shown by x-ray methods to be held together by the attractions of positive potassium ions. It is also known, however, that this mineral contains aluminum atoms. In black mica (*biotite*), aluminum atoms are also present, although magnesium and iron ions are present between layers. The micas are members of a vast class of minerals, called the *aluminosilicates*, in which aluminum atoms have taken the place of silicon atoms in the basic tetrahedral structure. Aluminum and silicon atoms are approximately of the same size, so that this substitution can be made without greatly distorting the tetrahedra. Aluminosilicates, then, may contain both SiO_4 tetrahedra and AlO_4 tetrahedra, in varying proportions. Silicate chain and layered structures, based upon SiO_4 tetrahedra, are negatively charged, since not all oxygen atoms present are bound to two silicon atoms (Figs. 25–5 and 25–7). To satisfy the valences of all oxygen atoms, extra electrons must be acquired, in number corresponding to the number of unshared tetrahedral corners present. In similar structures containing AlO_4 tetrahedra, however, a larger number of electrons is required, since the aluminum atom has only three valence electrons. Extended aluminosilicate ions, then, bear more negative charge than the silicate ions which correspond to them in size and structure. A single chain of SiO_4 groups, for example, has two units of negative charge per silicon atom present; a single chain containing both SiO_4 and AlO_4 tetrahedra would bear two negative charges for each silicon atom present, and three for each aluminum atom.

If each of the remaining unshared oxygen atoms in a layered silicate structure (Fig. 25–7) were to become part of a second SiO_4 tetrahedron, an indefinite, three-dimensional *framework* of tetrahedra would be formed. Since all silicon and oxygen valences would be satisfied within the structure, it would not be charged, and its composition could be represented by the formula SiO_2. Quartz and the other crystal forms of silica, in fact, consist of just such frameworks, and differ from one another only in the internal orientation of their tetrahedra. A similar structure containing aluminum atoms at the centers of some of the tetrahedra, however, would bear negative charge, and positive ions would have to be present in the crystal to preserve electrical neutrality. There are many aluminosilicate minerals which exhibit just this structure—three-dimensional frameworks with positive ions fitted into their larger openings.

The *feldspar* minerals, which are the principal constituents of many common rocks (Chapter 26), are all framework aluminosilicate structures. In common feldspar, or *orthoclase*, one-quarter of the tetrahedral units are

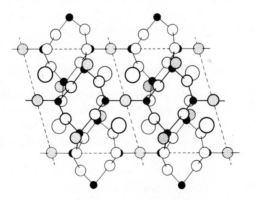

●   Al or Si atom (one in four is Al).

○   O atom in or above the plane of the paper.

◉   O atom below the plane of the paper.

○   K⁺ ion above the plane of the paper.

○   K⁺ ion below the plane of the paper.

FIG. 25–8. Structural plan of the crystal of orthoclase, a common feldspar. The two portions enclosed within dotted lines are identical; this structural unit is repeated indefinitely throughout the crystal. (Redrawn from A. F. Wells, *Structural Inorganic Chemistry*, 2nd ed., Clarendon Press, Oxford.)

AlO_4 groups, the rest SiO_4 groups. For each aluminum atom present the necessary extra electron has been supplied by a potassium atom, so that potassium ions are present in the crystal lattice. A schematic representation of this structure is shown in Fig. 25–8. The empirical formula for this mineral is simply $KAlSi_3O_8$. Other feldspars contain a higher proportion of aluminum atoms in the aluminosilicate framework. *Anorthite*, $CaAl_2Si_2O_8$, contains equal numbers of AlO_4 and SiO_4 tetrahedra, and doubly charged calcium ions to balance electrical charge. Since compact aluminosilicate frames extend throughout the crystals of these minerals, they are nearly as hard as quartz. In many aluminosilicate minerals, such as the *zeolites*, the framework is much more open than in quartz or the feldspars. These materials are much softer and their large openings are capable of taking up water molecules, which are loosely held and may be expelled by vigorous heating.

With this very brief discussion it is easy to see why there should be so many silicate minerals. There may be mineral structures containing discrete silicate ions of varying complexity but definite extent, others with indefinite, ionic chains, others with charged silicate sheets. There may be aluminosilicate chain, layer, or framework structures, and in these the proportions of aluminum to silicon atoms may vary. For all these possibilities positive ions must be present, and there is great variety to choose from. Mineral structures may contain two or more kinds of positive ions, and for these the relative proportions may vary.

25–4 Nonsilicate minerals

Most of the thousands of known minerals are both rare and unimportant. However, some uncommon minerals are economically important as *ores*, from which such materials as iron, aluminum, and uranium may be profitably recovered. Means of identification of particular minerals, important for many reasons, are based on a variety of properties. Hardness, density, and luster are particularly valuable indexes to identification. Color is sometimes reliable, although trace impurities may often impart different colors to disparate samples of the same mineral. Chemical analysis for the constituent elements is important, though not final; in the case of the three forms of silica, we have seen that different minerals may sometimes have the same composition. Optical properties, exemplified by the behavior of quartz toward polarized light, constitute an often valuable means of identification, and external crystal form, since it depends upon the internal arrangements of atoms and ions, is also important. Many crystals exhibit the property of *cleavage*, i.e., under the stress of a sharp blow, they break cleanly along well-defined planes. For example, the mica minerals show this property along the direction parallel to their

Fig. 25–9. A crystal of the feldspar mineral *microcline*. Note the two directions of cleavage. (Courtesy of Ward's Natural Science Establishment.)

aluminosilicate layers, while quartz fractures along curved surfaces or unevenly when struck, like glass (see also obsidian, Fig. 26–9). The feldspars show cleavage along two directions (Fig. 25–9), and this property is an important clue in the identification of these minerals.

Some of the silicate minerals, we have seen, consist of relatively simple ionic crystal lattices containing, for example, positive ions and negative (SiO_4^{-4}) ions. While most of the silicate mineral structures are more complicated than this, most nonsilicate minerals consist of simple ionic crystals. The classic example of an ionic crystal is sodium chloride, in which Na^+ and Cl^- ions are arranged in a regular cubic array (Fig. 20–9). Large crystals of sodium chloride in the form of the mineral *halite* are found mostly in arid regions, because of the solubility of this substance in water. Halite exhibits three very clean cleavage planes at right angles to one another (Fig. 20–7), a reflection of the cubic internal symmetry of its constituent ions.

Calcite, a very common and important mineral, is a crystal form of calcium carbonate, $CaCO_3$. The crystal is composed of Ca^{++} and CO_3^{--} ions, regularly arranged in the geometric form of a rhombo-

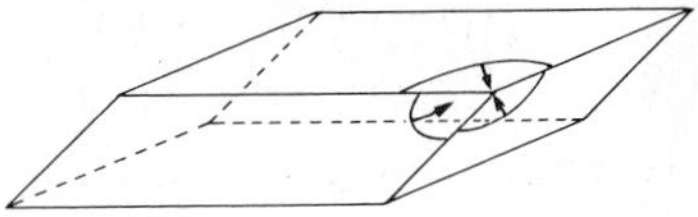

Fig. 25–10. Calcite, $CaCO_3$, crystallizes in the geometric form of a rhombohedron, in which none of the three characteristic interfacial angles (marked) is a right angle.

(a)

(b)

FIG. 25–11. Natural calcite crystals (a) may exhibit faces which do not correspond to the rhombohedron. The three cleavage directions are such, however, that any calcite crystal will form rhombohedra, as in (b), when struck. (Courtesy of Ward's Natural Science Establishment.)

hedron (Fig. 25-10). It shows excellent cleavage in three directions which are not at right angles to one another, so that crystal fragments are characteristically shaped as rhombic prisms (Fig. 25-11). An interesting consequence of the internal arrangement of ions in calcite is that the crystals are doubly refracting, i.e., electromagnetic vibrations in one plane are transmitted differently from those lying in another (Section 17-6). "Iceland spar," the name of the material Bartholinus and Huygens used in the first demonstration of the polarizability of light, is just another name for calcite. Calcite is the chief constituent of the rocks limestone and marble, although large, transparent crystals are rarely encountered in these materials. Calcium carbonate also occurs in the form of the rather uncommon mineral *aragonite*, whose crystalline form and properties are quite different from those of calcite.

Dolomite, a mineral which is often confused with calcite, is a mixed carbonate of calcium and magnesium, $CaMg(CO_3)_2$. Dolomite also shows three cleavages, and the angles between its cleavage planes are not quite the same as those observed in calcite. *Gypsum*, a very soft mineral, consists of calcium and sulfate ions interspersed with water molecules, $CaSO_4 \cdot 2H_2O$. It is the most abundant sulfate in the earth's crust. Gypsum exhibits very clean cleavage, but along only a single direction. *Hematite*, Fe_2O_3, and *magnetite*, Fe_3O_4, are two of the ores of the useful metal iron. The latter, it will be recalled, is "lodestone," well known since antiquity because of its permanent magnetic property. Its formula, Fe_3O_4, is misleading: out of every three iron ions present, two are ferr*ic*, one ferr*ous*. Other metallic ores of importance are *bauxite*, a mixture of hydrated aluminum oxides; *galena*, lead sulfide (PbS); *sphalerite*, zinc sulfide (ZnS); and *cassiterite*, stannic oxide (SnO_2). Only the most inactive of metals, such as copper and gold, are ever found as minerals in their free, metallic states.

While there are fewer nonsilicate than silicate minerals, the number of such known substances is still very large, and it would not be in keeping with our purposes to list and describe more than a few examples, as we have done.

25-5 The growth and significance of mineralogy

Although almost all solid matter is crystalline on at least a very small scale, perfect crystals of appreciable size are not commonly found among the materials of the earth's crust. The "stones" of curious shape or color that evoked wide interest in antiquity included mineral crystals, but most treatises that have come down to us from ancient and medieval times are concerned with their magical and curative powers, or consist of purely speculative, though imaginative, accounts of their origin. Early efforts to classify minerals were based primarily on color, a prominent and often attractive feature. Some simple minerals, such as iron pyrite ("fool's gold," FeS_2) do have distinctive colors, but color variations are produced in many minerals by the merest traces of impurity. Ruby, red garnet, and other deep red minerals were classed together as "carbuncle," despite wide divergences in properties other than color. Ruby is now known to be a form of aluminum oxide, Al_2O_3, which occurs in many colors, including sapphire; garnets are ionic silicate structures.

The growth in importance of mining during the 16th century led to careful descriptions of new minerals and their relations to each other. It was not until the 17th century, however, that the true, general regularities of crystal shapes were detected. Nicholas Steno (1636–1686) was the first to observe that corresponding faces of quartz crystals meet at the same angle in all crystals, regardless of size. The same property was verified in several other crystals within a few years of Steno's announcement. Steno also described the formation of crystals in terms of slow precipitation of solids from saturated solutions. Large and very perfect crystals of copper sulfate slowly form in saturated $CuSO_4$ solutions held under the proper conditions, for example, and if an irregularly broken crystal is added to such a solution it can be made to "heal," i.e., new, smooth faces grow onto the jagged portions. There are several other salts which can be made to form large, perfect crystals by this slow precipitation technique, although relatively few minerals have actually been crystallized in the laboratory in this way. The principle of characteristic crystal form is beautifully illustrated by such experiments, however.

Steno missed the second important expression of crystal form, cleavage, possibly because quartz, on which his discovery of constant angles was based, does not show cleavage planes. It was Rene-Just Haüy (1743–1821) who happened to drop a fine prism of calcite and noticed at once, with delight, that the pieces of various sizes were all rhombohedrons, of the same general form as those shown in Fig. 25–11(b). This discovery is a striking example of Pasteur's maxim that "chance favors the prepared mind." Haüy's studies in botany had impressed him with the similarities underlying complicated forms, and he felt that in crystals, too, some more simple regularities must underlie the apparent variety; it was while in this state of mind that the accident to his calcite prism occurred. He then proceeded to shatter many kinds of crystals, determined the cleavage properties of many minerals, and developed the first theory of crystal structure. Haüy advanced the idea that all the "molecules" of a crystal such as calcite have the same geometric form, and that these elementary forms may be grouped differently to yield crystal faces that are different from cleavage planes. Although this theory has required considerable modification, it is clearly the forerunner of the modern concept of a regular arrangement of atoms or ions, involving indefinite repetition of some basic structural unit.

It was Berzelius who secured the chemical basis for the science of mineralogy, and founded the modern chemical classification of minerals. He deduced chemical formulas for many minerals on the basis of quantitative analyses, and gave names to many of the silicates. He demonstrated the principle of *isomorphism*, that similar crystal forms may contain different combinations of atoms or ions. Modern techniques of analysis with x-rays have revealed many structural details which were hidden from Berzelius, but these details would have remained hidden without the chemical techniques he introduced.

The study of crystalline minerals has always been part of a larger effort, the study of the earth. It is no accident that the person who is generally considered to have been the first modern geologist, Steno, was the discoverer of the constancy of angles between quartz crystal faces. From our consideration of the element silicon we were led to the structures of silicates and other minerals; it is fitting that the subject of mineralogy should lead us to the study of the earth.

25–6 Summary

Silicon, second only to oxygen in abundance in the earth's crust, is second only to carbon in compound-forming ability. Its versatility is not based on bonds between silicon atoms, but on the highly stable silicon-oxygen bond. The most common minerals, silica and the silicates, contain silicon atoms bound to four oxygen atoms in a tetrahedral array, as the basic structural unit. These may be arranged in an indefinite, three-dimensional framework structure, as in quartz, or in layers or chains. Simpler silicates contain definite, discrete negative ions based on one or more SiO_4 tetrahedra. In the *alumino*silicates some of the positions which would be occupied by silicon atoms in a silicate structure are occupied by aluminum atoms. In the silicates and other minerals the arrangements of atoms inside the crystal are reflected in the relations between external crystal faces. These relations, whose constancy was first observed by Steno, are helpful in the identification of minerals. Among other properties which may be used for this purpose is the interesting one of cleavage, which is also a direct reflection of the internal structure of a crystal. The study of minerals, throughout its history, has been closely related to the science of geology.

REFERENCES

ADAMS, F. D., *The Birth and Development of the Geological Sciences*, especially Chapter VI, on the birth of modern mineralogy.

BRAGG, W. L., *The Atomic Structure of Minerals*. Difficult, but cited here because of its many excellent illustrations of mineral structures.

LEET, L. D., and S. JUDSON, *Physical Geology*, Chapters 2 and 3.

ROCHOW, E. G., and M. K. WILSON, *General Chemistry, a Topical Introduction*, Chapter 24.

SISLER, H. H., and others, *General Chemistry, a Systematic Approach*, Chapter 15.

1. To how many silicon or aluminum atoms is each oxygen atom bonded in a three-dimensional silicate or aluminosilicate framework structure? Does this same answer hold for all the oxygen atoms in a layer structure? a chain structure? Explain.

2. Talc and mica are both layered-structure minerals. What feature of their layers is responsible for the great difference in hardness between talc and mica?

3. Crystals will assume their characteristic forms, with external faces which express their internal structures, only when they are free to do so. The bounding surfaces of a crystal may be imposed by those of surrounding solids. How could you determine whether or not an irregular, transparent sample, which is known to have chemical formula $CaCO_3$, is the mineral calcite?

4. Ordinary glass is principally a mixture of silicates in the form of a super-cooled liquid. What does this statement mean? Would you expect SiO_4 tetrahedra to be present in glass?

5. Both diamond and graphite are composed of pure, elemental carbon. In diamond each carbon atom forms covalent bonds with four others in a tetrahedral array, while graphite contains a layered structure, with each carbon atom linked to three others in the same plane. Explain how this structural difference might account for the greater hardness and density of diamond, and the fact that diamond shatters irregularly on impact, while graphite shows ready cleavage along a single direction.

CHAPTER 26

ROCKS AND THEIR FORMATION

Much of the land surface of the earth is covered by a thin layer of soil which is essential to life processes and is itself a product of organic as well as inorganic activity. But the soil covering is very superficial, and the entire crust of the earth, from the highest mountains to the basin of the extensive oceans, is made essentially of rock. (We shall examine the evidence concerning the inaccessible interior of the earth in a later chapter.) Rocks are composed of minerals, usually in complex solid mixtures. Chemical and atomic structural analysis of rock is important to geology, as is knowledge of protein structure to biology but, similarly, it is by no means the whole story. The earth, like life, is something that is *happening*—it has a present as well as a history. Geology is the study of the earth as we find it today, and of how it came to be as it is. The origin of the earth is still largely a matter for speculation, and although the science of geology is not primarily concerned with such speculation, it inevitably yields important evidence bearing on that difficult problem. What we call "geological time," however, begins with an earth whose surface contained the essential features—rocks, soil, and oceans—observed today, but which was not at all the same in detail as we find it now. The history of geological change has been preserved in the rocks themselves, in their positions, gross structures, relations to each other, and their physical and chemical properties. We find in rocks biological remains that serve as documents of geological history, and at the same time contribute to the study of the evolution of life. We also find the radioactive elements that have served as tools for the exploration of atoms, stars, galaxies, and even rocks themselves.

In general, rocks are highly heterogeneous solids, consisting of mixtures of minerals of various kinds and crystal sizes, in varying proportions. One or a few minerals usually predominate, so that it is possible to classify rocks on the basis of composition. "Grain," or crystal size, forms another possible basis for division of rocks into categories. It is much more useful, however, to make the first broad classification on the basis of origin, in at least attempted answer to the question "what was this material just before it assumed the solid form in its present particular composition?" In this way, geological history is built into the very foundations of the study of rocks, and description of the earth around us involves recognition that it has not always been as we find it.

26–1 The beginnings of geology

The earlier civilizations on which our own is based had plenty of evidence that the earth is not static: Greece has long been a region subject to many earthquakes, and volcanos abound in the Mediterranean area. Moreover, the seashells still to be found in rocks high in the hills of Malta and elsewhere were taken to be evidence, as early as the 7th century B.C., that those rocks originated in the seas. Herodotus (484–425 B.C.) realized that the Nile delta was formed by deposition of silt, and actually tried to compute how long it would take for the Arabian Sea to be filled up if the Nile flowed into it. But since little was known in ancient times about the earth as a whole, and about the basic physical and chemical processes involved in geologic change, only casual, isolated observations of this sort were made. Later even these ideas were lost or ignored.

During the Renaissance a suggestion originally proposed by early Greek philosophers, that fossils are the remains of living things, was revived by such thinkers as Leonardo da Vinci and Giordano Bruno. The first geologist, in the modern sense of the term, was Nicolas Steno, or Niels Stensen (1638–1686), whose ideas were so far in advance of his time that most of them were rejected or overlooked until more than a century after his death. Steno's career was an exception to the general geographical trend of 17th century science toward the commercial north. Born and educated in Copenhagen, he made important anatomical discoveries in Holland and Paris before going to Italy, where his geological work was carried on and published. It was while nominally serving as physician to the Grand Duke of Tuscany that he became interested in rocks and fossils, and published (1669) the *Prodomus*, an "introduction" to geology which was also his last writing on the subject. Steno recognized that rocks contain a record to be deciphered, and formulated some of the principles which make the decoding of this record possible. He described the crystals he found in rocks and, as we have seen, the ways in which they can grow. From the fossilized remains and prints of plants and animals, he concluded that many rocks originated as sediments, at first as loose grains, later cemented together in layers, or *strata*. His knowledge of anatomy made it possible for him to compare fossils with living organisms, and to distinguish rocks formed from sediments laid down in the sea (Fig. 26–1) from those formed by consolidation of river silt, although he made no systematic study of the fossils themselves. Some of his conclusions may now seem very naive (he thought that mammoth bones found in the Alps were remains of Hannibal's elephants, for example) but he showed amazing clarity in the recognition of fundamental principles.

Steno's great contribution was his recognition that the rock strata form a chronology, or history, and he wrote the first geological history of a

FIG. 26-1. Fossil shells found in eastern Virginia. (U. S. Geological Survey.)

geographic region, that of Tuscany. From his observations of sediments
in the process of accumulation, he formulated two simple but basic laws,
both essential to any attempted unraveling of the rock record. First of
these is the *Law of Superposition*: in any *undisturbed* pile of strata the oldest
layer is at the base, the youngest on top. The second is the *Law of Original
Horizontality*: river or sea sediments are *originally* deposited in layers
which are horizontal or nearly so, roughly parallel to the surface on which
they accumulate. These laws are significant because rock layers are often
found tilted at large angles, folded, or even overturned. Tilting and folding of strata, according to Steno's principles, thus indicate movements
that took place long after sedimentation of the material they contain.

Steno refuted the notion, then prevalent, that mountains grow like biological organisms, and held that the rocks are elevated or depressed as a result of pressures exerted by other rocks.

Despite the rejection of Steno's work by his contemporaries, the idea that rocks are formed by the cementing of sediments was commonplace before the close of the century following his death. The man who systematized geology and secured its status as a science, Abraham Gottlob Werner (1750–1817), held that *all* rocks, with a few exceptions, were precipitated from primeval oceans. He and his numerous disciples were called "Neptunists." Others, called "Vulcanists," had held that rock strata were formed by a series of eruptions of liquid rock from a molten mass below the earth's surface, which trapped living things before becoming cool and hard. The strict Vulcanist view could not be sustained; its proponents soon simply emphasized the role of heat in rock formation, and did not deny the existence of cemented sediments. A great 18th century controversy between the Neptunists and the Vulcanists, in a sense, gave birth to modern geology. This controversy can be studied with profit only when we have learned something more of sedimentary rocks, however.

26–2 Sedimentary rocks

At least three-quarters of the rocks that cover the earth's land surface can be attributed, without ambiguity, to sediments. Some of them bear permanent testimony to their origin in the form of ripple marks and ancient mud cracks (Fig. 26–2). The single feature most characteristic of sedimentary rocks, however, is stratification, or bedding: sediments are almost invariably deposited in layers, usually having roughly parallel horizontal boundaries. This is particularly true of sediments laid down by water, the most important agent of sedimentation, but the action of wind also produces marked bedding. Glaciers also leave sediments with characteristic patterns of deposit. The various forms of sedimentary rocks may often be identified by comparison with recent, uncemented sediments. In such rocks the strata are preserved, although they have become *lithified* (hardened) into solid masses. The hardening may be brought about in several ways, one of the most common being the precipitation of cementing minerals from aqueous solution.

Sedimentary rocks differ from one another in color, hardness, density, size of grain or crystal, chemical composition, and other characteristics. Unlike their constituent minerals, which are chemical substances with fairly definite composition and structure, no two rocks are exactly alike. Nevertheless, it is only through their classification and grouping with respect to general characteristics that we can trace geologic history. Important and common sedimentary rocks are described in the reference

FIG. 26–2. Ripple marks in sandstone, Golden, Colorado. (U. S. Geological Survey.)

texts listed at the end of this chapter; here we shall discuss only a few familiar varieties.

Conglomerate, as the name implies, is a rock consisting of pebbles, or gravel, cemented together. Its sedimentary origin is obvious from the appearance of its component materials. The pebbles found in conglomerate are ordinarily rounded, presumably by wear during their transportation by the currents of water which deposited them in shallow seas, lakes, or stream channels.

Sandstone is a finer grained rock than conglomerate, consisting of cemented sand. Sand, for this purpose, is defined as a sediment composed of particles ranging from 1/16 mm to 2 mm in diameter. Quartz is the chief mineral present in sand and sandstone, since it resists division to smaller particle size by virtue of its hardness and chemical stability. Grains of silicate minerals are also common in sandstone. The wide variety of color observed in sandstones is related principally to the presence or absence of varying quantities of iron compounds or organic matter, although these materials make up a very small percentage of the whole. Sand deposits are laid down either by wind or by water.

Shale, a relatively soft rock that splits easily into layers, is hardened mud. Its mineral grains are extremely fine, consisting mainly of the hydrous aluminum silicates, or clay minerals.

Limestone, the most common nonsilicate rock, is composed mostly of calcium carbonate in the form of calcite. Some limestones consist of aggregates of the shells of marine animals, others appear to have been formed by precipitation from solution. The hardness of limestone cannot be greater than that of calcite, but it may be even less, as is the case in the very fine-grained, weakly cemented variety of limestone called *chalk*. The calcareous material in limestone is often found admixed with clay or sand. From our knowledge of processes now going on (e.g., the growth of coral reefs) and the properties of calcium carbonate, it seems evident that nearly all limestones must have been originally deposited in warm, shallow seas. Even so, we find thick layers of limestone, oriented at all angles, in the highest mountains!

26-3 Geological maps and their significance

Sedimentary rocks, characteristically, are rich in fossils, although the distribution of such direct evidence of former life is by no means uniform. The importance of fossils in geology arose from the gradual discovery that their distribution differs from one series of rock strata to another, and that a particular group of beds could be correlated, on the basis of its assemblage of fossils, with strata found in widely separated and different localities (Fig. 26-3). This observation has grown in importance from a practical method for identifying beds of rock that are exposed at the surface only here and there, to a principle for historical dating of the origin of rocks. The principles of correlation arose only as a result of systematic study and observation, and were arrived at independently and almost simultaneously by a group of French naturalists engaged in investigating the region around Paris, and by William Smith (1769–1839) in England. The French workers, especially Georges Cuvier (1769–1832), were more scientifically inclined than Smith, and made a more systematic study of the fossils themselves. Smith made his observations in the course of a quarter of a century devoted to practical surveying for the construction of canals. His data extended over a wider variety of geological formations and some of his conclusions were more general and inclusive than those of Cuvier and his colleagues.

By exploration and observation over wide regions, Smith and the French group deduced the patterns of consecutive layers of rock in those regions, despite the fact that the layers were hidden for the most part by soil at the top and by each other farther below the surface. These studies were suggested by observations made in excavations. In the 1780's Lavoisier published papers in which he pointed out that different layers of stone are found in similar relations to each other in quarries near Paris. During the next decade Smith was studying rock cuts made necessary for the con-

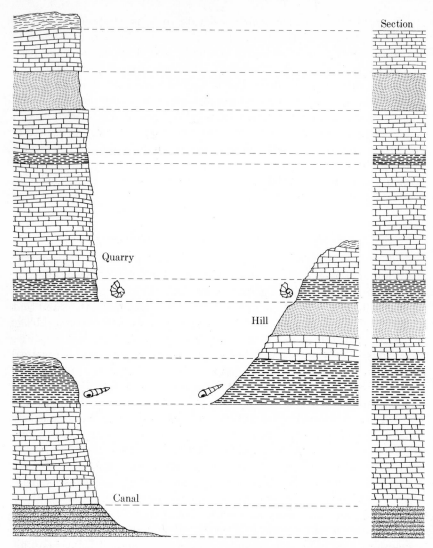

FIG. 26–3. Schematic representation of Smith's use of fossils to match beds in a canal, a hill, and a quarry. Result is the section diagram at the right.

struction of canals. Generalization from such direct observations to strata underlying whole areas was made on the basis of principles first formulated by Steno. In addition to the laws of superposition and original horizontality, there are two corollaries. One, called the *Law of Original Continuity*, states that layers of rock deposited by water must have extended sidewise to the edge of the basin in which they were laid down, unless they became thin because of lack of deposition. The second applies to observed departures from continuity: an abrupt break in a stratum, at a position other than at the edge of a basin, must have been made since deposition of the stratum, either by erosion or by a dislocation of the earth's crust.

The application of these principles generally requires astute detective work, inasmuch as rocks are usually buried except in mountains, where the patterns are often too complicated to be readily unraveled. Smith and the French geologists went looking for naturally exposed rocks, called *outcrops*, often found near streams and on hillsides. They watched for bits of rock in the soil, and carefully observed the rocks exposed during the digging of wells, canals, quarries, and mines. To report their information they indicated on maps of the regions investigated the kinds of rock nearest the surface; such were the first geologic maps, constructed almost simultaneously in England and in France. (Cuvier's map appeared in 1811, Smith's in 1815.)

It is obvious that geologic maps are useful for digging a shallow canal or building a road, but they have much more fundamental significance as well. Superposed on a contour map, showing the elevations of a region, a surface-rock map yields information about the rocks far below the surface. This information has economic value in connection with mineral production, but it also enables us to trace geologic history. Let us consider the simple map of Fig. 26-4, showing the contour lines in a small region where there are outcrops of shale and limestone below the crest of a sandstone hill. It may be inferred that the limestone extends under the shale, and a *geologic section* may be constructed as indicated in the figure. The section shows the layering that would be seen if a vertical cut were made through the earth along the line AB of the map. If, at the top of a limestone outcrop, bits of limestone were found embedded firmly in the base of the shale layer, one could be sure that the limestone was well hardened before the mud was deposited. In such ways one can deduce the time sequence of the deposit of strata. Since the layers in the formation are not horizontal, it is clear that the area has been tilted since its constituent sedimentary rocks were formed.

Our example is too simple to illustrate the importance of fossil content in the identification of strata. Many strata are discontinuous; they may have been eroded before the succeeding bed was deposited, or small beds may have been deposited locally, like sand banks, confusing the general pattern. Many such discontinuities are observed over large areas. Then, too, there may be numerous layers of the same kind of rock, e.g., limestone or sandstone, some of which are missing in one or more regions. Variations in the properties of sediments may occur over the area of a large basin and lead to variations within the rock strata formed from them. The problem of correlating layers despite these difficulties was solved when it was

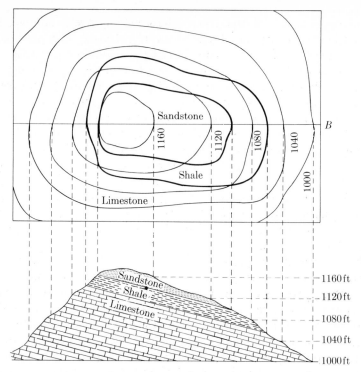

FIG. 26-4. Construction of a geologic section from a geologic map.

recognized that each closely related group of strata, or *formation*, can be identified by its fossil content. Smith and the French geologists found systematic differences in fossils from one formation to another. Cuvier and his co-worker Brongniart also noted that resemblance between the forms of fossils and those of animals living today decreases as one goes to lower strata. This was the first step taken in the direction of relative dating of sedimentary beds on the basis of the characteristic fossils they contain.

Implicit in the whole of our discussion of sedimentary rocks is, at least in limited form, a principle first clearly stated by James Hutton (1726–1796) in 1785, called the *Law of Uniform Change*. A partial statement of this principle is that the origin of rocks formed long ago can be understood in terms of processes now going on—that stratification, the embedding of fossils, and various degrees of cementation can be observed in the sediments of rivers and seas, and in sand piled up by winds. Although not stated explicitly by Steno, this assumption is implicit in his laws regarding sedimentary strata. Hutton's theory was not generally accepted in his day, partially because it was not believed that the earth could be as old as it must be if its surface has been altered significantly by the gradual processes of change now at work. Today, with a time scale for geologic change which has been vastly lengthened by important discoveries, its basic tenet is well established. Before we can generalize the law of uniform change to all rocks, or apply it to changes other than rock formation, we must consider rocks of other than sedimentary origin and note their distribution over the earth.

26–4 Igneous rocks

Ordinarily it takes a long time for sediments to be cemented together; the nature of the process is inferred from observations of the final result and of examples of incomplete cementation. The hot lava that pours from the fissure of a volcano, on the other hand, can be watched continuously while it solidifies into dark, dense rock called *basalt*. It is obvious, then, that not all rocks are sedimentary in origin. But volcanos, spectacular as they are individually, are not very widely distributed over the earth. There are, for example, no active volcanos in the whole of the United States today, although Mt. Lassen in California erupted briefly as late as 1915. The question thus arises whether the dark, fine-grained rocks that cover thousands of square miles in the northwest United States and elsewhere, indistinguishable in composition and texture from rocks which are obviously solidified lava, are also volcanic in origin. Moreover, masses of very similar rock are frequently found cutting through sedimentary beds that must have once been deeply buried. Sometimes rock strata strongly resembling basalt lie between layers of sediment.

It is now recognized that basalt is not sedimentary in origin, but has formed by direct solidification from a molten state. Its frequent occurrence in layers parallel to adjacent sedimentary strata, however, led to one of the most heated controversies in the history of science. We have mentioned Abraham Gottlob Werner, who was a professor at the Academy of Mines in Freiberg, Germany. Werner combined a passion for orderliness and method with great personal charm and persuasivemess as a teacher. Freiberg, as a result of his influence, became a world center for geological learning. It can be fairly said that Werner, more than any other, made geology a science in its own right, rather than a group of casual, unrelated observations of "naturalists." Yet, he is remembered today not so much for his many valuable contributions to science as for his quite erroneous theory of the origin of the earth's crust. Basalt had been known since Roman times, and the problem of its occurrence in regions far from volcanos had been the subject of considerable speculation. Werner's only acquaintance with basalt was in Stolpen, Saxony, where it occurs in roughly horizontal strata and forms conspicuous cliffs (Fig. 26–5). Werner examined the basalt in this area with great care, and found no trace of vol-

FIG. 26–5. The Scheibenberg, in Saxony, from which Werner concluded that basalt is sedimentary. He held that the whole series above the base rock was deposited by one of three "primeval oceans." (After Richard Beck.)

canic action. He concluded, with methodical finality: "After further more mature research and consideration, I hold that no basalt is volcanic, but that all these rocks . . . are of aqueous origin." Carrying his speculation further, he concluded that all rocks at or near the earth's surface were precipitated from three successive "primeval oceans" which had covered the entire surface of the earth at different times in the past, then subsided. What happened to the water between these times of universal flood was not made entirely clear in this theory. Werner's great mistake was to generalize to the entire world a theory based on observational evidence from no more than a small region of Saxony. It later became apparent that even in Saxony he had not looked for evidence *against* his universal system, which hinged on the assumed sedimentary origin of basalt and of another common rock called *granite*.

In other parts of Europe there was basalt whose volcanic origin was so obvious that Werner's views were challenged from the start; still, he could be answered conclusively only by contrary evidence. By the time the wordy battle began to abate, early in the 19th century, the French government worker Nicholas Desmarest (1725–1815) had identified several basalt deposits with recognizable, ancient volcanic craters, and had concluded that they consist of "flows." He also determined that the nature of such rock flows can, in general, be determined by careful examination of their boundary surfaces. If hot, molten rock flows on the surface of the earth, it should "scorch" the earth below it, and evidence of the effect of heat should be visible in the underlying rock. Fragments of the original surface, and probably bubbles of trapped gas, should also be found in the rock flow near its base. If the top surface of the flow is still intact (i.e., if it has not been worn down by erosion since the rock solidified), it could be expected to contain holes due to the rapid expansion and escape of gases from the hot, molten rock. All these features are observed in the basalt cliffs of Werner's Saxony, as well as in central France where Desmarest's observations were made.

Some layers of basalt and other very similar rocks show the effects typical of lava flows on the sedimentary rocks adjacent to their top surfaces, as well as at the bottom. It is clear that rock layers such as these solidified in place from a molten state, but not at the surface of the earth. Rather, the liquid must have been forced through solid rock layers which had already formed, like grease from a grease gun separating sheets of metal. Molten material that flows between sedimentary strata, forces them apart, and then congeals, results in formations called *sills*. The Palisades, a cliff across the Hudson River from New York City, is the eroded cross section of a vast sill nearly 1000 feet thick in some places, which extends westward between layers of the shales and sandstones of New Jersey (Fig. 26–6).

Fissures filled with rock which has solidified from a molten state and which cut across layers of sediments or other older rock, instead of being parallel to them as in the case of sills, constitute formations known as *dikes* (see Fig. 26–7). Exposed dikes often rise above the ground like ruined walls, in areas where softer, neighboring rocks have worn away. The Flume, a narrow gorge in the White Mountains in New Hampshire, on the

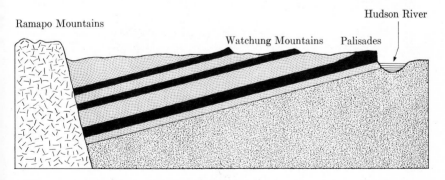

Fig. 26–6. Schematic section through the Palisades and two lava beds whose outcrops form the Watchung Mountains in New Jersey. Note that the whole series breaks off sharply on the west.

FIG. 26–7. Dikes in sedimentary strata on Alamillo Creek, Socorro County, New Mexico. (U. S. Geological Survey.)

other hand, marks a dike that has been eroded by a stream; the material of this dike is softer than the granite walls its ancestral fluid originally pushed apart. All rocks such as those constituting dikes and sills, that have solidified below the surface of the earth, are said to be *intrusive;* they have intruded into space formerly occupied by other, older rocks. Lava, by definition, is pushed out of the earth to become solid on the surface; geological formations which originated as lava flows are said to be *extrusive.* An extrusive formation may become buried by sediments; the distinguishing features of an intruded sill and a buried lava flow, both parallel

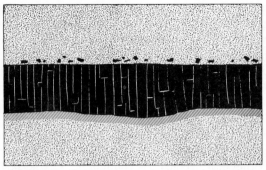

Igneous fragments
in sediments

Buried lava flow

"Scorched" contact

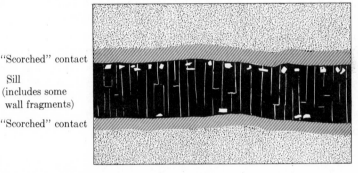

"Scorched" contact

Sill
(includes some
wall fragments)

"Scorched" contact

Fig. 26–8. Distinguishing features of a sill and a buried lava flow.

to the beds of their neighboring sediments, are indicated in Fig. 26–8. The sill is a younger rock (sometimes much younger) than either of the adjacent strata, while the lava flow must be older than any sedimentary rock formed above it.

Intrusive rocks are often found in shapes that are much more irregular and complicated than layers or fissures. In a variant of the sill known as a *laccolith*, molten rock has spread between sedimentary strata and then lifted the upper rocks into a dome before hardening. An elaborate classification of intrusions according to shape is not very helpful, but we must take note of *batholiths*, which are the largest of all intrusive masses. The word *batholith* means "deep stone," and batholiths are said to be bottomless in the sense that they have no well-defined floor. We shall have to consider some of the rock forms again in connection with both volcanic activity and the origin of mountains.

Rocks which originate by solidification from a molten state are called *igneous*. The word literally means "pertaining to fire," and is used in this sense because liquid rock is intensely hot. Molten rock itself is called *magma*, from a Greek word meaning "to squeeze," or "to knead," emphasizing the fluid properties of the material rather than its temperature. Actually, the word magma is usually reserved to designate fluid rock below the surface of the earth, where its degree of fluidity is probably enhanced by high pressures and temperatures. The temperature of magma ranges roughly from 500°C to 1400°C. Chemically, magma is composed mainly of silicates; some of its constituents may remain in solid form even though the mass as a whole is fluid.

Hardening of magma to solid rock always involves cooling, and the texture or grain size of all igneous rocks depends markedly on the rate at which they have cooled. If the molten rock is cooled with great rapidity it becomes glassy and has no crystal structure at all; igneous rocks of this sort are examples of amorphous solids, or supercooled liquids (see Chapter 20). *Obsidian* (Fig. 26–9), a volcanic glass sometimes used for inlaid jewelry, and *pumice*, a glass froth, are well-known amorphous rocks. Intrusive rocks that have hardened at great depth, such as those constituting batholiths, probably required centuries to crystallize; these are typically coarse in texture, and contain many crystals visible to the naked eye. Most dykes and sills have solidified nearer the surface, and have relatively fine texture. Granite is a typical coarse-grained rock, predominantly of igneous origin. Basalt is fine-grained, but not glassy.

TABLE 26–1

SUBDIVISIONS OF IGNEOUS ROCK ON THE BASIS OF TEXTURE
AND CHIEF MINERALS (MUCH SIMPLIFIED)

Chief Minerals / Texture	feldspar quartz	ferromagnesians little feldspar no quartz
glassy	obsidian pumice	basalt glass
very fine-grained	rhyolite dacite	basalt
granular	granite granodiorite	dolerite (also called diabase) gabbro (coarser than dolerite)

(a)

(b)

FIG. 26–9. Photographs of (a) obsidian, showing curving fracture, and (b) gabbro. (Courtesy of Ward's Natural Science Establishment.)

The subdivisions of the whole class of igneous rocks are made on the dual basis of average grain size and chemical composition. There are many gradations and intermediate types on both counts, and the number of subdivisions is somewhat arbitrary. Table 26–1 illustrates as simply as possible the way these divisions are made. It is desirable to have a classification that can be used "in the field" by the working geologist without recourse to elaborate apparatus, and rocks can be readily classed as coarse-grained, fine-grained, or glassy by visual observation. Approximate chemical composition, or mineral content, is usually indicated by color and density: the ferromagnesian minerals are denser and darker than the alkali feldspars and quartz, and the rocks in which these minerals predominate are correspondingly dense and dark colored. To distinguish between the two most common types of igneous rock:

Basalt, a fine-grained rock of black, brown, very dark gray, or green color, is commonly encountered in extrusive lava flows, and intrusive dikes and sills. Ferromagnesian minerals predominate in basaltic rocks. Later we shall review the evidence for the existence of basaltic rocks underlying the ocean basins, and of a basaltic layer under the vast continental masses.

Granite (i.e., "grainy") is coarse-grained, and is less dense and lighter in color than basalt; its dominant minerals are feldspars and quartz. An almost equally common coarse-grained rock with a somewhat greater proportion of ferromagnesian minerals than true granite is known as *granodiorite.*

Note that the only minerals we have mentioned in connection with igneous rocks are silicates—only small amounts of other minerals are found in them. Since silicates are based, structurally, on the oxygen-silicon tetrahedron, the overwhelming abundance of oxygen and silicon in the earth's crust is easily accounted for.

26–5 Metamorphic rocks

A third class of rocks, called metamorphic, comprises those formed by radical alteration of either sedimentary or igneous rock at great depths within the earth (see Table 26–2). Under conditions of high temperatures and pressures, changes in patterns of crystallization or marked rearrangements of crystal structures may occur in a variety of ways. High temperatures affect rocks by increasing reaction rates, thereby encouraging chemical transformations which would not take place at lower temperatures. High temperature also increases the plasticity and deformability of the minerals in rocks, and thus permits their rearrangement. High pressure will cause *any* solid to become plastic, i.e., capable of flowing to at least some extent; differences in pressure can also produce flow, in the course of which minerals may become rearranged. Crystallization during flow, or

TABLE 26–2

MOST COMMON METAMORPHIC ROCKS

Name		Commonly derived from	Chief minerals
Unfoliated	Hornfels	any fine-grained rock	variable
	Quartzite	sandstone	quartz
	Marble	limestone, dolomite	calcite, magnesium and calcium silicates
Foliated	Slate	shale	mica, quartz
	Schist	igneous rocks and shale	mica and other platy silicate minerals
	Gneiss	granite, shale, etc.	feldspar, quartz, mica, garnet, etc.

when a rock is under great stress, tends to produce minerals with platy (layered) structures. For this reason, many metamorphic rocks have layered, or *foliated*, appearances. The most familiar foliated metamorphic rock is *slate*, which splits readily along parallel planes and is therefore much used for roofing. Slate is mostly metamorphosed shale, but its foliation planes bear no relation to the original bedding planes of the cemented mud, since they have been produced by a much later, independent process. The chemical content of slate is not essentially different from that of shale, but the mineral content is changed. Characteristically, the clay minerals of shale are substantially replaced by tiny crystals of mica, oriented in planes which constitute the foliation planes of slate.

The most abundant foliated rock in which the crystals are large enough to be clearly visible to the naked eye is called *schist*. Schist results from more intense metamorphism than slate; it derives from fine-grained igneous rocks as well as from shale.

The temperatures involved in metamorphism, although high compared with those at the earth's surface, are not sufficiently great to produce truly molten rock, or magma. If they were, all traces of the previous origin of the rock would be lost, and the resultant rock would have to be classified as igneous, not metamorphic. Some degree of metamorphism always results, to be sure, from the contact of older rocks with magma. The "scorching" which occurs at the bases of lava flows and at the boundaries of intrusive igneous rock formations (Fig. 26–10) is metamorphism, as are

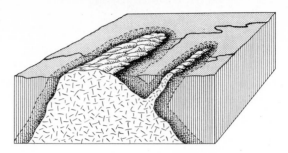

FIG. 26–10. Zone of metamorphism surrounding an igneous intrusion.

the changes in chemical content that may result from gaseous emanations given off by the magma. As examples of metamorphic rocks found at igneous contacts we may mention *hornfels*, a hard, fine-grained rock recrystallized mostly from shale, and *quartzite*, a hard mass that results from the interlocking of quartz grains in sandstone. These rocks, especially quartzite, are also found in mass well away from igneous contacts.

Most metamorphism takes place far below the surface of the earth, and metamorphic rocks become exposed by subsequent processes of uplift and erosion. This is true of almost all *marble*, which is metamorphosed limestone or, if the mineral is chiefly calcium magnesium carbonate instead of calcite, metamorphosed dolomite.

The changes that take place during metamorphism all represent equilibrium shifts in directions which tend to relieve the "stresses" of high pressure and temperature, in accordance with LeChatelier's principle. Metamorphic rocks, in general, are more dense and compact than their unaltered counterparts, although limitations on density are imposed by the nature of possible crystal structures. The heavy mineral garnet is often found in metamorphic rocks, since its structure occupies less space than any other mineral with equivalent chemical composition. Chemical changes which accompany metamorphism, characteristically, are those which absorb heat, provided that such changes are compatible with pressure conditions. An example is the formation of anthracite coal, the metamorphic equivalent of the sedimentary bituminous (soft) coal. The constituent compounds of anthracite are much higher in chemical energy content than are those of bituminous coal.

26–6 Weathering and the rock cycle

The constant destruction of existing rocks is more obvious than the processes of rock formation: cliffs crumble, building stones decay, soils are replenished. Yet, there is a continuous cycle of both formation and decay, as was pointed out clearly in 1785 by James Hutton. In his words: "This world is thus destroyed in one part, but it is renewed in another; and the operations by which this world is continually renewed are as evident to the scientific eye, as are those in which it is necessarily destroyed." In these operations, according to Hutton, "we find no sign of a beginning, no prospect of an end."

The chief processes by which rock decay takes place is called *weathering*. Weathering of rock consists of changes, at or near the surface of the earth, which result from exposure to air, water, and the action of plants and animals. Mere physical disintegration with little or no accompanying chemical change, such as the spalling of slabs of granite from exposed knobs or the cracking loose of fragments from cliffs in mountains, is called *mechanical weathering*. A rock crusher is the ideal agent for mechanical weathering, but in nature the most effective single agent is frost. The expansion of water on freezing enables it to exert such great pressure, if ice forms in cracks or crevices, that fragments of rock are broken away. The roots of plants can also exert sufficient pressure to dislodge rocks. Natural cracks are often found in large exposed rock masses, as a result of various internal stresses.

More important than mere physical disintegration is *chemical weathering*, which involves transformation of rock-forming minerals to those characteristic of soil. The chemical changes involved may be very complex, but the most important single factor is the action of carbon dioxide or, more precisely, of carbonic acid, since CO_2 is an active weathering agent only in water solution. When CO_2 gas is in contact with water, the following equilibria are established:

$$CO_2 + H_2O \rightleftharpoons H_2CO_3; \tag{1}$$

$$H_2CO_3 + H_2O \rightleftharpoons H_3O^+ + HCO_3^-. \tag{2}$$

Calcite, the chief constituent mineral of limestone, is virtually insoluble in water, i.e., the equilibrium

$$Ca^{++} + CO_3^{--} \rightleftharpoons CaCO_3 \downarrow \tag{3}$$

is ordinarily shifted far to the right. If hydronium ions are present, however, they tend to donate protons to carbonate ions:

$$H_3O^+ + CO_3^{--} \rightleftharpoons HCO_3^- + H_2O, \tag{4}$$

and in the attempt to restore the carbonate ion concentration, equilibrium (3) is shifted to the left. $CaCO_3$ thus tends to pass into ionic solution.

Even the very dilute solution formed by rainwater with atmospheric CO_2 is capable of dissolving limestone slowly. In the course of centuries, vast caverns and sinkholes are formed by carbon dioxide-bearing water which seeps through rock, and dissolves and carries it away. Calcium carbonate which has been dissolved in this way will stay in solution only so long as dissolved CO_2 is also present. Any change of conditions (e.g., reduction of pressure or increase of temperature) which tends to drive equilibria (2) and (1) to the left, and release CO_2, will simultaneously shift equilibrium (4) to the left, and (3) to the right, precipitating $CaCO_3$. The spectacular stalactites and stalagmites seen in limestone caverns consist of calcite which has been redeposited from underground water solution; when the water enters the large volume of the cavern, it experiences a drop in pressure, releases CO_2, and $CaCO_3$ precipitates.

The chemical weathering of silicate minerals is much more complex and varied than that of calcite, and quartz itself weathers extremely slowly. Silicate minerals, such as the feldspars and ferromagnesians, on weathering, generally combine with carbonic acid and water to yield the clay minerals, silica (either in solution or as quartz grains), and soluble inorganic carbonates or bicarbonates. The clay minerals which form are usually *hydrous*, i.e., water molecules are incorporated into their soft crystals. One of the simplest examples is the weathering of the feldspar mineral orthoclase, for which we may write the following equation, indicating only initial reactants and end products:

$$2KAlSi_3O_8 + (H_2O + CO_2) + nH_2O \longrightarrow$$
(orthoclase)   (carbonic acid)

$$Al_2(OH)_2Si_4O_{10} \cdot nH_2O + 2SiO_2 + 2K^+ + CO_3^{--}.$$
(hydrous clay mineral)

Weathering of the ferromagnesian minerals eventually gives rise to the iron oxide minerals, yellow limonite and red hematite. These minerals, together with humus (organic material) are often responsible for the characteristic colors of soils.

By far the largest volume of products from the weathering of rock consists of clay minerals, quartz, and soluble salts. These and other products are being produced continuously everywhere on the earth's surface, at rates that depend on the nature of the exposed rock and on climate, hence vary widely. The most important determining factor in rate of weathering is the presence of moisture; rock decays most slowly in warm, arid climates, such as that of Egypt. A striking example is provided by a granite obelisk called Cleopatra's Needle (Fig. 26–11), thought to have been carved in about 1500 B.C., which was moved to New York City in 1880. Exposed to frost and moisture, the stone has weathered much more during three-quarters of a century in New York, despite attempts to preserve it, than during the many centuries of its previous existence.

After the constituent materials of rocks have been mechanically fragmented or chemically altered, they may be easily transported by water, wind, and ice. Wherever they are deposited by these agents in large quantity, beds of sediments gradually develop. In time, the sediments become lithified, forming new sedimentary rocks. If buried to sufficient depth in the earth, some of these new rocks may become metamorphosed or even, perhaps, melted to reconstitute magma. Ultimately, the magma may crystallize on or near the earth's surface, forming new igneous rock. Here, then, is the rock cycle described by Hutton in 1785. As we have indicated in Fig. 26–12, there is actually more than a single rock cycle, since all kinds of rock are subject to weathering, and since both sedimentary and igneous rocks may be metamorphosed. The diagram of Fig. 26–12, in a sense, is a shorthand account of the dynamic physical processes which shape the earth's surface. By the process of *erosion*, the rock debris resulting from mechanical and chemical weathering is constantly being removed from some areas and transported to others, where *sedimentation* occurs. This process, constantly at work, tends to level the earth. Inverse processes, whose detailed nature we shall consider in Chapter 28, are simultaneously at work uplifting parts of the earth's crust, creating and maintaining the irregularities of its surface. Without these irregularities, the large-scale transport of sedimentary materials would have ceased long ago.

Many of the rocks visible at the surface of the earth and exposed by shallow cuts are sedimentary; it is from the study of these that most of our detailed knowledge of geological history has been deduced. There are some areas of the earth, such as those in the western United States (Arizona, New Mexico, and several states in the Northwest), which are covered by extrusive layers of the igneous rock basalt. These layers are often superficial, however, and are generally found to overlie a sedimentary base. There are many huge areas of exposed *intrusive* rocks, consisting of granite or of the somewhat darker, related rock granodiorite. These are what we have called batholiths. They extend along the cores of most of the major mountain ranges, and show themselves in regions of metamorphism such as are found in northern Canada and Scandinavia. Their compositions are far from uniform, a fact which has given rise to some debate as to the origin of granite. It is possible that these vast intrusions of magma have "swallowed up" large quantities of sedimentary rocks, or have so completely changed the states of crystallization of the latter as to make them indistinguishable from crystallized magma. Of all intrusive formations, batholiths are bordered by the thickest blankets of

FIG. 26–11. Weathering of Cleopatra's Needle. The photograph above was taken in Egypt before 1880, that on the opposing page was taken in New York in 1918. (Courtesy of the Metropolitan Museum of Art.)

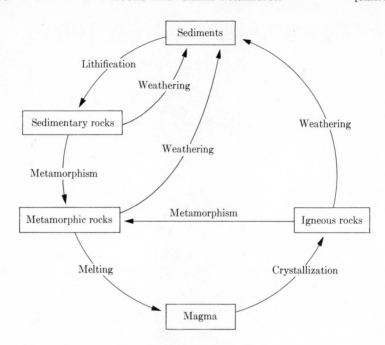

FIG. 26–12. The Rock Cycle.

recognizably metamorphic rocks, as might be expected from their size and the long periods which they must have required to cool at considerable depths. The origin and movement of magma are the subject of an unsolved geological problem. Some rock undoubtedly becomes melted upon deep burial, as suggested in Fig. 26–12. This may account for much of the variation observed in the chemical content of the molten rock exposed as lava. Yet, on the whole, magma contains more of the heavier elements than are usually found in surface rock, and magma apparently flows upward from very great depths. As we shall see in the next chapter, the earth's crust is mostly solid; melted rock is present only in relatively small pockets. The question of magma will arise again in our discussion of mountain building. We must note here, however, that the rock cycle, important as it is for the understanding of geological transformation, has validity only in describing changes at or near the earth's surface. There is no evidence that large masses of igneous rock have been completely regenerated from rock that was once at the surface; instead, such masses seem to have derived, at least in part, from the deeper interior of the earth. To pursue these matters further, however, we must turn our attention from individual rocks and rock masses, and look at the earth with greater perspective in both space and time.

26–7 Summary

That the earth has a history whose story is preserved in rocks was first clearly recognized by Steno in the 17th century, but the science of geology was not developed systematically until the 19th century. Apart from a superficial layer of soil, the crust of the earth is almost entirely composed of rocks, mainly aggregates of silicate minerals. Calcite also plays a very important role, despite its relative scarcity. Rocks are classified by origin as sedimentary, igneous, and metamorphic. Much of earth history is traced with the aid of geological maps combined with principles of sediment formation arrived at by comparison of sedimentary rock structure with processes now going on; relative dating of sedimentary rocks is possible from their fossil content. Igneous rocks are solidified *magma,* and may be intrusive or extrusive. Metamorphic rocks arise by radical alteration of other rocks under conditions of high pressure and temperature. Subdivisions of the three main classes are made on the basis of chemical composition (dominant minerals) and by size of grain or crystal. Surface rocks disintegrate by the process of weathering, both mechanical and chemical, and the resultant particles may be deposited as sediments and cemented to form sedimentary rock. There is thus a "rock cycle," which also involves igneous and metamorphic rocks.

REFERENCES

ADAMS, F. D., *The Birth and Development of the Geological Sciences.* A standard work.

FENTON, C. L., and M. A. FENTON, *The Story of the Great Geologists.* A popular account with an excellent bibliography.

GEIKIE, A., *The Founders of Geology.* An interesting history, written by a famous geologist.

GILLULY, J., A. C. WATERS, and A. O. WOODFORD, *Principles of Geology.* A text that lives up to its name; principles are emphasized, although not at the expense of examples and illustrations.

LEET, L. D., and S. JUDSON, *Physical Geology.* An interesting text with many excellent illustrations.

MATHER, K. F., and S. L. MASON, *A Source Book in Geology,* pp 33–44 (Steno), 90–91 (Desmarest), 92–100 (Hutton), 188–193 (Cuvier), 194–200 (Cuvier and Brongniart), 201–204 (Smith).

1. Like mud cracks, fossilized tracks of prehistoric animals are sometimes found in shale and related rocks. Does this mean that lithification (consolidation into rock) took place at the earth's surface? Suggest a possible reason for the preservation of these tracks.

2. From a consideration of the predominant mineral structures, can you explain why sandstone is generally more permeable to water than shale?

3. Why should the Palisades form a ridge that is conspicuously higher than its surroundings?

4. If two igneous rocks have essentially the same mineral content, but one is coarse-grained, the other fine-grained, what can you say of their probable origin?

5. With reference to Fig. 26–6, where would you expect to find most extensive metamorphism? Where would you expect fragments of igneous rock as inclusions in a sedimentary layer?

6. In some regions large areas of metamorphic rocks (e.g., slate, marble, etc.) are exposed at the surface of the earth. What conclusion can you draw about erosion in such an area?

7. How are calcite, limestone, and marble related? Quartz, sandstone, and quartzite? Can you name a corresponding series beginning with the clay minerals?

8. What is the difference in origin between *stratification*, found in shale, and *foliation*, found in slate? How is this difference related to characteristic mineral content?

CHAPTER 27

THE EARTH AS A WHOLE

In this chapter we shall discuss the earth as we find it today, with little regard to the changes, extremely slow but no less important on that account, which are constantly taking place within it. First, let us consider the main features of the surface; then we shall inquire about the inaccessible interior of the earth, and the means which geology has developed for its indirect exploration. In the next chapter we shall examine the earth's surface in greater detail, the processes which cause it to change, and the long record of geological history it contains.

27-1 General features of the earth's surface

The general shape of the earth, as was known in ancient times, is spherical. It is not a true sphere, however, but is slightly flattened at the poles, and possesses an "equatorial bulge." As we have noted in Chapter 4, this fact was crucial in Newton's interpretation of the precession of the equinoxes. The actual amount of flattening is not large, since the radius of the earth at its equator is nearly 4000 miles (3963.3 miles, or 6386.0 kilometers), and its radius at either pole is only 13.3 miles shorter. This is a variation of only one-third of one percent, and the earth is indeed a very close approximation to a sphere. From the perspective of inhabitants on the earth's rugged surface it may seem difficult to imagine our planet as a *smooth* sphere, but again, the variation in elevation of the surface is very small in comparison with the radial dimension of 4000 miles. Mt. Everest, the highest mountain, rises about 5.5 miles (29,000 feet) above sea level, and the greatest known ocean depth is approximately 6.5 miles. The maximum *relief* of the earth's surface is thus only 12 miles, smaller than the variation in the earth's radius due to departure from sphericity. Moreover, the area occupied by mountains of altitude greater than 10,000 feet, and by ocean "deeps"—depressions 23,000 feet or more below sea level—is extremely small. Virtually all the solid surface lies within an altitude range of 6 miles.

The continents and ocean basins establish a natural division of the earth's solid surface into two ranges of altitude, as can be seen in Fig. 27-1. The division is an unequal one, as the figure shows; nearly 71 percent of the

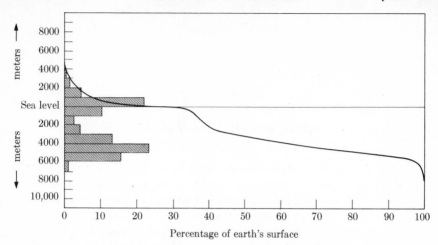

FIG. 27–1.   Graph showing altitude distribution of earth's surface.   The contour line represents the percentage of the surface lying *at least* as high as indicated by the scale on the left, while the histogram shows the percentages lying between the respective altitudes at intervals of 1000 meters. (Redrawn from Sverdrup, Johnson, and Fleming, *The Oceans*, Prentice-Hall, Inc., 1942)

earth's surface lies under the seas. If the surface were only slightly more uniformly distributed, with respect to altitude, it would be entirely covered with water. Associated with each continental mass, and at approximately the same level, is a continental *shelf*, which would be uncovered if the earth were to lose but a small fraction of its water. Continental shelves are portions of continents which simply happen to be submerged, and are rather sharply differentiated from the oceans. They participate in the dynamics of sedimentation and uplift as integral parts of continents. There is surprising uniformity in the altitude distribution of the continents. More than a quarter of the earth's surface, an area approximately equal to that of all the land, lies within a range of 1000 meters (3300 feet), with submerged shelves approximately equalling inland plateaus and low mountains in area. High mountains, exceeding 3000 meters (10,000 feet) in altitude, occupy so little area that they hardly show on the graph of Fig. 27–1.

As the continents are predominantly flat, the oceans are predominantly deep. Well over half the earth's surface lies between 3000 and 6000 meters below sea level, and nearly one-quarter is found within the narrower limits of 4000 to 5000 meters. The ocean floors are by no means smooth, but are crossed by great ridges and deep troughs. The altitude variation of the submerged portions of the earth's surface, as a whole, is roughly the inverse of that of the continents, i.e., the distribution of surface below sea level, in the one case, is approximately analogous to that above sea level, in the other. Some of the greatest plateaus and mountain-like ridges on earth are submerged. The mid-Atlantic Ridge, perhaps the most notable underwater mountain-like feature, roughly bisects the Atlantic Ocean from north to south, contains a vast bend corresponding to the general contour of the ocean's shores, and rises well over 10,000 feet along much of its length. A few of its highest points rise above the water surface to form islands; of these, the Azores are the best known. In addition to long chains, the oceans cover many smaller mountain systems, usually fairly near continents, whose exposed peaks form island arcs and enclose seas. The Antilles, which mark the outer boundary of the Caribbean Sea, form a typical example of this kind of mountain system. Island arcs are especially numerous in the Pacific, and nearly overlap along the entire west and northwest coasts of that ocean. Not all the seas enclosed by island arc formations are shallow and, interestingly enough, most of the known ocean deeps (7000–15,000 meters below sea level) lie along the convex sides of such systems. Despite the presence of vast irregularities in the ocean floor, it is possible to speak of a predominant ocean depth, i.e., the average variation in depth is not large.

Why the earth's surface should be distributed over two general altitude levels, rather than a single level, is still a puzzling question to geologists, although *how* it can be so has become clear. The average density of continental surface rock has been found to be about 2.7 gm/cm^3. A given volume of granite, which may be taken to represent the average, thus weighs 2.7 times as much as an equal volume of water. Are continents, then, supported from below with nearly three times greater force than oceans? Or, are there underlying differences in the composition, and structural strength, of the earth's crust beneath oceans and continents? Interpretation of the earth's surprising surface configuration depends upon knowledge of the pressures, composition, and strengths of materials *inside* the earth. Is there any way to find out what the interior of the earth is like? If so, what *is* it like?

27–2 Irregularities and gravity

If both mind and eye are receptive, many geological questions can be answered by following Desmarest's advice, offered during the controversy over the origin of basalt, to "go and see." Ocean floors are more difficult to explore than land masses, but so many devices and techniques have been developed for this purpose that, in a sense, the bottom of the sea is accessible to direct observation. Deep mines and borings for deep wells (particularly oil wells) have netted useful information concerning rocks whose presence in continents cannot be inferred from surface observations, and they are also used to check the inferences drawn from surface outcrops. Only a very thin outer layer of the earth is accessible to direct observation, however (the deepest wells extend no farther downward than about 4 miles), and to find out what lies below this layer requires the interpretation of indirect evidence. The two general methods which have proved most fruitful of such evidence are determinations of g, the acceleration of gravity, and the study of those disturbances called earthquakes. The two kinds of information which have resulted from these methods supplement each other, and have yielded most of our knowledge about that part of the earth we cannot "see."

The *plumb bob*, which consists simply of a weight suspended by a string, is a surveying instrument that has been used since the days of some of the earliest civilizations. The direction taken by the taut string, called a *plumb line*, should establish the vertical direction at its point of suspension; on a perfectly regular, spherical earth, all possible plumb lines would be directed radially toward the center. It has been clear as long as the law of universal gravitation has been known, however, and was first remarked by Newton, that the irregularities of the earth's surface can affect the direction taken by a plumb line. Moreover, the weight itself, i.e., the gravitational force on the suspended mass, varies in magnitude in a manner reflecting differences in the positions and densities of nearby masses, as has been mentioned in Chapter 4. Thus there is important information to be gained by observing variations in both *direction* and *magnitude* of gravitational force at different points of the earth's surface. Let us first find what can be ascertained by noting deviations in the direction of weight from one place to another.

The plumb bob is used as a device for the determination of latitude. For simplicity in visualizing the method, let us suppose that the measurement is made with the sun at equinox, so that at noon it is directly overhead at the equator. A plumb line at the position whose latitude is to be determined presumably passes through the center of the earth, in the absence of sideward pulls, and thus the angle between the line of sight to the sun at noon and the vertical is just equal to the latitude angle, as indicated in Fig. 27–2. (In practice, the sun is rarely used; observations on the relative position of a known star are much more accurate, because a star is remote and subtends a vanishingly small angle.) The linear distance of point A (Fig. 27–2) from the equator or, almost as simply, the distance between any two points on a north-south line, can also be determined by this method, since the radius of the earth is known. This is the reverse of Eratosthenes' method of determining the size of the earth.

In this method of determining latitude it is tacitly assumed that the earth's surface is regular; nearby mountains either to the north or to the south of the observation point would produce apparent deviations in latitude by virtue of their gravitational attraction on the bob. About a quarter of a century before Cavendish measured the constant of universal

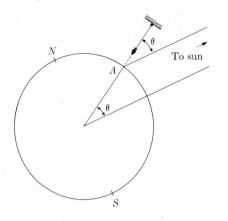

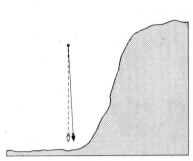

FIG. 27–2. Measurement of latitude by use of a plumb line.

FIG. 27–3. Showing the deflection of a plumb line by a nearby hill (exaggerated).

gravitation, the British Astronomer Royal, Nevil Maskelyne (1732–1811), had attempted to "weigh the earth" by measuring such deviations. Maskelyne found the difference in apparent latitude between two stations, one to the north and one to the south of a steep granite mountain, Schehallian, in Scotland (Fig. 27–3). The mass of the mountain could be estimated from its volume and average density, and Maskelyne compared the downward pull of the earth as a whole with the small sideward pull of the mountain. Assuming that apart from this one hill the earth is an approximately symmetrical sphere of known size, he concluded that its average density is about 4.5 times that of water. This result was some 20 percent smaller than that of Cavendish, and considerably less accurate. Maskelyne's qualitative conclusion provides an interesting sidelight on the status of scientific thought at the time (1774): "It appears from this experiment that the mountain Schehallian exerts a sensible attraction; therefore, from the rules of philosophizing we are to conclude that every mountain, and indeed every particle of earth, is endued with the same property, in proportion to its quantity of matter." It was not that 18th-century scientists doubted Newton's law of gravitation, but that experimental proof on a terrestrial scale was recognized as important.

Latitude determination can also be used to check the results of trigonometric surface surveying for the preparation of maps. It was a failure to achieve just such a check that led to one of the most important and interesting conclusions of modern geology. In the middle of the 19th century Sir George Everest organized what was called the Trigonometrical Survey of India, in order that accurate maps might be made of the whole region. Most of the work was done by the careful triangulation methods regularly used in land surveys, and plumb-line determinations of latitude were made at several points. These points included Kaliana, in the north near the Himalayas, and Kalianpur, some 375 miles due south of Kaliana (see Fig. 27–4). The distance between the two points as determined by the latitude angles and the known radius of the earth did not check with the results of direct land survey; the discrepancy was small, but well above any error of observation. The obvious explanation, in the light of Maskelyne's experiment, was to be found in the differential pull of the vast Himalayan mountains. Kaliana is nearer the mountains, so that an error in latitude measurement due to deviation of the plumb line would be greater there than at Kalianpur. A correction was therefore computed, based on the estimated volume and disposition of the mountains and plateaus to the north, but it turned out to be three times too large. Any reasonable calculation overcompensated to make an error twice as large as before, and in the opposite direction!

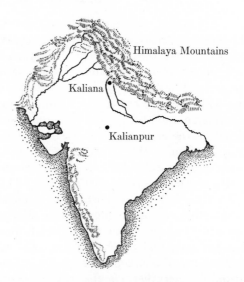

Fig. 27–4. The plumb line is deflected more at Kaliana, but not as much as would be expected from the estimated mass of the Himalayas.

Two somewhat different versions of a possible explanation for this curious result were put forward in 1855. It had been assumed, in computing the gravitational corrections, that rock of the same density was involved everywhere—under the plain, in and under the mountains. But it was already known that the earth as a whole is more dense than its surface rocks. Geologists had also been puzzled about how high mountains could be supported without crushing the rocks underneath them. It was now

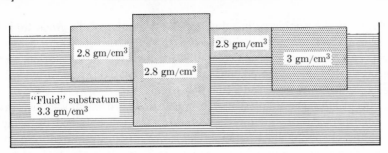

FIG. 27–5. Flotational equilibrium of blocks of different sizes and one of density unlike the others.

pointed out that this problem of stress could be solved, along with that presented by the triangulation discrepancy, if it were assumed that masses of crustal rock float in a denser liquid, like icebergs in the sea. Most of the mass of a floating object is below the surface and, for objects of like density, those that rise highest also extend deepest into the fluid, as indicated in Fig. 27–5. If it is assumed that a large volume of the mountain-forming rock, of relatively low density, extends farther into the dense interior than does the surface rock of the continental plain, then the required gravity correction due to nearness of the Himalayas would be decreased, and the latitude measurements brought into agreement with the results of the land survey. A part of the difference might also be due to somewhat greater density for the rock underlying the plain than that composing the mountains.

The hypothesis that emerged from the difficulties encountered in the survey of India should apply generally if it is correct. Stated simply, it is that the rock masses composing the crust of the earth are in flotational equilibrium in a fluid of greater density. Areas of high altitude stand higher than low-lying areas, on this interpretation, because they are more massive and hence sink more deeply into the subcrust, or because they are less dense than the surrounding lowlands, or both. The condition of flotational equilibrium among crustal rock masses is called *isostasy*, almost exactly the Greek equivalent of the Latin *equilibrium*. The force equilibrium involved is between fluid pressure exerted upward on a rock mass and its weight, the net downward gravitational pull exerted on it by the rest of the earth.

Postponing the issue of whether the earth is really fluid beneath its crust, let us examine some other evidence for and against isostasy. To do so we must consider variations in the magnitude of the earth's gravitational pull as well as variations in direction. We have noted in Chapter 4 that g, the acceleration of gravity, varies slightly with altitude above or below sea level, and varies with latitude for two reasons. The first of these is variation in the earth's radius, due to polar flattening of the globe, and the other is a variable centrifugal effect due to the earth's rotation. All these effects can be very accurately computed for any observation station, and a "theoretical" value of g predicted for that station. To this idealized value, the experimentally observed g must be compared.

Conceptually, the simplest way to measure g is to weigh a known mass on a spring balance, but more accurate values are obtained by using a pendulum of special construction. The *period*, or time required for a complete swing of a pendulum, depends on g in a way that was first set forth by Huygens, who communicated to the Royal Society, in 1664, a measurement of the acceleration of gravity performed by timing a pendulum. In our day a gravity meter, with built-in features to facilitate readings, is a standard piece of geological equipment, and portable models are used in commercial prospecting. Corrections may be applied to an observed value of g to account for local variations in the distribution of mass, and for the quantity of matter between the point of observation and sea level. If the "theoretical value" computed for the altitude and latitude of the station is then subtracted from the measured value, as corrected, the difference is called the *gravity anomaly* for that position of observation.

Individual variations in observed gravity anomalies often have only local significance, but a generalization has emerged from many widespread measurements: continental stations, as a rule, yield values of g which are *lower* than expected, while most sea stations yield values somewhat *larger* than the theoretical predictions. Since the measured values have already been corrected for surface features, this general difference invites interpretation in terms of the underlying rock. In making the calculations needed to correct measured values of g to sea level, it is assumed that below sea level the earth is constructed of materials of the same density, below both oceans and continents. But if the rock underlying ocean basins should be more dense than that underlying the continents, the trend of variation in values of the gravity anomaly, described above, can be understood. The low continental values would be caused by the presence in the continents, both above and below sea level, of rock having less density than the average for the crust as a whole. We shall see that there is additional evidence for this conclusion. If true, the conclusion is consistent with isostasy: the continents behave, on the whole, like relatively light masses which "float" at a higher level, and perhaps extend deeper, than the denser rocks underlying the oceans.

Many *local* variations of g, however, are not compatible with the assumption of a pressure equilibrium, and can only mean that isostasy, if the idea is valid, cannot be complete for all regions of the earth. A study of departures from isostatic equilibrium is a part of the consideration of geological change: *complete* equilibrium would imply a static surface, which we know is not the case. There is some truth in the witty description given by one geologist, who said that isostasy is "a sort of hydrostatic equilibrium, with the water left out and the equilibrium somewhat doubtful." That there is a *tendency* toward isostasy is certainly well established, but there are forces at work other than those given consideration in the development of this principle. To the changes produced by these forces, some familiar, some not as yet understood, we shall return in the next chapter.

27-3   Earthquakes and the interior of the earth

Earthquakes have been known since the earliest times. The Greek *seismos*, whence come our words seismology and seismograph, simply means earthquake. Those quakes whose stories have come down to us were great human catastrophes. The great Lisbon earthquake of 1755, in which North African cities were destroyed as well as Lisbon itself, was experienced with some violence throughout most of Europe and northern Africa. It was probably the most widely felt earth disturbance within historic times. Although by no means the strongest, the most famous earthquake in the United States was that at San Francisco in 1906, which was also important for its effectiveness in focusing attention on the nature of such disturbances. As a result of the intensive study of earthquakes carried out during our century, we have some notion of the nature of the deep interior of the earth. Unfortunately, this knowledge has not yet brought with it the capacity to predict the occurrence of such catastrophic disturbances.

The immediate cause of most earthquakes is the fracture and subsequent relative movement of rock in or near the earth's crust. Commonly, the relative movement of rock masses takes place along an old fracture, known as a *fault*. In the case of the San Francisco earthquake, the fracture occurred right at the surface, and relative movement along it was obvious. Often there is no rupture at the surface, but the fact that underground faults have been discovered lends credibility to the idea that fracture and relative movement are always associated with earthquakes.

Faults, surfaces along which there has been relative displacement of rock, are detected by observing abrupt offset, or even termination, of sedimentary strata or other kinds of rock. Most faults are so old, i.e., movement along them has taken place so long ago, that the fracture has "healed." Where a fault is exposed at the surface, the rock on one side of the line of displacement often erodes faster than that on the other, giving rise to a pattern of differential erosion. The series of sediments and igneous layers shown in Fig. 26–6 terminates in a fault. Figure 27–6 shows an old fault with displaced sediments. In some cases relative motion along a fault may take place so gradually that no noticeable tremors

FIG. 27–6. Faulted sandstone beds, Colorado, with vertical displacement of about 10 ft. (U. S. Geological Survey.)

are produced. Deep wells are sometimes sheared gradually and silently, for example. There is generally some adhesion between the layers of rock on the two sides of a fault, however, which will resist shearing under moderate stress. When stress sufficient to cause movement does build up there may be a sudden break, and consequent release of enough energy to set up a major (or minor) earthquake. This energy is propagated through the earth as a series of waves, similar to those described in Chapter 16.

Seismic (earthquake) waves present more complicated possibilities than do sound and light waves. In the first place, solids may transmit longitudinal (pressure) waves like those of sound, and also transverse waves. In addition, the earth can propagate waves along its surface. These surface waves, more complicated than either longitudinal or transverse interior waves, yield important information about the nature of the earth's crust.

By learning to distinguish the kinds of seismic waves, and by measuring the times required for each kind to reach a series of observers at various distances and directions from a given center of disturbance, geologists have determined their characteristic wave patterns and velocities. From extensive observations made at large numbers of stations, it has proved possible to make deductions about the nature of the earth's interior. After a brief look at the main features of the methods of observation, we shall proceed to the conclusions that have been reached about this fascinating topic.

Earthquakes are recorded on instruments called seismographs, which are now constructed with such sensitivity that they are able to indicate vibrations much too small to be felt with the unaided senses. While much ingenuity is required to design instruments of great accuracy, in principle the seismograph is very simple—it merely takes advantage of Newton's first law, the principle of inertia. A mass is supported in a manner that makes it as free as possible to stand still while motion takes place in the earth at the position of support. A record of the relative motion between the nearly still mass and the moving earth may then be obtained. A possible way in which this could be accomplished is indicated in Fig. 27–7(a). The case and support shown in the diagram are mounted on a concrete block, which is anchored firmly to bedrock. The mass is suspended from the case by a flexible spring which does not transmit tremors experienced by the case, i.e., by the earth. In practice, recording of the relative motion is done by less crude means than the pointer (attached to the mass) indicated in Fig. 27–7. An amplifying device is usually used to increase accuracy, and a continuous record, on which time intervals are marked, is

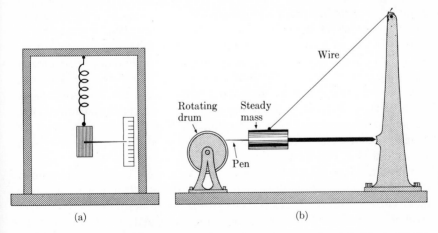

Fig. 27–7. The principle of (a) the vertical seismograph, and (b) the horizontal pendulum seismograph.

obtained on paper rolled on a slowly turning drum. The seismograph of Fig. 27-7(a) will respond only to vertical motions, and to record vibrations in a horizontal plane a "horizontal pendulum" [Fig. 27-7(b)] is used. With three instruments, one for vertical vibrations and two for vibrations in each of two mutually perpendicular horizontal directions, a complete record of all the components of earthquake motion can be obtained.

It is possible, of course, that a suspended weight or a pendulum may execute vibrations of its own. In either case, however, motions other than those *characteristic* of the given mass suspension system are difficult to set up and will not continue. The characteristic vibration period of a horizontal pendulum is determined largely by its mass and length, and the vibration rate of a spring-suspended weight depends on its mass and the stiffness of the spring. If the characteristic vibration period of a mass suspended in either way is long compared with that of the earth tremors to be recorded, the inertia of the mass is highly effective, and the vibrations recorded will portray faithfully the motions of the earth itself.

By intercomparison of many seismograph records and application of the general theory of elastic waves in solid and fluid media, geologists have learned to recognize and interpret these earthquake vibration patterns. Waves of various kinds originate simultaneously at the source of the disturbance, and are propagated along or through the earth at velocities that depend on the density and elasticity of the media traversed as well as on the nature of the wave. Those seismic waves transmitted with greatest velocity through a given medium are longitudinal or pressure waves (designated P), like sound in air. These are the first to reach a distant station, hence are recorded first by the seismograph. The transverse, or "shear" waves (designated S) travel more slowly and are received later. Seismographic patterns are often complicated by reflections of pressure waves from the surface of the earth, and by the fact that shear waves are also reflected by a boundary of solid matter, much as light is reflected from an air-glass surface. Last of all to arrive from a given point of disturbance at a seismograph station are the surface waves. These travel most slowly, and the vibrations transmitted along the surface are relatively slow. Each surface vibration makes a long wave on the recorded pattern, hence surface waves are designated L, for "long." The patterns that might be received at different stations from a disturbance at a point A in the earth are indicated in Fig. 27-8.

The path of each signal corresponding to a wave transmitted through the earth's interior (P or S) is curved, not straight. The reason for this is made clear in Fig. 27-9. As a wave spreads out from its source, the corresponding wave front would be a sphere if the propagation velocity were the same in all parts of the medium. Actually this velocity increases with depth below the earth's surface, because of increasing pressure. Since the

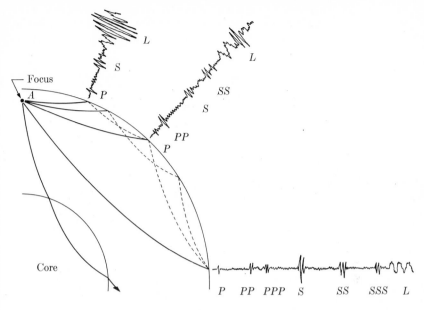

FIG. 27–8. Showing seismograph records that might be received from an earthquake focus. *PP* is a once-reflected pressure wave, etc. The paths of *L* waves are not shown. (After Umbgrove, *Pulse of the Earth*, Martinus Nijhoff, 1947.)

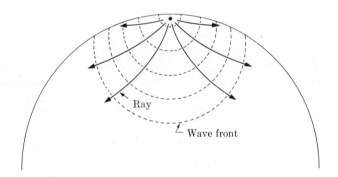

FIG. 27–9. Section through the earth showing that the wave fronts of a seismic wave are not spherical, but spread faster with increasing depth. The path of the wave toward any particular station (a ray) is therefore curved.

direction of any wave propagation always remains perpendicular to the wave front, the path of any "ray" is curved, as shown.

Now, what can be ascertained about the interior of the earth from a study of seismic records? Neglecting some of the complications, we shall note the behavior of each of the three kinds of waves separately, assuming

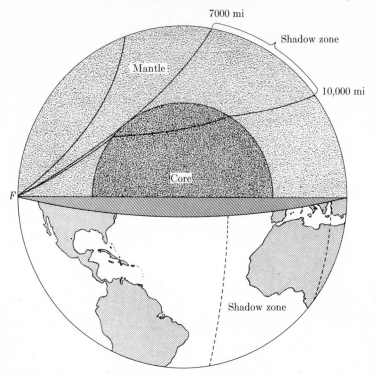

FIG. 27–10. Structure of the interior and shadow zone for a wave whose focus is at F.

that these have been properly identified by seismologists and traced to an origin, or focus, at some point at or near the earth's surface. Let us first consider the longitudinal pressure wave, usually the first to be recorded by a distant seismograph.

Suppose there is an earthquake at the focus F (Fig. 27–10) which sets up compressional P waves in the earth. Stations up to 7000 miles away, as measured on the earth's surface, will receive these waves at times which the geologist would find consistent with his past experience with P waves. The wave spreads out with increasing speed below the surface, and its signal to any particular station follows the curved arc shown by one of the solid lines. At stations beyond 7000 miles, however, these waves will arrive much later than would be predicted on the basis of a velocity which increases gradually with the density of the earth, and at greatly reduced intensity. At a distance of about 10,000 miles the waves are again received in strength, but as much as 4 minutes later than would be expected if they traveled as fast as they do to the nearer stations, i.e., to those 7000 miles or less from the origin. The region of the globe lying from

7000 to 10,000 surface miles away from the center of any quake has there-fore been called the "shadow zone" for P waves. The existence of such a zone can be understood on the basis of an optical analogy: if a glass sphere or a spherical flask filled with water is suspended near a source of light, it will produce a ring of shadow on a nearby screen (Fig. 27–11). Light which is not intercepted by the sphere will illuminate the screen in the normal way, but those rays which pass through the sphere are refracted, or "bent," in a manner that concentrates them within a central spot. This case is simpler than that of the earth's shadow zone; here, the rays follow straight paths, since air, water, and glass have uniform optical properties. Still, the analogy is striking. The sphere corresponds to what is called the *core* of the earth, an internal region which must have a rather sharp boundary, marking a discontinuity about 1800 miles below the surface.

We have said that the speed of the P waves increases with increasing pressure, other things being equal. But P waves are *slowed* in passing through the core, much as light waves are slowed in passing through the sphere shown in Fig. 27–11. Is the pressure in the core less than that in the outer part of the globe? This is extremely unlikely. Is it therefore com-posed of material of a different kind? A clue to this question is provided by the behavior of S waves, the transverse, or shear, vibrations.

The thick layer of the earth lying outside the core, now called the *mantle*, transmits shear waves in much the same way that P waves are transmitted, although somewhat more slowly. Seismograph stations up to 7000 surface miles from an earthquake center record S waves, a fact of great significance, since transverse mechanical waves can be transmitted only by rigid media (solids). Fluids, which by definition do not resist changes of shape, are quite incapable of supporting waves of this kind. The con-clusion can therefore be drawn that at least the outer 1800 miles of the earth is essentially solid. The evidence of earthquake records has thus

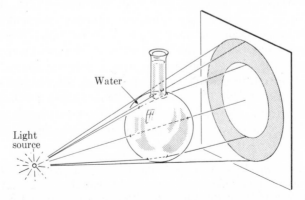

Water

Light source

FIG. 27–11. Optical analogy of the shadow zone.

made untenable an older conception of an earth consisting of a thin crust of rock surrounding a molten interior. In the light of this evidence, we shall have to review the subject of isostasy, or flotational equilibrium. Magma that occasionally appears at the surface or has crystallized to form igneous rocks most probably can have its origin only in isolated pockets.

The behavior of S waves is especially revealing with respect to the earth's core: stations more than 7000 miles from a center of disturbance receive no direct S waves at all. Any transverse waves that do arrive at such distant stations can be identified as S waves which have penetrated a relatively small distance within the earth and have been reflected from the surface. It seems certain that the core cannot transmit shear waves although it does carry compressional waves, and in this respect it behaves like a true liquid. Actually, one can conclude from this evidence only that the core is fluid at its outer boundary. It could contain a liquid sheath, opaque to S waves, and still possess further layering, or even a solid center. Such a structure would not be accessible to the kind of indirect examination we have discussed.*

Information about the exterior layers of the earth is derived from the study of all three types of seismic waves, perhaps most significantly the "long" surface (L) waves. The material immediately underlying continents, down to an average depth of about 10 miles, exhibits considerable uniformity in its seismic wave transmission properties. Apart from very local variations due to the presence of unusually deep layers of sediments, this uniformity is sufficient to justify classification of the rock material as a single type, called granitic. This does not mean that it necessarily consists of granite, but that its wave transmission properties are very similar to those of granite. In the rock layer immediately underlying ocean basins, earthquake waves are propagated at speeds which differ markedly from those observed in the granitic layer under continents. The difference is most evident in the Pacific region, but again there is sufficient uniformity so that all ocean basin rock may be classified together. Since its wave transmission properties resemble those of basalt, the rock layer underlying oceans is called *basaltic*. This layer reaches a depth of approximately 20 miles and apparently extends under the granitic continental masses, as indicated in Fig. 27–12. This outermost 20-mile layer is called the *crust* of the earth. Its existence as a rather distinct region has been made probable by the detection of a fairly sharp discontinuity at its base: L

---

*Very faint P waves received within the shadow zone do indicate the presence of an inner core of radius about 800 miles. For a nontechnical account of internal structure details of the earth which have been omitted here, see K. D. Bullen, *The Interior of the Earth*, Scientific American, September, 1955.

waves are transmitted *only* by the crust. Earthquakes that originate at depths greater than 20 miles, i.e., inside the upper part of the mantle, set up extremely faint surface waves if any at all. The detailed behavior of P and S waves also shows that the earth's crust and mantle are sharply differentiated, i.e., the same *discontinuity* is betrayed.

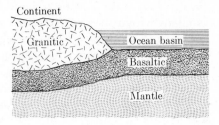

FIG. 27–12. Apparent general structure of the earth's crust.

A general picture of the body of the earth, embodying three main divisions, has thus evolved from the long and careful study of seismic wave transmission. First of these divisions is the *core*, of radius slightly exceeding one-half the radius of the earth itself, and liquid at least in its outer regions. Second is the *mantle*, rigid enough to support transverse waves, extending from the core to within approximately 20 miles of the surface. Last is the *crust*, composed of rocks similar to those we see on the surface itself, in which continental masses are distinguishable from a lower basaltic layer by the presence of a granitic layer which is absent, or nearly so, under the ocean basins. Within both the mantle and the core there are gradual variations in pressure, density, and probably in chemical composition. These regions also are known to contain further discontinuities, although none of them as major in character as those setting off the three principal divisions.

There is no evidence of rock fracture at very great depths in the earth. Seismologists are able to locate what is called the "depth of focus" for each earthquake, and it is known that the great majority of quakes originate in the crust. The frequency of occurrence decreases with increasing depth, but earthquake foci have been established at depths ranging from the surface down to 435 miles, roughly one-tenth the distance to the center. In our discussion of crustal deformation in Chapter 28, we shall return to the possible significance of seismic disturbances of deep focus.

27–4 Density, composition, and plasticity

Henry Cavendish found that the earth has an average density 5.5 times that of water; his result was in very good accord with the accepted modern value of 5.52. The average density of rocks in the crust is found to be only about 2.7, less than half the density of the earth as a whole. The interior of the earth, then, must be very much more dense than the materials we find occurring naturally at the surface. The densest ores, for example, are generally no greater in density than the earth's average. It is true that rocks are compressible under great pressure, but compression alone could hardly produce the high densities which must be present in central zones, as inferred from the average of the whole. There is a gradual change in density with depth in the mantle which may be largely due to pressure, but it is likely that the core is predominantly composed of the heaviest of the common elements, more dense, because of tremendous pressures, than they would be at the surface.

Careful analysis of seismic data, together with inferences concerning the distribution of the earth's mass drawn from the way it behaves gravitationally as a part of the solar system, yield the variation of density with depth which is shown in Fig. 27–13. The details of the graph are not entirely certain, especially within the core, but there is little doubt that it represents the earth's general mass distribution. The question of density variation in the earth is much less difficult to answer than that of the variation in composition which accompanies it. A hint as to the internal composition of both mantle and core may come from the analysis of meteorites, on the assumption that many of these pieces of extraterrestrial matter are fragments of a planet that was somehow broken up in the distant past. This assumption is consistent with the fact that most meteors travel in the same direction as the planets. Most meteorites, called

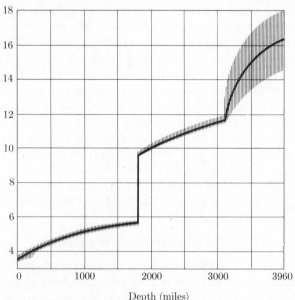

Depth (miles)

FIG. 27–13. Density of the earth varies with depth. The gray region indicates uncertainty. The discontinuity within the core is shown by behavior of very faint pressure waves in the shadow zone, but its nature is still in doubt. (After K. E. Bullen, *Scientific American*, September, 1955.)

"stony," are much like our own crustal rocks, but others, called "iron," consist predominantly of iron and nickel in a concentration not otherwise found in the earth's crust. It seems probable that the earth's heavy core may be composed almost entirely of molten iron and nickel. Elements of even greater density are not ruled out, of course, but they are probably rare in comparison with iron and nickel.

Now let us return to some of the questions raised by the hypothesis of isostasy. Is it possible for the mantle to act like a liquid in the establishment of flotational equilibrium, and like a solid in the transmission of transverse waves? There is still another argument for a rigid mantle which cannot be ignored. If the earth were fluid beneath its thin crust it would be subject, as a result of the gravitational attractions of the moon and sun, to tides similar to those observed in the ocean. The tidal bulge on each side of the earth, roughly in line with the centers of the earth and moon, as indicated on the exaggerated diagram of Fig. 4–9, should then be of a size corresponding to fluid flow. Earth tides have been detected and measured quantitatively, and their extent is no greater than that to be expected if the earth were a solid sphere of hard steel!

We have noted that any solid can become somewhat plastic under sufficient pressure, and that amorphous solids such as glass actually tend to flow a little in all circumstances. Cold pitch or tar will shatter like glass under the stress of a sharp blow, but if left alone it gradually assumes the shape of its container or spreads out on its supporting surface. Thus rigidity of the mantle is possible with respect to sudden changes, even the daily changes of the tides, but at the same time the mantle may flow enough to provide a slow trend toward flotational equilibrium, especially if the material it contains is glassy rather than crystalline. The discontinuity marking the boundary between the mantle and the crust may then very possibly result from a change in the state of crystallization of materials present, rather than a sharp change in chemical composition. Major crustal movements take place extremely slowly. As a single example of relatively rapid motion, consider the Scandinavian peninsula, which, in some places, is rising out of the sea at rates of a foot or more per century. As little as 10,000 years ago an ice cap covered that part of the globe, and added its vast weight to the crust. Now that the ice cap has melted and its mass is distributed uniformly over the oceans, upward crustal movement of the formerly glaciated area takes place in the direction of restoring equilibrium. The rise of the peninsula is apparently a trend toward isostasy, not yet completed after 10,000 years. Such a time scale is compatible with the concept of the mantle as an amorphous solid, slightly plastic, yet sufficiently rigid to transmit shear waves readily.

27-5 Temperatures within the earth

The question of the temperature of the interior of the earth is closely related to theories of its origin and its age. It was once held, with considerable conviction, that the earth originated as a molten mass, perhaps white hot, and that a calculation of the probable time of cooling would give us an idea as to how long ago the earth was born. This relatively simple view is now held in serious doubt, and the discovery of sources of energy other than purely thermal (e.g., radioactivity) has brought in question whether the earth is even cooling at all at the present time. It *is* known, at least, that the earth is hotter inside than at its surface. Measurements made in deep mines and wells indicate that the temperature increases by about 1°C per 100 feet, although there are wide geographical variations in the rate of increase. The existence of hot springs and geysers shows that in many places there are relatively high temperatures very near the surface. Molten rock emerges from volcanos at temperatures of 1000°C or more, although, as we have said, magma probably exists only in pockets in the crust.

The relation of molten magma to the earth's rigid mantle has been the subject of much speculation. Unlike ice, which occupies a smaller volume when it has turned to water, rock expands on melting, so that an increase of pressure would raise its melting point. Since high pressure would therefore tend to maintain the solid state in rock at higher temperatures than would otherwise be possible, it is conceivable that the base of the crust is at about 1400°C, and is solid only because of the pressures that are ordinarily experienced at that depth. If the pressure were lowered locally, melting might take place. The accompanying volume increase could be accommodated most readily in an upward direction, further melting of crustal rock could take place, and volcanic activity at the surface could finally result. Although the argument is plausible, it is by no means sure that most pockets of magma are produced in this way. As an alternative, the melting might be produced by an unusually large local supply of energy from a concentration of radioactive material.

The interior temperatures of the mantle and of the core are largely a matter of educated guesswork—guesswork within the limits of logical possibilities. The temperature probably increases with depth in the mantle, in a manner consistent with the existence of the solid state at such great pressures. The core is molten, at least on its outside, where melting could probably occur at about 3000°C. Temperatures within the core cannot be estimated from evidence now at hand.

Is the earth cooling off? A body warmer than its surroundings always loses heat, and it would seem that this question should be answered in the affirmative. While the earth's surface temperature is maintained primarily by heat from the sun, there is some warming of the crust from below. Moreover, heat energy is supplied continuously by radioactivity (see Chapter 29). There is a paradox here: if the interior of the earth were as rich in radioactive elements as the crust is known to be, we should expect the heat supplied in this way to overbalance that conducted through the crust to the outside. Perhaps the temperature of the interior is rising, not falling! In any case, the rate of change in internal temperature must be very small. The earth must have been much as it is now, with respect to interior temperature distribution, as long as it has had its present structural characteristics.

This chapter has been devoted to the characteristics of the earth that do *not* change, or at least have probably not changed very much during geologic time. To obtain any estimate of the probable duration of that time, we must now examine the changing features of the globe.

27-6 Summary

The surface of the earth is divided rather sharply into two levels characteristic of the continents and the ocean basins. One important tool for determining what lies below the visible surface is the plumb bob or simple pendulum, by means of which the direction and magnitude of g, the acceleration of gravity, can be measured. The gravitational force on any object is affected by the configuration and density of matter in the neighborhood of the object, and small variations in g yield information on the distribution of rock masses with respect to density. It was thus found that mountains have "roots," and tend to "float" in more dense rock; this is an application of the concept of *isostasy*, or flotational equilibrium. Most of our knowledge of the deeper interior of the earth comes from analysis of earthquake waves. Earthquakes apparently originate in motion along fractures in the earth's crust called *faults*; the disturbance sets up longitudinal and transverse waves in the body of the earth, together with surface waves, unless the earthquake focus is too deep. These waves are transmitted in such a way as to indicate discontinuities in earth structure: a dense *core*, probably liquid, a plastic *mantle*, and a crystalline crust, mainly basaltic, in which the continents have granitic roots. Variations in density, pressure, and temperature which would yield the observed wave transmission are inferred indirectly.

REFERENCES

BULLEN, K. E., "The Interior of the Earth," *Scientific American*, Sept., 1955.
DALY, R. A., "Strength and Structure of the Earth."
GILLULY, J., A. C. WATERS, and A. O. WOODFORD, *Principles of Geology*, especially Chapters 3 and 18.
HEISKANEN, W. A., "The Earth's Gravity," *Scientific American*, Sept., 1955.
LEET, L. D., and S. JUDSON, *Physical Geology*, especially Chapter 13.
SHAPLEY, H., and H. E. HOWARTH, *A Source Book in Astronomy*, pp. 133–139 (Maskelyne).

1. Why would an equal-arm balance necessarily fail to determine g?

2. The radius of the earth is about 4000 mi. A gravity meter in a plane a mile above the earth shows that g is smaller, by about 2 parts in 4000 (0.05 percent), than at the surface. At the bottom of a mine a mile deep g is also smaller than at the surface, although only by about 1 part in 8000 (0.0125 percent). Both differences from surface readings may be interpreted in terms of a spherically symmetric earth, i.e., one that shows no local irregularities. How?

3. Some places have been found where a plumb line is deflected away from a hill toward a plain. Can you suggest a possible explanation for such behavior?

4. A floating body displaces its own weight of fluid. From this principle and the definition of density as mass per unit volume, find what fraction of a granitic mass, density 2.7 gm/cm³, would be submerged in a fluid of density 3.3 gm/cm³ under conditions of isostasy. [$Ans.$: approximately 0.8]

5. Assume for simplicity that a mountain range, of average elevation 10,000 ft, is buoyed up by a granitic "root" in a substratum of density 3.3 gm/cm³. How deep is the root, on the average?

6. If the mountain range of Exercise 5 lost 5000 ft by erosion, what would its elevation be when isostatic balance had been restored? [$Ans.$: 9000 ft]

7. Why are three different seismographs necessary for the full recording of earthquake vibrations at a given station? The displacement in pressure waves is at right angles to that in shear waves; how can it happen that both kinds of waves may be recorded by the same single instrument?

8. The time lag between receipt of the first P and S waves may be used to compute the distance of a quake focus from a seismographic station. Can a single station locate the focus in this way? Explain.

9. With reference to Fig. 27–13, suppose the true density in the inner core were represented by the lower boundary of the shaded area, while that of the outer part of the core is represented by the upper boundary of shading. How could the total mass be accounted for in this way, even though the change from the black line is so much greater in one place than another?

10. List all the arguments you can against the idea that the earth is a molten mass covered by a thin layer of crustal rock.

CHAPTER 28

THE GEOLOGIC PAST

The deciphering of geological history is not altogether different from research in human history, or human prehistory, except that the documents are of another sort and the time scale is enormously greater. The techniques of geological investigation involve almost all the principles and devices of physics and chemistry, yet its interaction with biological science is even more profound. The sciences of the earth and of life have contributed to each other in a very fundamental way; it was from geological data that the concept of the evolution of living forms arose. Charles Darwin was a geologist before he became a biologist, and he was greatly influenced by the ideas of Hutton and his geological school of "gradualists."

28-1 Fossils and the geologic column

The practical use of fossils in the correlation of geological strata led to the fundamental idea of evolutionary chronology, first in geology, then in living forms. William Smith's recognition of characteristic assemblages of fossils may be called empirical; he used them simply as convenient identification marks. Cuvier and Brongniart, with greater prior knowledge of biologic forms, saw not only that there were systematic differences in the fossil contents of various rock strata, but also that fossils in upper and presumably younger sedimentary beds are more like the animals now living than are those in deeper layers. In other words, they recognized a succession of living forms, each apparently corresponding to the duration in time of a particular species of living organism, most typically a shelled marine animal. These successions were by no means regular or of equal span in time, but the generalization seemed broadly applicable to all observed species, both in the Paris basin and in England.

Geologists next asked themselves whether the principle of relative dating of strata, on the basis of fossil content, applies on a world scale or only locally. Many difficulties and false clues were encountered in the search for an answer, but it soon became firmly established that sedimentary rocks could be correlated the world over by the observation of similar assemblages of fossils. There are actually relatively few fossils found in every continent, and due attention must be paid to differences in climate. Still, there seems to have been plenty of time in each geologic age for free-swimming marine forms to traverse all available parts of the globe. The overlapping of fossil content from one age to another, and from one temperature zone to another, is often as helpful as the occurrence of a species which survived for a relatively short time, although the latter serves as an excellent time marker whenever it is found. Marine sediments interbedded with land-laid strata make it possible to correlate land fossils, but the greatest contribution to the over-all geological picture has come from remains of animals which once inhabited the changing margins of the seas. Literally hundreds of thousands of fossil species have been identified and classified with respect to their duration in geological history. A much smaller number of *guide*, or *index*, fossils serve to determine the period of deposition of sedimentary rock layers anywhere in the world.

It was by application of the laws of superposition and original horizontality, the techniques of geologic mapping, and a study of the succession of fossils that the geologists of the 19th century were able to piece together what they called a "standard geologic column." At any given place sediments corresponding to a particular age might be missing either because they were never deposited or because they were uplifted and eroded away before the next age, but the entire column was designed to represent the various layers of rock that would be found, one above the other, in an ideal section where no erosion had ever taken place. The subdivisions are somewhat arbitrary, and the number of such divisions has been changed as information has increased. Initially they represented, for the most part, recognizably different formations found in Great Britain and on the continent of Europe. Gaps have been filled in as a result of geological exploration in other parts of the world, but it is perhaps more astonishing that the general scheme has continuing world-wide applicability than that modifications and extensions have been necessary. Table 28–1 shows the main divisions of the column in the terminology recognized by the U. S. Geological Survey. Most of the divisions called *periods* are designated by place names where characteristic rocks were found. This table does not have to be memorized for our purpose; it is inserted in the text as a reference to aid our discussion of geologic history.

Two features of the geologic column must be noted at the outset. First, we must understand that fossils can supply only *relative* dates, without regard to absolute time intervals in years. Ancient rock systems in which fossils are lacking or at least very sparse can only be grouped together, on this basis, at the bottom of the column. Second, the column is made up exclusively of sedimentary rocks; igneous rocks can be included in this system only on the basis of their positions in relation to sedimentary strata. At first it was thought that the rocks below the Cambrian (see table), in which no fossils could be found, represented the original crust formed by the cooling of molten earth and were thus in a sense igneous. This turned

TABLE 28–1

GEOLOGIC COLUMN AND TIME SCALE

Era	Period	Dominant life	Years ago (in millions of years)
Cenezoic ("recent life")	Pleistocene (Quaternary) Tertiary (5 subdivisions)	Man Mammals Flowering plants	1 60
Mesozoic ("middle life")	Cretaceous Jurassic Triassic	Reptiles (Dinosaurs)	200
Paleozoic ("ancient life")	Permian Carboniferous Devonian Silurian Ordovician Cambrian	Fish Invertebrates	500
Precambrian { Proterozoic Archeozoic	Oldest rocks	Fossils rare or absent	3500(?)

out to be quite wrong. Much of Precambrian rock is indeed undifferentiated, and intense search for fossils has yielded substantial evidence only for some algae and a few wormlike creatures, but it is now clear that geologic change took place in those ancient times as well as more recently, the only difference being the absence or paucity of living forms. The earliest records of geological history are thus difficult to read, but evidence has been established of sediments, seas, and vast mountain ranges, all long since leveled and largely covered over. The study of geology throws no direct light on the nature of an "original crust," if indeed there ever was such a thing. It is as true today as it was for James Hutton that "we find no sign of a beginning."

Before considering the kind of changes that bring into being the landscape of any given age, let us consider the fundamental Law of Uniform

FIG. 28–1. Wall of the Grand Canyon of the Colorado River. The dotted lines indicate buried erosion surfaces, called *unconformities*, which mark missing chapters of the rock record. Two faults are also indicated on this photograph. (U. S. Geological Survey.)

Change in a more general way than we were able to do in Chapter 26. Simply stated, it is that past changes in the earth's crust were brought about by forces now in operation. These changes are not really uniform, but they are extraordinarily slow. For example, it is estimated that the Grand Canyon (Fig. 28–1), as much as 6000 feet deep, was cut by the Colorado River at the rate of about one foot per 3000 years; the Himalaya Mountains may have been elevated at the greater rate of one foot per 500 years. There have been periods of great mountain building and periods of widespread submergence of continents by shallow seas, periods of great igneous activity and other times of relative quiet. But "catastrophes" have been infrequent and certainly local; the earthquakes and volcanic eruptions of our own day may easily be more violent than is typical of the geologic past as a whole, although less common than during some periods. The climate of the earth has varied—again slowly; at some periods it has been much more mild than at present, while continental glaciation has taken place several times, at least twice in the Precambrian era as well as much later. All these changes seem to have occurred in vast cycles, never repeating in detail but involving the same general processes again and again. Some of the forces at work to produce the changes are easily understood; for others we have as yet only the most vague and unsatisfactory hypotheses.

The right-hand column of Table 28–1 contains absolute dates in years, although only relative dating can be achieved by means of rock fossil content. The principles involved in the absolute dating of rocks are those of radioactivity and of crystallization. Some minerals present in igneous rock contain radioactive elements such as uranium, presumably segregated into crystals at the time the rock solidified. Uranium "decays" at a measurable rate, as we shall see in Chapter 29, into a series of identifiable products, so that analysis of a suitably fresh and previously unexposed sample to find the ratio between the original element and its products may be used to determine the age of the crystal. Thus, in favorable circumstances, an absolute date may be given for the formation of an intrusive rock. The sedimentary strata that have been invaded by the magma must be older than the measured igneous sample, hence a lower limit can be placed on their own absolute age. The durations of the various eras in years are only rough estimates, designed to be consistent with the measured ages of igneous rocks formed within the respective eras.

28–2 Some gross movements of the earth's crust

Many sedimentary rocks, by their fossil content of marine animals, show clearly that they were originally deposited in shallow seas, yet most of the rocks that we can see are well above sea level, some at altitudes of thousands of feet. Since lithification these strata have been somehow uplifted to their present elevations. On the other hand, the most obvious processes taking place around us are those of *gradation*, or leveling; mountains are scoured by snow, rain, ice, and wind, and the debris is carried downhill toward the seas and deposited as sediments. The processes of erosion and sedimentation constantly tend toward uniformity—toward the reduction of vast mountains to level plains. There is actual evidence that such leveling has been accomplished, not once but many times.

Much of what we call scenery is due to *differential erosion*. No two kinds of rock are equally resistant to the effects of water, ice, or wind, and it is the harder rock that gives rise to cliffs, isolated hills, and the ledges over which streams plunge to produce waterfalls. Most kinds of sedimentary strata are eroded more easily than hard igneous rock, and what we see of many high mountains is primarily their granite "cores." But in time even the hardest rock succumbs to erosion and weathering, and in the long run our landscape depends as much on the forces of uplift, the undoing of gradation, as on erosion itself. As a rule the processes of uplift are less obvious than the visible silt in streams, and they are of several kinds. Actually, movements of the earth's crust can go in either direction, toward *subsidence* as well as uplift, and horizontal crustal movements are observed as well.

Evidence of vertical movement of the earth's crust is often particularly noticeable in coastal regions. Shorelines vary greatly, but most of their features are due either to deposition or to erosion. A typical erosion feature is a wave-cut cliff, often with sea caves or arches produced by differential erosion. Sandy beaches and tidal flats are typical of seashore deposition. Either or both of these formations are found well above the present shoreline in California, Maine, Scotland, and many other places. In tropical climates they are frequently accompanied by elevated coral reefs. These features result from land uplift, not from a shrinking of the oceans, as is clear for two reasons. In the first place, their occurrence is extremely uneven. Secondly, there is equally convincing evidence of the submergence of old coastlines. The estuaries of numerous rivers along the north central part of the eastern coast of the United States (Hudson, Delaware, Chesapeake Bay, etc.) are clearly submerged valleys. Submerged rivers that once flowed through San Francisco Bay and some of the seas in the neighborhood of Borneo and Java can be seen from the air under favorable conditions. In many places, such as the coast of Maine, there is evidence of a succession of past periods of submergence and elevation. Some of the movements now going on are sufficiently rapid to be measured. We have mentioned the elevation of most of Scandinavia, occurring at the rate of about one foot per century, and the base of the Danish peninsula is subsiding at a measurable rate. An interesting example of crustal movement is furnished by the water level of Lake Superior. Old coastlines have emerged in the north, while stream inlets are being submerged in the south; the whole basin thus appears to be slowly tilting.

While slow "warps" of the earth's crust are most readily measured in coastal areas, the most conspicuous record of cumulative movements lies in the crumpled folds of sedimentary rock strata visible in mountain chains. When we remember that these sedimentary beds must have been deposited in horizontal layers, their present positions and orientations constitute evidence for vast changes in the crustal rocks. As a rule, the folds have been greatly modified by erosion, even during the periods of folding, so that reconstruction of the missing portions is sometimes necessary for visualization of an entire series of strata (see Fig. 28–2). It is certain that the gentle tilting accompanying broad warps of the crust can develop into the sharp convolutions visible in mountains, since some strata can be traced continuously from plains to highly distorted layers. The rock layers overlying some continental areas may often be older than the mountain ranges which border them, however. There has been much variety in the intensity of crustal movement in any geological age, and equally great variety from one age to another. Many of the broad warps can be attributed to isostatic adjustment, made necessary by loss of weight caused by erosion or the melting of vast glaciers. Others cannot be so easily explained, and the whole question of the intense folding accompanying the formation of most mountains is so complicated that we shall postpone it until we have considered other manifestations of crustal movement.

Broad crustal warping is apparently not accompanied by any fracture of rock masses; the forces involved do not exceed the flexibility of the rocks. In our discussion of the origin of earthquakes, however, we have seen that breaks in the crust do occur, and we have called any such break along which there has been relative motion a *fault*. Motion along a fault

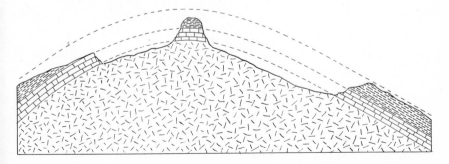

Fig. 28–2. Erosion modifies the landscape as the strata are warped.

may be sudden, setting up a tremor, or it may be imperceptibly slow. Even in the most severe earthquakes, observable fault displacements are small—rarely more than a few feet. Old faults are found, however, along which the relative motion has amounted to many miles. An important kind of fault involved in mountain building is developed from a sharp fold, as shown in Fig. 28–3; the fold has been ruptured, and the upper rocks have apparently moved over those underneath. An oblique fracture of this kind, in which the upper segment of rock is moved up over the lower, is called a *thrust* fault. In other kinds of fracture, the displacement may be in the opposite direction, or the motion may be very nearly horizontal. Whatever the kind of fault, the amount of relative motion can be determined by measuring the offset of formations that were once continuous. A horizontal displacement of roughly 65 miles along the Great Glen Fault in Scotland (Fig. 28–4) has been inferred from such measurements. The vast thrust fault shown in Fig. 28–4, a relic of a great mountain range that once continued from Scotland toward Scandinavia, older than the Great Glen Fault, has been broken and displaced by motion along the latter. Other evidence for the motion has been deduced by matching the schist and granite formations on either side of the Great Glen. There is little or no indication of how much time was required for this displacement, and of course one cannot conclude that the remainder of the coastline has been unchanged; modern details are shown on the hypothetical map only to identify the extent of the motion. This is an extreme example of relative horizontal movement along a single fault.

Some mountain ranges, although not most, are based on structures called *"fault blocks."* Classic examples are furnished by the Basin Ranges in the United States, west of the Rockies. Of these, the most conspicuous example is the Sierra Nevada range, which runs north and south in eastern

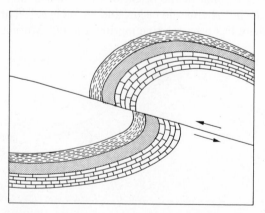

FIG. 28–3. A thrust fault developed from a sharp fold.

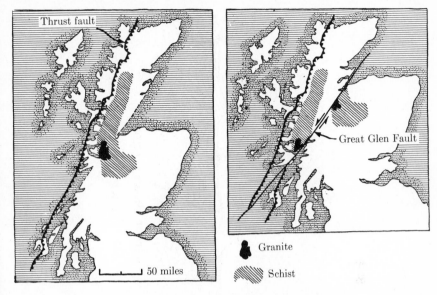

Granite

Schist

50 miles

Fig. 28–4. On the left is a map of Scotland before movement along the Great Glen Fault as inferred from the present formations, indicated on the right. (After W. A. Kennedy.)

California. There has been extensive relative vertical movement along a great system of fractures which reaches deep into the crust. The rock mass on one side of a fault line has been greatly elevated with respect to that on the other side, by this movement. Some of these fault-block systems are represented schematically in Fig. 28–5. The surfaces have now been modified by erosion—glacial erosion in the most elevated areas. The Sierras themselves have been sculptured from a tilted block of crust some 400 miles long and 40 to 60 miles wide, whose eastern edge has been lifted about 2 miles relative to the adjoining block. The western edge of the tilted block has been buried beneath the sediments of the central California valley. Much of the rock consists of a great igneous batholith (see Section 26–6) which must once have been covered by sedimentary strata, but which was essentially undistorted by the tilting.

Fault-block mountains, or remnants of them, are found in many parts of the world. They have been formed from time to time throughout all geologic eras. Evidence of fault-block mountains of Precambrian age is found in the Grand Canyon of northern Arizona, for example. One of the most magnificently exposed series of rocks in the world is to be found in the Grand Canyon. It is often taken as an example of the process of piecing together the geologic history of a particular region. The canyon has been cut by the Colorado River to a depth of a mile or more below the

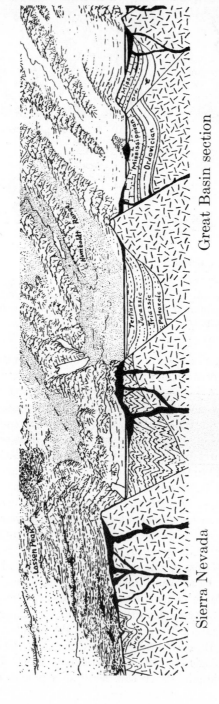

Sierra Nevada

Great Basin section

FIG. 28–5.   Block-fault mountains in western United States.   (After A. K. Lobeck, courtesy of The Geographical Press, a division of C. S. Hammond & Company, Maplewood, N. J.)

present level of a plateau, exposing rocks of many different geologic ages. Let us trace the main outlines of the history of this region, as revealed in the canyon walls.

A diagrammatic representation of a cross section through the wall and inner gorge of the Grand Canyon is shown in Fig. 28–6. Most of the canyon wall is cut through nearly horizontal sediments of varying thickness, terraced by differential erosion to form the colorful cliffs and the many picturesque features within the canyon. The inner gorge is cut through ancient folded schists and granite, the original structure of which is difficult to trace in detail. A series of tilted sediments shows in many places, underlying the main canyon wall as indicated. What is not shown in this figure is that the angle of tilt is quite different at different parts of the canyon. Some of the stages in the geologic history of the region, reconstructed from a study of these exposed rocks, are shown schematically in Fig. 28–7. The details are inevitably uncertain, and no attempt is made here to use an accurate scale. The granite and metamorphic rocks of the inner gorge are the oldest, of course, and apparently constitute the roots of an ancient mountain range, complete with folds, faults, and igneous intrusions similar to those found in most great mountain systems of the present. These mountains, long since vanished, have been called the Vishnu, and their remaining rock is known by that name. The details of their upper structure, indicated in Fig. 28–7(a), are quite imaginary, for they were in time worn down to the level plain indicated in (b); in geological language, they were *peneplaned*. The whole region then subsided and was slowly

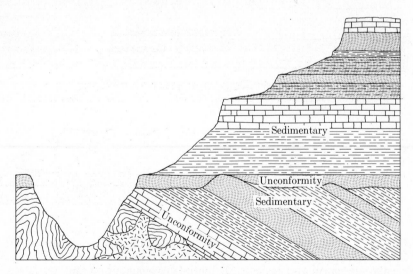

FIG. 28–6. Schematic section through gorge and wall of the Grand Canyon.

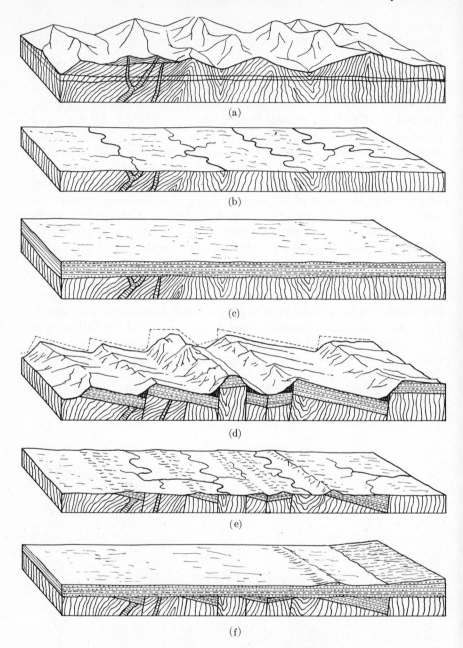

FIG. 28–7. Six stages of early history of the Grand Canyon area. (After C. O. Dunbar.) (a) The Vishnu mountains. (b) Erosion of the Vishnu to a plane. (c) Sediments spread over region. (d) Block-fault mountains form. (e) Leveling of the block mountains. (f) Younger rocks are formed.

covered with sediments characteristic of shallow seas, to a depth of more than two miles in some places. These sediments are indicated in (c).

After a long time the area was uplifted, not by warping, but in fault blocks which were comparable in size to that now forming the Sierra Nevadas. It is impossible to know how high these mountains were, for they were eroded at the top as they were lifted, but it is probable that they compared with the present Sierras. These mountains, too, were in time leveled to an almost flat plain, as shown in (e), and the region again subsided to sea level. All of these cycles had occurred before the dawn of Cambrian times, more than 500 million years ago, including the long period needed for the leveling of the fault-block mountains. It is possible that this leveling required as much time as has actually elapsed since the beginning of the Cambrian period.

During the time of its remaining history, the region has been relatively quiet. As the area subsided it was again covered with sediments, some marine in origin and others land-laid. There were several periods of interruption, in which the land lay high enough for erosion to take place instead of sedimentation. These beds can be accurately dated by their fossil content of sea forms, and by the tracks of animals, preserved in rocks which were once mudflats. Gradual uplift of the region to a plateau and the concurrent cutting of the canyon by the Colorado River are relatively recent geologic events which took place in the last few million years.

It is obvious that much work has gone into the reconstruction of this history, even though the Grand Canyon is virtually a geologist's paradise because of its very open display of most of the relevant data. Although it is much more difficult to piece together the geologic history of most other areas, there are many regional histories that are now unambiguously reconstructed. No matter how much the details differ, rocks constitute the documents for only part of the history, and there are always immense gaps in the story, corresponding to periods in which erosion was destroying the documents. These gaps do not necessarily correspond to the same times in different areas, however, and as geological investigation proceeds, our record of the geologic past of the earth as a whole becomes ever more continuous and complete.

28-3 Volcanos and igneous activity

The changes considered in the last section generally take place very, very slowly. At times, more rapid changes in natural landscape have been effected by igneous activity, especially in the formation and explosive eruption of volcanos. Although the greatest volcanos were active before human history began, a few have come into existence in modern times.

The most recent has been Paricutin in Mexico, born in February, 1943, which grew to a height of 1410 feet in its first year, but after nine years of activity became a dead cone of cinders. A volcano is a mountain, usually conical in shape, which is formed by the eruption of material from the interior of the earth through a vent (or series of vents) in the surface rock. This material may be liquid or it may previously have solidified, but its temperature is always high; the immediate explosion is usually due to the expansion of gaseous substances. Apparently the magma originates at considerable depth and forms a reservoir of molten rock which works its way upward, melting or enveloping other rocks, until it finally spreads out through existing fissures or through forced vents which lead to the surface. After the fact, the advent of Paricutin does not seem so very surprising. There are many volcanic cones in the region of this baby volcano, and not far away another volcano, Jorulla, arose in the middle of a plantation as recently as 1759. It seems evident that there is a persistent reservoir of magma underlying this part of Mexico. The magma reservoir which has been inferred to be associated with the Italian volcano Vesuvius is shown in Fig. 28–8. An outer cone, older than Vesuvius, once formed a volcano now known as Mt. Somma, which may have been fed by the offset central vent shown. The magma has worked upward at many positions to form dikes, as indicated, which traverse the local sedimentary strata.

Volcanic activity has almost invariably accompanied mountain building to some extent, and some of the most beautiful peaks of the Andes, the Caucasus, and other mountain systems are volcanic cones. Only rarely, however, has volcanic activity been the predominant factor in the formation of mountains. The Cascade Mountains in the northwest United States form a conspicuous exception. This range consists entirely of pic-

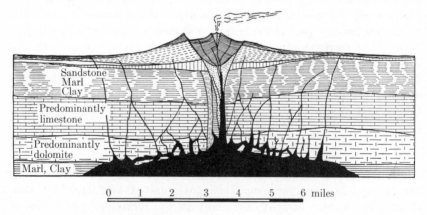

Sandstone
Marl
Clay
Predominantly limestone
Predominantly dolomite
Marl, Clay

0   1   2   3   4   5   6 miles

FIG. 28–8. Section through Vesuvius. The reservoir of magma is inferred from the activity. (After A. Rittmann.)

turesque volcanic cones, now no longer active—Mt. Ranier, Mt. Hood, Mt. Shasta, and many others.

Desmarest was able to trace the old lava beds in southern France to ancient volcanic craters, but the most extensive basalt layers erupted through fissures, not through vented volcanic cones. We have mentioned the Columbia Plateau, which extends over parts of Washington, Oregon, Idaho, and northern Nevada, altogether some 200,000 square miles in extent. Originally built up in layers due to a succession of vast lava flows, this formation is as much as 5000 feet thick in some places. An even greater area of lava flow still stands, the Deccan Plateau of India; it has been greatly altered by erosion since its solidification, however. Similar formations are found in Africa, Siberia, and Australia, but the only recent recorded fissure flow took place in Iceland during 1783. The whole of Iceland is part of an extensive basalt plateau of the north Atlantic which also shows itself in northern Ireland and southern Greenland.

Volcanos and broad surface lava flows are only one manifestation of pockets of molten rock in or just below the earth's crust. Dikes and sills are often found in areas which contain no evidence of surface vents. Such intrusions must have produced lateral movement or elevation of the rock they invaded, and elsewhere, at the same or a somewhat later time, there must have been consequent collapse or sinking, for there can be no empty holes deep within the earth.

There are many questions concerning igneous activity which have as yet no satisfactory answers. We have noted that enough heat may be generated by radioactive substances to produce magma, although variations in pressure must certainly play a role in the motion of magma, and may even account for its formation. There are even more challenging and puzzling features of mountain building than the origin of magma, however, and we shall next examine some of the formations found in the most typical mountains.

28–4 The folded mountain chains

We have seen that mountains can be formed by fault blocks like those of the Sierras, and that accumulation of material from the interior of the earth can form volcanic mountains such as the Cascades. Erosion always plays a major role in shaping the landscape as we find it, and some impressive mountains have been formed entirely by the differential erosion of plateaus. The Ozarks, to name a single example, are the eroded remnants of a plateau. But the greatest mountain systems of the world, e.g., the Appalachians, Rockies, Andes, Alps, and Himalayas, have much more complicated histories than any of these lesser ranges. All involve sharply folded sediments, great thrust faults, and evidence of vast igneous activity, even where there are relatively few volcanos. Scientists have come a long way in deciphering much of the history of these great ranges, although the forces that produce them are not yet adequately understood.

An important clue was observed by the American geologist James Hall (1811–1898) in 1859. He found that certain sedimentary strata, identifiable by their fossils as having been laid down in the Paleozoic era (see Table 28–1), occur in much thicker beds in the Appalachians than in the lowlands to the west of these mountains. In some places, beds thousands of feet thick in the mountains could be correlated with those only hundreds of feet thick in the lowlands. The rocks of the mountain belt also include fragments of old rocks, apparently washed down from highlands on the east, to a greater extent than those of the lowlands. Moreover, there is much more metamorphism observed in the mountains than in the plains. A combination of the features of thick beds of sediments which have been folded, extensive faulting, and metamorphism has since been observed in all the great mountain systems we have mentioned. The fossils found in these mountains are mostly those of marine forms that inhabit shallow seas.

If the thick sedimentary beds now found in high mountains were originally deposited at about sea level, the basins in which they formed must have been sinking slowly during the long period of their deposition. The first drawing of the series in Fig. 28–9, showing stages of formation of the Appalachians, indicates what must have happened. Thickening of the layers in the depressed basin would have been brought about by gradual subsidence of the great trough. That most of the material came from a land mass on the east is deduced from observation of a gradual coarsening of the deposited material from west to east. It is obvious that a stream carrying both coarse and fine solids into a body of water will tend to deposit coarse particles first, and to carry fine silt farther out. The name given to a vast, down-bent structure of sediments such as that shown in Fig. 28–9(a) is *geosyncline* ("world" syncline). Any downward rock fold is called a *syncline*, in contrast to an upward fold or arch, called an *anticline*. A syncline of great proportions is designated as a "world" syncline even though its actual extent is purely regional. The sediments in a geosyncline often reach to depths of several miles. There is evidence that all the great folded mountains began with geosynclines, thick beds of sediments that had accumulated for millions of years. Some very ancient thick sediments are found which have never been transformed into mountains, so that a geosyncline appears to be a necessary though not sufficient condition for the formation of great mountain systems. In parts of the Appalachian region and in the Alps, there is evidence for some preliminary folding of the geosyncline rocks during the time when sediments were still being deposited, but on the whole the sedimentation period is thought to have been one of relative geologic quiet.

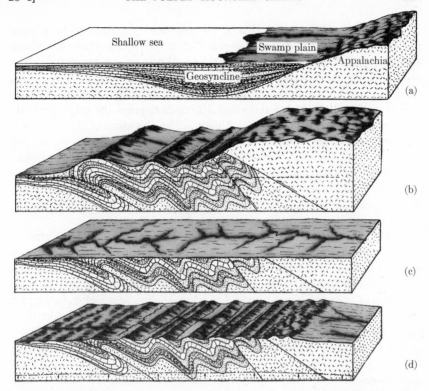

FIG. 28–9. Four stages in the evolution of the Appalachians. The early highland to the east from which the sediments came has been called Appalachia. (Reprinted by permission from Longwell, Knopf, and Flint, *Physical Geology*, John Wiley and Sons, Inc., 1948.)

In the formation of the Appalachians and other great mountain systems, the next stage was one of very extensive folding and frequent faulting, so that some of the rocks were lifted thousands of feet above sea level. This process also must have required a very long time, and was undoubtedly accompanied by erosion of the uplifted strata. In the figure representing this state of formation of the Appalachians (28–9b), the contours of the surface are purely hypothetical, for we cannot know what they were really like. The folds themselves are far from uniform, but their axes are oriented predominantly in a particular direction. The process of folding brings about considerable shortening of the earth's crust, which has often been regionally diminished by 20% or more along a direction perpendicular to the folds, just as the area of a piece of cloth is decreased by wrinkling. In areas containing large thrust faults, of which very few are shown in Fig. 28–9, portions of a surface that was once continuous are frequently found overlapping one another, sometimes in multiple layers.

In the case of the Appalachians, all large-scale folding had been completed by the end of the Paleozoic era. While the folds in these mountains are thus more than 200 million years old, the range we know today has certainly not survived the ravages of erosion for so long a time. From studies of the levels of the present ridges and the general pattern of drainage, it is clear that during their first 100 million years the original mountains were reduced to a fairly level plain. The elevation of this plain was probably not much above, and may even have been slightly below, sea level. Toward the end of the Mesozoic era the entire region was uplifted by gradual, gentle warping movement, as shown in Fig. 28-9(d). The ridges we find in the Appalachians today are outcrops of rock layers which have proved more resistant to erosion than the strata which once lay between them.

The general history of the original Appalachians is similar to that of other great mountain systems, although in most cases there is evidence of more extensive igneous activity than in this region. (The section diagrams of Fig. 28-9 are representative of the central area, in which no evidence of such activity is exposed to view; the igneous and metamorphic zone of the Appalachians is exposed farther to the south.) Frequently a great intruded batholith of igneous rock, beneath the folds of sedimentary strata, forms the "core" of a mountain range. In many parts of the Rockies, for example, and even more strikingly in the Canadian Coast Range, the mountains we find today have been nearly completely denuded of thick sediments by erosion, and consist of largely undifferentiated masses of granite which extend to indefinite depth. Where sedimentary strata remain, past intrusion of magma is often detected by the presence of dikes and sills. In some mountainous regions molten rock has broken through to flood the surface at some points during the period of folding. While the flow of some of the magma which is now congealed as igneous rock in mountains probably took place during times of folding and faulting, in many regions it is known to have occurred later.

Slow as all processes of mountain building undoubtedly were, they could not have taken place uniformly throughout geologic time. Past periods in which extensive mountain building has taken place in some parts of the earth, times during which rates of crustal movement have been much greater than average, are called *revolutions*. Let us emphasize that there is no evidence that sudden vast catastrophes have occurred. It is probable that our own time will qualify as one of revolution to geologists of the distant future. Geologic changes in most of the areas bordering the entire Pacific Ocean are now taking place as rapidly as any past changes, in other areas, for which we have evidence. Despite their long durations, the periods of great mountain building in the past are convenient mileposts for the division of geologic time into *eras*, characterized by long intervals of relative quiet between revolutions. Thus the first Appalachians were formed toward the end of what is called the Paleozoic era; rocks whose fossil contents are characteristic of a later time are not found in that region. The Ural Mountains of Russia were folded at about the same time, and general continental uplift, rather than subsidence, seems to have taken place. Because of this, relatively little sedimentation was occurring, and consequently, in the fossil record over most of the earth, there is a distinct gap corresponding to the period of rapid crustal movement. It is actually on this basis that division of the "geologic column" is made, and the Mesozoic era introduced.

The end of the Mesozoic era is marked by another time of widespread uplift and disturbance, the most striking result of which was folding of the Rocky Mountains of North America. The Andes were folded at about the same time, but both the Rockies and the Andes owe their present great height to further uplift which occurred during the more recent Cenezoic era, after the original ranges had been almost leveled by erosion. The Alps and the Himalaya Mountains are younger than the Rockies and the Andes. The sediments of the geosynclines from which they developed were being deposited in the Mesozoic era, but their actual folding and uplift did not take place until after the beginning of the Cenezoic, roughly 60 million years ago. In all these cases there is evidence that folding took place in many stages and occupied a very long time. It has not yet been proved possible to correlate changes that were taking place simultaneously at different places on the earth, or the rise and fall of the vast mountain systems in Precambrian time, more than 600 million years ago, of which we have only fragmentary evidence.

All great mountain systems show evidence of uplift subsequent to folding, although few have been so completely leveled as the Appalachians were before their most recent rejuvenation. The uplift involved is usually broad warping, often increasing the elevation of neighboring plains as well as the mountains themselves. (Sometimes not all parts of the folds are elevated; the Appalachian folds disappear in the south beneath the coastal plain of Alabama, for example.) Upward warping may be due, at least in part, to the forces which tend to restore isostatic balance. The rocks of which mountains are made, on the whole, are less dense than the crustal average, so that as their tops are eroded off, mountains tend to be pushed up again. The lateral thrusts that produce mountains in the first place cannot be due to forces tending to attain stable equilibrium, however; if geological change is continuous, there must be forces that cause great deviations *from* isostasy. Some deviations, such as those produced by erosion, can be easily understood, but interpretation of the folding and faulting of sediments to form mountains is much more complicated.

We have noted that deviations from isostasy are indicated by local

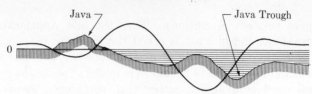

FIG. 28–10. Cross section through the Java trough, with a graph of the gravity anomaly superposed. The sea-level line is also the line of zero anomaly. (After Vening-Meinesz.)

values of the gravity anomaly. Some of the most striking anomalies which have been observed are associated with the ocean deeps found near island arcs. In the example shown in Fig. 28–10, the line denoted "gravity profile" can be understood only by assuming that some very light rocks are being held down north of the Java trough, while on either side the dense rocks are nearer the surface than would be expected. Deep focus earthquakes are also associated almost exclusively with island arcs and ocean trenches (Fig. 28–11). Ocean deeps themselves must be geologically young, since otherwise, at the rate material is being deposited, they would by now have filled with sediments. All these facts point to the conclusion that the crust along these island arcs is being deformed relatively rapidly. Is a mountain system in process of formation along the arcs? Despite the many suggestive indications, geologists cannot answer this question definitively.

The nature of the forces which produce crustal folds can still be treated only speculatively. For many years it was thought that these complex events could be explained in terms of a shrinking earth. The idea was that the earth is a cooling, hence a contracting, body, and that wrinkles appear on its crust just as they appear on the skin of a withering apple. The wrinkles on an apple are much more uniformly distributed than are

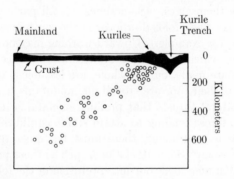

FIG. 28–11. Section at right angles to the Kurile island arc showing the foci of deep earthquakes. (After H. H. Hess.)

mountains on the earth, it is true, but localization of crustal folds was explained by the assumption that crumpling would take place only where the crust is weak, along the weak sedimentary rocks of geosynclines. There are serious objections to this theory. As we have noted, it is not probable that the earth *is* cooling appreciably—it *may* even be warming up. Another objection is that, given the distribution of folded mountains known today, a shrinking earth could not have maintained its spheroidal shape, since the great circles would not all have been shortened by the same amount. Moreover, the earth's crust does not seem strong enough to have transmitted the forces which are produced by uniform shrinking from one mountain system to the next. Finally, the theory does not account for the initial formation of geosynclines. For all these reasons the shrinking-earth hypothesis is not widely believed today, although an elaborately modified form of the theory is held by some prominent geologists.

Early in the 20th century a theory of *continental drift* was very popular as an explanation for certain similarities in plant fossils and patterns of very ancient continental glaciation. The eastern coastal contours of North and South America fit roughly into the western contours of Europe and Africa, and Africa, Australia, and Antarctica might once have fitted around India, if one judges only by general geographic outlines. If the continents have drifted in the past, it was thought, the Himalayas and related mountains could have been formed by a push on India, against the main mass of Asia. The long line of mountains bordering the western edge of the American continents were thought to have been produced by crumpling of the eastern edge of these land masses as they drifted away from Europe and Africa, leaving the Atlantic Ocean. The trouble with this theory is that it raises as many questions as it answers. What about the much older mountain systems, whose roots have now been traced? Most continental details, indeed, require special explanations in addition to the general hypothesis of drift. The hypothesis is itself difficult to accept, in view of the nature of the ocean floor. However picturesque, the idea of an ancient single land mass cannot now be taken seriously.

A theory of mountain building has been developed within the past 20 years which postulates *convection currents* within the mantle of the earth. We have seen in the previous chapter that the mantle, while rigid enough to transmit shear waves, is nevertheless plastic. If at some particular place near the core the mantle became unusually hot, it would tend to expand and rise, eventually gaining velocities which could be as great as one inch per year. These convection currents would be mainly below the crust, and motion would take place until the uneven heating became dissipated. What *might* happen at the crust, as a result of two such currents, is shown in Fig. 28–12. A geosyncline could be formed by downward motion of external parts of the mantle, originally relatively cool, and these could

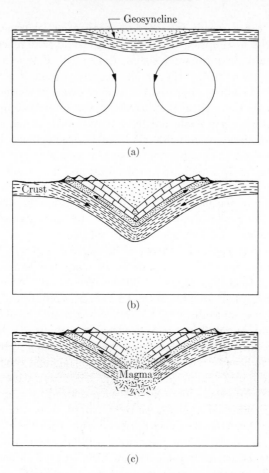

FIG. 28–12. Three stages of thrust-fold mountain building according to the convection theory. (a) Formation of geosyncline. (b) Folding. (c) Uplift and igneous activity.

tend to drag the crust along. As the mantle rocks became warmer, the crust would be sufficiently deformed to produce folding and breaking in the weak rocks of the geosyncline, as shown in part (b) of the figure. Meanwhile the viscous mantle would tend to become still, since the temperature differences farther down would have become more nearly equalized. The cracks involved in the folding and faulting could relieve some of the pressure from below, so that some of the rock, mantle and crust, is able to melt. Rise of this magma to regions near the surface would then be the final cause of uplift.

The convection theory is obviously most ingenious. Lateral forces that might be produced in the crust by this mechanism could also account for parallel ranges of mountains, such as the system consisting of the Himalayas, the Kunlun Mountains, and the Tibetan Plateau. The most serious objection to the theory is that, thus far, careful mathematical calculation has failed to predict reasonable intervals of time for the various phases. Formation of most geosynclines, in particular, has required much longer periods of sedimentation than would be predicted by this theory on the basis of the properties of the mantle which have been inferred from seismic data. Because of these discrepancies it must be admitted that there is as yet no satisfactory theory to account for lateral crustal forces.

The fundamental problem in geologic change is to trace the energy transformations involved in the vast and apparently endless modifications which take place on the globe. It is probable that the main source of renewed heat energy deep within the earth is radioactive energy, the manifestation of changes in the energy states of atomic nuclei. On the surface of the earth, however, very nearly our sole energy source is the sun. Coal is fossilized plant life, made possible by sunlight, and oil is almost certainly derived from organic remains. Heat from the sun evaporates the water that descends as rain or snow to produce erosion and carry sediments. Solar energy is also basically responsible for the work done by winds and ocean currents. Geologic processes, as well as life processes, thus depend heavily on energy from the sun. But where does the sun get its energy?

Again we are led to the consideration of atoms, those units of matter which were once thought to be indivisible. Before we can engage in further interpretation of very large systems, e.g., the sun, we must learn more about certain submicroscopically small systems, atomic nuclei and their component parts.

28–5 Summary

The basic principle of geology is that changes in the earth's crust were brought about by forces now in operation. Geological history can be traced in large measure by means of the fossil content of sedimentary strata, which can be correlated on a world-wide scale. On this basis earth history is divided into eras and periods, according to what is called the standard geologic column. Igneous intrusions and extrusions can be compared with neighboring rocks of sedimentary origin; analysis of radioactive minerals in igneous rocks permits absolute dating, to supplement the relative ages derived from fossils laid down in sediments. The surface features of the earth at any given time are the product of the competing processes of gradation and uplift. Mountains have originated in a variety of ways, including gradual uplift followed by erosion and the differential motion of great fault blocks. Volcanos and other kinds of igneous activity, which originate from local pockets of magma in the earth's crust, play an important role in mountain building. The greatest mountain systems involve folded and uplifted sediments of unusual thickness that must have been deposited in shallow sinking basins. The history of these mountain systems can be traced, but no fully satisfactory theory exists to account for the forces that produced them.

REFERENCES

There are numerous interesting and reliable modern textbooks of geology in which the reader will find many details which have been omitted here. Especially recommended are:

DUNBAR, C. O., *Historical Geology.*
GILLULY, J., A. C. WATERS, and A. O. WOODFORD, *Principles of Geology.*
LEET, L. D., and S. JUDSON, *Physical Geology.*
STOVALL, J. W., and H. E. BROWN, *The Principles of Historical Geology.*

1. Limestone in a deep quarry and sandstone on a distant hill are found to contain some of the same index fossils. List all the conclusions that can be drawn from this fact.

2. One of the ideas attacked by Steno was that mountains grow, much as a tree grows. What arguments could he have used in his attack? In what sense *do* mountains grow?

3. Especially in the Alps there are many "recumbent folds" which result in nearly horizontal layers of sedimentary rock in which younger strata lie below those of greater age. List all the ways you can think of for detecting this condition in a highly eroded area.

4. An *unconformity* is a buried erosion surface. How many unconformities can you find in Fig. 28–5? How could an unconformity be distinguished from a fault?

5. How can you reconcile the Law of Uniform Change with the "revolutions" that are conventionally used to mark the terminations of the various geologic eras?

6. Figure 28–13 represents a cross section with correlated sediments designated by the same letter and igneous rocks given by name.

(a) Which is the older of the two igneous rocks?

(b) Which is the older of the two faults?

(c) Which is the oldest rock shown?

(d) Which is younger, *A* or *F*?

7. Write as completely as you can a geologic history of the region represented by the diagram of Fig. 28–13.

8. What is a geosyncline? What is its role in mountain building?

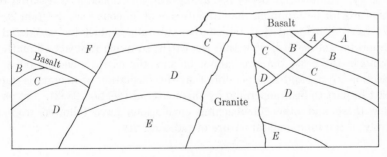

FIGURE 28–13.

CHAPTER 29

INTRINSIC ENERGY OF MATTER: NUCLEAR PROCESSES

In Chapter 18 we saw how Becquerel was led to his discovery of radioactivity in the "gold rush" of investigation that followed the discovery of x-rays. We also outlined Rutherford's analysis of the three kinds of radioactive "rays," alpha, beta, and gamma, and his later use of alpha particles to discover that each atom has a positively charged nucleus carrying nearly all the atomic mass. We will recall that alpha particles are identical with helium nuclei (charge number $Z = 2$, atomic weight 4), that beta particles are electrons, and that gamma rays consist of penetrating electromagnetic radiation, indistinguishable from very high energy x-rays. In Chapter 18 our primary interest was the structure of atoms, however, and radioactivity was treated more as a research tool than as a phenomenon of great interest in its own right. Once we had discussed the essential role played by alpha particles in establishing the existence of an atomic nucleus we could temporarily neglect internal nuclear structure, for *chemical* properties are determined by the outer electronic structures of atoms. The periodic table of chemical elements can be interpreted by treating the nucleus of each atom as though it were an indivisible whole.

We have been returned to the subject of radioactivity by our study of geology. Radioactive decay has again been mentioned as a research tool, this time for determining the absolute age of igneous rock (Section 28–1). We have also found that radioactive substances must be considered an important source of heat within the earth; so much radioactive matter is found in the crust that we cannot be sure the earth is cooling off at all (Section 27–5), and it is possible that the formation of magma is due at least in part to heat generated by this material (Section 28–3). Let us see how these and other far-reaching conclusions have followed from the study of the fundamental nature of radioactivity.

29–1 Natural radioactivity

Becquerel discovered the radioactive properties of the element *uranium*, we have noted in Chapter 18, and Pierre and Marie Curie discovered the elements *polonium* and *radium*. At about the same time, other investigators found the element *thorium* to be radioactive and discovered the new radioactive element *actinium*. Early in the 20th century Rutherford found radioactive gases associated with both thorium and radium. He was able to isolate enough of the gas associated with radium to determine that it could be condensed only at low temperatures, and that it seemed to be chemically inert. He concluded that a new element in the inert gas family was present, the element now called *radon*. He was only able to study its properties by making measurements of its radioactivity, and he found that the radioactive strength of a sample of radon gas, as determined by its effect on a charged electroscope, declines rapidly after it is isolated from radium. New radioactive gas was found to develop, at a slow rate, over the original radium sample. Furthermore, Rutherford found that freshly purified samples of radium compounds emit only alpha particles and gamma rays, but that beta particles make their appearance soon after purification.

The heating effect of radioactivity was discovered in 1903, by the Curies. They found that even a small sample of radium may maintain a temperature higher than that of its surroundings, and quantitative measurements showed that the quantity of energy given off per unit mass of radium, in unit time, is extremely substantial. There was no apparent diminution of this heating effect with time, and the observation caused much excitement. It was generally agreed that the energy of radioactive decay must either be assimilated from outside and released in this way, or must represent a hitherto unsuspected source of energy *within* the atoms of radioactive elements. Rutherford and Frederick Soddy introduced a hypothesis, in 1903, which encompassed both the latter view and the experimental observations Rutherford had made on radium and radon. Their hypothesis was that radioactive emission accompanies *transformation* of an atom of an element of one kind into an atom of another element. Radium atoms, for example, may undergo transformation, with loss of mass, charge, and energy, to form radon atoms. In Rutherford's own words:

"On this theory, the atoms of the radio-elements, unlike the atoms of the ordinary element, are not stable but undergo spontaneous disintegration accompanied by the expulsion of an alpha or a beta particle. After the disintegration, the resulting atom has physical and chemical properties entirely different from the parent atom. It may be in turn unstable and pass through a succession of transformations each of which is characterized by the emission of an alpha or beta particle."

Any given sample of radioactive material, uranium, for example, may be found to emit alpha and beta particles and gamma rays, and among these a wide range of penetration power, i.e., energy, may be observed. This complexity of radioactive emission, in the view advanced by Rutherford and Soddy, arises from a chain of consecutive changes, all of which may go on simultaneously within a single sample, once the sequence has begun. This view has been completely substantiated by observations made since the year of its proposal, 1903.

Let us consider the radioactive decay of initially pure uranium, which is known to emit alpha particles. If a uranium atom emits an alpha particle, it must lose two units of positive charge and four units of atomic weight, since the alpha particle is known to be identical with the doubly charged ion of helium. The uranium atom contains 92 units of positive charge, and its atomic weight is approximately 238; after emission of an alpha particle, then, its charge number is 90, its atomic weight 234. If this new atom emits a beta particle, its charge number will be raised from 90 to 91, since loss of the one unit of negative charge on the electron is equivalent to gain of one unit of positive charge. The mass change associated with beta-particle emission is negligible for our purposes, however, since the electron mass is only $1/1840$ of an atomic weight unit. Each change occurring in the uranium radioactive decay chain will be one of these two kinds. The emission of gamma rays, electromagnetic radiation of short wavelength, leaves the charge of an atom intact and does not appreciably affect its mass. Some kinds of radioactive atoms are found to emit gamma rays along with alpha particles, others along with beta particles. Invariably, in radioactive transformation, the new atoms formed have lower energy than the original atoms; this energy difference is reflected in the kinetic energies with which alpha or beta particles are expelled and, frequently, in the emission of gamma radiation as well.

Radioactive transformation seems to occur in a purely random manner. One expression of this is that the number of disintegrations occurring per unit time in a pure radioactive sample is directly proportional to the total number of radioactive atoms present. The rate of decay is always such that *half* of the atoms present will have undergone transformation in a time which is unique to the particular radioactive material present, but independent of the size of the sample. This time is called the *half-life* of the material. The half-life of radium is rather long, 1620 years, which accounts for the fact that the Curies were unable to detect diminution in its rate of energy release with time. The half-life of radon, on the other hand, is only 3.82 days, and Rutherford was able to detect rapid depletion in the radioactive intensities of radon samples soon after he had discovered this element. In the uranium decay chain, uranium itself has the longest half-life, 4.5×10^9 years. Initially pure uranium gradually builds up a mixture of all of its "daughter" substances, the progeny of its decay, each contributing its own mode of radioactivity.

The number of units of positive charge on the nucleus of an atom, it will be recalled, is called its *atomic number*; each such number is associated with a particular element which can be identified by reference to the periodic table. When a uranium atom emits an alpha particle, and its atomic number changes from 92 to 90, it must have been transformed into an atom of the element thorium. In accepted nomenclature for identification of atomic nuclei, the atomic mass (really *mass number*, see Section 29–2) is written as a superscript after the appropriate chemical symbol, while the atomic number is shown as a subscript before the symbol. A uranium atom is represented as $_{92}U^{238}$ and ordinary hydrogen as $_1H^1$, for example. In

TABLE 29–1

RADIOACTIVE DECAY CHAIN OF URANIUM

Radioactive atom and particle emitted	Half-life
$_{92}U^{238}$	
$\downarrow \alpha$	4.5×10^9 years
$_{90}Th^{234}$	
$\downarrow \beta$	24.1 days
$_{91}Pa^{234}$	
$\downarrow \beta$	1.1 minutes
$_{92}U^{234}$	
$\downarrow \alpha$	2.5×10^5 years
$_{90}Th^{230}$	
$\downarrow \alpha$	8.0×10^4 years
$_{88}Ra^{226}$	
$\downarrow \alpha$	1620 years
$_{86}Rn^{222}$	
$\downarrow \alpha$	3.82 days
$_{84}Po^{218}$	
$\downarrow \alpha$	3.05 minutes
$_{82}Pb^{214}$	
$\downarrow \beta$	27 minutes
$_{83}Bi^{214}$	
$\downarrow \beta$	19.7 minutes
$_{84}Po^{214}$	
$\downarrow \alpha$	1.6×10^{-4} second
$_{82}Pb^{210}$	
$\downarrow \beta$	22 years
$_{83}Bi^{210}$	
$\downarrow \beta$	5.0 days
$_{84}Po^{210}$	
$\downarrow \alpha$	138 days
$_{82}Pb^{206}$	

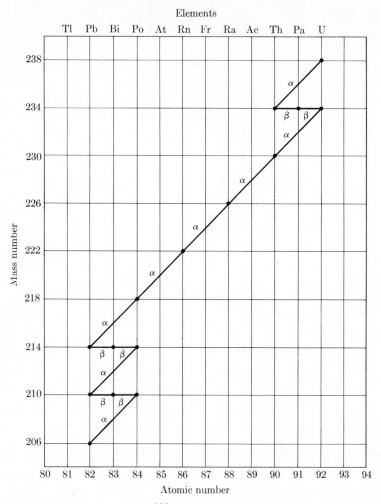

FIG. 29–1. Diagram of the U^{238} radioactive series. The effect of alpha emission is to shift the nucleus two places to the left in the periodic table and reduce its mass number by 4. Beta emission leaves the mass number unchanged but increases the charge number.

this nomenclature, the chain of radioactive decay events which begins with uranium, along with the measured half-lives of all its participants, is shown in Table 29–1. The chain is also shown schematically in Fig. 29–1. The atoms of lead, $_{82}Pb^{206}$, which mark the end of the sequence, are stable against radioactive decay.

Uranium is the most abundant radioactive element found in rocks, and one method of dating rocks depends upon the uranium decay chain in a simple way. Some of the intermediate steps in the uranium-lead sequence take much longer than others, but the material of greatest half-life in the series is uranium itself. Since decay of uranium atoms initiates the whole chain of events, the half-life of uranium determines the rate of production of $_{82}Pb^{206}$. If at the time of its formation a mineral contained uranium but no lead, measurement of the ratio of $_{82}Pb^{206}$ to $_{92}U^{238}$ could be used to determine its age. A ratio of $1:1$, for example, would mean that the mineral crystallized 4.5 billion years ago, just time for half the uranium atoms initially present to decay to lead. Not as much as half the original uranium has been converted to lead in any rock found thus far, but ages of more than 2 billion years have been measured by this method. In practice, the measurement technique is usually complicated by the presence of kinds of radioactive elements other than those found in the $_{92}U^{238}$ series, and by other kinds of lead.

The phrase "other kinds of lead" raises a question that is fundamental to the interpretation of radioactivity. The atomic weight of the lead ordinarily found in nature is 207.21, not 206. Moreover, the uranium series (Fig. 29–1) contains two radioactive members that we have shown as $_{82}Pb^{214}$ and $_{82}Pb^{210}$. Two kinds of each of the elements uranium, thorium, and bismuth, and three kinds of polonium also appear in this series. The discovery that there may be several kinds of atoms of a single element was one of the important fruits of the investigation of radioactivity.

29–2 Isotopes

In Dalton's version of the atomic theory it was assumed that all atoms of any particular element are alike in every respect. Atoms were thought to be indivisible, and it followed that matter is made up of as many kinds of "particles" as there are elements. As the number of known elements increased, this view led to increasing complication. We have noted in Chapter 9 that Prout, soon after Dalton's proposal of the atomic theory, endeavored to introduce simplicity into the growing complexity by postulating that the hydrogen atom is the primary substance of which all other atoms are made. Prout's hypothesis had to be abandoned, however, because atomic weights were found not to be integral multiples of the atomic weight of hydrogen, even though some are very nearly so.

After the discovery of radioactivity, several pairs of substances, the members of which were clearly different in radioactive properties but inseparable chemically, were found. $_{90}Th^{230}$, for example, was at first thought to be a new element and was given the name *ionium*. It was first prepared from pitchblende, the ore in which radium was discovered, and it was found that freshly separated ionium gradually gives rise to new radium. The thorium ordinarily found in its ores has atomic weight 232.12, and does not give rise to radium of the kind that was discovered by the Curies. In chemical behavior, however, thorium and the new ionium could not be distinguished, and no difference between the bright-line spectra of the two substances could be detected. The two atomic weights were determined with great care, and there was no doubt that the atomic weight of ionium is lower than that of thorium. This and several other similar examples led Soddy to declare in 1910 that

"Chemical homogeneity is no longer a guarantee that any supposed element is not a mixture of several [elements] of different atom weights, or that any atomic weight is not merely a mean number."

Soddy thus proposed to recognize thorium and ionium as different forms of the same chemical element, unlike in mass but identical in chemical properties. He suggested the name *isotopes* (Greek *iso*, "same," *topos*, "place") for such cases of unlike atoms which occupy the same position in the periodic table. He also posed the possibility that *any* element may consist of a mixture of unlike atoms, and that measured atomic weights may be no more than mean values, depending on the individual atomic weights and relative numbers of two or more isotopes. In 1913 this hypothesis was verified by J. J. Thomson for the case of the nonradioactive element *neon*. Applying the same principles he had employed in his measurement of the charge-to-mass ratio of the electron, Thomson found that neon ions, all of the same charge, exhibit *two* distinct charge-to-mass ratios. He thus proved the existence of two isotopes of neon, one of approximate atomic weight 20, the other 22. (Thomson missed a third isotope, approximate atomic weight 21, which is much rarer than the other two.)

The apparatus Thomson used in his experiments with neon was the precursor of a modern instrument of exceptional versatility and precision, called the *mass spectrometer* (Fig. 29-2). In this instrument, the isotopes of any element may be separated on the basis of their slight differences in charge-to-mass ratio, and their relative masses may be determined with great precision. Oxygen, the standard of chemical atomic weight, was found to consist of three isotopes, and for expression of relative *isotopic* masses a new standard, in which the most abundant oxygen-isotope is assigned the value 16.00000, was adopted. The difference between the two scales is slight, since the abundances of the two heavier forms of oxygen, $_8O^{17}$ and $_8O^{18}$, are very small. The relative masses of most of the known kinds of atoms have been carefully determined by use of the mass spectrometer, and it has turned out that Prout's hypothesis had validity after all! The masses of individual atoms are all very nearly, though not quite exactly, integral multiples of the mass of the hydrogen atom. The nomenclature we introduced in Section 29-1, e.g., $_{92}U^{238}$ for a uranium atom, is necessary for the representation of isotopes and for drawing clear distinctions between them. As we have seen, there are two kinds of uranium atoms in the uranium decay series, $_{92}U^{238}$ and $_{92}U^{234}$. The superscripts used in this system, called *mass numbers*, are not atomic weights but the integers nearest the exact *isotopic* weight in each case. The use of integers for this purpose has deeper significance, as we shall learn in Section 29–4.

The known stable isotopes of several elements are listed in Table 29–2, with mass numbers to identify each, the relative abundances of the different forms usually found for the element as it occurs naturally, and the *chemical* atomic weight of each element. The atomic weight of chlorine, for example, 35.46, reflects the fact that natural chlorine is a mixture of two kinds of atoms of mass numbers 35 and 37, in approximately 3:1 ratio. The atomic weight of lithium, 6.94, results from the presence of a small percentage of atoms of mass number 6 among the predominant variety of mass number 7. It is interesting to note that even the very light elements hydrogen and helium exist in two stable isotopic forms. Heavy hydrogen, called *deuterium*, symbol $_1H^2$, was not discovered until 1933 for the very good reason that ordinary hydrogen atoms outnumber deuterium

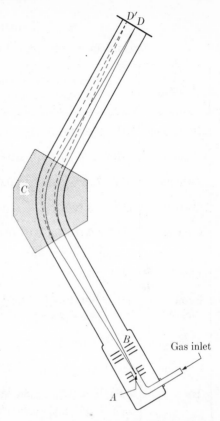

Fig. 29–2. Diagram of a mass spectrometer. Ions formed by electron bombardment of gas molecules at A and passing through slits B are bent by a magnetic field in region C. Those of a particular charge-to-mass ratio are brought to D, while those of slightly larger mass and equal charge are brought to D'. This type of spectrometer brings to a focus ions of the same charge-to-mass ratio.

atoms in natural sources of the element by about 6000 to one. Atmospheric helium contains only about one ten-thousandth percent of atoms of mass number 3, $_2He^3$.

The concept of isotopes proved invaluable to the task of clarification of natural radioactive decay. The decay chain shown in Fig. 29–1, for example, cannot be fully interpreted without it. Difficulty was compounded for the early investigators by the fact that there are *three* natural radio-

TABLE 29–2

STABLE ISOTOPES OF A FEW SELECTED ELEMENTS

Element	Symbols and abundances of known stable isotopes	Chemical atomic weight of the element
Hydrogen	$_1H^1$ (99.9849%), $_1H^2$ (0.0151%)	1.008
Helium	$_2He^3$ (1 × 10^{-4}%), $_2He^4$ (99.9999%)	4.003
Lithium	$_3Li^6$ (7.98%), $_3Li^7$ (92.02%)	6.940
Carbon	$_6C^{12}$ (98.89%), $_6C^{13}$ (1.11%)	12.010
Oxygen	$_8O^{16}$ (99.758%), $_8O^{17}$ (0.0373%), $_8O^{18}$ (0.2039%)	16.0000 (defined)
Fluorine	$_9F^{19}$ (100%)	19.004
Neon	$_{10}Ne^{20}$ (90.92%), $_{10}Ne^{21}$ (0.257%), $_{10}Ne^{22}$ (8.82%)	20.183
Aluminum	$_{13}Al^{27}$ (100%)	26.97
Chlorine	$_{17}Cl^{35}$ (75.4%), $_{17}Cl^{37}$ (24.6%)	35.46
Tin	$_{50}Sn^{112}$ (0.95%), $_{50}Sn^{114}$ (0.65%), $_{50}Sn^{115}$ (0.34%), $_{50}Sn^{116}$ (14.24%), $_{50}Sn^{117}$ (7.57%), $_{50}Sn^{118}$ (24.01%), $_{50}Sn^{119}$ (8.58%), $_{50}Sn^{120}$ (32.97%), $_{50}Sn^{122}$ (4.71%), $_{50}Sn^{124}$ (5.98%)	118.70
Lead	$_{82}Pb^{204}$ (1.48%), $_{82}Pb^{206}$ (23.6%), $_{82}Pb^{207}$ (22.6%), $_{82}Pb^{208}$ (52.3%)	207.21

active decay chains among the heavy elements. In addition to the series beginning with $_{92}U^{238}$, there is a second whose long-lived parent isotope is the rarer form of uranium, $_{92}U^{235}$. After a long series of alpha and beta emission steps, this series ends in the lead isotope $_{82}Pb^{207}$. The third naturally occurring chain begins with the most common form of thorium, $_{90}Th^{232}$, and ends with another stable lead isotope, $_{82}Pb^{208}$.

The evolution of energy which accompanies radioactive transformation of atoms, which proved so exciting to the scientific community of the early 20th century, did not become completely comprehensible until it was interpreted in terms of Einstein's relativity theory, originally quite unrelated to nuclear processes. The whole subject that is now called "atomic energy," in fact, is related to this theory in a rather fundamental way. Before we can proceed further with our consideration of atomic masses and their meaning we must survey some of the principal contributions of this remarkable theory.

29–3 Special relativity—an apparent digression

Again and again in this book we have followed one line of scientific advance until we have found that it converges with another chain of research that had previously seemed quite independent. The proliferation of science into many branches, in a sense, seems always to have been a transitory, although historically necessary, phase. Simplification and deeper understanding comes with the recognition of underlying interrelations in areas of thought where there had previously appeared to be contradictions. (At the same time, of course, new and more powerful generalizations open new, unexplored regions to view, and the process of elaboration starts over again on a higher level.) We have seen that this consolidation process took place in the transition from Ptolemaic to Newtonian astronomy, from phlogiston to oxygen chemistry, and in the introduction of the quantum hypothesis. But there is no better example in the whole history of science than the rise of the special theory of relativity, a theory whose consequences turned out to be much more far-reaching than the immediate understanding it was designed to gain. It was an apparent paradox concerning the transmission of electromagnetic waves that gave rise to the theory; Einstein's resolution of that paradox affected, in some degree, all of science and its most fundamental concepts.

We have noted (Chapter 17) that the idea of an *ether* as a medium for transmitting light was not only useful to Young and Fresnel, but was also extended by Faraday and Maxwell to account for light and all other electromagnetic phenomena. The ether had to be a "subtle fluid" which could penetrate matter, and through which material bodies could move with no perceptible resistance. Since light waves are transverse, and only solids can transmit transverse vibrations, literal mechanical properties of the ether had to be dispensed with. The absence of resistance to motion in a solid is too absurd to be taken literally. Still it was natural, in view of the great successes of mechanics, to suppose that the behavior of electromagnetic waves was at least *compatible* with the principles of Newtonian mechanics. This assumption turned out not to be fully justified by experience. The contradiction may be made clear by comparison of the behavior of sound waves and light waves.

Let us consider an attempt to measure the speed of sound on one car of a train moving uniformly on a straight track (Fig. 29–3). This can be

FIG. 29–3. Measuring the speed of sound on an open flat car. B sees the flash of A's gun and notes the time interval until he hears the sound; by this time, however, he is at B'

easily done: have one person fire a blank cartridge from a gun at one end of the car, while another person times the interval between the flash and the sound of the gun, with an accurate timer, at the other end. By measuring the length of the car, the data needed for determining the speed of sound will be completed. But there are two possibilities. If the observers were in a closed car, in which the air is carried along with the train, they would obtain the same answer as if the car were standing still. Suppose they are on an open flat car, however. Although the air that transmits the sound may be very still with respect to the earth, the observers are now moving with respect to this transmitting medium. Even though the car is of the same length as before, the time interval between the instant the flash is seen and the instant the report is heard will be different. In the case pictured in Fig. 29–3, the time interval will be greater than if the car were standing still, for the sound signal has actually traveled in air from A to B', instead of simply from A to B. If the length of the car is taken to be the distance traversed by the signal, the calculated value for the speed of sound, distance over time, will be smaller than the correct value.

If an ether is assumed necessary as a transmitting medium for light, a situation analogous to the above example for sound should arise in measuring the speed of light. The earth moves in its orbit about the sun at a rate of about 30 km/sec, and if we move with respect to the ether, the velocity of light should be slightly different in directions along and at right angles to this motion. Apparatus carefully designed to detect this difference was set up by A. A. Michelson (1852–1931) and E. W. Morley (1838–1923) in 1887; to their surprise and that of scientists everywhere they found no difference at all between the speeds measured in these two directions. It was as if we ride through the universe in a closed car, carrying our ether with us! This conclusion was contradicted by other experiments, however. The measured velocity of light in a moving medium such as a stream of water can be explained in terms of the ether theory only if it is assumed that the ether stands still.

The Michelson-Morley experiment remained a major paradox in science unitl 1905, when Einstein suggested an apparently simple but very revolutionary solution. The special theory of relativity is based on two almost deceptively simple postulates. The first is that *the velocity of light in space is a constant of nature, and remains the same regardless of any motion of the source of light or of the observer.* This means that the analogy with sound is not justified, and implies that the idea of an ether may be discarded entirely; the electromagnetic *fields* Maxwell employed to explain light waves are retained, but no transmitting medium need be involved. The other postulate becomes clear by comparison of the ether theory with Newtonian mechanics.

In the mechanics of Galileo and Newton rest and *uniform* (unaccelerated) motion are indistinguishable; a body interacts with the rest of the world only as it undergoes *changes* of motion. In this sense Newtonian mechanics is *relativistic.* For example, a person has no more difficulty in eating his lunch on a plane flying smoothly at 200 miles per hour than in his dining room at home, and in a sealed cabin with no windows he could not detect his motion by anything that takes place inside the plane. Even with a speedometer, the pilot can directly determine only his *relative* speed with respect to the surrounding air, and when there is wind his ground speed can be found only indirectly. The wave theory of light had introduced a new feature that seemed to destroy this relativity. The ether was thought to be a universal medium, one which either moves or stands still, but in any case something against which *absolute* motion could in principle be measured. Einstein's second postulate was simply a return to pre-ether relativity: *it is impossible to distinguish between rest and uniform motion except in relation to each other; there is no standard against which absolute motion can be determined.* (Note that *accelerated* motion is clearly distinguishable from unaccelerated motion, just as in Newtonian mechanics. It is this restriction to motion at uniform velocities that characterizes Einstein's *special,* or restricted, theory of relativity.)

The two postulates of special relativity do far more than merely explain the Michelson-Morley experiment, which can be viewed simply as a test of the first postulate. They also make necessary a reconsideration of the fundamental concepts of *space* and *time.* Let us suppose that, contrary to fact, they were true not just of light but also of sound, and again consider Fig. 29-3. If the observers were constrained to find the same ratio of distance to measured time interval for sound transmission at all speeds of the flat car and at rest, some very drastic changes would have to be made in their clock, the length of their car, or both. Moreover, since the signal would have to reach B to be observed by him *at all,* he certainly could not travel faster than sound itself. These restrictions are *not* true of sound— our previous analysis of the measurement of sound is correct—but the analogy is useful, since they are true for light. Lengths and clocks *do* change with velocity *in comparison with those "at rest,"* and the maximum limit for all velocities is the velocity of light. The reason such changes have been detected only in the 20th century is that the speed of light, 3×10^{10} cm/sec, is virtually the equivalent of *infinite* speed for most practical purposes. It is in connection with certain finite, though large, maximum speeds that the relativity consequence of greatest importance to nuclear processes, the relation between mass and energy, is most evident.

Although the postulates of relativity imply a finite maximum speed, they put no limitations on the amount of force that may be exerted on a body. Why shouldn't an unlimited amount of force, or a finite force of unlimited duration, be able to produce an unlimited velocity? The prediction given by the theory of relativity is that matter's resistance to changes in motion, the property called inertia, increases as its velocity increases, in just such a way that the upper limit of this velocity is that of light. This conclusion follows logically from a mathematical application of Einstein's postulates to the motions of bodies, although we will be content here to state it only in words. Now *mass* is a measure of inertia, and the same conclusion can be stated by saying that when work is done on a body by an external force, not all of it goes into increasing the speed of the body, but some goes into increasing its mass. In other words, some of the energy expended by a force acting through a distance may be converted into additional mass. According to the theory, the quantity of additional mass multiplied by the square of the speed of light is equivalent to the energy transformed to mass.

It is true that a particle has the *additional* mass considered above only by virtue of its velocity. If mass can be equivalent to energy in any circumstances, however, may the mass of a body at rest also represent energy? The theory does not answer this question unequivocally, but Einstein had the courage to give this opinion as early as 1905: "The mass of a body is a measure of its energy content . . . It is not impossible that with bodies whose energy content is variable to a high degree (e.g., with radium salts) the theory may be successfully put to the test." This is the origin of the now famous equation

$$E = mc^2, \qquad \qquad (29\text{--}1)$$

where E represents the energy content of a body, m its mass (variable according to whether the body is at rest or in motion, but always a measure of its inertia), and c is the velocity of light. Numerically, one gram of mass is equivalent to 9×10^{20} ergs of energy, or 25×10^6 (25 million) kilowatt-hours.

Increase in the mass of a particle with velocity, predicted by Einstein, was first observed in the form of a decrease in the charge-to-mass ratio measured for very high-speed electrons. In his reference to radium salts Einstein was interpreting radioactive energy in terms of his prediction of mass-energy equivalence. The atom produced by radioactive decay should have less mass than its parent atom, in amount corresponding to the mass of the particle emitted *plus* the amount of kinetic and radiant energy that appears in the radioactive transformation. This interpretation is known today to be correct, but the mass equivalence of the energy given off in a single radioactive transformation is extremely difficult to measure, and a quantitative verification of the applicability of Einstein's equation to *rest* mass was not possible at first. The experimental test of the generality of Eq. (29–1) was made possible by increased knowledge of the structures of light atomic nuclei.

29–4 Nuclear reactions: "artificial" transmutation

After the hypothesis that radioactivity consists of spontaneous transformations of atoms was definitely established, it was believed by some that transformations might be accomplished by "artificial" laboratory procedures. It was recognized after 1913 that such transformations must take place in the atomic nucleus, since the chemical nature of an atom is determined by the quantity of positive charge its nucleus contains. Rutherford, in thinking about this possibility, realized that he might use the high-speed alpha particles from radioactive atoms as projectiles. He also realized that heavy nuclei would repel the positively charged alpha particles very strongly by virtue of their own very high positive charge, and that alpha particle projectiles would be able to penetrate only very light nuclei, if any at all. In 1919, this line of reasoning led him to perform a very simple and profoundly meaningful experiment. His apparatus, shown in Fig. 29–4, consisted of a gas-filled box equipped with a movable source of alpha particles; at one end there was an opening covered with thin silver foil on which a fluorescent zinc sulfide screen was mounted. Alpha particles were known to cause small light scintillations on striking

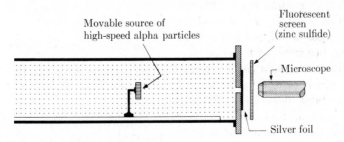

FIG. 29–4. Plan diagram of Rutherford's apparatus for detection of nuclear reaction.

such a screen, and Rutherford mounted a microscope in a position enabling him to look for scintillations. When the box was filled with carbon dioxide or oxygen, and the source was 7 or more centimeters away from the screen, no scintillations were observed; the gas and the silver foil were sufficient to absorb all alpha particles directed toward the screen. When the box was filled with nitrogen, however, Rutherford observed scintillations with the source as far removed as 40 centimeters from the screen! He knew that alpha particles could not traverse this distance in the gas, and concluded that alpha particles were colliding with nitrogen atoms and causing the expulsion of some new, more penetrating particles from them.

Rutherford's experiment had brought about the first laboratory-induced *nuclear reaction*: helium nuclei and nitrogen nuclei, in close proximity, had produced some third particle. Rutherford carried out magnetic deflection experiments which showed that the scintillations were caused by high-speed hydrogen ions, or *protons*. His was the first direct evidence that protons exist as such in atomic nuclei, and the first experimental verification of Prout's hypothesis. Another product of this reaction was later identified as an isotope of oxygen.

This identification, achieved by P. M. S. Blackett in 1925, was accomplished with an important and fascinating instrument, called the *cloud chamber*, which permits one to "see" high-energy particles.

The cloud chamber (Fig. 29–5) was designed by C. T. R. Wilson in 1912. Wilson had studied the formation of fog for many years, and noted that supersaturated water vapor readily forms droplets in the presence of ions. Ions are produced in a gas by collision of alpha or beta particles, or gamma rays, with gas molecules. When the density of water vapor is adjusted properly, each ion becomes the nucleus (condensation center) of a visible drop of water, which can be photographed under suitable illumination. In this way tracks of individual charged particles can be seen and permanently recorded. The tracks of alpha and beta particles, as well as of fast

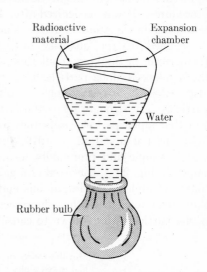

FIG. 29–5.   Simple apparatus for demonstrating the principle of the cloud chamber. Water vapor in the air above the liquid is first compressed; droplets are formed along the path of the radioactive rays when the pressure is released quickly and the gas expands. Practical cloud chambers designed for high-precision work are much more elaborate.

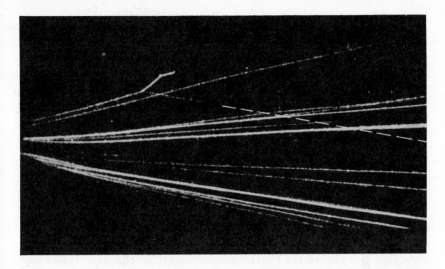

FIG. 29–6. Blackett photograph showing the ejection of a proton from a nitrogen nucleus on collision with an alpha particle. A dashed line along the faint proton track has been added to enhance its visibility. The short thick track is that of oxygen 17. (Courtesy of Prof. P. M. S. Blackett, from *Radiations from Radioactive Substances* by Lord Rutherford, J. Chadwick, and C. D. Ellis, Cambridge University Press.)

protons, can be distinguished from one another by the density of droplets; in general, a massive charged particle creates more ions per unit length of its path than a lighter one. Figure 29–6 is a reproduction of one of the original pictures taken by Blackett; the tracks were photographed simultaneously from two directions at right angles, so that each event was recorded in three dimensions, although only one view is reproduced here. The source of alpha particles is just at the left of the photographic field in Fig. 29–6. One alpha particle has been stopped, and has given rise to a track thinner than those of alpha particles, identified as the track of a proton. In addition, there is a short, irregular track, thicker than that of the alpha particle, emanating from the point at which the latter was stopped. Note that there is no third track which corresponds to the alpha particle itself after the collision. Blackett could only conclude that the alpha particle does not escape, and that the short track was produced by the atom involved in the collision. Detailed analysis of such photographs showed that momentum conservation requirements are satisfied if the mass number of the particle which produced the short, thick track is 17.

We may now write an equation for the reaction studied by Rutherford and Blackett, represented schematically in Fig. 29–7, as follows:

$$_2\mathrm{He}^4 + {}_7\mathrm{N}^{14} \rightarrow {}_8\mathrm{O}^{17} + {}_1\mathrm{H}^1. \tag{29–2}$$

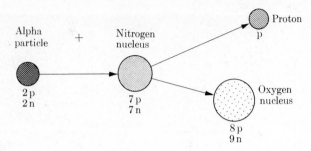

FIG. 29–7. Diagram of the reaction described by Eq. (29–2), indicating the numbers of protons and neutrons in each nucleus. The oxygen produced here, O^{17}, is stable but not abundant in nature.

Here the symbols need represent only the nuclei of the atoms involved, since it is in the nucleus that fundamental change occurs in this process. Note that the sum of the charge numbers must be the same before and after the transmutation; charge is strictly conserved. The sum of the mass numbers of the participants is also unchanged, but we remember that these integers represent the actual masses only to a fairly close approximation. The atomic masses before and after the reaction are not *quite* the same; if Einstein's equation is correct, this difference in mass should check with the gain or loss of kinetic energy in the reaction. Neither Rutherford nor Blackett was able to measure accurately the energies and masses of all the particles participating in this first nuclear reaction, but if one "artificial" transmutation is possible there must be others. Rutherford's experiment opened a new field of research, and thousands of nuclear reactions have been investigated since 1919.

All nuclei are positively charged, and thus repel each other. The reason alpha particles from radioactive substances are good tools for probing atoms near their nuclei is that they are very energetic, and despite the repulsive force can get close enough to affect the nucleus, especially if it is a light nucleus with low atomic number. High-energy protons, hydrogen nuclei, would be even better projectiles, but protons are not given off by radioactive materials. There is no natural source of high-energy protons, but the problem of producing them has been solved by the design of *particle accelerators*. A variety of giant accelerators, with such names as the *cyclotron* and the *synchrotron*, are now in use for the production of high-speed protons, deuterium atoms, alpha particles, and other nuclear projectiles.

It was with an early accelerating machine that the British physicists J. D. Cockcroft and E. T. Walton were able to make the first quantitative verification of the relation $E = mc^2$, in 1932. Their accelerator was very simple in principle: charged particles gain kinetic energy in falling through an electrical potential, just as a massive sphere would gain kinetic energy in falling through a gravitational potential, i.e., from the top of a tower. The machine was designed to supply a very high potential difference, and protons were injected so that they could acquire high kinetic energies. One unit for measuring the resultant particle energy is the *electron volt* (ev), defined as the energy that would be acquired by a particle having one electronic unit of charge in falling through a potential difference of one volt. This unit is too small for convenience in nuclear processes: from the equation $E = mc^2$, 1 atomic mass unit (amu) is calculated to be equivalent to 931 million electron volts. The energy unit ordinarily applied in nuclear calculations is one million electron volts, usually written as 1 Mev. Cockcroft and Walton succeeded in accelerating protons only to 0.6 Mev in their machine, but produced a reaction well suited to measurement. When lithium is bombarded by protons, alpha particles are produced in accord with the equation

$$_3\text{Li}^7 + {_1}\text{H}^1 \rightarrow {_2}\text{He}^4 + {_2}\text{He}^4. \qquad (29\text{–}3)$$

The masses of all these particles are well known from mass spectrometer measurements. The sum of the two masses on the left is 8.0263 amu, while the two alpha particles on the right have total mass 8.0077 amu. In this reaction, then, 0.0186 amu of mass is lost. By observing the reaction in a cloud chamber, Cockcroft and Walton were able to measure the combined kinetic energies of the alpha particles as 17.2 Mev. From Einstein's equation we have calculated that 1 amu = 931 Mev, hence this relation predicts that $0.0186 \times 931 = 17.3$ Mev of energy is equivalent to the mass lost in this reaction. This value is in excellent agreement with the experimental result, and it was thus that the equation $E = mc^2$ was first verified quantitatively.

In general keeping with Prout's hypothesis that all elements are made up of hydrogen, it was at first thought that all nuclei are composed of protons and electrons. An alpha particle, for example, could contain 4 protons and 2 electrons, the protons contributing virtually all the mass and the electrons present to cancel the excess of two units of positive charge. This idea was not satisfactory in detail, however, and as early as 1920 Rutherford suggested the possible existence of the *neutron*, an uncharged particle of unit mass number. Assuming this particle, a model of a nucleus could be built up in which a number of protons equal to its atomic number, and enough neutrons to make up the difference between the atomic number and the mass number, are present. Isotopes of a single element would differ only by the number of neutrons in their nuclei (see Fig. 29–8). This model of the nucleus remained speculative until 1932, when an uncharged particle having all the necessary properties was actually discovered by

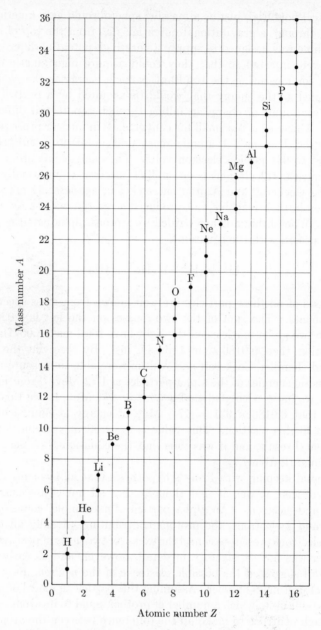

Fig. 29–8. Chart of the known stable nuclei of atomic numbers 1 to 16. The number of neutrons in each nucleus is given by $A - Z$.

James Chadwick. The presence of neutrons in all nuclei is now established beyond doubt, and the hypothesis that nuclei are composed of
neutrons and protons is completely accepted. The *mass number* of any
atom, in terms of this model, may be regarded as the sum of the numbers
of protons and neutrons in its nucleus. The *atomic number*, which determines chemical properties, corresponds to the number of protons present,
and the number of neutrons is simply the difference between the mass
and atomic numbers.

In 1933 Irene (1897–1956) and F. Joliot-Curie produced the first "artificially" radioactive substances. Unstable atoms, as well as stable ones, may
be produced in nuclear reactions. Since 1934 a very large number of radioactive isotopes have been produced, and radioactive forms of all the
elements are known. The beta rays emanating from many of these radioactive isotopes are not negatively charged electrons, but *positrons*, particles having the same mass and quantity of charge as electrons, but *positively* charged. Neither negative nor positive electrons are present in
nuclei as such, but they may be created, during radioactive decay, as a
mode of liberating energy. Charge is strictly conserved in positron emission; the atomic number of an atom is *decreased* by one unit by this mode
of decay. For example, the radioactive phosphorus isotope $_{15}P^{30}$ emits
positrons to form stable atoms of silicon, $_{14}Si^{30}$.

The positron was not first observed in artificial radioactivity, but as the
result of interactions of very high-energy gamma radiation with matter.
The energy of a gamma ray may be converted into a positron-electron
pair, two particles of opposite charge but similar in all other respects
(Fig 29–9). This process constitutes very direct evidence for the mass-
energy equivalence predicted by the special relativity theory. The minimum energy a gamma ray must have in order to create a "pair" is twice
that equivalent to the "rest" mass of an electron; any excess goes into
kinetic energy of the particles. The inverse of this process accounts for the
fact that although they may be created, positrons are not common; when
a positron and an electron meet, they may "annihilate" each other, with
the production of a gamma ray. Since electrons and positrons may be
created by processes outside nuclei, it is reasonable to suppose that either
may be created within a nucleus. Emission of either kind of particle must
be regarded as a step toward greater internal nuclear stability, i.e., lowered
nuclear energy.

The creation of particles from other forms of energy has become almost a commonplace of modern physics, and there are many possibilities. Electrons and
positrons are always created as members of pairs, although the second member of
an electron pair is not necessarily a positron if creation takes place so that charge
can be conserved in some other way. A neutron may emit an electron and a

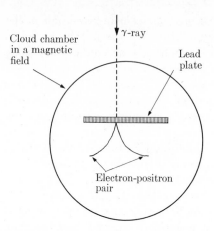

Fig. 29–9. An electron-positron pair is created in the lead plate by the incident γ-ray. Since the electron and positron are opposite in charge they are bent in different directions by the magnetic field (direction of field is perpendicular to plane of diagram).

chargeless particle called the *neutrino*; what results is no longer a neutron but a proton, however. If this process occurs within a nucleus, the nuclear charge has been increased by one unit, i.e., this is what happens inside a nucleus that is about to emit a beta particle. Conversely, a proton in a nucleus may emit a positron and a neutrino to become a neutron, as in the transmutation of $_{15}P^{30}$ to $_{14}Si^{30}$, mentioned above.

29–5 Binding energy and nuclear stability

Nuclei, then, seem to be composed of protons and neutrons, particles which may themselves possess substructure. The number of protons in a nucleus is its atomic number, and the number of protons plus the number of neutrons its mass number. At very short distances, of the order of 10^{-13} centimeter, these particles must attract each other sufficiently to provide the cohesive force that holds the nucleus together. Work must be done to separate a nucleus into its constituent protons and neutrons, and the quantity of such work is a measure of the *stability* of a particular nucleus. This quantity is called the "binding energy," an amount of energy that a nucleus *does not have* in comparison with the total energy of its separated protons and neutrons. This is exactly analogous to the energies involved in chemical compound formation, but the amount of work required to separate the components of nuclei is generally more than a million times greater than that needed to separate the constituent atoms of molecules. The energies of nuclear reactions are about a million times greater than those of chemical reactions, on the average.

A quantitative measure of nuclear binding energy is found by measuring what is called *mass defect*. The masses of the neutron and the proton, as these particles exist *outside* nuclei, are known:

$$m_{\text{proton}} = 1.00814 \text{ amu},$$

$$m_{\text{neutron}} = 1.00898 \text{ amu}.$$

If these particles correspond to Prout's universal atomic building blocks, we might naively expect the sum of the masses of neutrons and protons present in a nucleus, calculated from these numbers, to correspond exactly to the mass of the nucleus. Nuclear masses, as we have said, have been determined very accurately with mass spectrometers; for nuclei of all kinds it is found that this sum is *greater* than the measured value, and it is the difference that is called mass defect.

The alpha particle, or helium nucleus, contains two neutrons and two protons ($_2\text{He}^4$). Its mass is known to be 4.00396 amu. The sum of the masses of two protons and two neutrons, calculated from the values given above, is 4.03425 amu. This sum is greater than the measured mass by 0.03039 amu, the mass defect of the helium nucleus. Since mass is equivalent to energy, we may calculate that this mass difference corresponds to $0.0304 \times 931 = 28.3$ Mev of energy. This is called the *binding energy* of the protons and neutrons in the alpha particle. To break up this nucleus into its constituents, 28.3 Mev of energy would have to be supplied. Conversely, if one could somehow *synthesize* helium neuclei from neutrons and protons, 28.3 Mev of energy would be released per nucleus formed. For comparison with chemical energies, the energy released in the combustion of one carbon atom to form carbon dioxide is only 4.4 ev, more than six million times smaller.

Relatively few of the infinite number of mathematically possible combinations of protons and neutrons actually form stable nuclei. Many of the stable nuclei of lighter elements contain equal numbers of protons and neutrons, e.g., $_2\text{He}^4$, $_5\text{B}^{10}$, $_8\text{O}^{16}$, $_{10}\text{Ne}^{20}$. As we go to heavier elements the neutrons become increasingly more numerous than the protons. $_{53}\text{I}^{127}$, for example, has 74 neutrons to 53 protons, and $_{82}\text{Pb}^{206}$ has 124 neutrons to 82 protons. $_{92}\text{U}^{238}$, which is not a stable nucleus, has 146 neutrons to 92 protons. It appears that the specifically nuclear forces, those responsible for holding the nucleus together, act most strongly in light nuclei containing equal numbers of protons and neutrons, even though at the very short distances of separation within a nucleus the protons must repel each other strongly because of their like charges. This repulsion would account for the relative shortage of protons and excess of neutrons found among stable nuclei of high atomic number. Among the very heaviest atoms, this same strong repulsive force becomes reflected in radioactive instability. For all elements of atomic number 84 and above, no excess of neutrons, which contribute only attractive force, is sufficient to offset this repulsive force entirely.

The binding energy of any nucleus is a measure of its stability, although not directly. The binding energies of very heavy nuclei are higher than those of lighter nuclei simply because they contain more particles, but they are not necessarily more stable. To compare the stabilities of different nuclei, the *binding energy per particle*, total binding energy divided by mass number, is used. This quantity is plotted against mass number in Fig. 29–10. The points shown correspond to the most stable nuclei known for each of the mass numbers considered; the points have been derived from the results of many careful mass measurements. Since the binding energy axis has been arranged negatively, the *lowest* points correspond to nuclei of greatest binding energy per particle, hence with *greatest stability*. It will be noted that the nuclei of greatest stability have mass numbers in the range 50 to 60 (iron and nickel) although the region of greatest binding energy per particle forms a rather wide and shallow trough. Matter in its

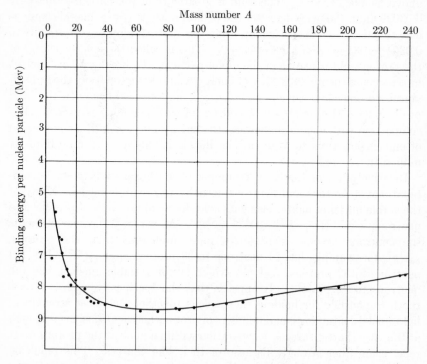

Fig. 29–10. Binding energy (in Mev) per nuclear particle (proton or neutron) for the most stable isotopes of the whole range of mass numbers.

stage of lowest energy would contain only atoms whose nuclei lie within this trough.

The curve of Fig. 29–10 shows us what general kinds of nuclear reactions may be expected to release energy. When a heavy nucleus emits an alpha particle, for example, its mass number is decreased; the new atom lies farther toward the left along the curve and has less energy. Remember that binding energy corresponds to energy given up when a nucleus is formed, so that nuclei of high binding energy *contain* less energy than those of lower binding energy. If an atom of very high mass number could somehow be split in two, the new nuclei would necessarily lie closer to the stability "trough" of Fig. 29–10 than the original. Splitting, or *fission* reactions, in heavy nuclei should therefore release energy. We can also see from the curve that the very lightest nuclei have smaller binding energies per particle than nuclei that are somewhat heavier. Accordingly, if light nuclei could somehow be made to combine to form heavier ones, in a *fusion* reaction, energy should also be released.

Nuclear reactions of the fission type were first detected and correctly identified, early in 1939, by O. Hahn and F. Strassman. Spontaneous fission is very rare, but in some kinds of heavy atoms fission can be readily induced by neutrons. The uranium isotope $_{92}U^{235}$ is one of these. There are many possible ways in which the atom may split, one of which is represented schematically in Fig. 29–11, and by the equation

$$_{92}U^{235} + _{0}n^1 \rightarrow _{36}Kr^{94} + _{56}Ba^{140} + 2_{0}n^1 + 200 \text{ Mev.} \qquad (29\text{–}4)$$

(Here the neutron is represented by n, with charge number 0 and mass number 1.) These isotopes of krypton and barium are not stable, but decay radioactively into stable nuclei; many kinds of radioactive nuclei are produced by fission reactions. The neutrons that are produced by

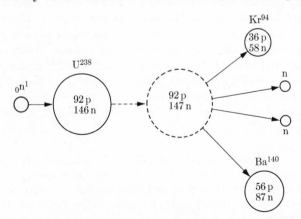

Fig. 29–11. Diagram of the reaction described by Eq. (29–4).

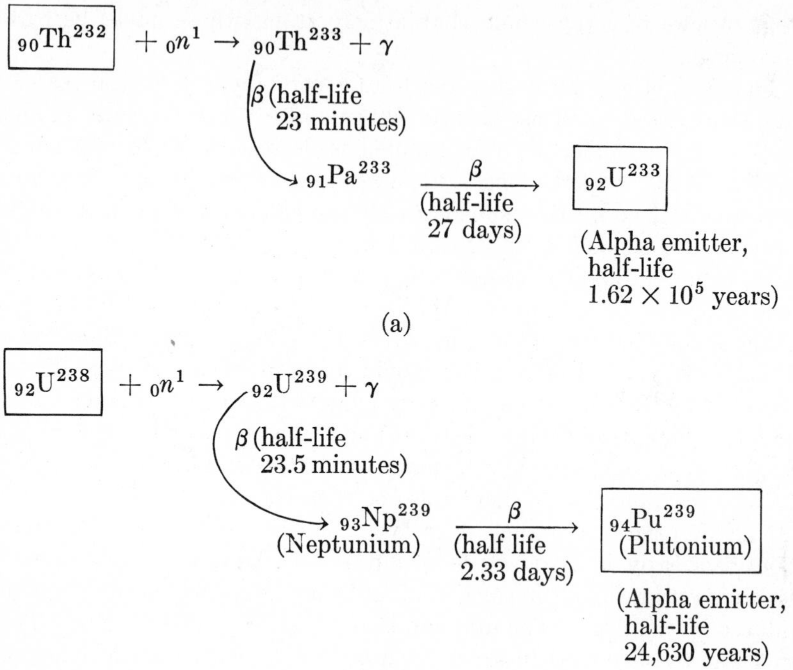

$$\boxed{_{90}Th^{232}} + _{0}n^{1} \rightarrow {_{90}Th^{233}} + \gamma$$

β (half-life
23 minutes)

$\searrow {_{91}Pa^{233}} \xrightarrow[\text{(half-life}]{\beta} \boxed{_{92}U^{233}}$
27 days)

(Alpha emitter,
half-life
1.62×10^{5} years)

(a)

$$\boxed{_{92}U^{238}} + _{0}n^{1} \rightarrow {_{92}U^{239}} + \gamma$$

β (half-life
23.5 minutes)

$\searrow {_{93}Np^{239}} \xrightarrow[\text{(half life}]{\beta} \boxed{\begin{array}{l}_{94}Pu^{239}\\ \text{(Plutonium)}\end{array}}$
(Neptunium)   2.33 days)

(Alpha emitter,
half-life
24,630 years)

(b)

FIG. 29–12. Neutron reactions which lead to production of fissionable $_{92}U^{233}$ (a), and $_{94}Pu^{239}$ (b).

fission can induce fission processes in other atoms of $_{92}U^{235}$. This is what makes possible the controlled chain reaction of the nuclear reactor, or *pile*, and the uncontrolled reaction of the atomic bomb. Only a few kinds of nuclei are so readily fissionable that they can maintain chain reactions, and $_{92}U^{235}$, an isotope amounting to less than 1% of naturally occurring uranium, is the only one found in nature. Other fissionable materials can be manufactured in quantity, however, notably $_{92}U^{233}$ and an isotope of the new element called plutonium, $_{94}Pu^{239}$. The first of these two isotopes is produced in nuclear reactors by reaction between neutrons and thorium, and the second is made similarly from the abundant uranium isotope $_{92}U^{238}$, as shown in Fig. 29–12.

In Section 5–2 we mentioned the possibility of transmuting other elements into gold. Only one isotope of gold, $_{79}Au^{197}$, is stable, but a variety of radioactive isotopes have been formed and their properties studied. For example, if mercury is bombarded with $_{1}H^{2}$ (heavy hydrogen nuclei, called *deuterons*), the following reaction is found:

$$_{80}Hg^{200} + _{1}H^{2} \rightarrow {_{79}Au^{198}} + _{2}He^{4}.$$

The resulting radioactive gold has a half-life of 2.7 days. Other unstable isotopes of gold can be formed by bombarding platinum with high-energy particles. Artificial gold is much more expensive than the ordinary kind, and hardly what the alchemists sought!

29–6 Fusion and the energy of the stars

If very light atoms can be combined (fused) to form heavier ones, according to Fig. 29–10 energy will be released. This kind of *thermonuclear* reaction can occur only at very high temperatures; the particles must be traveling at enormous speeds to get close enough to react despite their mutual electrical repulsion. Thus far, such reactions have been studied in detail only by the use of the high-energy particles produced in cyclotrons and other accelerating machines. In the so-called "hydrogen" bomb, a fission ("atomic") bomb is used to provide the high temperature necessary for the initiation of thermonuclear reactions. Sufficiently high temperatures occur in the sun and other stars, and nuclear fusion is almost certainly the source of stellar energy.

Let us consider some of the facts known about the sun, the star in which we have the greatest interest and with which mankind is best acquainted. By application of the law of gravitation it has been determined that the mass of the sun is approximately 333,000 times that of the earth. Its volume, which can be found from a measurement of the angle it subtends at the earth and knowledge of the distance from the earth to the sun, is about 1.3 million times the volume of the earth. Its average density is thus less than a third that of the earth, only about 1.4 gm/cm^3. The variations in density which occur in the sun are much greater than those of the earth, however, for several reasons. In the first place, the sun is white hot; the temperature of its surface, as determined by the whiteness, is about 6000°C. (This method for temperature determination will be discussed in Chapter 30.) It is at this temperature that light is emitted, to reach us and the rest of the universe. All forms of matter are known to be vaporized at this temperature, and most chemical compounds are dissociated into atoms. The sun, then, is a sphere of extremely hot atomic gas, and those portions of it so external as to produce the Fraunhofer absorption lines (Section 18–7) are much more rarefied than our own terrestrial atmosphere. But under the vast internal pressures that must accompany such a great total mass, the density of the solar gas in the sun's interior must be much greater than that of the liquids or solids found on earth.

The most significant feature of the sun is its continuous outpouring of energy. At the earth about 2 calories of energy reach each square centimeter of surface at right angles to the sun's rays, per minute. By a simple geometric calculation, it is found from this value that approximately 150,000 calories are given off from each square centimeter of the sun's surface every minute. This enormous outpouring of energy could take place only if the interior of the sun were much hotter than its surface; it is estimated that at the center of the sun the temperature is probably as high as 20 million degrees. From spectroscopic analysis of sunlight scientists have determined the composition of the outer layer of the sun: it contains about 95% atomic hydrogen and 4% helium, while the remaining 1% comprises sixty or more of the elements known on the earth. The sun is thus composed of familiar atoms, but in unfamiliar proportions and existing under conditions quite unknown terrestrially (except very partially and ephemerally in the explosion of a "hydrogen" bomb).

The question of the origin of the sun's heat and light, and thus, indirectly, of our own sources of useful energy—indeed, of our very existence—is probably as old as human speculation itself. Traditionally, the sun has been referred to as a "ball of fire," but actually it is much too hot to burn; small amounts of carbon and oxygen are present, but carbon dioxide is unstable at such temperatures. Heavy, naturally radioactive atoms, e.g., uranium and radium, are not present, at least not in sufficient quantities to account for the sun's energy output. It was once thought that solar energy represents the cooling of an initially much hotter body, or of a body which is continuously contracting gravitationally so that its outer constituents constantly lose kinetic energy. These possibilities are ruled out by geological evidence; from the rock record it is clear that the earth has been receiving energy from the sun at about the same rate for at least half a billion years, probably much longer. A calculation of the energy emitted by a cooling or contracting sun shows that the rate of emission would necessarily exhibit very marked changes in a much shorter time.

Conditions inside the sun are favorable for the fusion of light elements, however, and the great abundance of protons (hydrogen) constitutes a possible source of the raw material needed. Several alternative, possibly competing processes have been proposed to account for the detailed nature of the fusion reactions which produce solar energy. One possible mechanism of this energy production, consisting of reactions which have been investigated on a small scale with particle accelerators, consists of the following steps:

$$\text{(a)} \quad {}_1H^1 + {}_1H^1 \rightarrow {}_1H^2 + e^+ + \gamma,$$

$$\text{(b)} \quad {}_1H^1 + {}_1H^2 \rightarrow {}_2He^3 + \gamma,$$

$$\text{(c)} \quad {}_2He^3 + {}_2He^3 \rightarrow {}_2He^4 + 2({}_1H^1).$$

In the first step two protons react to form a deuteron (hydrogen of mass number 2), with the emission of a positron (e^+) and radiant energy designated by γ, i.e., a gamma ray. A deuteron thus formed may react with another proton as in step (b), producing the known light isotope of helium, $_2\text{He}^3$. If the He^3 nuclei become sufficiently abundant so that there is possibility of a high-energy collision between pairs of those atoms, reaction (c) may take place, producing ordinary, highly stable helium nuclei, and releasing two of the original protons. The *net* reaction is the synthesis of helium nuclei from protons, with an over-all energy release near that we have computed in Section 29–5. Production of this energy must be accompanied by loss of an equivalent quantity of mass.

Whatever the details of the process, solar energy is almost certainly produced by conversion of hydrogen to helium. From the mass-energy relationship $E = mc^2$, it has been calculated that the energy production rate of the sun corresponds to the loss of about four million tons of mass every second! In terms of particles, this means that roughly 3×10^{39} protons are converted into a quarter that number of helium nuclei per second. It is estimated that there are about 10^{56} protons in the sun, which would provide fuel for some 30 billion years even at this unbelievably prodigious rate of consumption. It is possible that a noticeable change in the sun's energy production rate may take place only a few billion years hence, however, as its composition changes toward a preponderance of helium, rather than hydrogen.

Consideration of nuclear processes and the mass-energy relationship has thus led us back to astronomy, although on a level very different from that of the Greeks and Copernicus. The fruitful applications of nuclear science to astronomy, geology, practical power production (most promising, but still in its infancy), and even as a tool in tracing life processes, have all been possible on the basis of relatively little knowledge, of a truly fundamental kind, about nuclei. Scientists have not yet determined the *nature* of the forces that bind nuclear particles together—no entirely satisfactory *theory* of nuclei has yet been devised. This challenging and important problem is being pursued simultaneously with the nuclear applications that have related all fields of natural science more closely than ever before.

29–7 Summary

In radioactivity atomic nuclei undergo spontaneous transmutation from one element to another; all elements of atomic number greater than 83 exist only in radioactive forms. Atoms of a given element (i.e., of the same atomic number) may have several different mass numbers; these atomic varieties are called *isotopes* of the element. Energy released in radioactive change is converted from mass according to the formula $E = mc^2$ derived by Einstein in the special theory of relativity. Induced nuclear changes (nuclear reactions) first confirmed quantitatively that mass is a form of energy, in accord with Einstein's equation. All nuclei are apparently made up of protons and neutrons, bound together in such a way that their energy (and thus their mass) is less than if they existed separately. This is a revival, on a refined level, of Prout's hypothesis that all elements are composed of hydrogen. The most stable (lowest-energy) nuclear species are those near the middle of the periodic table, but helium has great stability relative to protons and neutrons. The synthesis of hydrogen to form helium, with consequent release of energy as radiation, accounts for the energy of the stars.

References

Gamow, G., *The Birth and Death of the Sun*. The earlier chapters review some of the nuclear physics necessary to gain an understanding of solar energy.

Hecht, S., *Explaining the Atom*, especially as revised and enlarged by E. Rabinowitch (3rd ed.).

Humphreys, R. F., and R. Beringer, *First Principles of Atomic Physics*. Chapters 25 through 29. An elementary account.

Marshak, R., in *The New Astronomy* (a *Scientific American* book). Contains a nontechnical account of the various nuclear reactions that may take place in stars.

Oldenburg, O., *Introduction to Atomic Physics*.

Semat, H., *Physics in the Modern World*, Chapter XII.

Semat, H., *Introduction to Atomic and Nuclear Physics*.

1. What is meant by the "half-life" of a radioactive element? The half-life of the radioactive gas radon is 3.82 days. Suppose that a sample of pure radon is collected; what percentage of the gas will remain after 7.64 days? After 11.46 days? [*Ans.*: 25%, 12.5%]

2. In mass spectroscopic determinations the common isotope of oxygen is taken as 16.00000, whereas in chemistry the mixture of naturally occurring oxygen isotopes (see Table 29–2) is taken as 16.00000, thus giving rise to two slightly different atomic weight scales. On which scale would the values for atomic weights be larger? (The actual ratio between the two scales is not quite 1.0003, but the small difference of this ratio from unity is significant in nuclear work.)

3. On the basis of conservation of both charge and mass numbers, complete the equations for the following nuclear reactions:

(a) $_9F^{19} + {_1H^1} \rightarrow {_8O^{16}} + ?$

(b) $_6C^{12} + {_1H^1} \rightarrow ? + \gamma$

(c) $_5B^{10} + {_0n^1} \rightarrow {_3Li^7} + ?$

(d) $_7N^{14} + ? \rightarrow {_5B^{11}} + {_2He^4}$

(e) $_7N^{14} + {_1H^2} \rightarrow {_7N^{15}} + ?$

4. The masses of the atoms involved in Eq. (29–2) are known to be 14.0075 for $_7N^{14}$, 4.0039 for $_2He^4$, 17.0045 for $_8O^{17}$, and 1.0081 for $_1H^1$. Is the reaction endothermic or exothermic? By how much? [*Partial answer*: 0.0012 amu of mass is gained]

5. The kinetic energy of the alpha particles used in Rutherford's experiment, Eq. (29–2), was estimated to be 7.7 Mev. Find the total kinetic energy of the products, taking into account the gain in mass (Exercise 4).

6. The equation for the reaction in which the neutron was discovered is

$$_4Be^9 + {_2He^4} \rightarrow {_6C^{12}} + {_0n^1}.$$

The masses involved are now known to be 9.0149 for Be^9, 4.0039 for He^4, 12.0038 for C^{12}, and 1.0090 for the neutron (all to the fourth decimal place only). Is kinetic energy lost or gained in this reaction? How much?

7. A nuclear reactor, or pile, produces power as the result of fission of U^{235} or other fissionable material, which is then called nuclear "fuel." What would correspond to nuclear "ashes" in such a power plant?

8. Why are high temperatures necessary for thermonuclear reactions if the products of the reaction are in lower energy states than the initial reactant nuclei?

9. The natural radioactive decay series which begins with the thorium isotope $_{90}Th^{232}$ proceeds by a series of alpha- and beta-particle emission steps, as follows:

$A\,({}_{90}\text{Th}^{232})$

$\quad\downarrow \alpha$

B

$\quad\downarrow \beta$

C

$\quad\downarrow \beta$

D

$\quad\downarrow \alpha$

E

$\quad\downarrow \alpha$

F

$\quad\downarrow \alpha$

G

$\quad\downarrow \alpha$

H

$\quad\downarrow \beta$

I

$\quad\downarrow \beta$

J

$\quad\downarrow \alpha$

$K\,({}_{82}\text{Pb}^{208},\text{ stable})$

Identify the atomic number, mass number and elemental symbol for each

nuclear species B through J. Construct a diagram similar to Fig. 29–1 for this series.

10. The radioactive substance called I in Exercise 9 has alternative modes of decay. About two-thirds of the I atoms which decay in any interval of time emit beta particles, as shown in Exercise 9, but about one-third emit alphas. The final product, ${}_{82}\text{Pb}^{208}$, is thus achieved by an alternative route:

$$I$$
$$\downarrow \alpha$$
$$L$$
$$\downarrow \beta$$
$$K\,({}_{82}\text{Pb}^{208})$$

This constitutes one of several "branches" which are observed in the radioactive decay chains. Identify the nuclear species L, and show this branch on the diagram you have constructed for the thorium decay series.

CHAPTER 30

STARS AND GALAXIES

We have seen that the study of radioactivity, atomic spectra, and other related phenomena has brought, within little more than half a century, profound understanding of the submicroscopic aspects of atoms and molecules, and of the very large manifestations of change in rocks and stars. Rocks and stars are more closely related than might appear at first sight. Geological history is defined as beginning with an earth much as we find it now, in broad character although not in detail. What happened earlier? How was the earth formed? There are no definitive answers to such questions as yet, but one thing is clear: the answers will depend on a study of the stars and interstellar matter; the earth, and even the solar system as a whole, cannot be regarded in isolation.

In this book we began with astronomy as the oldest physical science in the modern (i.e., rational) sense of the word. Ancient astronomy was essentially confined to the solar system, as the stars themselves were considered fixed on their crystalline sphere, and immutable. Men like Bruno came to shatter the crystal sphere and to imagine the stars to be distributed through an infinity of space. More recently has come the realization that stars are in a state of constant change. The very fact that we see them is evidence of this, for they must lose energy in order to emit the radiation which reaches us. But the rate of change in most stars is so slow that their main characteristics have not been observably affected within the span of human history and much of the basis for deciphering stellar history must come from a synthesis of information concerning many different stars. The techniques for distinguishing stellar motions and composition have been developed only in the last century, so that stellar astronomy, strictly speaking, is a new science, in contrast to the ancient science of the solar system. Let us begin by identifying some of the most important of these new techniques.

30-1 New astronomical tools and methods

Since early in the 17th century the telescope has been the traditional instrument for extending our information about the heavens. The primary advantage of a well-constructed large telescope is its light-gathering power; millions of stars too faint to affect the eye can be detected by such an instrument and photographed for detailed study. The earliest telescopes made use of lenses, and these *refracting* telescopes are still useful. The use of a simple magnifying glass is limited to the magnification of objects that can be placed near it. For distant objects, such as stars, the trick is to use another lens to produce an image that can be viewed with a magnifier at a short distance. The lens that first receives the light behaves like that of a camera, except that no plate or film need be used where the image is formed. It is advantageous to make this first lens wide in aperture, to gather as much light as possible, and also of very long focal length, to produce a large image. Figure 30–1 is a diagram of Kepler's telescope, which was of this kind. The chief difficulty with refracting telescopes is that different wavelengths of light are brought to a focus at different distances, so that the resulting image is blurred. This difficulty is called *chromatic aberration*. In modern instruments this defect is largely overcome by the use of *achromatic* lenses, combinations of lenses of different kinds of glass such that the separation of colors by one component lens is canceled by that of another.

The largest telescopes are based on the principle that light entering along the axis of a parabolic mirror is reflected to a point focus. Reflection does not separate colors, so that chromatic aberration is not introduced. The first reflecting telescope actually constructed was made about 1668 by Newton, whose experiments with color (see Section 17–3) led him to believe that achromatic lenses were impossible. Figure 30–2 is a diagram of Newton's telescope; a prism was used to deflect the focused image to the side, although a plane mirror at an angle would have done as well. The simple magnifier by which the image is viewed introduced relatively little color separation. The largest of all telescopes at the present time is a reflector of 200-inch diameter on Mt. Palomar in southern California, and

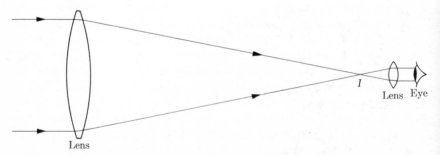

Fig. 30–1. Kepler's telescope (a refractor). Light from a distant star enters the lens on the left and is brought to a focus at I; in other words, the first lens acts like that of a camera. This image is viewed through a simple magnifier.

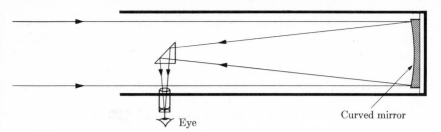

Fig. 30–2. Newton's reflecting telescope. The prism was used to reflect light to the side; a plane mirror at an angle would have done as well.

its possibilities for extending astronomical information have only begun to be realized. Smaller telescopes, not capable of collecting so much light, have compensating advantages for certain kinds of measurements, and many different varieties of telescopes are needed to round out our knowledge of the stars.

Astronomical records are now almost exclusively made by photography, and not by visual observation of an enlarged telescopic image. The simple magnifier, or *eyepiece*, of a reflector or a refractor may be removed and a photographic plate inserted to record the image; the telescope thus becomes a gigantic camera. Photography has the advantage that the record is permanent and that long exposures can be made, while films of various color sensitivity give a more accurate account of color than can be obtained visually.   Photographic plates sensitive to the ultraviolet or the infrared record information that the eye is incapable of receiving.   The photoelectric cell is also employed for determining accurately the amount of energy received from any particular star.

The combination of telescopes with prisms or diffraction gratings makes it possible to photograph the spectra of the stars, and thus to obtain information concerning their chemical composition and several other properties. Most stars, including the sun, give *dark-line* spectra, indicating the presence of a relatively cool outer layer of gas that absorbs some of the light emanating from the main body of the star (cf. Section 18–7).   It is always the composition of the external envelope that is primarily determined by spectral analysis. Some stars give *bright-line* spectra, but again we see only the lines originating in the outer layers.   The study of stellar spectra also results in information on the speed of the star and its temperature. Let us see qualitatively how this information is derived.

If a given star is observed over a long period, changes in its position may be detected, from which it must be inferred that the star is in motion. This observed motion would have to be perpendicular to the line of sight, since motion toward or away from us would result in no apparent change in position.   But in many cases speeds along the line of sight can be determined from stellar spectra, by application of what is known as the *Doppler principle*, after its discoverer, Christian Johann Doppler (1803-1853). This principle applies to wave motion of all kinds: if a source of waves is approaching the observer the received frequency is increased, i.e., the successive vibrations need to travel shorter and shorter distances, and are therefore received at shorter intervals than those at which they are actually emitted. Conversely, if the source is receding from the observer, the successive vibrations arrive at longer time intervals. The first case is indicated in Fig. 30–3; if the source remains at A the wave pattern at a given instant is that shown by the solid line, but if A travels to A' with one-fourth the speed of wave transmission, the same number of vibrations as before sets up a pattern of shorter waves in the direction of the observer at B. The observed change in frequency due to motion of the source depends on the velocity of the source but not on its distance. In the spectrum of a particular star a certain configuration of lines can be recognized as characteristic of some one element, as noted in Section 18–7, except that all the lines may be displaced toward the red or toward the blue in comparison with their frequencies as known from laboratory sources. The amount of "Doppler shift" of each line is consistent with a particular speed of recession or approach, and thus this speed can be computed.

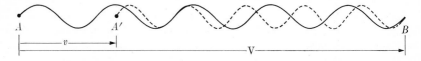

FIG. 30–3. Wave pattern in the direction of B corresponding to waves emitted during one second by a source at rest (solid line) and one which moves from A to A' during the interval.

Spectral lines may be shifted for other reasons as well, so that considerable care must be exercised in the interpretation of spectra, but the Doppler effect has been applied without ambiguity to determine the line-of-sight velocities of thousands of stars.

A sufficiently good formula for the Doppler shift is easily derived with reference to Fig. 30–3. Source A emits vibrations at frequency n (5 vibrations per second in the diagram) and moves with speed v, while the speed of the waves is V. Each wavelength is shortened by an amount v/n, the distance traveled by the source during one vibration. The wavelength λ when A stands still satisfies $V = n\lambda$ (Eq. 16–1), while the observed wavelength λ' is given by

$$\lambda' = \lambda - \frac{v}{n}$$

$$= \lambda - \frac{v\lambda}{V},$$

when V/λ is substituted for n. This equation may be written in the form

$$\frac{\lambda - \lambda'}{\lambda} = \frac{v}{V},$$

that is, the ratio of the change in wavelength to the customary wavelength is equal to the ratio of the speeds of the source and the wave transmission. If the source is receding the wavelength is lengthened, but the ratio of the change in wavelength to the unchanged wavelength is still v/V.

———————

One method of determining the temperatures of stars—at least the temperatures of their exteriors from which we receive radiation directly—depends on an application of Wien's displacement law (Wilhelm Wien, 1864–1928). It is a familiar fact that the color of an incandescent body is an indication of its temperature: a white-hot body is hotter than one that is only red hot, and the color becomes bluer and less yellow as the temperature increases. There are several ways of making this observation quantitative, but all depend on spreading out the radiation, according to wavelength, by some spectroscopic instrument. The intensity of the radiation may then be plotted against frequency, as in Fig. 30–4, and the resulting curve shows a maximum at some particular frequency range. According to Wien's law, the absolute temperature of the emitter is directly proportional to the frequency at which most radiation is given off (and thus inversely proportional to the wavelength of this maximum of radiated energy). Such determinations of temperature can be applied to stellar spectra, although care must be taken to allow for possible distortions of the energy distribution that might be due to absorption in the atmosphere or in the optical instruments used.

The atmosphere absorbs much of the ultraviolet radiation and that in the far infrared, so that astronomical information that might be derived from those parts of the electromagnetic spectrum (see Section 17–8) is denied to observers on the earth's surface. A very wide range of radio waves is transmitted by the atmosphere, however, and the most recent revolution in astronomical technique has consisted of the development of radio telescopes. As is well known, radio waves can penetrate materials that are opaque to ordinary light. Modern astronomers have discovered

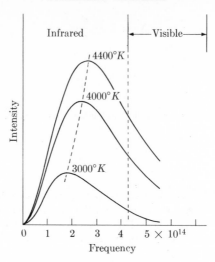

Fig. 30–4. Intensity of radiation plotted against frequency for three different source temperatures. The peaks lie in the infrared for these terrestrial sources, but for some stars they lie in the visible or ultraviolet.

much opaque material in interstellar space that makes certain parts of the sky behave like dense curtains toward visible radiation. Radio waves can penetrate these curtains, however. Furthermore, many stellar and interstellar sources of radio waves produce so little radiation in the optical range that their existence has been detected only through radioastronomy. Radio telescopes are instruments that can collect and focus long electromagnetic waves, so that details of "celestial transmitters" can be mapped out and compared with photographs of the skies. Radioastronomy is so new that its possibilities are as yet difficult to appraise, but it opens a whole new window on the universe. Some of the information already available by radio techniques is included in the sections that follow.

30–2 Stellar characteristics

The few thousand stars that can be seen with the naked eye differ in brightness and somewhat in color, but closer examination reveals much greater and more significant differences. The many millions of stars brought within range by the telescope add to the great variety observable. All individual stars must differ from each other to some degree, but they have certain properties by which they may be classified as to type. Let us first note that to describe a star itself we must try to eliminate any factors that would depend on our position with relation to the star. *Apparent* brightness depends on the distance of a star as well as on how much light it actually radiates, and a knowledge of distance is thus important. The measure of radiated energy is given as the *intrinsic* brightness or *luminosity* of the star, or, even more technically, as its *absolute magnitude*. (Note that *magnitude* in this technical sense is a measure of brightness, and is not defined as the size or mass of a star.)

Stellar distances are conveniently measured in *light years*, one light year being the distance light traverses in one year, or 5.88×10^{12} miles. All stellar distance determinations depend on parallax (see Section 1–7), but only for the nearest stars can parallax be measured directly. The base line of the earth's orbit, with the aid of high-precision techniques, permits the direct parallax determination of about 5000 stars against the more distant background. This sampling of stars fortunately includes almost all recognizable types of stars, so that greater stellar distances can be found indirectly, by a series of comparisons. If the intrinsic brightness of a star can be determined by correlation of some feature of its spectrum, for example, with that of a star at known distance, a comparison of apparent and absolute magnitude will yield the actual distance. We shall return to this point.

For stars whose distance can be measured directly, the intrinsic brightness may be readily computed from the apparent brightness. There would be no difference between apparent and intrinsic brightness if the stars were all at the same distance from the earth, as, for example, on the crystalline sphere of Greek cosmology. When we determine apparent brightness we are measuring the light received from a star per unit area; the area utilized may be that of the pupil of the eye or of the telescope tube. The radiation received from any source is proportional to that actually emitted but it is distributed over a sphere that expands with the velocity of light, and the energy received per unit area at any particular distance

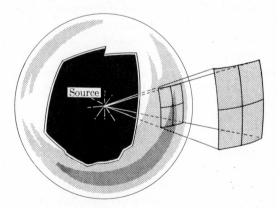

FIG. 30–5. The area of spherical surface over which energy is distributed varies as the square of its distance from the source.

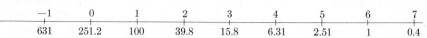

Conventional
magnitude

−1	0	1	2	3	4	5	6	7
631	251.2	100	39.8	15.8	6.31	2.51	1	0.4

Amount of
light received

FIG. 30–6. The amount of light corresponding to magnitude numbers is shown on an arbitrary scale on which unity corresponds to magnitude 6, the faintest magnitude visible to the unaided eye. Each magnitude is a little more than $2\frac{1}{2}$ times as bright as the one to its right. Hipparchus established the use of magnitudes 1 to 6 in his catalog of stars, but the numbers are now extended as far as necessary. The (apparent) magnitude of the sun on this scale is −26.7.

from the source is inversely proportional to the square of that distance. (The area of the spherical surface over which the energy is distributed varies as the square of its radius, as shown in Fig. 30–5. Hence the energy per unit area at distance r varies as $1/r^2$. The same law governs the distribution of light from an unshaded reading lamp; if you double the distance from the lamp the amount of light received on your book, for example, decreases by a factor of four.) If brightness were measured on a linear scale, all energy measurement could be transformed from apparent to absolute by multiplying the amount of light received by the square of the distance in some appropriate units. Luminosity is, in fact, measured on a scale that substitutes factors (multiples) for additive increments, in a way shown in Fig. 30–6. This is called a logarithmic scale. Such scales represent the intensity of sensation more accurately than do linear scales, and have the additional advantage of compressing the range of large variations so that graphical representation is facilitated.

Let us now turn to the question of stellar masses. Once the gravitational constant and the mass of the earth are known, the mass of the sun, as we saw in Chapter 4, can be determined by equating the force of attraction to that necessary to keep the earth in its orbit. The same method cannot be applied to individual stars in general, because the forces acting on them are not known. At least in our neighborhood of the universe, however, there are many stars that are double, or members of multiple systems. A pair of stars that rotate about each other is called a binary system, or simply a *binary*; if their orbits and speeds can be found, either visually or by application of the Doppler principle, the laws of gravitation and mechanics can be applied to determine their masses. (The details are straightforward but rather complicated, and may be found in either of the astronomy textbooks listed at the end of this chapter.) There are double stars of all the types we shall meet in Section 30–3, and generalizations concerning mass can be extended to stars that are single.

The sizes of stars (as distinct from their masses) cannot be measured directly, for each star appears as a single point on a photographic plate; the area of the image reflects only the amount of light received. But size can be determined indirectly by the use of a relation that governs the emission of radiation. Figure 30–4 shows that it is not only the color of a body that changes as its temperature is raised; the total *amount* of light that it gives off also increases. A lamp filament that is only red hot radiates very little energy in comparison with the same filament when it is white hot. Physicists have worked out a formula (called the Stefan-Boltzmann law) relating the temperature to the energy radiated *per unit area*, exactly valid only for an ideal radiator known as a "blackbody," but approximately valid for all radiating bodies. According to this law, the *total* energy emitted per unit area varies as the fourth power of the temperature. If we interpret intrinsic brightness as the total rate of emission of energy, we find the size of the star by comparison with the theoretical prediction for the radiation per unit area at the observed temperature. For some stars size may be estimated from other considerations, and the results strengthen our confidence in the application of the radiation law.

Stars may be distinguished by further characteristics which we shall discuss in later sections, but we must note the wide variations in size, mass, brightness, and temperature. The greatest variation is in energy radiated; the very brightest stars give off as much as 10^{12} (a million million) times as much light as the faintest. Surface temperatures of stars range from less than 2000°C to about 100,000°C. The masses of known stars vary by a factor of only about 1000, but their diameters differ by as much as a factor of 300,000; the very largest stars are the most diffuse, so that they are not correspondingly massive.

30–3 Classification of stars

In view of the tremendous differences in the simple stellar characteristics we have considered, it is of great interest to note any regularities or relations among the various properties of stars. Let us temporarily disregard size and mass, and consider only brightness and temperature. The Danish astronomer Ejnar Hertzsprung found a way of arranging stars on a diagram according to brightness and temperature which demonstrated the existence of a very clear grouping. This result was confirmed independently by the great American astronomer Henry Norris Russell in 1913, and this method of representing stars is called the Hertzsprung-Russell (or simply H-R) diagram. Figure 30–7 is such a diagram; brightness is plotted on a vertical scale, decreasing downward, and temperature horizontally, decreasing toward the right. The scales are not linear, but

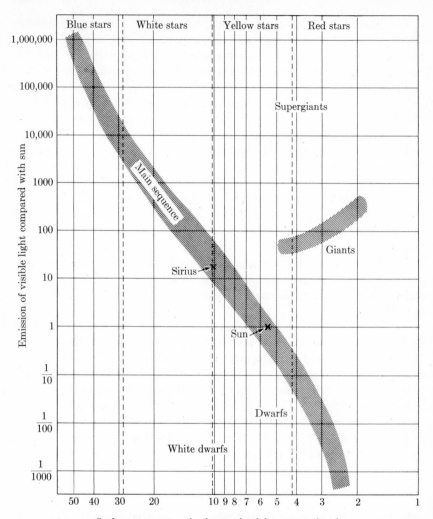

FIG. 30–7. H-R diagram of our neighboring stars, with the shaded portions corresponding to greatest density of stars (Type I).

logarithmic, and are chosen so as to represent the great variety of temperature and energy radiation most simply on a single graph. As we have seen, temperature is correlated with color; the dotted vertical lines roughly divide the stars into four relative color groups, ranging from blue on the left to red on the right. Note that the brightness scale relative to the sun is marked in equal steps, but that each step represents a factor of 10, not a constant increment. When the stars in our neighborhood are represented by dots on this diagram, the majority of points fall into the diagonal band running from the upper left to the lower right. This band is called the *main sequence*. Note the position of the sun itself, which is a rather average yellow star in the sequence. The only concentration other than that observed in the main sequence appears in an isolated band of bright stars toward the right of the diagram. These luminous red stars, named "giants" by Hertzsprung, are brighter than those of the same surface temperature in the main sequence, and hence must be greater in size than equally bright stars in the main sequence. Very few of our neighboring stars fall into other parts of the diagram; those to the far upper right are called *supergiants*, and a smaller number of *white dwarfs*, much hotter than the average for their brightness, is found on the lower left.

Figure 30–7 bears the designation *Type I*, and we have been careful to specify that it represents the stars in our own neighborhood. Since these are just the stars most available to us for study and classification, it was thought for a long time that the general contour of Fig. 30–7 represented all stars. Inconsistencies began to arise, however, which were resolved in 1944 by Walter Baade of the Mt. Wilson Observatory. Baade discovered that stars fall into two broad types, or *populations*. Population I, characteristic of our particular neighborhood, occurs in the spiral arms of galaxies (see Section 30–4) where there is considerable interstellar matter either in the form of interstellar gas or as tiny cosmic "dust" particles. Population II occurs in dust-free regions, including galactic centers; its most luminous stars are red, and not as bright as the luminous blue stars at the upper left of the main sequence on the H-R diagram. There are also differences in composition; spectroscopic analysis shows that Population I stars are richer in metals. The temperature-luminosity characteristics of the two populations are compared in Fig. 30–8; the brightest stars of Population II are more luminous than Hertzsprung's giants, but not as bright as the relatively rare supergiants at the same temperature.

The method of determining stellar masses described in Section 30–2, although not reliable for Population II, has been extensively applied to Population I. It is instructive to make a diagram of brightness against mass for Population I. The result is as indicated qualitatively in Fig. 30–9, where the scale is again logarithmic; it is striking that the giants and main sequence stars now fall in the same narrow band. This relation, first noted by Sir Arthur Eddington (1882–1944), is known as the mass-luminosity law, and indicates that Population I stars of the same mass have the same intrinsic brightness, whether they are ordinary (main sequence) or relatively dilute and swollen (giants). The white dwarfs are exceptional; they are much too faint for their masses to satisfy the mass-luminosity relation.

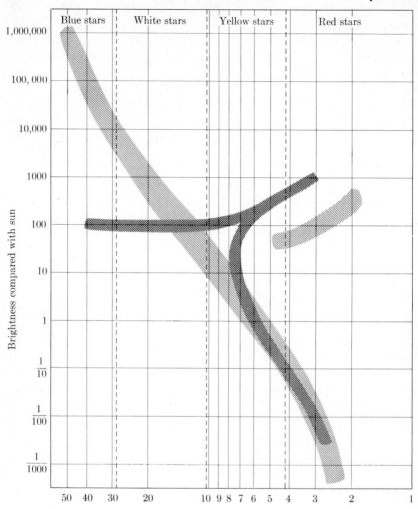

Temperature in thousands of degrees centigrade

FIG. 30–8. Typical H-R distribution of Population II, superposed on the faintly shaded concentrations of Population I.

It has already been indicated that detailed analysis of stellar spectra yields information on chemical composition, although the identification of atomic species by their characteristic spectra is complicated by the prevalence of temperature conditions not readily attainable on the earth. It is evident from these studies that stellar atoms are ordinary atoms; no evidence has been found of matter in stars or in interstellar space which is different from that to which we are accustomed around us. There is

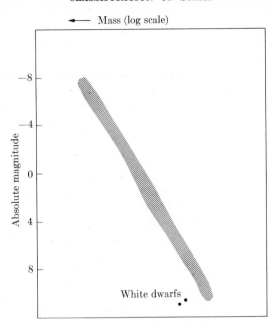

Fɪɢ. 30–9. On a mass-luminosity diagram all Population I stars fall into the shaded portion except the white dwarfs.

relatively much more hydrogen and helium than on the earth, apparently, and there are very few molecules except on the coolest stars. Perhaps the most astonishing result, because it is not immediately apparent from the variety of stellar spectra corresponding to such wide variations of temperature, is that practically all stars seem to be made up of essentially the same kinds of matter in approximately the same proportions. Such differences as that of metal atoms between Populations I and II amount to no more than a small fraction of one percent, but differences even of this small magnitude must be considered significant. It is difficult to estimate the relative abundance of the various kinds of atoms in the universe, since we can get no direct information as to the composition of the interiors of stars. The general uniformity of matter extends to the material distributed throughout interstellar space, however, as well as to the outer layers (at least) of the stars themselves.

We should note that stars are classified by astronomers according to what is called *spectral type*, in addition to a luminosity classification. Each type of spectrum is represented by a letter of the alphabet in the order *O B A F G K M* (with some additions for unusual stars). This classification is almost identical with that based purely on temperature, with the order as written above representing decreasing temperature. The observed spectral differences are in the main due simply to temperature differences; the same kinds of atoms radiate differently according to the temperature of the gas, reflecting different degrees of excitation and ionization. Spectral type is so familiar to astronomers that stellar properties are usually shown in reference texts in relation to this series of letters instead of a temperature scale. It will suffice in using these references to remember that the hottest stars are those of type O, the next hottest B, etc.

30–4 Galaxies and stellar clusters

Starlight is not received in equal intensity at the earth from all parts of the heavens; a large part of it comes from the luminous band called the Milky Way. Even a small telescope or a pair of good binoculars reveals that the vast circle of the Milky Way is made up of many faint individual stars, and it is thus clear that the stars we can distinguish are not distributed uniformly throughout space. We see most readily the stars nearest us, of course, and these stars are grouped in a huge system that is rather flattened. It is this system that is called our *galaxy*, a word derived from the Greek equivalent of Milky Way.

Galaxy is the term now applied to all such aggregates of stars, together with their accompanying luminous interstellar gas and dark dust. Millions of galaxies are observable with techniques already at hand, all differing in size and content, but each containing millions of stars. Some are irregular in shape, others symmetrical in a way that suggests that they are rotating. Many have spiral arms, probably as a result of nonrigid rotation. The great galaxy in the constellation *Andromeda*, shown in Fig. 30–10, has typical spiral form. This galaxy is nearer our own Milky Way than any other. Figure 30–11 is a photograph of a galaxy in the constellation *Ursa Major*, and shows spiral structure with exceptional clarity. Figure 30–12, another galaxy found in the vicinity of *Andromeda*, is seen in edge-on view. Its spiral arms cannot be distinguished, but other features of galactic structure are brought out. The galaxy consists of a relatively thin disk, but with a very dense concentration of stars which thickens the disk at its center.

Our own galaxy is larger than most, although not quite so large as the great Andromeda Nebula. It has been difficult to get as clear an idea of its over-all shape as we have of other galaxies, just because we are inside it. Moreover, many of its stars are obscured from our view by intervening clouds of dust. Nevertheless it has become evident that the galaxy has spiral form; a preliminary map of spiral arms is shown in Fig. 30–13. The sun lies in one spiral arm, toward the edge of the galaxy, but there are at least two other arms farther from the galactic center than we are. The speed of rotation of the solar system about the galactic center has been estimated

Fig. 30–10. Great Nebula in *Andromeda* (Messier 31), photographed with a 48-inch telescope. (Courtesy of Mt. Wilson and Palomar Observatories.)

FIG. 30–11. Spiral galaxy in *Ursa Major* (Messier 81), photographed with the 200-inch telescope. (Courtesy of Mt. Wilson and Palomar Observatories.)

Fig. 30–12. Spiral nebula in *Andromeda* (NGC 891), seen edge on. Photographed with a 60-inch telescope. (Courtesy of Mt. Wilson and Palomar Observatories.)

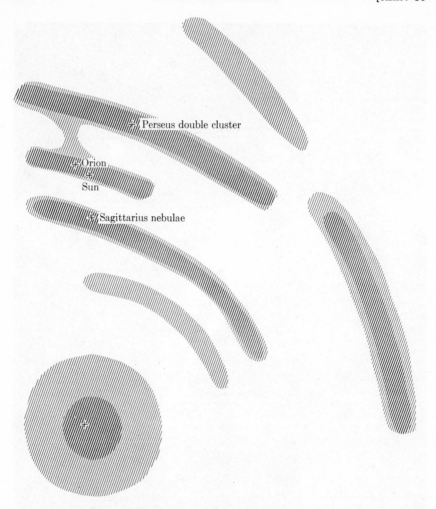

Perseus double cluster

Orion

Sun

Sagittarius nebulae

Fig. 30–13. A preliminary map of the spiral arms of our galaxy, showing the position of the sun. (Courtesy of *Scientific American*.)

to be about 200 km/sec. The absolute size of our galaxy is too large to be easily comprehended: estimates run up to 100,000 light years for the diameter, and about a tenth as much for the thickness at the center. The galactic center is bright, but obscured from us visually by dust; we know of it only by radioastronomy. The stars in the spiral arms are accompanied by much dust and by luminous gas, often concentrated into bright *diffuse nebulae*. Figure 30–13 is constructed to show that the average density of detectable matter is very much lower in the region between galactic spiral arms than within the arms themselves. These regions are not entirely

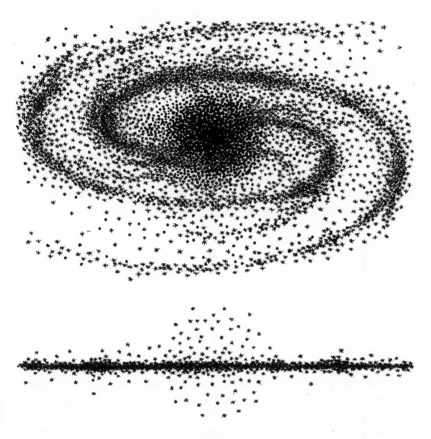

Population I

Population II

Fig. 30–14.　Distribution of populations in a spiral galaxy.　Dots represent stars of Population II, "stars" those of Population I.　(Courtesy of *Scientific American*.)

empty, however, but contain numerous Population I stars similar to our sun, often called "Common Stars." There is very much less interstellar gas and dust between spiral arms than within them.

Aggregates of stars known as *galactic clusters* are observed in or near the plane of the Milky Way; they belong to Population I, and constitute small knots in the spiral arms. The most familiar galactic cluster is that called the Pleiades, shown on the star map of Fig. 1–2. Many galactic clusters are sufficiently near so that the motions of their individual stars may be studied in detail; they move as a group, which suggests that they had a common origin. Galactic clusters also partake of the galactic rotation, as does the gas and interstellar dust. In contrast to the known galactic clusters, *globular clusters* are more compact, larger, much more populous, and more distant; some 100 globular clusters have been found in our galaxy, but the fact that they are more distant means that they are more rare than galactic clusters. Globular clusters are singularly free of interstellar dust, and their brightest stars are red, not blue; their stars belong to Population II. These clusters are a part of the galaxy, but have motions apparently independent of the galactic rotation. Figure 30–14 shows a simplified typical distribution of Populations I and II in the same galaxy; the spherical nucleus is shown here as a globular cluster, but in an actual galaxy with millions of stars there may be many smaller clusters of this sort as well.

Figure 30–14 could not have been constructed on the basis of our knowledge of our own galaxy, as is clear from the incomplete and preliminary character of Fig. 30–13. General information on galactic structure is derived from the study of external galaxies. These vast systems are found throughout all space the largest telescopes can explore. Most of them are

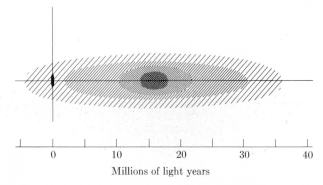

Millions of light years

FIG. 30–15. Schematic cross section of our supergalaxy, whose center is toward Virgo (see Fig. 1–2). The vertical plane of our galaxy, shown at the left from the edge and in much exaggerated scale, is approximately at right angles to the central plane of the supergalaxy. (Courtesy of *Scientific American*.)

regular, either elliptical or spiral. Almost all galaxies are well separated from each other, but they often form clusters, and there is recent evidence that our Milky Way system is a member of a supergalaxy (Fig. 30–15), some 40 million light years wide and a few million light years thick, that comprises perhaps ten thousand or more individual galaxies! But the mere recital of these dimensions raises the question of how such large distances, and those even greater, can be measured. Astronomers have found their "yardstick" in the variability of certain stars, which we shall consider only qualitatively.

30–5 Visible stellar changes

The stars as a whole change very slowly, by standards of human life-time. If one of the Babylonians came back tonight and had a look at the sky, he would have no difficulty at all in finding his familiar constellations, and only after some very careful checking against the old records would he be able to find any indications of change. The bright stars described in Hipparchus' catalog are still bright stars. There have been famous exceptions, of which the most spectacular have been "new stars," or *novae*. (Novae really do not change the sky picture at all, because they are short-lived.) Two novae so bright that they undoubtedly occurred in our own galaxy were significant in the struggle to overthrow the limited cosmology inherited from the Greeks: Tycho's new star (1572) and that of Kepler (1604). Many novae have been observed in modern times, although less spectacular than these because farther away, and it has been established that the phenomenon results from the explosion of a star. In an ordinary nova a star loses only a fraction of its matter in the explosion; it is probably as though a star of mass similar to that of the sun shoots off an amount of gas equivalent to the mass of the earth. Occasionally a star disintegrates to a very large extent, forming what is called a *supernova*. The new stars of Tycho and Kepler must have been supernovae, for no remains have been detected despite search with powerful telescopes. The greatest known supernova in our galaxy appeared on July 4, 1054, as we know from excellent Chinese records. The remains are still visible tele-scopically, and are known as the Crab Nebula. This nebula is one of the most powerful radio-wave emitters in the sky.

Much more common than novae are the variable stars, those that pulsate in brightness more or less rhythmically, growing brighter and then fading again, over and over. Of particular interest, because they have furnished us with distance scales for stars very far away, are the Cepheid variables, named for one of their number, a visible star in the constellation Cepheus, near the pole opposite the Great Dipper. The periods of Cepheid variables range from as little as a day to more than a month, many of them brightening gradually and dimming rather suddenly, others changing more smoothly. Let us see how they came to be "yardsticks" for distances too great to be measured in any ordinary way.

Very few Cepheid variables are near enough so that their distances may be readily measured, and what is observed, of course, is only their apparent magnitudes. In the study of Cepheid variables in a relatively small galaxy known as the Lesser Magellanic Cloud (first reported to northern civilizations by members of Magellan's crew on the famous circumnavigation of the globe), the American astronomer Henrietta S. Leavitt (1868–1921) discovered a striking relation: *the variables with longer periods appear brighter.* Now the stars in a single remote galaxy are close together in comparison with their distance from us, and Miss Leavitt concluded that the long-period stars must be really brighter, and that the period must be correlated with *intrinsic* brightness. If this is true, it should be possible to measure the period of any Cepheid variable and thus determine its absolute magnitude, regardless of its distance. Since the apparent magnitude is actually observed, comparison with this calculated intrinsic brightness would yield the distance!

The distance calibration presented a difficult problem, but Harlow Shapley was able to determine a distance scale in absolute terms from the study of Milky Way variables. The method has been refined since Miss Leavitt's original work in 1905, and two distinct classes of Cepheids are now recognized, corresponding to stars of Populations I and II as distinguished at the end of Section 30–4. It is by determining the periods of these variables in distant galaxies that their actual distances are found. Individual stars can be resolved only up to distances of 20 million light years, even with the 200-inch telescope, and therefore this is as far as the method can be applied directly. Beyond this distance astronomers extrapolate on the assumption that galaxies in one large region of space are as intrinsically bright, on the average, as those in any other region. There is no real justification for this assumption, but on the other hand there is no reason to believe that the nature of space and its contents change just at the limit of resolution of present-day telescopes.

We should note that the reason for the observed pulsation of variable stars is not clear. The material of which a star is made is held together by gravitation, but it is also subject to tremendous pressures as a result of the internal energy release. It may be that these pressures become so great that expansion takes place to relieve them, and after relief the star contracts again. But why some stars should have begun this kind of periodic expansion and others not is a matter for future scientists to ascertain.

30–6 Stellar evolution

It is abundantly clear that even nonvariable stars are changing, and that in some way this change constitutes a history. There is much evidence that the stars, like members of a human population, are of widely different individual ages. Stellar history is one of the most fascinating problems of modern science, but the subject is so new that it still involves much uncertainty and speculation. Fortunately, excellent nontechnical accounts are accessible, especially in the magazines *Sky and Telescope* and *Scientific American*, by means of which it is possible for the layman to keep well abreast of current developments. Here we give a brief resumé of some of the ideas astronomers found most acceptable in 1956, which may serve as a background for keeping up with exciting new theories and discoveries. Much fuller accounts are contained in the references listed at the end of this chapter, especially those of most recent date; it is particularly important in such a young science that sources of information be up to date as well as professionally responsible.

Historically it was inevitable that the source of solar energy should become a subject for scientific inquiry once the principle of conservation of energy was established. In 1854 Helmholtz advanced the hypothesis that the mutual gravitational attraction of the particles composing a star (specifically, the sun) may cause it to contract, and in this process gravitational potential energy would be converted into kinetic energy, that is, into heat. This process is undoubtedly an important one in stellar changes, but it cannot account for the facts. Lord Kelvin showed that the sun could last only about 40 million years on the heat generated in this way, whereas geological evidence that the sun has been shining a much longer time is unambiguous. Henry Norris Russell attempted to improve and refine the Helmholtz hypothesis to account for the main sequence of stars on the H-R diagram, which was thought to indicate the various stages in stellar evolution, but the energy transformations involved could not be satisfactorily explained.

Knowledge of nuclear reactions as sources of stellar energy has established the first firm foundation for an understanding of stellar evolution. Conditions in the interior of stars permit the transformation of hydrogen to helium, with consequent release of kinetic and radiation energy. This process may take place by the steps outlined in Section 29–7 or by some alternative series of reactions. In some stars it is possible that somewhat heavier atoms, e.g., lithium and boron, may combine with hydrogen or helium to form more stable nuclei, those nearer the bottom of the energy trough of Fig. 29–10. All these processes may compete, and the dominance of any one of them depends on conditions of pressure and temperature as well as on the abundance of atomic varieties.

The total age of a star can be approximately computed from its mass and the rate at which it is giving off radiation, assuming that conversion from mass to radiation is accomplished by the most probable processes. What is meant by age here is how long the star can last at the rate it expends energy, with changes in composition taken into account as well as possible. The mass-luminosity law (Section 30–3) indicates that at least for Population I the greater the mass of a star the more rapid its rate of change. Even though it has more hydrogen to spend, the rate of conversion is so rapid for a large, bright star that the most massive stars apparently die youngest, having been extremely prodigal of their substance. The very hottest and most luminous stars (called O and B by astronomers, or simply *blue giants*) should find themselves spent in as little as 10 million years, perhaps even less. Some rocks on the earth are 300 times as old! It may be reassuring to note that the sun's life expectancy would be about 10 billion years on this basis.

Some of the stars in our galaxy are so very bright, spending energy at rates up to 100,000 times that of the sun, that they cannot have been shining very long. These stars tend to occur in groups, and make up some of the open galactic clusters known as O-associations. Some stars of each group are moving very fast and others are not, and their motions taken together indicate that they started from a common center, in some cases as little as a million and a half years ago. These O-associations sometimes contain stars that lie at lower temperatures on the main sequence, and they always contain very dense clouds of gas and dust. It seems likely that all stars are formed from such clouds, which may condense by gravitational attraction. Bart J. Bok has called attention to small dense clouds of material that appear on many photographs, from which it seems probable that stars evolve; these are called *globules*. To explain why some of the stars move rapidly away from each other once they are formed, Jan H. Oort has suggested a plausible theory. Assume that the central stationary stars of the association were formed first. As they began to generate and pour forth large amounts of energy they would make the neighboring gas very hot, so that it would expand rapidly against the cooler surrounding gas. As more stars formed from this gas they would have continuing motion with respect to the first stars. Although this theory is plausible, it is not wholly substantiated in a quantitative way by the present data.

Since some of the stars in an O-association are moving rapidly, the group will disperse; old associations of this kind thus do not exist, and in order to trace later stages in stellar evolution we must examine the true galactic clusters mentioned in Section 30–4. These are more stable dynamical entities, held together principally by the mutual gravitational attraction between the stars, so that it is possible to find "old" clusters as well as young ones. Within each cluster is always found a sequence of stars whose brightness and color are closely related; this, together with analysis of their relative motion, suggests that the stars of a given cluster are of about the same age. Different clusters may be compared as to approximate age; one indication of old age, for example, is the absence of blue giants, which spend their energy so fast that they cannot maintain their status very long, astronomically speaking. The older clusters do, however, often include stars that fit the red giant category of Population I (Fig. 30–7), whereas those clusters that contain blue giants do not. From this it is inferred that the evolutionary path of a very hot bright star on the H-R diagram is a horizontal track to the right; that is, after a certain time the energy output of a star remains constant, but its temperature decreases. On exactly what then happens to the red giants of Population I and how stars evolve which initially contain less material than do the blue giants, there is much less evidence and consequently no well-established theory.

Type II stars behave quite differently. It will be remembered that these stars are characteristic of globular clusters; careful analysis of the stars in a single large globular cluster has led Allan R. Sandage and Martin Schwartzchild to propose a theory that is compatible with what is known of stellar energy processes. On an H-R diagram the distribution of stars belonging to this cluster (known as $M3$) is indicated in Fig. 30–16. Sup-

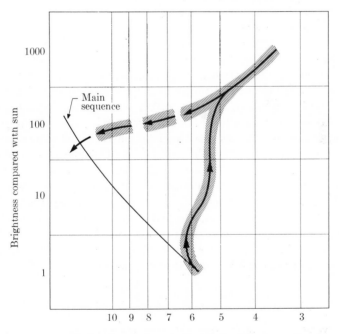

FIG. 30–16. An H-R diagram showing the density of stars in globular cluster $M3$, showing a probable evolutionary path. Note the similarity to Fig. 30–8.

pose the stars of the cluster were formed at about the same time and had the same composition. Like the stars of Type I they first appeared in the main sequence, but with less material than the blue giants, so that their positions on the sequence ranged along a band somewhere near the position of the sun. At first the energy was produced by nuclear processes near the core of the star, but at length the hydrogen in the core became exhausted. Conversion then took place in a thin shell around this core of very hot "ashes," but the pressure was less in this shell and the star began to expand. This expansion converted the stars into giants, brighter on the whole than the red giants of Population I. At some point in their hydrogen conversion they began to shrink, and to return relatively rapidly along the broken horizontal line toward the main sequence. Along this path the star may become so unstable as to form a variable, or perhaps explode as a supernova. It is generally believed that the dense white dwarfs represent the final stage of stellar evolution of both populations, rarely seen because the stage is brief. The more massive stars would have to shed a considerable portion of their materials before they could condense in this way.

This abbreviated account omits many well-substantiated points, but it does reflect the absence of any complete or wholly general picture of stellar evolution. Many diverse but intimately related problems are involved. The changes in stars and in the interstellar gas that plays such an important role in the birth and death of stellar systems also reflect an evolution in matter itself. The origin of the elements is only one of the puzzles that now engage the attention of astronomers and astrophysicists. One of the most intriguing of these problems is that of the origin of the solar system. Many hypotheses of origin of the solar system have been advanced, but no theory has been entirely successful in accounting for all the observed details. It has been held by some that the planets were formed by a "catastrophe" which caused separation of matter from the sun, by others that they developed in a gradual evolutionary process which accompanied the formation of our sun. The latter view appears the more probable at the present time. In one of the most successful quantitative expositions of the evolutionary theory, Gerard P. Kuiper has been able to account for the observed orbits and rotations of planets, satellites, asteroids, comets, and many other details of the solar system. An account of Kuiper's theory may be found in Baker's *Astronomy*.

30–7 A glimpse of modern cosmology

The universe is obviously very different from the mental picture developed by the Greek philosophers. It is particularly clear in the field of astronomy that expanding knowledge continually widens our view of the unknown—the more we know, the more we have yet to discover. With the

200-inch telescope on Palomar Mountain astronomers can gaze more than two billion light years into space, yet find no evidence that the matter of the universe thins out with distance. And we must assume, since we have no excuse for thinking otherwise, that the universe must look much the same from a galaxy two billion light years away as it looks to us from our vantage point in the Milky Way.

At the present time there is no single well-established cosmological model that is acceptable to all astronomers. One reason is simply that the universe is so vast that our detailed information about it is necessarily meager. On one broad and spectacular generalization, however, all are agreed. This is the *red-shift* phenomenon, announced by Edwin P. Hubble (1889–1953) in 1929. Spectroscopes detect the characteristic line spectra of known atoms in the light reaching us from all parts of the universe, even that from the most distant of galaxies. There is a strange regularity in such spectra, however: all the familiar lines are shifted toward the red end of the spectrum, and to an extent which increases with the distance of the galactic source of light. The only interpretation that can be placed on this fact in terms of our knowledge of light is that the red shift is an example of Doppler effect, and that the distant galaxies are receding from our own, at rates which increase with distance. A galaxy 720 million light years away is apparently receding at a velocity of 38,000 mi/sec, one-fifth the speed of light! It is the red-shift phenomenon that has led to the theory of the *expanding universe*. We cannot conclude that ours is a unique position, but must assume that an observer anywhere in the universe would detect a red shift such that all other galaxies would appear to be running away from his own.

Since the red-shift phenomenon implies that the universe is expanding, many astronomers have concluded that the matter it contains must once have been concentrated, at enormous density, in a small portion of space. This conclusion leads to the cosmological belief that the universe experienced a moment of "creation" at the instant expansion began. The "age" of the universe, or elapsed time since this moment of creation, has been calculated on the basis of red-shift observations. The result, about five and one-half billion years, is at least greater than the apparent age of the earth (Chapter 28). The calculation is a highly speculative one, however. Several scientists have attempted to account for the observed abundance of the chemical elements in terms of assumed conditions immediately after the moment of "creation."

Wherever the astronomer directs his telescope, he gathers light which he feels certain has been produced in nuclear reactions within stars. Throughout the universe, matter is being converted to energy, and cosmologists who believe that the universe has been expanding since some initial moment of "creation" also believe it probable that it is "running down." An alternative view has been advanced in recent years by a group of British cosmologists, who propose that the universe is in a *steady state*. According to this theory, energy is being continuously converted to matter, and the average density of matter in any given large region of space remains about constant despite the mutual recessions of galaxies. The problem of deciding between the two modern cosmologies cannot be settled by classical Newtonian mechanics, which leads to absurd paradoxes when naively applied to the vast scale of the universe. The very nature of space and time, as well as that of matter and energy, must be examined more closely and with greater subtlety before any model of the universe can be accepted with confidence greatly beyond that inspired by intellectual or emotional appeal. Einstein's general theory of relativity has already provided the framework for some of the necessary calculations. Even more necessary, however, are more observational facts with which to develop the detailed cosmological theories of the future.

Modern speculation about the universe may seem as uncertain as the cosmological theories of Greek philosophy, and in a sense it is. There are two great differences: the scope is vastly broader now, and the dependence of theory on observational data is fully recognized. The main difficulty lies in obtaining enough data to serve as a sound basis for cosmological theory. Meanwhile, existing theories, speculative as they are in large part, serve as a guide for further exploration as man seeks to satisfy his boundless curiosity about his restless physical environment.

30–8 Summary

New astronomical tools have made it possible to examine stars in relatively great detail and to get information on those at enormous distances. Spectroscopic studies indicate that stellar and interstellar matter is made up of the same kind of atoms that we know on earth. Stars vary greatly in size, mass, intrinsic brightness, and temperature. If stellar brightness is plotted against temperature, most of our neighboring stars fall into a narrow band called the *main sequence*. Other kinds of stars are the diffuse *red giants*, brighter than average for their temperature, and *white dwarfs*, hotter than average for their intrinsic brightness. Our region of space has considerable interstellar gas and dust, and is populated by stars called Type I. Other stars, notably those in dust-free globular clusters, belong to what is called Population II. Stars are grouped into vast aggregates known as galaxies, many of which have spiral arms consisting of gas and stars of Population I. The sun is in such a spiral arm of the local galaxy, whose plane is indicated by the Milky Way. There are many variable stars that show periodic or erratic changes, but more generally both the individual stars and their groupings are in process of evolutionary change. Inferences about stellar evolution and galactic history may be drawn from observations of the variety of features found in the present configurations of stars and galaxies, but these changes are only beginning to be understood.

REFERENCES

The New Astronomy, a Scientific American book containing nontechnical articles by ranking astronomers. Highly recommended in connection with recent developments in stellar astronomy.

BAKER, R. H., *Astronomy.* 6th ed. An excellent elementary text.

BLAAUW, Adriaan, "Young Stars," *Scientific American,* February, 1956.

BOK, B. J., and P. F. BOK, *The Milky Way.* The new version of this popular book for the layman brings the subject matter up to date.

HARGREAVES, F. J., *The Size of the Universe.* Traces the problem in a nonmathematical fashion from primitive ideas to those of 1948, the date of publication.

HOYLE, FRED, *Frontiers of Astronomy.* A nontechnical and well-written survey of many recent developments in astronomy.

PAYNE-GAPOSCHKIN, C. H., *Stars in the Making.* Also *Introduction to Astronomy,* an elementary textbook, with references to history and literature.

"The Universe," *Scientific American,* September, 1956. An issue devoted to new work in extragalactic astronomy in relation to modern cosmology.

1. The focal length of a camera lens is the distance from lens to plate for a sharp image of an object that is far away. Can you show that for ordinary cameras the size of a photograph of a distant scene is proportional to the focal length of the lens used? (No particular properties of the lens need be invoked, except that for any lens the angle subtended by the object is equal to that subtended by the image, as indicated in Fig. 30–17.) Why should a refracting telescope have a lens of long focal length and also of wide aperture?

2. If the sun were twice as far away, how large would its apparent area be in comparison with that actually observed?

3. Two stars A and B are both of absolute magnitude 1. The apparent magnitude of A is also 1, but that of B is +6. With the help of Fig. 30–4, find the ratio of their distances from the solar system. [Ans.: B is 10 times as far as A]

4. A nova may change from absolute magnitude 1 to absolute magnitude —7. By what factor is its rate of energy radiation changed?

5. Suppose that a stellar spectrum contains a line of measured wavelength 6006 angstrom units that is identifiable with a line 6000 A from a terrestrial source. What is the radial speed, on the assumption that the shift is due to the Doppler effect? [Ans.: 3×10^7 cm/sec, or 300 km/sec, in a direction away from the earth]

6. The sun, whose temperature may be assumed as 6000°K, emits maximum energy at a wavelength of 5000 A. On the basis of Wien's displacement law, what is the temperature of a star which emits maximum energy at a wavelength of 10,000 A? At 2500 A?

7. On the assumption that the temperature of the sun's surface is 6000°K, what is the surface temperature of a star that radiates 81 times more light per unit area than the sun? One that radiates 1/16 as much light per unit area as the sun? [Ans.: 18,000°K and 3000°K]

8. List some of the reasons why the structure pattern of our own galaxy is less well known than that of galaxies many light years away.

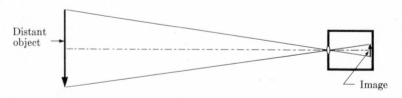

Distant object →

Image

FIGURE 30–17.

CHAPTER 31

CONCLUSION

It is fitting that we should conclude our story as we began it, by considering cosmology. Throughout man's history, the universe and its "mysteries" have inevitably raised "ultimate" questions—about its structure, its extent, its past, and about the position which man himself occupies in the vast scheme of things. There have always been questions which appear, by their nature, beyond the reach of science, and we confidently predict that there will always be such questions. Many of the questions that seemed "ultimate" to the Greeks have long since been answered by science, only to be replaced by new ones. Modern man's answers to the questions that appear "ultimate" today are no less personal and speculative than were those of the Greeks to their own "ultimate" questions. What has not changed between ancient times and the present is man's driving desire to interpret his world, to create an image in his mind that he believes to correspond to the universe. Where there are gaps in his knowledge, he has never hesitated to fill them by speculation.

When we predict that there will always be realms that appear impenetrable to science we cannot pretend to foresee what any of them may be, one or a hundred generations hence. We can predict, however, that the future of science is surely greater than its past. Great future progress has already been foreshadowed by current progress in many branches of science, including stellar astronomy and biological chemistry. Although Francis Bacon's vision of man bending nature to his command has not become reality, mankind has achieved a remarkable degree of control over his environment, and the role of science in civilization has gradually become a dominant one. Its present importance is such that science must be increasingly understood, for it is highly improbable that this role will be relinquished. On the contrary, both science and its technological consequences are expanding at a greater rate now than in any previous age.

Fundamental scientific discoveries have been frequent in the 20th century, and many of them have led quickly to important applications. Although nuclear fission was discovered only in 1939, for example, power from nuclear reactors, operating on fission energy, is already being commercially distributed. Military application of nuclear fission, of course, was achieved in 1945. Because scientific progress, through its applications, has more or less immediate impact upon the general public, awareness of science is more widespread than at any time in the past. The notice accorded science today is by no means uniformly favorable, however. Because science has made possible the development of dreadfully devastating weapons, there has arisen some tendency to distrust science itself, despite the generally recognized fact that the construction of military devices rests upon political, not scientific, decisions. Moreover, since many concepts of modern science are not readily identified with what we have been taught to call common sense, there is also a tendency to regard scientific abstractions as immutably beyond ordinary comprehension. From this conclusion it is one short and dangerous step to the conclusion that science achieves its admittedly remarkable results by procedures that are not quite rational, and must therefore be either taken on faith or distrusted. We have noted constantly, however, that the highly creative work of great scientists is continuously subject to the checks of observation and experiment and to the discipline of mathematical logic. It is just this combination of creativity and rationality that has permitted science to triumph where magic and witchcraft failed.

To illustrate that the growth of science today depends upon the interacting roles of imagination and experiment as much as it has in the past, let us consider the present plight of the science of nuclear physics. As we have said in this text, nuclei are thought to consist of neutrons and protons. These and the electron are called "fundamental" particles, since they were long believed to be the ultimate building blocks of all matter. The nature of the forces which hold nuclei together has been recognized as an important problem as long as the existence of the nucleus has been known. Noting that an electromagnetic field of force may be interpreted in terms of discrete photons, the Japanese physicist Hideki Yukawa, late in 1934, proposed that forces between nuclear particles might be interpreted in terms of a new, hitherto undetected kind of particle. On being rapidly exchanged between neutrons and protons, the new particles could serve as a nuclear "glue." He predicted that such particles, if they existed, should have masses intermediate between those of the proton and the electron, and showed that they should be unstable outside the nucleus. In 1938 a particle whose properties were in substantial accord with Yukawa's description was discovered in the study of cosmic rays; it was called the *meson*, and was at first thought to be unique in the same sense that electrons and protons are unique. Since that time, however, a whole series of new particles has been discovered, some lighter than protons, others heavier, some neutral, others charged. Exactly how these particles contribute to the nuclear "glue" remains unknown, but the idea that neutrons and protons are "fundamental" has broken down. Without achieving an answer to the original question, nuclear physics has acquired

CONCLUSION 703

a new and much broader problem, that of interpreting the many new particles.

Several particles of recent discovery are collectively called "strange particles." The use of this odd terminology does not mean that the particles are unwelcome, but simply that they are new and unexpected, and that their role in the general scheme of things is not yet understood. Nature herself has provided more surprises and greater variation than Yukawa's brilliantly creative mind had imagined, and now new creativity is required to devise a theory that will encompass the whole body of new knowledge. The unexpected discovery of the many new particles is but one more example of the constant change that is so characteristic of science. Throughout the 19th century, atoms were considered indivisible. This belief was destroyed by the discovery of radioactivity, and gradually a new model, granting substructure to the atom, was developed. Neutrons and protons long appeared to be the basic structural units of nuclear matter, but now it seems certain that they are themselves structured in some manner, for the "strange particles" can be created in nuclear interactions. No one now knows how or why they are produced, but understanding will surely come in the future. By its very nature, science is perpetually penetrating unexplored frontiers. No scientist can anticipate what lies immediately ahead, nor can he be sure that the science of his youthful years of training will be adequate for the research of his middle age.

In this book we have not stressed the practical utility of science, although the historical interrelations of science and technology have been frequently mentioned. One compelling reason for our emphasis on principles rather than practical applications is that the "benefits" of science are *not* all to be found in the comforts and amenities of modern technological civilization. Equally spectacular have been the profound effects of science on the whole of human thought. Man's concept of himself in relation to the rest of the universe has been revolutionized by the work of Copernicus, of Darwin, and, in our own century, by that of Einstein, for example. The reciprocal dependence between science and other aspects of our culture is often not fully recognized, although it must gain more and more recognition as civilization becomes increasingly dependent upon scientific achievement. Another reason for our emphasis on science itself rather than its applications is the paradox that while science borrows ideas as well as methods from technology, the body of fundamental scientific knowledge grows much faster if it is not tied to the solution of explicit practical problems. In this sense the great creative men of science, Kepler, Galileo, Newton, Faraday, Rutherford, and the rest, have been philosophers, although they might more accurately be called lovers of truth than lovers of wisdom. Practical inventiveness is not enough to support science, and it is a necessary condition for the flourishing of science in any age that those who are determined to follow truth, wherever it may lead, find sufficient encouragement and freedom from intellectual restraint.

Along with the many conveniences that we can now only call the necessities of life, science has given human beings greater responsibility. We have seen, for example, that the earth which supports us so abundantly evolved, through an almost unbelievably long period of time, with no help from us. It is important that we understand the forces responsible for this evolution, for they continue to act. But the very knowledge that enables us to exploit the earth's resources for our well-being carries with it the responsibility for utilizing them as wisely as possible. And science itself is rapidly becoming the most valuable resource of all, as the welfare of the world becomes increasingly dependent upon technological achievement. As such it is much too important to be left to the scientists alone—science is everybody's business.

We have come down a long and sometimes tortuous path since we set out, in the introduction, to sketch in the broad outlines of physical science. We have tried to hew closely to our expressed purpose of giving principles priority over details, but we hope that the reader may have been tempted, from time to time, to seek further details in other sources. Even more important, we hope that he may have acquired a desire to maintain continuing acquaintance with the progress and accomplishments of physical science. Since change is one of its most characteristic attributes, science must be kept up with to be appreciated. Here we have seen, in a limited way, how the endless frontier of science has been pushed back in the past. It will be even more exciting to watch, and to take some part, however small, in the developments of the future. It is a continued story we have here begun to trace, and while every stage is rooted firmly in the past it is also, in a sense, a threshold. For truly, to quote Laplace, "What we know here is very little, but what we are ignorant of is immense."

APPENDIX

TECHNIQUES OF MATHEMATICS AND MEASUREMENT

According to Galileo, mathematics is a language one must learn in order to read the book of natural phenomena. Perhaps what he meant is that nature is much too complicated to be comprehended without taking advantage of the simplified representation, the economy of thought, and the logic inherent in mathematics. Here we merely summarize some of the useful elementary mathematical concepts and relations which will facilitate the general discussion of physical science, most of which will be already familiar to the reader. For a charming discussion of mathematics itself, we recommend *Mathematician's Delight* by W. W. Sawyer, which is "designed to convince the general reader that mathematics is not a forbidding science but an attractive mental exercise."

A-1 Proportionality

One quantity is said to be directly proportional to another if their ratio (arithmetical quotient) remains unchanged as the quantities themselves vary. For example, if an automobile travels at constant speed, the distance it has traversed at any instant is directly proportional to the time elapsed since it passed the point at which measurement was begun. In mathematical notation, we may write

$$\frac{d}{t} = \text{constant}, \tag{A-1}$$

or, equivalently (multiplying both sides of the equation by t),

$$d = \text{constant} \times t, \tag{A-2}$$

where d represents any distance from the point at which measuring is begun and t is the time required to travel this distance. The constant in this case is the speed itself, whose magnitude we may represent by v. The direct proportionality between distance and time may then be represented by

$$\frac{d}{t} = v, \tag{A-3}$$

where v is understood to be constant. The size of this constant depends on the actual performance of the automobile and driver, and on the units in which distance and time are measured. The speed of an automobile traveling 60 miles per hour (mi/hr) may also be expressed as 88 feet per second (ft/sec), and the speedometer of a European automobile at this speed would indicate 96 kilometers per hour.

Suppose that several drivers traverse the same distance, each at constant speed of his own choice. The time required for the journey will be greater for those traveling at smaller speeds. In this case, the distance d is constant, but both time t and speed v vary from driver to driver. Rearranging Eq. (A–3), we obtain

$$t = \frac{d}{v} = \frac{\text{constant}}{v} \; ; \qquad (A\text{–}4)$$

this time, t is said to be *inversely* proportional to speed v. One quantity, time, increases as another, speed, decreases, in a way that conforms to the relation (A–4). Another way of looking at this relation is to say that time t is *directly* proportional to the *reciprocal* of speed v, since

$$t = \left(\frac{1}{v}\right) \times \text{constant} \qquad (A\text{–}5)$$

says exactly the same thing as Eq. (A–4) and has the form characteristic of direct proportionality (Eq. A–2). Equation (A–4) may be rearranged in another way, by multiplying both sides by v, to give

$$tv = \text{constant.} \qquad (A\text{–}6)$$

In inverse proportionality, the arithmetic product of two quantities remains unchanged as the quantities themselves vary.

For the above example, we have taken a series of individual drivers, but in many cases physical quantities are found to vary *continuously* in inverse proportion. In Chapter 12, for example, Boyle is reported to have discovered that at constant temperature the volume of a gas is inversely proportional to the pressure:

$$V = \frac{\text{constant}}{P} = \frac{K}{P} \, , \qquad (A\text{–}7)$$

or

$$VP = K, \qquad (A\text{–}8)$$

where V represents the volume of the gas and P the pressure. K is a constant quantity, if temperature does not change, for any given quantity of gas. Its numerical magnitude depends upon the temperature, the quantity of gas and the units in which P and V are measured. In principle, any conceivable combination of P and V, corresponding to any one of an infinite number of states of compression of the gas, will lead to the same value of K as any other.

Other kinds of proportionality may be expressed in the form of equations, in terms of proportionality constants. Galileo discovered that the total distance from its starting point of a freely falling object starting from rest is proportional to the square of the time of fall:

$$d = Kt^2. \tag{A–9}$$

(In Chapter 2 it is shown that here $K = \frac{1}{2}g$, where g is the "acceleration of gravity.") Newton found that the force exerted by the sun on a planet is inversely proportional to the squares of their distances, r, from the sun:

$$F = \frac{K}{r^2}. \tag{A–10}$$

An important and useful general rule about proportionality is that if any quantity is proportional to a second quantity *and also* to a third, it is proportional to their product. Newton's second law of motion asserts that the force F on a body needed to produce acceleration a is proportional to a and also to the mass m of the body:

$$F = \text{constant} \times ma = Kma. \tag{A–11}$$

Another example is his law of gravitation, according to which the gravitational attraction between two bodies of masses M and m is proportional to the product of the masses, as well as inversely proportional to the square of the distance r between them:

$$F = KMm/r^2. \tag{A–12}$$

The constant of proportionality in every case is determined by measurement of the variable quantities themselves. Its size, as in the first case of the moving automobile, depends on what is being described and on the units used in the description. In some cases, as in $F = Kma$, units may be defined for some one of the quantities to make the constant itself equal to unity; given standards for m and the measurement of a, the unit of force can be defined so as to make $F = ma$. Ordinarily the constant of proportionality that appears in a physical law relates quantities for which units have already been agreed upon, and its value is then determined by experiment.

A–2 Units

In the metric system, various units of length are related by powers of 10, as are units of mass. The centimeter (cm) is defined as one-hundredth part of the standard meter. Other metric units of length frequently employed are the millimeter (0.1 cm), and the kilometer (1000 meters). The most useful relations to English units are:

$$1 \text{ m (meter)} = 39.37 \text{ inches,}$$

$$1 \text{ inch} = 2.54 \text{ cm.}$$

The unit of mass in the metric system is the gram (gm), defined as one-thousandth part of the standard kilogram. The relations between metric and English units of mass are:

$$1 \text{ kgm (kilogram)} = 2.205 \text{ lb,}$$

$$1 \text{ lb} = 453.6 \text{ gm.}$$

For most purposes, the basic unit of time is the mean solar day, defined as the average interval between successive passages of the sun across the meridian. The second is 1/86,400 part of the mean solar day.

Derived units often carry the names of the basic units; e.g., velocity is measured in cm/sec, volume in cm^3 or some multiple thereof, momentum in gm·cm/sec. Units of force and energy require careful consideration. In problems involving only static masses it is permissible to measure force in grams or pounds, and the terms are interpreted as the *weight* of a gram or a pound of matter, respectively. In dynamical problems the dyne is defined to make $F = ma$, and thus one dyne is the same as one gm·cm/sec^2. Since the acceleration of gravity is 980 cm/sec^2 at sea level, a one-gram weight is equivalent to 980 dynes. Analogously, work may be expressed in gram·centimeters, but (in the system of units we employ) kinetic and potential energy must be expressed in dyne·cm, or ergs. The joule is defined as 10^7 ergs. For measuring power, the watt is defined as 1 joule/sec. The English unit of power is the horsepower, and 1 horsepower = 745 watts.

A–3 Graphs

As a device for showing the relation between one quantity and another, graphs are probably more familiar to the reader than equations. They have the advantage of indicating visually the behavior of one quantity with respect to another even when no "formula" is known, as in the case of the annual production of oil or steel over a period of years. In physical science a simple algebraic relation (a "proportion" of some kind) may be discovered or verified by plotting observational data. For a trivially simple example take observations of mile posts and clock times in an automobile that happens to have no speedometer. These may be:

Distance (miles)	Time (minutes)
0	0
2	3
4	6
10	15
24	36

If on squared paper (graph paper) the vertical axis is marked off in miles and the horizontal axis in minutes, each set of observations may be represented as a single point on the plane (Fig. A–1). The second observation in the table, for example, is shown as a point 2 units up and 3 to the right of the axis intersection, or origin. The most striking thing about the resultant graph is that all the points fall on a straight line which passss through the origin. It is easy to see from the table that for this case the distance is directly proportional to the time. *Every* direct proportionality results in a

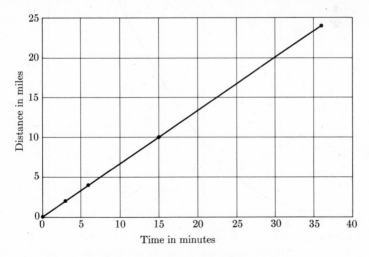

FIG. A–1. Plotting distance against time.

straight-line graph.   For actual observations, where there is some uncertainty in taking precise readings, the best test of proportionality is to
plot the data to see if the relation can be represented by a straight line,
within the limits of accuracy of the measurements.

For a freely falling body the graph of distance against time is not a
straight line, but would resemble Fig. A–2. From this plot it is seen that
the distance increases more rapidly than if it were in direct proportion
to the time, and we might guess that it is proportional to the square of the
time.   This guess could be checked by plotting the distance against the
square of the time, i.e., d against t^2.   The same observational data represented in Fig. A–2 are shown again, in this way, in Fig. A–3.   For the first
part of the fall, the points lie nicely on a line, and then they begin to fall
below it.   Distance is strictly proportional to the square of time, then, only
in the earlier stages of the body's fall, when its speed is small.   The deviation in later stages is due to air resistance, which increases as the velocity
increases.

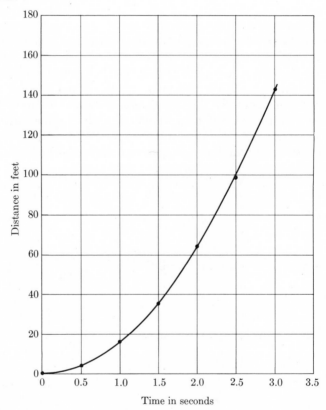

Fɪɢ. A–2.   Graph of distance against time for a freely falling body.

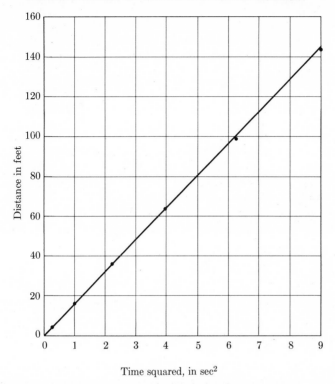

FIG. A–3. Graph of distance against the *square* of time for a freely falling body.

Inverse proportion is shown graphically in Figs. A–4 and A–5, which represent the variation of the volume of a gas with pressure. The variation of P with V is shown in Fig. A–4, and the points fall on a curve known as a hyperbola. The test of the inverse relationship is to plot P against $1/V$, for in that case P is directly proportional to $1/V$. The result is as shown in Fig. A–5. The points are numbered so that those on one graph may be identified with those on the other.

A–4 Representation of large and small numbers

Science deals with both the very large and the very small, from the vast reaches of interstellar space to the minute dimensions of atoms and their constituent particles. Masses, time intervals, electric charge, even pure numbers of the kind determined by counting, all have tremendous ranges of size. In writing and manipulating these numbers, it is almost imperative that we take advantage of a shorthand notation called *exponential*. The velocity of light in empty space, for example, is about 186,000 mi/sec

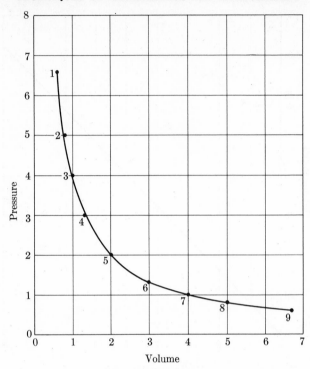

FIG. A–4. Graph of pressure against volume for a sample of gas. (Units are arbitrary.)

or, more exactly, 29,979,290,000 cm/sec. For many purposes it may be sufficiently accurate to call it 30,000,000,000 cm/sec, but this method of expressing the number is both awkwardly long and potentially misleading. Even in 29,979,290,000 cm/sec, the last zeros are added to make the decimal place right and do not represent the result of measurement; there is actually experimental uncertainty about the last number 9, with the precision available at present. To avoid this, we may express the velocity of light as 3×10^{10} cm/sec, or 2.997929×10^{10} cm/sec, depending on the accuracy required. Let us find out what makes this exponential notation work.

It is clear that $10^2 = 100$, $10^3 = 1000$. Similarly, $10^6 = 1,000,000$ (one million), etc. The exponent, or power, of ten in each case represents the number of zeros needed to fill out the number. Multiplication with these numbers follows a simple rule which can be seen by noting that

$$10 \times 100 = 10 \times 10^2 = 1000 = 10^3,$$

that

$$100 \times 1000 = 10^2 \times 10^3 = 100,000 = 10^5,$$

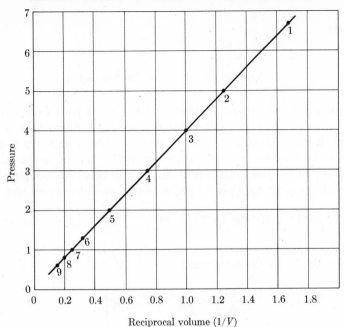

FIG. A-5. Plot of pressure against the *reciprocal* of volume for a sample of gas. Numbers along the line relate these points to those on the curve of Fig. A-4.

etc. Since 10 is the first power of 10, the rule is easily seen: in multiplying powers of ten the correct result is obtained by *adding* the exponents. Similarly,

$$3 \times 10^{10} \times 2 \times 10^3 = 6 \times 10^{13},$$

the powers of ten having been multiplied in the usual way.

We may also find the rule for dividing from a few examples.

$$\frac{100,000}{100} = \frac{10^5}{10^2} = 1000 = 10^3.$$

The answer, 10^3, is equal to $10^{(5-2)}$; in other words, the exponent in the denominator has been *subtracted* from that in the numerator. An extension of this rule enables us to express decimal fractions as powers of ten:

$$\frac{100}{100,000} = \frac{10^2}{10^5} = \frac{1}{1000} = 0.001 = 10^{-3}.$$

The exponent in the answer, -3, is the result of subtracting 5 from 2.

Similarly,

$$0.1 = 10^{-1},$$

$$0.000001 = 10^{-6} \text{ (one-millionth)},$$

etc.

Negative exponents thus represent *reciprocals* of positive powers, and negative powers of ten represent decimal fractions. The rules for multiplying and dividing remain the same. For example, a unit much used in biological work with the microscope is the *micron*, defined as one-millionth of a meter, 10^{-6} meter. To find the number of centimeters equivalent to one micron we must multiply by the number of centimeters per meter, 10^2:

$$10^{-6} \text{ meter} \times 10^2 \text{ cm/meter} = 10^{(-6+2)} \text{ cm} = 10^{-4} \text{ centimeter.}$$

On the other hand, if there were occasion to divide 10^{-6} by 10^2 the answer would be 10^{-8}. By the same rule,

$$\frac{10^2}{10^{-6}} = 10^{2-(-6)} = 10^8.$$

These rules for multiplying and dividing with exponents apply to any "base" number, not just 10:

$$a^n \times a^m = a^{n+m}, \tag{A-13}$$

and

$$\frac{a^n}{a^m} = a^{n-m}. \tag{A-14}$$

A-5 Angular measure and triangulation

In describing the positions of the sun and moon, stars and planets, angles constitute the only direct measurement that has the same meaning for everybody. To say that the moon is as big as a plate or an orange is to state a purely subjective impression. Our knowledge of distances between members of the solar system is indirect, determined from measurable distances on the earth combined with angular measurements. Angular measure is also useful terrestrially, for surveying, for location (latitude and longitude), etc. The elevation of Mt. Everest was determined accurately long before the mountain was ever scaled, by what is known as triangulation. (Mt. Everest's status as the world's highest mountain was discovered by computation from the observed data in a surveyor's office, not by looking at it.) Let us review the principles of angular measure and their use.

A circle is divided into 360 equal parts, called degrees. The size of the circle does not matter, for what we are here concerned with is the angle between two radii, subtended by the arc of the circle. Each degree consists of 60 minutes of arc (not to be confused with minutes of time!). Surveyors and especially astronomers work to such accuracy that it is convenient to subdivide each minute into 60 seconds of arc, but we shall rarely be concerned with such high precision. An angle of seven degrees, fourteen minutes, and fifty seconds is written $7°14'50''$.

Angular measure is required to determine the distance to the moon, for example. To do this we take advantage of what is called *parallax*, the fact that an object appears to move against a more distant background if the observer moves. Figure A–6 illustrates this principle, which is the geometrical proposition that two angles and one side determine a triangle. For small angles the problem is further simplified. The straight-line distance from Greenwich to the Cape of Good Hope is about 5400 miles. In the simple case shown, the moon is equally distant from the two observatories, but the observer at the Cape finds it is $1°20'$ farther north among the stars than does the Greenwich observer. In other words, the angle designated by B is $1°20'$ larger than that designated by A, and thus the angle M is $1°20'$. Since this angle is very small, a circle centered at the moon and passing through the two observatories would very nearly coincide with the line between them. If X is the radius of this circle, its circumference is $2\pi X$. To find X, the distance from the earth to the moon, we need only remember that the circumference $2\pi X$ corresponds to a full circle, 360° of arc, and the distance 5400 mi to $1°20'$, or 1.33° of arc. From the simple proportion

$$\frac{5400}{2\pi X} = \frac{1.33°}{360°} \tag{A–15}$$

the distance X is found to be approximately 240,000 mi.

Knowing the distance from the earth to the moon, the size of the moon may also be estimated. The angle it subtends to an observer on the earth

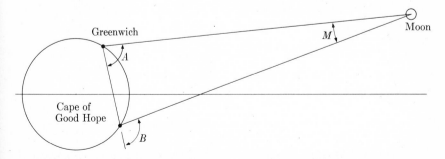

Fig. A–6. Measurement of distance to the moon by triangulation.

is about 31', or 0.52°. The proportion in this case is

$$\frac{0.52°}{360°} = \frac{y}{240,000(2\pi)} , \qquad (A\text{–}16)$$

from which y, the diameter of the moon, is found to be roughly 2150 mi. (More careful measurments yield a value of 2160 mi.)

When larger angles or more oblique triangles are involved, the geometrical problem involved in triangulation can be solved by making a diagram to scale, but it is more convenient and accurate to compute the required quantities trigonometrically. Trigonometry is an algebraic expression of geometry in which all triangles are essentially broken up into right triangles.

Consider the right triangle ABC of Fig. A–7, with sides a, b, c opposite the angles A, B, C, respectively. In a right triangle, with $C = 90°$, $B = 90° - A$, so that all angles are known if A is known. A triangle similar to ABC will, in general, have sides of different lengths, but the *ratio* of any two sides depends only on the size of angle A. These ratios are fixed for a given A, and are called *trigonometric functions* of A. The name given to the ratio of the opposite side to the hypotenuse is called the *sine* of angle A, often abbreviated to *sin*:

$$\frac{a}{c} = \sin A. \qquad (A\text{–}17)$$

The value of $\sin A$ depends on the size of A, of course, but it is independent of the size of the triangle so long as it is a right triangle with A as one acute angle. Tables of sines are extremely useful for solving practical problems. Suppose, for example, that a railroad is built along a 5° slope, and it is desired to know the vertical rise per 100 ft of track. If it is known that $\sin 5°$ is 0.08716, it follows that the rise per hundred feet is 8.716 ft.

It is a relatively simple matter to derive a formula involving sines for use in oblique triangles. Consider the oblique triangle ABC of Fig. A–8;

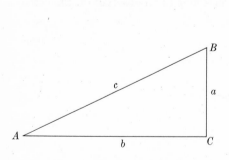

FIG. A–7. Right triangle.

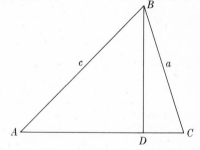

FIG. A–8. Oblique triangle resolved into two right triangles.

a perpendicular is dropped from B to the opposite side. Since $BD/c = \sin A$ and $BD/a = \sin C$, we may write

$$c \sin A = a \sin C,$$

or

$$c/\sin C = a/\sin A. \tag{A–18}$$

But we could just as well draw a perpendicular from C to the opposite side, from which we can prove that

$$a/\sin A = b/\sin B. \tag{A–19}$$

Thus the ratio of any side of a triangle to the sine of the angle opposite that side is the same for all sides of the triangle. This rule enables us to find the distance to an inaccessible point if we have what is known as a base line and can measure the angles between the base line and the lines of sight to the unaccessible point. Suppose that it is desired to find the distance BC in Fig. A–9. The angles A and B can be measured, and angle C is determined by the condition that the sum of all the angles is 180°. The distance AB is also known, and therefore

$$BC = AB \sin A/\sin C. \tag{A–20}$$

A table of sines permits the immediate computation of the required length.

In principle, all other right triangle ratios (trigonometric functions) are known if the sines are known, since the third side of any right triangle may be determined by the theorem of Pythagoras,

$$a^2 + b^2 = c^2. \tag{A–21}$$

In practice, it is also convenient to have access to the ratio of the adjacent side to the hypotenuse, known as the *cosine*:

$$b/c = \text{cosine } A, \text{ or } \cos A. \tag{A–22}$$

The ratio of the side opposite the angle to the adjacent side is also useful; a/b is called the tangent of A, abbreviated to $\tan A$:

$$a/b = \tan A.$$

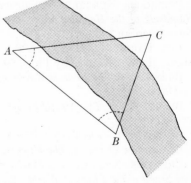

FIG. A–9. Determination of distance to an inaccessible point.

Tables of sines, cosines, and tangents will be found in any mathematical handbook or trigonometry text.

BIBLIOGRAPHY

Magazine articles noted earlier as appropriate for the various chapters are not cited in the general bibliography. Many of these articles will be found in *Scientific American*, an excellent publication which we recommend highly, as a regular reading diet, to all who like science and wish to keep themselves informed about current scientific progress. The book references listed below, for convenience, are divided into three categories, although this division is somewhat arbitrary. Taylor's *Physics, the Pioneer Science* and Holton's *Introduction to Concepts and Theories in Physical Science*, for example, contain much historical material, but are designed as texts of scientific subject matter and are therefore so listed. On the other hand, classical original papers and source books are listed as historical material; these are among the most valuable collateral readings, but only in rare cases do they furnish self-contained explanations of the subject matter they treat, especially for the uninitiated. It is also impossible to distinguish sharply between biography and history, since biographies of scientists must include accounts of their work, and histories of science often give biographical data on great scientists. Nevertheless there are differences in emphasis and in the ordering of material, and the distinction is often useful in the selection of references. The list in Part III, while far from complete, does include biographies of many of the most outstanding figures in the history of physical science.

I. Works Dealing Primarily with Scientific Subject Matter

BAKER, R. H., *Astronomy*. 6th ed. New York: D. Van Nostrand, 1955.
BERNHARD, HUBERT J., DOROTHY A. BENNETT, and HUGH S. RICE, *New Handbook of the Heavens*, Rev. ed. New York: McGraw–Hill, 1948. (Mentor, New American Library, 1954.)
BOK, BART J., and PRISCILLA F. BOK, *The Milky Way*. 3rd ed. Cambridge, Mass.: Harvard University Press, 1956.
BORN, MAX, *The Restless Universe*. London: Blakie & Son, 1935. (Reprinted by Dover, 1951.)
BRAGG, W. L., *The Atomic Structure of Minerals*. Ithaca: Cornell University Press, 1937.
BRAGG, W. L., *Electricity*. New York: Macmillan, 1936.
BRAGG, SIR WILLIAM, *The Universe of Light*. London: G. Bell and Sons, 1933.
CHERONIS, NICHOLAS D., JAMES B. PARSONS, and CONRAD E. RONNEBERG, *The Study of the Physical World*. 2nd ed. Boston: Houghton Mifflin, 1950.
COWLING, T. G., *Molecules in Motion*. London: Hutchinson's University Press, 1950.
DALY, R. A., *Strength and Structure of the Earth*. New York: Prentice-Hall, 1940.
DAVIDSON, MARTIN, *From Atoms to Stars*. 3rd ed. London: Hutchinson's Scientific and Technical Publications, 1952.

DUNBAR, CARL O., *Historical Geology*. New York: John Wiley & Sons, 1949.

EINSTEIN, A., and L. INFELD, *The Evolution of Physics*. New York: Simon and Schuster, 1938.

FARADAY, MICHAEL, *Experimental Researches in Electricity*. London: J. M. Dent & Sons, 1914, 1951 (Everyman's Library).

FEARNSIDES, W. G., and O. M. B. Bulman, *Geology in the Service of Man*. Harmondsworth: Penguin, 1950.

GILLULY, JAMES, AARON C. WATERS, and A. O. WOODFORD, *Principles of Geology*. San Francisco: W. H. Freeman, 1951.

GLOCKLER, GEORGE, and RUBY C. GLOCKLER, *Chemistry in Our Time*. New York: F. S. Crofts, 1947.

HARGREAVES, F. J., *The Size of the Universe*. Harmondsworth: Penguin, 1948.

HECHT, SELIG, *Explaining the Atom*. New York: Viking Press, 1947. Revised and enlarged by Eugene Rabinowitch, 1954.

HOFFMAN, BANESH, *The Strange Story of the Quantum*. New York: Harper and Brothers, 1947.

HOGBEN, LANCELOT, *Science for the Citizen*. New York: W. W. Norton, 1938.

HOLTON, GERALD, *Introduction to Concepts and Theories in Physical Science*. Reading, Mass.: Addison-Wesley, 1952.

HOYLE, FRED, *Frontiers of Astronomy*. New York: Harper and Brothers, 1955.

HUMPHREYS, RICHARD F., and ROBERT BERINGER, *First Principles of Atomic Physics*. New York: Harper and Brothers, 1950.

JEANS, SIR JAMES, *Science and Music*. New York: Macmillan, 1937. Also Cambridge University Press.

KRAUSKOPF, KONRAD BATES, *Fundamentals of Physical Science*. 3rd ed. New York: McGraw-Hill, 1953.

LEET, L. DON, and SHELDON JUDSON, *Physical Geology*. New York: Prentice-Hall, 1954.

LONGWELL, CHESTER R., ADOLPH KNOPF, and RICHARD F. FLINT, *Physical Geology*. 3rd ed. New York: John Wiley & Sons, 1950.

LUHR, OVERTON, *Physics Tells Why*. Lancaster: Jaques Cattell Press, 1943.

MACH, ERNST, *The Science of Mechanics*. Chicago: Open Court Publishing Co., 1942. (First published 1883.)

MENZEL, DONALD H., *Our Sun*. Philadelphia: Blakiston, 1949.

MICHELSON, A. A., *Light Waves and Their Uses*. Chicago: University of Chicago Press, 1903.

MILLER, D. C., *The Science of Musical Sounds*. New York: Macmillan, editions 1916 to 1944.

MILLIKAN, R. A., *Electrons (+ and −), Protons, Photons, Neutrons, Mesotrons, and Cosmic Rays*. 2nd ed. Chicago: University of Chicago Press, 1947.

OLDENBURG, OTTO, *Introduction to Atomic Physics*. 2nd ed. New York: McGraw-Hill, 1954.

PAULING, LINUS, *College Chemistry*. San Francisco: W. H. Freeman, 1952.

PAULING, LINUS, *General Chemistry*. 2nd ed. San Francisco: W. H. Freeman, 1953.

PAYNE-GAPOSCHKIN, CECELIA, *Introduction to Astronomy*. New York: Prentice-Hall, 1954.

PAYNE-GAPOSCHKIN, CECELIA, *Stars in the Making*. Cambridge, Mass.: Harvard University Press, 1952.

PFEIFFER, JOHN, *The Changing Universe*. New York: Random House, 1956.

RAMSAY, SIR WILLIAM, *The Gases of the Atmosphere*. London: Macmillan, 1920.

READ, JOHN, *A Direct Entry to Organic Chemistry*. London: Methuen, 1948.

ROCHOW, E. G., and M. K. WILSON, *General Chemistry, a Topical Introduction*. New York: John Wiley & Sons, 1954.

RUCHLIS, HYMAN, and HARVEY B. LEMON, *Exploring Physics*. New York: Harcourt, Brace. 1952.

RUSSELL, H. N., *The Solar System and its Origin*. New York: Macmillan, 1935.

SAWYER, W. W., *Mathematicians' Delight*. Harmondsworth: Penguin, 1943.

Scientific American Books: *Atomic Power, The New Astronomy, The Physics and Chemistry of Life*. New York: Simon and Schuster, 1955.

SEMAT, HENRY, *Introduction to Atomic and Nuclear Physics*. 3rd ed. New York: Rinehart, 1954.

SEMAT, HENRY, *Physics in the Modern World*. New York: Rinehart, 1949.

SHAPLEY, HARLOW, HELEN WRIGHT, and SAMUEL RAPPORT (Editors), *Readings in the Physical Sciences*. New York: Appleton-Century-Crofts, 1948.

SISLER, H. H., C. A. VANDERWERF, and ARTHUR W. DAVIDSON, *General Chemistry, a Systematic Approach*. New York: Macmillan, 1949.

SKILLING, WILLIAM T., and ROBERT S. RICHARDSON, *Astronomy*. Rev. ed. New York: Henry Holt, 1948.

STOVALL, J. W., and H. E. BROWN, *The Principles of Historical Geology*. Boston: Ginn and Company, 1954.

TAYLOR, LLOYD WILLIAM, *Physics, the Pioneer Science*. Boston: Houghton Mifflin, 1941.

TYNDALL, JOHN, *Heat, A Mode of Motion*. 6th ed. New York: Appleton-Century-Crofts, 1893.

WHIPPLE, FRED L., *Sun, Moon and Planets*. Philadelphia: Blakiston, 1941.

WHITE, HARVEY E., *Classical and Modern Physics: A Descriptive Introduction*. New York: D. Van Nostrand, 1940.

WHITE, HARVEY E., *Modern College Physics*. New York: D. Van Nostrand, 1948.

WOOD, ALEXANDER, *The Physics of Music*. New York: Dover, 1956.

II. WORKS THAT ARE MAINLY HISTORICAL

ABETTI, GEORGI, *History of Astronomy*. New York: Henry Schuman, 1952.

ADAMS, FRANK DAWSON, *The Birth and Development of the Geological Sciences*. Baltimore: Williams and Wilkins, 1938. (Reprinted by Dover, 1954.)

ARMITAGE, ANGUS, *A Century of Astronomy*. London: S. Low, 1950.

BERNAL, J. D., *Science and Industry in the 19th Century*. London: Routledge, K. Paul, 1953.

BERNAL, J. D., *Science in History*. London: Watts, 1954.

BROWN, G. BURNISTON, *Science, Its Method and Philosophy*. New York: W. W. Norton, 1951.

BUTTERFIELD, HERBERT, *The Origins of Modern Science, 1300–1800.* New York: Macmillan, 1951.

CHALMERS, T. W., *Historic Researches.* London: Morgan Brothers, 1949.

CHASE, C. T., *The Evolution of Modern Physics.* New York: D. Van Nostrand, 1947.

COHEN, M. R., and I. E. DRABKIN, *A Source Book in Greek Science.* New York: McGraw-Hill, 1948.

CONANT, J. B. (Editor), *Robert Boyle's Experiments in Pneumatics.* Cambridge, Mass.: Harvard University Press, 1950.

CONANT, J. B., *Science and Common Sense.* New Haven: Yale University Press, 1951.

CONANT, J. B., *The Overthrow of the Phlogiston Theory.* Cambridge, Mass.: Harvard University Press, 1950.

CREW, HENRY, *The Rise of Modern Physics.* Baltimore: Williams and Wilkins, 1935.

DAMPIER, SIR WILLIAM CECIL, *A History of Science.* 4th ed. Cambridge: Cambridge University Press, 1949.

DREYER, J. L. E., *A History of Astronomy (from Thales to Kepler).* Cambridge: Cambridge University Press, 1906. (Second edition reprinted by Dover, 1952.)

FARRINGTON, BENJAMIN, *Greek Science.* 2 vols. Harmondsworth: Penguin, 1944 (vol. 1), 1949 (vol. 2).

FARRINGTON, BENJAMIN, *Science in Antiquity.* Oxford: Oxford University Press, 1947 (Home University Library).

FINDLAY, ALEXANDER, *A Hundred Years of Chemistry.* New York: Macmillan, 1937.

FRASER, CHARLES G., *Half Hours with Great Scientists.* New York: Reinhold, 1948.

GALILEO GALILEI, *Dialogues Concerning Two New Sciences,* translated by H. Crew and A. de Salvio. New York: Macmillan, 1914. (Reprinted by Dover.)

GALILEO GALILEI, *Dialogue on the Great World Systems.* Georgio de Santillana (Editor). Chicago: University of Chicago Press, 1953.

GREGORY, SIR ARCHIBALD, *The Founders of Geology.* London: Macmillan, and Baltimore: Johns Hopkins Press, 1901.

GREGORY, J. C., *A Short History of Atomism.* London: A. and C. Black, 1931.

HALL, A. R., *The Scientific Revolution.* London-New York: Longmans, Green, 1954.

HEATH, SIR THOMAS, *Greek Astronomy.* London: J. M. Dent, 1932.

History of Science Society, *Sir Isaac Newton, 1727–1927.* Baltimore: Williams and Wilkins, 1928.

HOPKINS, A. J., *Alchemy, Child of Greek Philosophy.* New York: Columbia University Press, 1934.

JAFFE, BERNARD, *Crucibles, the Story of Chemistry.* Cleveland: World Publishing Co., 1930. (Reprinted by Dover, 1955).)

JEANS, SIR JAMES, *The Growth of Physical Science.* 2nd ed. Cambridge: Cambridge University Press, 1951.

KNEDLER, J. W., JR., *Masterworks of Science.* Garden City: Doubleday, 1947.

LEICESTER, H. M., and H. S. KLICKSTEIN, *A Source Book in Chemistry.* New York: McGraw-Hill, 1952.

LEICESTER, H. M., *The Historical Background of Chemistry.* New York: John Wiley and Sons, 1956.

LUCRETIUS, *De Rerum Natura* (On the Nature of the Universe). Many translations, e.g., by R. Latham, Harmondsworth: Penguin, 1951.

MACH, ERNST, *History and Root of the Principle of the Conservation of Energy.* Chicago: Open Court Publishing Co., 1911.

MAGIE, W. F., *A Source Book in Physics.* New York: McGraw-Hill, 1935.

MASON, S. F., *Main Currents of Scientific Thought.* New York: Henry Schuman, 1953.

MATHER, K. F., and S. L. MASON, *A Source Book in Geology.* New York: McGraw-Hill, 1939.

McKIE, D., and N. H. deV. HEATHCOTE, *The Discovery of Specific and Latent Heats.* London: E. Arnold, 1935.

MILLER, D. C., *Anecdotal History of the Science of Sound.* New York: Macmillan, 1935.

MILLER, D. C., *Sparks, Lightning, Cosmic Rays.* New York: Macmillan, 1939.

MOTT-SMITH, M. C., *The Story of Energy.* New York: Appleton-Century-Crofts, 1934.

MOULTON, F. R., and J. J. SCHIFFERES, *The Autobiography of Science.* Garden City: Doubleday, 1945.

NASH, L. K., *The Atomic-Molecular Theory.* Cambridge, Mass.: Harvard University Press, 1950.

NASH, L. K., *Plants and the Atmosphere.* Cambridge, Mass.: Harvard University Press, 1952.

NEEDHAM, JOSEPH, and WALTER PAGEL, (Editors), *The Background to Modern Science.* New York: Macmillan, 1938.

ORNSTEIN, MARTHA, *The Role of Scientific Societies in the Seventeenth Century.* Chicago: University of Chicago Press, 1928.

PARTINGTON, J. R., *A Short History of Chemistry.* London: Macmillan, 1948.

PASCAL, BLAISE, *Physical Treatises,* translated by I. H. B. and A. G. H. Spiers. New York: Columbia University Press, 1937.

PLEDGE, H. T., *Science Since 1500.* London: H. M. Stat. Off., 1939; New York: Philosophical Library, 1947.

RAMSAY, W., *The Gases of the Atmosphere, the History of Their Discovery.* London: Macmillan, 1902.

RANDALL, J. H., *The Making of the Modern Mind.* Rev. ed. Boston: Houghton Mifflin, 1940.

READ, JOHN, *Prelude to Chemistry.* London: G. Bell and Sons, 1936.

ROLLER, DUANE, *The Early Development of the Concepts of Temperature and Heat.* Cambridge, Mass.: Harvard University Press, 1950.

ROLLER, DUANE, and DUANE H. D. ROLLER, *The Development of the Concept of Electric Charge.* Cambridge, Mass.: Harvard University Press, 1954.

SARTON, GEORGE, *Ancient Science to Epicurus.* Cambridge, Mass: Harvard University Press, 1952.

SARTON, GEORGE, *A History of Science: Ancient Science through the Golden Age of Greece.* Cambridge, Mass.: Harvard University Press, 1952.

SCHORLEMMER, CARL, *The Rise and Development of Organic Chemistry.* London: Macmillan, 1894.

SEDGWICK, W. T., and H. W. TYLER, *A Short History of Science.* New York: Macmillan, 1939.

SHAPLEY, HARLOW, and HELEN E. HOWARTH, *A Source Book in Astronomy.* New York: McGraw-Hill, 1929.

SINGER, CHARLES, *A Short History of Science.* Oxford: Clarendon Press, 1941.

STENO, NICOLAS (STENSEN, NEILS), *Prodomus.* Ann Arbor: University of Michigan Studies, Humanistic Series, vol. 11, 1914.

TAYLOR, F. SHERWOOD, *A Short History of Science and Scientific Thought.* New York: W. W. Norton, 1949. (Published in England under the title *Science Past and Present.*)

TAYLOR, F. SHERWOOD, *The Alchemists.* New York: Henry Schuman, 1949.

VAN MELSON, A. G., *From Atomos to Atom, the History of the Concept Atom.* Pittsburgh: Duquesne University Press, 1952.

WEEKS, MARY ELVIRA, *The Discovery of the Elements.* 5th ed. Easton, Pa.: The Journal of Chemical Education, 1945.

WHITTAKER, E. T., *A History of the Theories of Aether and Electricity.* 2 vol. London-New York: T. Nelson, 1951 (vol. 1), 1953 (vol. 2).

WOLF, A., *A History of Science, Technology and Philosophy in the 16th and 17th Centuries.* 2nd ed. London: George Allen and Unwin, 1950.

III. BIOGRAPHICAL WORKS

ANDRADE, E. N. DA C., *Isaac Newton.* New York: Chanticleer Press, 1950. Also *Sir Isaac Newton.* London: Collins, 1954.

ARMITAGE, ANGUS, *Sun, Stand Thou Still.* New York: Henry Schuman, 1947. (Reprinted as *The World of Copernicus*, Mentor, New American Library, 1951.)

BELL, A. E., *Christian Huygens and the Development of Science in the Seventeenth Century.* London: Edward Arnold, 1947.

COULSON, THOMAS, *Joseph Henry, His Life and Work.* Princeton: Princeton University Press, 1950.

CROWTHER, J. G., *British Scientists of the 19th Century.* London: K. Paul, Trench, Trubner, 1935. (Reprinted by Penguin. Published in New York, W. W. Norton, as *Men of Science*, 1936.)

CROWTHER, J. G., *British Scientists of the 20th Century.* London: Routledge and K. Paul, 1952.

CROWTHER, J. G., *Famous American Men of Science.* New York: W. W. Norton, 1937.

CURIE, EVE, *Madame Curie.* Garden City: Doubleday, 1939.

DICKINSON, H. W., and H. P. VOWLES, *James Watt and the Industrial Revolution.* 2nd ed. London: Longmans, Green, 1948.

EVE, A. S., *Rutherford.* New York: Macmillan, 1939.

FAHIE, J. J., *Galileo, His Life and Work.* New York: James Pott, 1903.

FARRINGTON, BENJAMIN, *Francis Bacon, Philosopher of Industrial Science.* London: Lawrence and Wishart, 1951.

FENTON, CARROLL LANE, and MILDRED ADAMS FENTON, *The Story of the Great Geologists.* Garden City: Doubleday, 1945.

FRENCH, SIDNEY J., *Torch and Crucible, the Life and Death of Antoine Lavoisier.* Princeton: Princeton University Press, 1941.

GADE, JOHN ALLYNE, *The Life and Times of Tycho Brahe.* Princeton: Princeton University Press, 1947.

GEIKIE, SIR ARCHIBALD, *The Founders of Geology.* London: Macmillan, and Baltimore: Johns Hopkins Press, 1901.

HEATH, SIR THOMAS, *Aristarchus of Samos.* Oxford: Clarendon Press, 1913.

JAFFE, BERNARD, *Men of Science in America.* New York: Simon and Schuster, 1944.

LENNARD, P., *Great Men of Science.* New York: Macmillan, 1934.

McKIE, D., *Antoine Lavoisier.* New York: Henry Schuman, 1952.

MORE, L. T., *Isaac Newton, a Biography.* New York: Scribner, 1934.

MORE, L. T., *The Life and Works of the Honorable Robert Boyle.* New York: Oxford University Press, 1944.

OLDHAM, FRANK: *Thomas Young, F. R. S.; Philosopher and Physician.* London: Edward Arnold, 1953.

RAMSAY, W., *The Life and Letters of Joseph Black.* London: Constable, 1918.

SINGER, DOROTHEA W., *Giordano Bruno, His Life and Thoughts.* New York: Henry Schuman, 1950.

SULLIVAN, J. W. N., *Isaac Newton, 1642–1727.* New York: Macmillan, 1938.

THOMPSON, J. A., *Count Rumford of Massachusetts.* New York: Farrar and Rinehart, 1935.

TURNER, DOROTHY M., *Makers of Science: Electricity and Magnetism.* Oxford: Oxford University Press, 1927.

TYNDALL, JOHN, *Faraday as a Discoverer.* New York: Appleton, 1873.

WOOD, ALEXANDER, *Thomas Young, Natural Philosopher.* Cambridge: Cambridge University Press, 1954.

NAME INDEX

Adams, John Couch (1819–1892), 89
Alter, David (1807–1881), 382
Ampère, André Marie (1775–1836), 313 ff.
Arago, Dominique Francois Jean (1786–1853), 314, 360
Archimedes (287–212 B.C.), 38, 112, 243
Aristarchus of Samos (ca. 310–230 B.C.), 13
Aristotle (384–322 B.C.), 12, 37, 40, 43, 99, 114, 327
Arrhenius, Svante (1859–1927), 443, 450, 461
Avicenna (ibn-Sina, 980–1036), 102
Avogadro, Amadeo (1776-1857), 147 ff., 170, 266

Baade, Walter (b. 1893), 681
Bacon, Francis (1561–1626), 1, 49 ff., 103, 230
Baeyer, Adolf (1835–1917), 521, 528
Balmer, J. J. (1825–1898), 383
Bartholinus, Erasmus (Bartholin, Rasmus, 1625–1698), 358
Becher, Johann Joachim (1635–1682), 116
Becquerel, Henri (1852–1909), 378, 640
Bernoulli, Daniel (1700–1782), 260
Berzelius, Jons Jacob (1779–1848), 144, 150, 368, 459, 484, 535, 563
Berthelot, Marcellin (1827–1907), 463, 475
Berthollet, Claude Louis (1748–1822), 127, 135
Bessel, Friedrich Wilhelm (1784–1846), 22
Black, Joseph (1728–1799), 119 ff., 127, 224 ff., 231
Blackett, P. M. S., (b. 1897), 654

Bohr, Niels (b. 1885), 390 ff.
Bok, Bart J. (b. 1906), 694
Boltzmann, Ludwig (1844–1906), 261, 679
Boyle, Robert (1627–1691), 103 ff., 116, 121, 128, 134, 246 ff., 260, 342
Brongniart, Alexandre (1770–1847), 574, 615
Bronsted, J. N. (b. 1879), 450
Brown, Robert (1773–1858), 270
Bruno, Giordano (1548–1600), 22, 567, 671
Bunsen, Robert (1811–1899), 174, 382, 485
Butlerov, A. M. (1828–1886), 487

Cannizzaro, Stanislao (1826–1910), 150 ff., 485
Carnot, Sadi (1796–1832), 233, 281
Cavendish, Henry (1731–1810), 91 ff., 121, 127, 294, 597, 609
Chadwick, James (b. 1891), 659
Charles, Jacques (1746–1823), 252
Chevreul, Michel Eugène (1786–1889), 485
Claudius Ptolemy of Alexandria, see Ptolemy
Clausius, Rudolph (1822–1888), 261, 283
Cockcroft, J. D. (b. 1897), 656
Colding, Ludvig August (1815–1888), 234
Comte, Auguste (1798–1957), 382
Copernicus, Nikolaus (1473–1543), 2, 17 ff.
Coulomb, Charles Augustin (1736–1806), 294 ff.
Couper, A. S. (1831–1892), 487
Curie, Marie Sklodowska (1867–1934), 174, 378 ff., 640
Curie, Pierre (1859–1906), 378 ff., 640

SUBJECT INDEX

Absolute magnitude, stellar, 677
Absolute temperature, 253
Absolute zero, 253
Absorption spectra, 382
Acceleration, defined, 45
  centripetal, 69
  of gravity, 48, 70, 72, 89, 596
Accelerators, particle, 656
Acetylene hydrocarbons, 493
Acids, 165, 450, 511
Acid-base pairs, 452, 472
Activation energy, 561
Affinity, chemical, 475
  electron, 417
Air, composition of, 124
Alchemy, 100 ff.
Aliphatic hydrocarbons, 494
Alizarin synthesis, 521
Alkali metals, 180
Alkaline earth metals, 180
Allotropic modifications, 428
Alpha particles, 379, 640 ff.
Ammeter, 300
Amorphous solids, 425
Ampere, defined, 300
Analysis, chemical, 131
Angstrom unit, 358
Angular measure, 714
Angular momentum, 200, 391
Anticline, 630
Appalachians, formation of, 530
Archimedes' principle, 112, 243
Aromatic hydrocarbons, 494
Artificial radioactivity, 659
Asbestos minerals, 555
Astronomy, in ancient Greece, 6 ff.
  Copernican, 17 ff.
  Newtonian, 77 ff.
  stellar, 671 ff.
Atmosphere, composition of, 124
  pressure of, 245

Atomic mass unit, 657
Atomic number, 187, 397, 642
Atomic ratios, 143
Atomic theory, Dalton's, 143 ff.
  Bohr's, 390 ff.
Atomic volume, 183, 381
Atomic weights, 142 ff., 648
  determination of, 150
  table, 155
Atomic weight ratios, 143
Avogadro's hypothesis, 147, 266
Avogadro's number, 171

Balmer formula, 383, 394
Barometer, 247
Bases, 450
Basalt controversy, 575
Batholith, 579, 632
Battery, voltaic, 174, 298, 368, 477
Benzene, 494
Beta particles, 379, 640 ff.
Binding, chemical, 411 ff.
  nuclear, 660
Bohr atom, 390
Boiling point, 279
Bonds, chemical, 411 ff.
  covalent, 418
  double, 421
  ionic, 413
Boyle's law, 249, 262
  deviations from, 273
Bright-line spectra, 382
Brightness, stellar, 677
Brownian motion, 270
Buoyancy, 112
Buffer solutions, 482

Calcination, 114
Calcite, 358, 559
Caloric, 128, 230
Calorie, 225